Imaging Anatomy of the Human Brain

Imaging Anatomy of the Human Brain

A Comprehensive Atlas Including Adjacent Structures

Neil M. Borden, MD
Neuroradiologist
Associate Professor of Radiology
The University of Vermont Medical Center
Burlington, Vermont

Scott E. Forseen, MD
Assistant Professor, Neuroradiology Section
Department of Radiology and Imaging
Georgia Regents University
Augusta, Georgia

Cristian Stefan, MD
Medical Education Consultant
Former Professor, Departments of Cellular Biology and Anatomy,
* Neurology and Radiology*
Medical College of Georgia at Georgia Regents University
Augusta, Georgia

Illustrator
Alastair J. E. Moore, MD
Medical Illustrator
Clinical Instructor, Department of Radiology
The University of Vermont Medical Center
Burlington, Vermont

demosMEDICAL

New York

Visit our website at www.demosmedical.com

ISBN: 978-1-936287-74-1
e-book ISBN: 978-1-617051-25-8

Acquisitions Editor: Beth Barry
Compositor: diacriTech

Illustrations in Chapter 2 © Alastair J. E. Moore, MD

Medicine is an ever-changing science. Research and clinical experience are continually expanding our knowledge, in particular our understanding of proper treatment and drug therapy. The authors, editors, and publisher have made every effort to ensure that all information in this book is in accordance with the state of knowledge at the time of production of the book. Nevertheless, the authors, editors, and publisher are not responsible for errors or omissions or for any consequences from application of the information in this book and make no warranty, expressed or implied, with respect to the contents of the publication. Every reader should examine carefully the package inserts accompanying each drug and should carefully check whether the dosage schedules mentioned therein or the contraindications stated by the manufacturer differ from the statements made in this book. Such examination is particularly important with drugs that are either rarely used or have been newly released on the market.

Library of Congress Cataloging-in-Publication Data
Borden, Neil M.
  Imaging anatomy of the human brain : a comprehensive atlas including adjacent structures / Neil M. Borden, Scott E. Forseen, Cristian Stefan.
      pages ; cm
  Includes bibliographical references and index.
  ISBN 978-1-936287-74-1
  1. Brain—Anatomy. 2. Brain—Imaging. I. Forseen, Scott E. II. Stefan, Cristian (Medical Education Consultant) III. Title.
QM455.B67 2015
612.8—dc23
                                                                                    2015015004

Special discounts on bulk quantities of Demos Medical Publishing books are available to corporations, professional associations, pharmaceutical companies, health care organizations, and other qualifying groups. For details, please contact:

Special Sales Department
Demos Medical Publishing, LLC
11 West 42nd Street, 15th Floor
New York, NY 10036
Phone: 800-532-8663 or 212-683-0072
Fax: 212-941-7842
E-mail: specialsales@demosmedical.com

Printed in the United States of America by Bang Printing.
15 16 17 18 / 5 4 3 2 1

Contents

Contributors

Steven P. Braff, MD, FACR
Former Chairman, Department of Radiology
The University of Vermont Medical Center
Burlington, Vermont

Andrea O. Vergara Finger, MD
Clinical Instructor, Department of Radiology
The University of Vermont Medical Center
Burlington, Vermont

Dave Guy, AS, RDMS
Ultrasound Technologist
The University of Vermont Medical Center
Burlington, Vermont

Timothy J. Higgins, MD
Assistant Professor of Diagnostic Radiology
The University of Vermont Medical Center
Burlington, Vermont

Scott G. Hipko, BSRT, (R)(MR)(CT)
Senior MRI Research Technologist
UVM MRI Center for Biomedical Imaging
The University of Vermont Medical Center
Burlington, Vermont

Alastair J. E. Moore, MD
Medical Illustrator
Clinical Instructor, Department of Radiology
The University of Vermont Medical Center
Burlington, Vermont

Sumir S. Patel, MD
Department of Radiology and Imaging Sciences
Emory University School of Medicine
Atlanta, Georgia

Thomas Gorsuch Powers, MD
Clinical Instructor, Department of Radiology
The University of Vermont Medical Center
Burlington, Vermont

Mitchell Snowe, BS
The University of Vermont NERVE Lab
Burlington, Vermont

Ashley Stalter, BS, RDM
Ultrasound Technologist
The University of Vermont Medical Center
Burlington, Vermont

Richard Watts, DPhil
Associate Professor of Physics in Radiology
UVM MRI Center for Biomedical Imaging
The University of Vermont Medical Center
Burlington, Vermont

Fyodor Wolf, MS
Web Developer
IS&T Boston University
Boston, Massachusetts

Rachel Rose Wolf, MA
MS Candidate, Speech-Language Pathology
MGH Institute of Health Professions
Boston, Massachusetts

Preface

I am writing this preface having just left the annual meeting of the American Society of Functional Neuroradiology (ASFNR). My experience at this meeting has underscored the idea that we have come so far in the field of neuroimaging since the inception of the specialty of neuroradiology, yet we are only scratching the surface. We have gone beyond the scope of what we can grossly see with the most sophisticated neuroimaging tools available and are now investigating the brain on a microstructural/cellular, biochemical, genetic, metabolic, and neuroelectrical basis. Emerging techniques in functional "F"MRI, such as activation task-based fMRI, resting state connectivity fMRI, ultra-high resolution diffusion tensor imaging (DTI), positron emission tomography (PET), spectroscopy as well as magnetoencephalography (MEG), are providing us with an immense compilation of data to analyze. These advanced imaging techniques are pushing the limits of some of our brightest scientists to "make sense" of this immense volume of data.

Knowledge of neuroanatomy is and will always be an imperative, despite the new direction neuroradiology is taking. Knowledge of cerebral surface anatomy and moving deeper into the cortex and subcortical structures is the fundamental basis of traditional neuroimaging techniques. The incredible complexity of the deceptively bland appearance of white matter (WM) on standard high-resolution MRI imaging is now revealed using DTI. Previous neuroanatomists have dissected some of the large bundles of WM tracts making them visible to the human eye, yet only now are we able to see them using DTI MR techniques.

This atlas of cerebral anatomy will provide the reader with the basic building blocks one needs to move forward in the journey into the realm of neuroscience and advanced neuroimaging.

An "Introduction to the Development, Organization, and Function of the Human Brain" in Chapter 1 is followed by a meticulous presentation of neuroanatomy utilizing multiple imaging modalities to provide a solid framework and resource atlas for clinicians, researchers, and students in the neurosciences and related fields.

Neil M. Borden, MD

Acknowledgments

There are so many people I would like to acknowledge for their contribution in making this atlas possible. First and foremost is the loving support and encouragement of my wife, Nina, my son Jonathan, my daughter Rachel Wolf, and my son-in-law Fyodor Wolf (whom we call Teddy). Not only is Teddy my son-in-law he is a brilliant computer engineer and programmer. He along with my daughter, Rachel provided invaluable help and support streamlining the extensive manipulation of data during this project and making sure that it all came together at the end.

I want to acknowledge Dr. Steven P. Braff, former Chair of the Department of Radiology at the University of Vermont, who himself is a neuroradiologist. He believed in my efforts to enhance the education and stimulate the interest, which I possessed in the field of neuroradiology/neuroanatomy to other individuals. His leadership and encouragement have been a source of strength to me. Dr. Braff facilitated this project and helped make it a reality.

A special thanks goes to the incredibly hard working and intelligent individuals who run the UVM MRI Center for Biomedical Imaging, whom without their assistance many of the beautiful images in this atlas would not be possible. These include Dr. Richard Watts, Scott Hipko, and Jay Gonyea.

Alastair J. E. Moore, MD, a very talented medical illustrator and a Clinical Instructor in the Department of Radiology at the University of Vermont worked arduously to provide the beautiful color illustrations in Chapter 2.

I would like to thank my Publisher Beth Barry at Demos Medical for her patience, encouragement, and loyalty in making not only this book but also my previous books, *3D Angiographic Atlas of Neurovascular Anatomy and Pathology* and *Pattern Recognition Neuroradiology* a reality.

I want to acknowledge the contribution of my co-authors, Dr. Scott E. Forseen and Dr. Cristian Stefan. I first met these talented physicians while I was on staff at the Medical College of Georgia in Augusta. Both of these individuals are dedicated to advancing medical education as I am. I am proud to co-author a companion atlas of the spine with Dr. Scott E. Forseen, *Imaging Anatomy of the Human Spine: A Comprehensive Atlas Including Adjacent Structures*.

Of all of the people I have spent time with and trained under, Dr. Robert F. Spetzler was the most influential person in my career. My time training at the Barrow Neurological Institute in Phoenix, Arizona was the most valuable time in my life, which provided me the knowledge, and tools that enhanced my love for my chosen profession, and most importantly the desire to educate and inspire others, in the way that I was inspired through my interactions with Dr. Robert F. Spetzler, who is the Director of Barrow Neurological Institute.

Neil M. Borden, MD

Introduction

This atlas provides the reader a unique opportunity to learn the complex anatomy of the human brain in the context of multiple different neuroimaging modalities. In medical school, human brain anatomy is first taught through dissection labs and lectures. In the past several years, different neuroimaging techniques, such as computed tomography (CT) and magnetic resonance imaging (MRI), have been integrated into this initial education. This integration provides the student a clinically relevant educational approach to incorporate classroom and laboratory knowledge during the beginning of their medical education. This approach hopefully enhances the educational experience and makes for a more interested medical student or other individual in pursuit of this knowledge.

Presented in this book are color enhanced medical illustrations and virtually all of the cutting edge imaging modalities we currently use to visualize the human brain. This includes standard CT, including multiplanar reformatted CT images and 3D volume rendered CT imaging, standard MRI images, diffusion tensor MR imaging (DTI), MR spectroscopy (MRS), functional MRI (fMRI), vascular imaging using magnetic resonance angiography (MRA), CT angiography (CTA), conventional 2D catheter angiography, 3D rotational catheter angiography, and ultrasound of the neonatal brain. There are advantages and disadvantages to these various techniques, which the neuroradiologist is well versed in, and can make educated decisions regarding which one or several techniques should be used in a particular situation.

Detailed labeling of images in this atlas allows the reader to compare and contrast the various anatomic structures from modality to modality. Unlabeled or sparsely labeled images placed side by side with labeled images at similar slice positions has been provided in certain sections of this atlas to allow the reader an unobstructed view of the anatomic structures and allows the reader to test their knowledge of the anatomy presented.

This atlas is not targeted only to radiologists but to anyone interested in the neurosciences. Therefore, brief, simplified explanations of some of the various imaging techniques illustrated in this atlas are provided but I refer the interested reader to the "Suggested Readings" chapter if they seek more in-depth knowledge.

This "atlas" is meant to be just that, a pictorial method of presenting knowledge. I think of my life as a radiologist as a story told through pictures/images. There is no better way to learn anatomy than through the assimilation of knowledge within an image. When I first started my training as a radiologist CT was just beginning to revolutionize this field. Over the last 30 years since that time tremendous advances in technology have led us to the point where we can now look beyond the anatomy demonstrated through standard cross-sectional imaging techniques. We can visualize neural networks and look at brain biochemistry to diagnose and predict outcomes.

Our hope in writing this "atlas" is to provide the reader a detailed map of the human brain to allow the integration of most of the cutting edge tools we now have to visualize both the gross and microstructural details of the human nervous system.

Imaging Anatomy of the
Human Brain

Introduction to the Development, Organization, and Function of the Human Brain

The nervous system is divided into the central nervous system (CNS) and the peripheral nervous system (PNS). The nervous system could also be divided into a somatic nervous system (SNS) and autonomic nervous system (ANS). These two basic classifications of the nervous system have practical importance and are based on embryological, anatomical, histological, and functional considerations.

The CNS consists of the brain and spinal cord, which are well protected by bony structures (skull and vertebral canal, respectively), meninges and normal spaces related to them. This atlas will cover the contents of the cranial vault, in addition to adjacent anatomic regions, including the orbits, paranasal sinuses, temporal bones, and the intracranial and extracranial vasculature.

The brain contains approximately 1 trillion cells, 100 billion neurons, and weights about 1400 g. While it constitutes only about 2% of the total body weight, it receives 20% of the cardiac output.

GRAY AND WHITE MATTER OF THE BRAIN

The brain consists of both gray matter and white matter and reflects their appearance on gross visual inspection of the brain. Gray matter is located along the superficial surface of the cerebral and cerebellar cortex as well as in the basal nuclei, diencephalon, nuclei of the brainstem, and the deep cerebellar nuclei. Gray matter is composed of neuronal cell bodies, glial cells, neuropil (collective term for dendrites and axons), and capillaries. The blood supply ratio between gray and white matter is 4:1. White matter lies in the subcortical and deep brain regions and consists of variably myelinated neuronal processes that transmit signals to and from various gray matter regions of the brain. The high lipid content within the myelin sheaths imparts a whitish appearance on gross visual inspection. The myelin sheath acts as an insulator, which enhances transmission speed of the neuronal signal.

White matter is arranged in tracts, which are divided into: (a) Association tracts (interconnect different cortical regions of the same cerebral hemisphere), (b) Projection tracts (connect cerebral cortex to subcortical gray matter in the telencephalon, diencephalon, brainstem, and spinal cord), and (c) Commissural tracts (interconnect the right and left hemispheres and include the corpus callosum and the anterior, posterior, and habenular commissures).

EMBRYOLOGY/DEVELOPMENT OF THE CENTRAL NERVOUS SYSTEM (CNS)

The development of the nervous system starts early during organogenesis. At the beginning of the third week of intrauterine life, the ectoderm thickens and forms the neural plate under the inducing influence of the notochord. The flat neural plate then gives rise to the neural folds with the neural groove between them. The neurulation continues with the approximation and fusion of the neural folds in the midline in the region of the future cervical region and continues both cranially and caudally to form the neural tube. The closure of the cranial neuropore (which occurs approximately on the 25th day) and posterior neuropore (approximately on the 27th day) are essential milestones in the formation of the neural tube. The complete lack of closure of the cranial neuropore results in anencephaly, and the incomplete closure of the cranial neuropore results in meningocele/encephalocele. Problems with closure of the caudal neuropore results in a variety of abnormalities including in the order of increasing severity: spina bifida occulta, meningocele, meningomyelocele, and rachischisis. These defects are accompanied by increased alpha-fetoprotein in the maternal serum (except for spina bifida occulta).

The neural crest cells are cells at the tips of the neural folds that remain at the top of the neural tube. After the neural tube closes, the pluripotent neural crest cells start migrating to give rise to a multitude of derivatives, including sensory ganglia, autonomic ganglia, adrenal medulla, Schwann cells, glial cells, arachnoid, pia matter, bones and cartilages of the skull, as well as various other structures not directly related to the nervous system.

The neural tube (neuroectoderm) sinks under the surface ectoderm, deeper into the embryo. The developing general organization of this tube encompasses a mantle layer (the future gray matter) and a marginal layer (the future white matter). Furthermore, each side (right and left) of the mantle layer develops into a basal plate (the future anterior horn of the spinal cord) and an alar plate (the future posterior horn of the spinal cord), which are separated by a groove called the sulcus limitans. Some regions of the neural tube will contain clusters of autonomic (preganglionic) neurons positioned between the basal and alar plates. This general organization remains distinct in the spinal cord and brainstem and is no longer recognizable above the midbrain. However, the arrangement of various neuronal clusters that form the cranial nerve nuclei in the rostral medulla oblongata and pons will reflect the growth and changes in shape that characterize the brainstem, that is, the motor and sensory cranial nerves will follow a medial to lateral arrangement, instead of the anterior to posterior one in the spinal cord. As a basic rule in the pons and rostral medulla oblongata, the general somatic motor nuclei of cranial nerves will be situated closest to the midline (with the visceral motor nuclei lateral to them) and the somatic sensory nuclei of cranial nerves will be located most laterally (with the visceral sensory nuclei medial to them, but lateral to the sulcus limitans).

The growth and further development of the neural tube is very pronounced in the cranial portion (the future brain) compared with the caudal portion (the future spinal cord), which remains narrow. Two main processes contribute to the shape of the final brain: the development of brain vesicles (three primary and five secondary vesicles) and the foldings of the neural tube (cervical, mesencephalic, and pontine).

The cranial portion of the neural tube initially consists of three primary vesicles: the prosencephalon or forebrain (that will be located in the supratentorial compartment), the mesencephalon or midbrain (that will pass through the tentorial notch), and the rhombencephalon or hindbrain (that will occupy the infratentorial compartment). These three primary vesicles will give rise to five secondary brain vesicles as follows: the prosencephalon will become the telencephalon and diencephalon, and the rhombencephalon will develop into the metencephalon (which comprises the pons and cerebellum) and the myelencephalon or medulla. The mesencephalon or midbrain does not further divide. Among all brain vesicles, the midbrain grows the least in size and it also contains the narrowest portion of the ventricular system, the aqueduct of Sylvius. This explains why the most common cause of obstructive (non-communicating) hydrocephalus is related to the compression or obstruction of the cerebral aqueduct.

The brainstem consists of the mesencephalon, metencephalon (pons and cerebellum), and the myelencephalon (medulla).

The telencephalon or cerebral hemispheres consist of neurons in the cerebral cortex, arranged in three, five, or six (most common situation) layers and clusters of neurons buried in the subcortical white matter (including the caudate nucleus, putamen, globus pallidus, claustrum, nucleus accumbens, amygdala, and hippocampal formation).

The diencephalon is at the rostral end of the brainstem and comprises a group of structures symmetrically positioned around the midline consisting of the thalamus, epithalamus, hypothalamus, and subthalamus. The epithalamus consists of the stria medullaris thalami, habenular nuclei, habenular commissure, and pineal gland.

MENINGES, MENINGEAL SPACES, CEREBRAL SPINAL FLUID

The surface of the brain is covered by three membranes: pia, arachnoid (collectively referred to as the leptomeninges) and dura (pachymeninx). Unlike the leptomeninges, dura is pain sensitive and has its own blood supply (meningeal arteries).

Dura mater consists of two layers: periosteal (outer) and meningeal (inner). These two layers are tightly fused except for the dural reflections that surround and contain the dural venous sinuses. The periosteal layer is firmly attached to the inner surface of the skull, which means that the epidural space around the brain is always a potential space, where numerous pathological processes can be located. This is in contrast with the epidural space around the spinal cord, which is well defined and contains normal and expected anatomic structures.

The dural meningeal layer is closely apposed to the arachnoid; therefore, the subdural space is also a potential one. Moreover, it is currently accepted that the subdural space occurs within the inner meningeal layer of the dura rather than between dura and arachnoid. Small (bridging) veins that connect the cortical veins to the overlying dural venous sinuses pass through the arachnoid and inner layer of dura to reach the sinus (e.g., superior sagittal sinus). Under certain conditions (e.g., sudden acceleration or deceleration) these bridging veins could tear and produce a subdural hemorrhage. As the inner dural layer (lined by arachnoid) covers each cerebral hemisphere and extends into both the anterior and posterior interhemispheric fissures along each side of the falx cerebri, a collection of blood/fluid in this potential subdural space would extend into the interhemispheric fissure and will not cross the midline.

However, if there is bleeding into the potential epidural space, then the collection of blood could cross the midline because the outer layer of the dura crosses the midline, but is limited by the cranial sutures. It requires significant pressure for blood to separate the dura from the bone and therefore epidural hematomas generally require high pressure arterial bleeding, most often related to trauma to the middle meningeal artery (a branch of the maxillary artery, which in turn is a branch of the external carotid artery). Rarely (more often seen in children) are venous epidural hematomas related to fractures with injury to an adjacent dural venous sinus.

Pia is closely applied in a continuous fashion to the entire surface of the brain and, unlike the arachnoid, extends into the sulci, fissures, and fossae. As a result, the space between the arachnoid and pia (subarachnoid space that contains cerebral spinal fluid [CSF]) is wider in some areas, forming subarachnoid cisterns (e.g., cerebellopontine angle cistern, cisterna magna, interpeducular cisten, prepontine cistern, suprasellar cistern). The arachnoid (so named because of its spider-web appearance) extends arachnoid trabeculae that connect it to the pia. The subarachnoid space contains much of the cerebral arterial vasculature surrounded by CSF; therefore, a rupture of/or leakage from these arteries (often from an aneurysm) results in subarachnoid hemorrhages. The subarachnoid space extends around the perforating vessels as they penetrate the parenchyma of the brain (Virchow–Robin perivascular spaces), which greatly increases the interface between brain and CSF.

The CSF has multiple roles, including acting as a cushion for the brain, providing a route for removal of metabolic waste material and immunoregulation. The total volume of CSF in the adult is approximately 150–270 mL (50% intracranial and 50% spinal). It is produced at a rate of approximately 0.3 mL/min with about 500 mL produced per day; therefore, the CSF turnover rate is estimated at approximately 3 times per day. CSF is secreted mainly by the choroid plexi in the ventricles (proportionate with the size of each ventricle). The ventricular system derives from the hollow embryonic neural tube. Each of the two lateral ventricles communicates via an interventricular foramen (foramen of Monroe) with the single third ventricle, which in turn communicates via the aqueduct of Sylvius with the fourth ventricle. After exiting the fourth ventricle through the dorsal midline aperture (foramen of Magendie) and the two lateral apertures (foramina of Luschka), the CSF enters the cisterna magna of the subarachnoid space, and then circulates around the CNS and is finally reabsorbed in bulk (non-selectively) into the venous circulation through the arachnoid villi. Arachnoid granulations (arachnoid villi grouped together) are seen most often in a parasagittal location to either side of the superior sagittal sinus, parasagittally in the posterior fossa near the transverse sinuses, near the torcular herophili (confluence of the dural venous sinuses) and along the floor of the middle cranial fossa (near the sphenoid sinuses). The arachnoid (pacchionian) granulations often result in bony erosion/remodeling of the inner table and may simulate a bony destructive process.

The inner layer of dura, which is lined by arachnoid, form dural septa (falx cerebri, tentorium cerebeli, falx cerebelli, and diaphragma sellae). The falx cerebri separates the two cerebral hemispheres and its inferior margin is not attached to the corpus callosum; therefore, cingulate gyrus herniations (subfalcine herniations) can occur in the space between the inferior margin of the falx cerebri and corpus callosum. This space is widest anteriorly and narrows posteriorly and is no longer present at the falco-tentorial junction (junction of inferior falx cerebri and the dura along the posterior aspect of the tentorial incisura). This explains why subfalcine herniations of the brain decrease in size and occurrence from anterior to posterior and cannot occur posterior to the falco-tentorial junction. The tentorium cerebelli separates the supratentorial from the infratentorial compartment. The compartments communicate via an anteriorly oriented "U" shaped opening named the tentorial incisura (notch), through which the midbrain passes.

SUPRATENTORIAL COMPARTMENT

■ CEREBRAL HEMISPHERES

The cerebral hemispheres are conventionally divided into several lobes, which is useful from an anatomical, functional, and pathophysiological perspective. The most common division consists of four separate lobes: frontal, parietal, temporal, and occipital. Official nomenclature established by the Federative Committee on Anatomical Terminology (FCAT) in 1998 divides the brain into six lobes by adding the limbic and insular lobes to the previously-mentioned four.

Unlike the cerebellar cortex that is formed by three layers throughout the cerebellum and looks the same on its entire surface, the cerebral cortex varies from one region to another. In contrast to the cerebellum, the cerebral cortex varies in architecture with regions that have three, five, or six layers.

Most of the cerebral cortex consists of neocortex (also named allocortex), which is morphologically organized in six horizontal layers and functionally in vertical columns. Moreover, the six layers differ among cortical regions in terms of thickness, structure, and connections. The thinnest neocortex corresponds to the primary sensory cortex, the thickest to the primary motor cortex with association cortex in between. Furthermore, the significant differences in cortical cytoarchitecture form the basis for the classification initiated by Brodmann and continued by other researchers, a classification that is widely used when referring to topographical, morphological, and functional areas. The transition between these areas (Brodmann's areas) could be abrupt or very subtle. A careful distinction has to be made between Brodmann's areas and the anatomical limits of the gyri (the delineation of a Brodmann area to a specific gyrus/gyri is the exception rather than the norm). Furthermore, a wide range of normal variations exists between individuals. In addition, for the same individual, there are major differences (functional, not anatomical) between the homologous areas on the left versus right hemisphere, which explains the concept of lateralization and the difference in clinical manifestations according to which hemisphere is affected by a pathological process. The numbers related to Brodmann's areas reflect the order in which they were discovered and named; therefore, they do not follow an anterior to posterior, lateral to medial, or other systematic descriptive order.

Frontal Lobe

The largest lobe of the brain is the frontal lobe. This extends from the frontal pole posteriorly to the central sulcus. It consists of the superior, middle, and inferior frontal gyri separated by the superior and inferior frontal sulci. The superior frontal sulcus runs longitudinally and parallel to the superior frontal gyrus. It most often terminates posteriorly into the horizontally oblique pre-central sulcus. Posterior to the pre-central sulcus is the pre-central gyrus or primary motor strip (Brodmann area 4). Just anterior to the pre-central gyrus, there are two parts of the Brodmann area 6: the premotor cortex (on the lateral, convex aspect of the hemisphere) and the supplementary motor region (on the medial aspect). Brodmann area 8 is found anterior to Brodmann area 6 on both the lateral and medial aspects of the cortex. It includes the frontal eye field (FEF), which is located mainly on the middle frontal gyrus. The middle frontal gyrus can occur as a single gyrus or may be divided into a superior and inferior segment separated by the middle frontal sulcus. If there is only a single middle frontal gyrus the middle frontal sulcus does not exist. The inferior frontal sulcus separates the middle from the inferior frontal gyri. The inferior frontal gyrus is a triangular-shaped grouping of three gyri called from anterior to posterior the pars orbitalis (Brodmann area 47), pars triangularis (Brodmann area 45), and pars opercularis (Brodmann area 44). The anterior horizontal ramus of the Sylvian fissure separates pars orbitalis from pars triangularis and the anterior ascending ramus separates pars triangularis from pars opercularis. Pars opercularis and pars triangularis in the dominant hemisphere correspond to Broca's area, which is involved in the generation of speech (expressive, motor, or productive speech center). On the nondominant hemisphere, this area is responsible for the expression or production of prosody (the intonation and inflection used in speech).

The prefrontal cortex (Brodmann areas 9, 10, 11, 12, and 46) could be further divided into three regions: dorsolateral, orbitofrontal, and ventromedial. Each of these regions is characterized by specific connections and functions; they have key roles in emotional responses, mood regulation, memory, personal and social behavior, judgment, planning, decision making, categorization, error detection, and empathy.

Anatomically, the basal portion of the frontal lobe consists of the gyrus recti (straight gyri) located paramedian to either side of the midline, just above the cribriform plates. The remainder of the basal forebrain consists of the orbital gyri often arranged around a sulcal pattern in the shape of an "H" (cruciform sulcus of Rolando). The medial orbital gyrus lies lateral to the gyrus rectus and is separated from the gyrus rectus by the olfactory sulcus where the olfactory bulb and tract run in an anterior to posterior direction. Lesions in this area could result in olfactory dysfunctions as well as changes in personality, emotions, and behavior. Lateral to the medial orbital gyrus are the anterior and posterior orbital gyri separated by a transverse sulcus (the transverse limb of the "H"). The lateral orbital gyrus is lateral to the anterior and posterior orbital gyri. The posterior orbital gyrus extends medially and merges with the medial orbital gyrus to form the posteromedial orbital lobule.

Usually the central sulcus does not extend all the way down to the Sylvian fissure. A bridge of brain tissue called the subcentral gyrus connects the inferior aspects of the pre and post central gyri and is the primary gustatory cortical area.

Similarly, the central sulcus does not extend on the medial aspect of the hemisphere beyond the vertex. The limited view of the central sulcus at the vertex can be identified as the first sulcus anterior to pars marginalis (ascending ramus of the cingulate sulcus). The paracentral lobule is only identified along the medial aspect of the cerebral hemisphere extending from pars marginalis to the paracentral sulcus and superior to the cingulate gyrus.

Taken together, the inferior frontal gyrus, the subcentral gyrus, and the anterior–inferior aspect of the supramarginal gyrus overlie the superior aspect of the insular cortex and represent the frontal and parietal operculum.

The representation of the motor homunculus on area 4 includes the face, upper limb, and trunk on the pre-central gyrus on the lateral aspect of the hemisphere (in the territory of the middle cerebral artery) and the lower limb on the medial aspect in the anterior part of the paracentral lobule (in the territory of the anterior cerebral artery).

Temporal Lobe

The temporal lobe is inferior to the Sylvian fissure. It extends from the temporal pole, which lies in the middle cranial fossa along the greater wing of the sphenoid bone anteriorly and extends back to the temporal-occipital junction. The lateral convexity surface of the temporal lobe consists of the superior, middle, and inferior temporal gyri and their separations, the superior and inferior temporal sulci. The inferior temporal gyrus is seen along the inferolateral as well as the lateral part of the inferior aspect of the temporal lobe.

The lateral aspect of the temporal lobe is formed by Brodmann areas 38 (temporal pole), 41 (part of the primary auditory cortex as most of the primary auditory cortex is on the superior surface of the temporal lobe), 42 (secondary auditory cortex), 22 (most of the superior temporal gyrus; with the posterior part of area 22 belonging to Wernicke's region on the dominant hemisphere), 21 (middle temporal gyrus), and 20 and 37 (inferior temporal gyrus). Buried within the lateral sulcus (Sylvian fissure) is the insula. The M2 segments of the middle cerebral artery (divided into upper and lower trunks) and the origins of its cortical branches are located in this sulcus. The presence of the M2 segment of the middle cerebral artery in the lateral sulcus (Sylvian fissure) poses difficulties regarding the neurosurgical approach to the insula.

The cerebral cortex that covers the undersurface (inferior or ventral aspect) of the temporal lobe is subdivided into various Brodmann areas: 38 (temporal pole), 36, 35 (perirhinal cortex), 34, 28 (entorhinal cortex), 20 and 37 (posterior part of perirhinal and entorhinal cortex). These areas are associated with various and intricate functions, including olfaction, memory processing, analysis, categorization and association of visual stimuli, face recognition and emotional perception, language, and empathy.

From lateral to medial, the undersurface of the temporal lobe consists of the inferior temporal gyrus, the lateral occipitotemporal gyrus (fusiform gyrus), and the parahippocampal gyrus (found only more anteriorly in the temporal lobe). An important feature of the parahippocampal gyrus is formed by its bulging antero-medial extremity called the uncus, the most medial portion of the temporal lobe. The uncus forms the lateral aspect of the suprasellar cistern. The structure underlying the uncus is the amygdala. The proximity and connections between the cortex of the temporal pole and surrounding areas and other structures of the limbic system and cortical areas responsible for the interpretation of visual stimuli (related to shape, color, and especially the processing of information regarding the face) make the parahippocampal cortex a key player in the processing of visuospatial information, memory, cognition, emotions, and spatial and nonspatial contextual association. Posteriorly in the temporal and temporal-occipital regions, the lingual gyrus, also called the medial occipitotemporal gyrus (part of the occipital lobe inferior to the calcarine sulcus) intercalates itself between the posterior parahippocampal gyrus/isthmus of the cingulate gyrus and the lateral occipitotemporal gyrus. The lateral occipitotemporal sulcus separates the inferior temporal gyrus from the lateral occipitotemporal gyrus, while the collateral sulcus separates the parahippocampal gyrus from the lateral occipitotemporal gyrus in the anterior temporal lobe. Posteriorly where the lingual gyrus/medial occipitotemporal gyrus intercalates between the parahippocampal gyrus/isthmus of cingulate gyrus and the lateral occipitotemporal gyrus, the collateral sulcus remains along the medial margin of the lateral occipitotemporal gyrus separating this gyrus from the lingual gyrus. The anterior extension of the calcarine sulcus separates the lingual gyrus/medial occipitotemporal gyrus from the isthmus of the cingulate gyrus. The occipitotemporal sulcus rarely extends as far back as the occipital pole because it is interrupted and often divided into two or more parts. The anterior portion of the lateral occipitotemporal sulcus often bends medially to join the collateral sulcus. The lateral occipitotemporal gyrus extends along the basal surface of the temporal lobe with its posterior lateral margin adjacent to the inferior occipital gyrus.

Along the lateral convexity surface, the temporal-occipital junction is a poorly defined region without discrete anatomical landmarks to define its location. Creating an imaginary line between the pre-occipital notch along the inferior lateral convexity of the cerebral hemisphere and the superior extent of the parieto-occipital fissure can approximate this junction. This line is referred to as the lateral parietotemporal line, delimiting the occipital lobe posterior and the temporal lobe anterior to this line. Another poorly demarcated separation occurs along the lateral convexity surface separating the parietal from the temporal lobe. This division can be approximated by drawing an imaginary line (the temporo-occipital line) from the posterior aspect of the Sylvian fissure to perpendicularly intersect the previously described lateral parietotemporal line along the anterior margin of the occipital lobe. The tissue above this line is in the parietal lobe and that which lies below this line is temporal lobe.

The basal surface of the temporal lobe is also poorly delimited by anatomic landmarks, but can be approximated by an imaginary line (basal parietotemporal line) extending from the pre-occipital notch to the junction of the parieto-occipital sulcus with the calcarine sulcus. The temporal lobe is anterior and the occipital lobe is posterior to this line.

Heschl's gyrus or transverse temporal gyrus (primary auditory cortex, Brodmann area 41) can be solitary or multiple and is/are the dominant structure(s) lying along the superior surface of the temporal lobe. Not only can there be single or multiple transverse temporal gyri (Heschl's gyri), there is right to left asymmetry. Heschl's gyrus is more often larger on the left, however, this asymmetry does not correlate with handedness. It courses from posteriomedial to anterolateral (toward the convexity). The flat superior surface of the temporal lobe from the anterior margin of Heschl's gyrus anteriorly is called the planum polare while the flat superior surface from the posterior margin of Heschl's gyrus to the posterior Sylvian fissure is called the planum temporale. Planum temporale is often asymmetric in size and larger on the left correlating with the side of language dominance.

The stem of the temporal lobe is an important anatomic region, which provides a direct connection between the white matter of the temporal lobe, and the inferolateral basal ganglia region (inferolateral frontobasal region). This neuronal connection allows pathologic processes of the temporal lobe or alternatively the inferolateral frontal basal region to spread through the stem of the temporal lobe to cross and involve either of these two anatomic regions.

Parietal Lobe

The anterior margin of the parietal lobe at the vertex and lateral convexity is demarcated from the frontal lobe by the central sulcus. Posteriorly the parietal lobe is clearly separated from the occipital lobe along the medial hemisphere by the parieto-occipital sulcus (fissure). The subparietal sulcus separates the posterior cingulate gyrus (a part of the limbic lobe) from the parietal lobe above along the medial hemispheric surface. Posteriorly and inferiorly along the lateral convexity surface of the brain, the division between the parietal lobe and temporal and occipital lobes is poorly demarcated and one should use the technique of creating imaginary lines as described in the section on the Temporal Lobe using the lateral parietotemporal and temporo-occipital lines.

Subdivisions of the parietal lobe include the superior parietal lobule and the inferior parietal lobule (consisting of the supramarginal gyrus and the angular gyrus). The superior parietal lobule extends along the superior-medial portion of the parietal convexity from the post-central sulcus anteriorly to the cranial end of the occipital lobe (superior occipital gyrus) demarcated by the parieto-occipital sulcus. Along the medial surface of the hemisphere, the superior parietal lobule is continuous with the precuneus (a medial extension of the superior parietal lobule). The margins of the precuneus are the ascending ramus of the cingulate sulcus (pars marginalis) anteriorly; posteriorly the parieto-occipital fissure and inferiorly by the subparietal sulcus. The superior parietal lobule is separated from the inferior parietal lobule (along the superolateral convexity surface) by the obliquely oriented intraparietal sulcus. This sulcus runs in an anterior to posterior (AP) oblique direction from anterolateral to posteromedial. The intraparietal sulcus often extends posteriorly and inferiorly to become the intraoccipital sulcus, separating the superior occipital gyrus from the middle occipital gyrus. Anteriorly the intraparietal sulcus continues to the inferior portion of the post-central sulcus. The supramarginal gyrus is just posterior to the post-central gyrus along the lateral convexity of the brain and is the tissue surrounding the posterior ascending ramus of the Sylvian fissure. The angular gyrus is located posterior to the supramarginal gyrus over the superolateral convexity surface and surrounds the horizontal distal portion of the superior temporal sulcus.

Occipital Lobe

Variability in the gyral and sulcal pattern (particularly along the lateral surface), and in the nomenclature is greater in the occipital lobe than any other region/lobe of the brain. This variability has led to confusion and disagreement on how this lobe is depicted and named in the vast number of anatomical textbooks available.

The separation of the parietal lobe from the occipital lobe is clearly defined along the medial hemisphere by the parieto-occipital fissure (sulcus). The division of the occipital lobe into the cuneus and the lingual gyrus is also clearly defined by the calcarine sulcus. Confusion and poor anatomic landmarks clearly delineating the lateral convexity surface and the basal surface of the occipital lobe leads to vagueness in these regions when localizing a lesion. The approach described in the Temporal Lobe section of creating imaginary lines, such as the lateral temporoparietal, basal temporoparietal, and temporal-occipital lines, helps to create these artificial boundaries. Just as there is confusion as to these boundaries there is also significant intrinsic variability in the sulcal and gyral anatomy of the occipital lobe. Depending upon the sulcal and gyral anatomy, some anatomists divide the occipital lobe into two or three major gyri. The two-gyrus pattern consists of dividing the lateral aspect of the occipital lobe into two main parts, the superior and inferior occipital gyri separated by the lateral occipital sulcus. The three-gyrus pattern divides the lateral surface into two longitudinally oriented (in the AP direction) gyri, the middle and inferior occipital gyri separated by the lateral (or inferior) occipital sulcus while the superior occipital gyrus is more posteriorly and medially along the interhemispheric fissure with all three converging at the occipital pole. The middle and superior occipital gyri are often separated by the intra-occipital sulcus, a posterior continuation of the intraparietal sulcus.

Insular Lobe

The insula (Isle of Reil) is found at the base of the Sylvian fissure. It is covered laterally and superiorly by the frontoparietal operculum and laterally and inferiorly by the temporal oper-culum (formed by the superior temporal gyrus). The anterior boundary of the insular lobe is the fronto-orbital operculum. The limen insulae is at the anterior–inferior aspect of this pyramid/triangle (shape of insular) at the junction with the parahippocampal gyrus of the temporal lobe. It is the transitional region between the insula and the basal aspect of the fron-tal lobes. The lateral surface of the insula resembles an upside down pyramid (or triangle). This is divided into a larger anterior lobule commonly consisting of three gyri (but may be variable in number) named the anterior short, middle short, and posterior short gyri and a smaller posterior lobule commonly consisting of two gyri (but may be variable in number) named the anterior long and posterior long gyri. There is considerable variability in the number of insular gyri with most studies demonstrating four to seven in all, together with right and left asymmetry in this number. The inferior ends of the short gyri of the anterior lobule converge to create the apex of the insula. The central sulcus of the insula separates the larger anterior from the smaller posterior lobules of the insula and approximates the inferior continuation of the cerebral central sulcus.

The insula is associated with multiple functions, including gustatory, vestibular, somatic and visceral sensation, visceral motor functions (especially cardiovascular), motor speech (left side), emotion, and cognition.

Limbic Lobe

Inclusion of the limbic system as a distinct lobe was introduced in the publication created by the FCAT in 1998.

The structures included in the limbic lobe involve cortical, subcortical, and nuclear structures, which are anatomically and functionally diverse and include areas within the telencephalon and diencephalon. Limbic structures include the cingulate gyrus, the parahippocampal gyrus, the hippocampal formation (hippocampus proper, subiculum, dentate gyrus), and the frontal mediobasal cortical area (paraterminal gyrus and paraolfactory gyri or subcallosal area). The hippocampal formation and its circuitry are involved in the conversion of short-term to long-term memory. The amygdala and its connections are involved with emotions and through connections with the hypothalamus affect the autonomic, neuroendocrine, and motor systems. The cingulate gyrus is a C-shaped structure curving around the corpus callosum beginning below the rostrum of the corpus callosum, arcing around the genu of the corpus callosum and continuing posteriorly and then inferiorly around the splenium of the corpus callosum where it is contiguous with the parahippocampal gyrus. The isthmus of the cingulate gyrus refers to the area of thinning that normally occurs beneath the splenium of the corpus callosum.

Due to the different connections and functions, a distinction is made between the anterior part of the cingulate gyrus (with important connections with the prefrontal cortex, septal nuclei, amygdala, mammillary bodies via the thalamus, and other parts of the hypothalamus) and the posterior part (especially with the hippocampus, precuneus, and cerebellum). Furthermore, the anterior part could be subdivided into an anterior-inferior component (related mainly with affect) and an anterior-superior one (related mainly with cognition). Although the cingulate gyrus works as a whole, the different parts have defined influences in terms of control of somatic and visceral function. For example, efferent axons from the anterior part of the cingulate gyrus run into the corticospinal, corticobulbar, and corticoreticular tracts. This fact explains why a patient with an intact anterior part of the cingulate gyrus who has a supranuclear facial palsy due to a lesion in the primary motor cortex, could still have a spontaneous transient smile on the paralyzed side of the face in response to a joke.

In addition, the anterior part of the cingulate gyrus is described as having a role in detecting errors and conflicts, and modulating goal-directed behavior.

The parahippocampal gyrus constitutes the medial surface of the temporal lobe. The uncus is the most anterior-medial aspect of the temporal lobe in the lateral aspect of the suprasellar cistern covering the bulbous deep gray matter nuclear group called the amygdala. The amygdala lies just anterior and superior to the head of the hippocampus. The flat superior surface of the parahippocampal gyrus represents the subiculum. The hippocampus is lateral to the subiculum and consists of Ammon's horn and the dentate gyrus. The hippocampus projects into the floor of the temporal horn of the lateral ventricle. The hippocampal sulcus or fissure separates the subiculum (inferior to sulcus) from the dentate gyrus (superior to sulcus) of the hippocampus. Ammon's horn has been subdivided into the Cornus Ammonis (CA) I, II, III, and IV. CA1 represents Sommer's sector or the vulnerable sector. The hippocampus in general is a region of higher metabolic demand with the most sensitive region being CA1. As such this region is most susceptible to hypoxic/ischemic injury. A thin layer of white matter fibers called the alveus cover the superior surface of the hippocampus within the temporal horn from which the fimbria of the fornix arises (along the medial margin of the alveus) which serves as the primary efferent from the hippocampus. The collateral sulcus separates the lateral margin of the parahippocampal gyrus from the lateral occipitotemporal gyrus (fusiform gyrus) in the anterior temporal lobe. Posteriorly the lingual gyrus (medial occipitotemporal gyrus) intercalates between the posterior parahippocampal gyrus/ isthmus of the cingulate gyrus and the lateral occipitotemporal gyrus. The collateral sulcus in this region separates the lingual gyrus (medial occipitotemporal gyrus) from the lateral occipitotemporal gyrus and the anterior calcarine sulcus separates the lingual gyrus from the posterior parahippocampal/isthmus. The indusium griseum is a thin layer of gray matter running along the superior aspect of the corpus callosum. Below the level of the rostrum of the corpus callosum, the indusium griseum is continuous with the paraterminal gyrus, located just posterior to the subcallosal area. Posteriorly the indusium griseum (supracallosal gyrus) encircles the splenium of the corpus callosum and connects with the posterior aspect of the dentate gyrus.

The mediobasal frontal cortical area consists of the paraterminal gyrus and the paraolfactory gyri (subcallosal area) and is included in the limbic lobe. The paraterminal gyrus is located along the mesial surface of both cerebral hemispheres facing the lamina terminalis. The subcallosal area also called the parolfactory gyrus is delimited by the anterior and posterior parolfactory sulci. The septal nuclei are contained within the paraterminal gyri and referred to as the septal area. The septal nuclei functionally connect the limbic system with the hypothalamus and brainstem primarily through the hippocampal formation.

The last area of the limbic lobe to be discussed will be the olfactory cortical area. This encompasses the olfactory nerves, bulb, tract, trigone, striae, the anterior perforated substance, the diagonal band of Broca and the piriform lobe. The anterior perforated substance is bounded anteriorly by the olfactory trigone and the lateral and medial olfactory striae, posteriorly by the optic tracts, medially by the interhemispheric fissure and laterally by the uncus of the temporal lobe and limen insulae (the transition between the insular lobe and the basal forebrain). The anterior perforated substance is located above the bifurcation of the internal carotid artery and the proximal A1 and M1 segments of the anterior and middle cerebral arteries. The lenticulostriate arteries (perforating arteries) arise from the A1 and M1 segments and penetrate the anterior perforated substance to enter the basal forebrain. On gross inspection, the surface of the anterior perforated substance is scattered with small holes representing the site of penetration of the basal perforating arteries along with their perivascular spaces (Virchow–Robin spaces). Along the posterior aspect of the anterior perforated substance lies the ventral striatum, which anatomically includes the substantia innominata. The ventral striatal region, a region of the basal forebrain, extends from the anterior perforated substance to the anterior commissure. Its lateral boundary is the stem of the temporal lobe and superiorly the anterobasal portion of the anterior limb of the internal capsule borders it. Medially it borders the septal region and hypothalamus. The ventral striatum includes the nucleus accumbens (located at the caudal connection of the caudate nucleus with the putamen and globus pallidus) and the basal nucleus of Meynert. The ventral striatum modulates neuropsychiatric functions.

Basal Nuclei

Although the traditional term of basal ganglia is still in use, these structures are nuclei, not ganglia, as they consist of clusters of neuronal bodies within the CNS.

Anatomically, they refer to subcortical structures formed by gray matter within the cerebral hemispheres (telencephalon). However, because the amygdala and claustrum are considered parts of the limbic system, the term basal nuclei currently refer to the caudate nucleus, putamen, ventral striatum (including nucleus accumbens), and globus pallidus. Moreover, due to the important connections between the anatomical basal nuclei and the subthalamic nucleus and substantia nigra, these two entities are engulfed functionally into the concept of basal nuclei, although anatomically they belong to the diencephalon and midbrain, respectively.

The caudate nucleus and putamen are collectively referred to as the striatum or corpus striatum. They have similar internal organization although participate in different circuits. Due to their proximity, the two parts of globus pallidus (internal and external) and the putamen are collectively referred to as the lentiform (lenticular) nucleus. The caudate nucleus bulges into the lateral ventricle on the same side and consists of a head, a body, and a tail.

Several circuits involving basal nuclei have been described in the literature. Although they have different distinct functions, they involve a similar rule regarding the progression of information: from a certain region of the cerebral cortex to a certain part of the striatum to a certain part of globus pallidus (or similar structure) to a certain thalamic region that projects in turn to cerebral cortical areas. Additional connections involve the subthalamic nucleus and substantia nigra pars compacta (different than pars reticulata that resembles the organization and functions of the internal part of globus pallidus).

At least four parallel functional loops (circuits) that involve basal nuclei are described: a motor loop (via the putamen, with a direct and an indirect circuit that work together), a cognitive circuit (via the head of the caudate nucleus), an oculomotor circuit (via the body of the caudate nucleus), and a limbic circuit (via the ventral striatum). Pathological processes could affect predominantly one or more of these functional loops. The motor clinical manifestations due to lesions that affect the basal nuclei on one side manifest on the contralateral side of the body (e.g., as in hemiballismus).

The topographical relationship of the basal nuclei and thalamus with the internal capsule is also clinically important, regarding vascularization, pathological processes in the region, and for neurosurgical and neurointerventional approaches.

Due to its location and clinical significance, the internal capsule deserves particular mention. It is topographically divided in five parts: anterior limb, genu, posterior limb, retrolenticular part, and sublenticular part. Not all of these parts are seen on the same anatomic dissection/imaging slice (e.g., axial or coronal). The anterior limb is located between the lentiform (lenticular) nucleus and the head of the caudate nucleus, while the posterior limb is located between the lentiform nucleus and the thalamus. The genu represents the junction between the anterior and posterior limbs. As their names imply, the sublenticular and retrolenticular parts of the internal capsule run under and posterior to the lentiform nucleus, respectively. A diversity of fibers/tracts run within certain portions of the internal capsule, with a precise topography, including corticospinal, corticobulbar, corticopontine, corticothalamic, thalamocortical, and so on. Even small lesions in the internal capsule (e.g., often due to lacunar strokes) could result in important functional deficits compared with those produced by cortical damage of comparable size.

The two most important tracts running in the anterior limb of the internal capsule are the corticopontine and anterior thalamic radiations.

For example, the anterior limb contains corticopontine (more precisely frontopontine) fibers and thalamocortical (to prefrontal and anterior cingulate cortex) fibers. The genu (i.e., the junction of the anterior and posterior limbs of the internal capsule) contains corticobulbar, frontopontine, and thalamocortical fibers (to the motor/premotor cortex). The posterior limb of the internal capsule mainly contains topographically arranged corticospinal, corticopontine (e.g., parietopontine), and thalamocortical (to motor, somatosensory, insular, and other cortical areas) fibers. The sublenticular part contains auditory as well as optic radiations. The retrolenticular part contains optic radiations.

Diencephalon

The diencephalon is located between the telencephalon and midbrain and it is formed by four distinct anatomical and functional parts: the thalamus, hypothalamus, epithalamus, and subthalamus.

The only part of the diencephalon visible at the inspection of the uncut brain is the hypothalamus, which presents important landmarks on the inferior (ventral) view of the brain: the optic nerves, optic chiasm, optic tracts, infundibulum, and mammillary bodies (this last structure appearing in the interpeduncular fossa). However, a midsagittal section of the brain would show all parts of the diencephalon with the exception of the subthalamic nucleus which, as the name implies, is positioned symmetrically and more laterally, just caudal to ("under") the thalamus and rostral to the substantia nigra. On the midsagittal view, the diencephalon extends from several anterior landmarks (interventricular foramen, anterior commissure, lamina terminalis, and the rostral margin of the optic chiasm) to an imaginary line connecting the caudal margin of the mammillary body with the posterior commissure. There is no clearly visible delineation between the diencephalon and the midbrain. Diencephalic features on the midsagittal view include the hypothalamic sulcus (that indicates the border between the thalamus and the hypothalamus, anterio-inferior to the sulcus, both of these structures forming the lateral wall of the third ventricle), the oval-shaped medial aspect of the thalamus with the stria medularis thalami and the often seen massa intermedia or interthalamic adhesion (which is gray matter; therefore not a commissure), the habenula, habenular commissure, and the pineal gland. The C-shaped stria terminalis is located at the border between the thalamus and the body of the caudate nucleus, in the lateral ventricle. Axial, coronal, and parasagittal sections show the lateral surface of the thalamus being separated from the lentiform nucleus by the posterior limb of the internal capsule, not to be confused with the external medullary lamina of the thalamus (white matter) that contains clusters of neuronal bodies that are together known as the thalamic reticular nucleus. Due to the anatomical proximity, the thalamus, internal capsule (posterior limb and genu), and lentiform nucleus largely share a common vascular supply; therefore, certain vascular lesions could affect more than one of these structures and with significant clinical manifestations, even if they are relatively small in size.

The internal medullary lamina of the thalamus (also white matter) anatomically divides the thalamus into anterior, medial, lateral, and intralaminar nuclear groups. In addition, there are midline nuclei, situated on the medial surface of the thalamus and representing a rostral continuation of the periaqueductal gray.

With the exception of the reticular, intralaminar, and midline nuclei (which are collectively considered nonspecific nuclei), the rest of the thalamic nuclei (thus specific) could be classified from a functional point of view into relay and association nuclei, based on their input and especially output.

As their name implies, the relay nuclei are intermediary stations that convey information from specific systems (e.g., somatosensory, visual, auditory, motor, limbic) to the corresponding specialized regions of the cerebral cortex. The association nuclei are different than the relay nuclei due to their input (largely from cortical areas with contributions from subcortical structures) and output (to association cortical areas).

The relay nuclear groups are: anterior (important input includes the mammillothalamic tract; output to the cingulate gyrus); ventral anterior and ventral lateral nuclei (both are collectively known as the motor thalamus, which receives input from the ipsilateral basal nuclei and contralateral cerebellum and projects to motor cortex); ventral posterolateral nucleus (relays somatosensory information from the body); ventral posteromedial nucleus (relays somatosensory information from the face, as well as taste); lateral geniculate nucleus (part of the visual pathway); medial geniculate nucleus (part of the auditory pathway); and lateral dorsal nucleus (input largely from hippocampus, output to the cingulate gyrus).

The largest association (and also the largest thalamic) nuclear group is the pulvinar, which forms the posterior part of the thalamus, which is well connected with the large parieto-occipitotemporal association cortex. The dorsomedial nuclear group (important connections with the prefrontal cortex) and lateral posterior group (connections with the parietal lobe) are also association nuclear groups. The lateral dorsal nucleus is sometimes included in this category as well.

The nonspecific nuclei exert modulatory influences at cortical and subcortical levels (bilaterally). The reticular nuclear group is different than the other thalamic nuclei because, although it receives input from cortex (corticothalamic fibers) it has no cortical output (no thalamocortical fibers); instead, it projects to and has a modulatory influence on other thalamic nuclear groups.

Due to the crossing of various pathways, the clinical manifestations of the thalamic syndrome (sensory ataxia, anesthesia and intense, wide-spread "thalamic" pain) are contralateral to the affected (posterior) thalamus.

The hypothalamus consists of clusters of neurons, forming nuclear groups that are mainly related to the control of visceral functions through both neural (autonomic) and endocrine mechanisms and coordinates drive-related behaviors. It has important neural connections including the thalamus, neurohypophysis (posterior lobe of the pituitary gland), amygdala, septal nuclei, hippocampus, retina, motor and sensory centers in the brainstem, and spinal cord and reticular formation nuclei.

Some of the most important connections of the hypothalamus are via the fornix (mainly with the hippocampal formation and thalamus), stria terminalis and ventral amygdalofugal bundle (mainly with amygdala), medial forebrain bundle, dorsal longitudinal fasciculus, and the mammillotegmetal and mammillothalamic tracts. Another important connection is through the hypothalamo-hypophyseal portal system, modulating the activity of the anterior hypophysis (anterior lobe of the pituitary gland). Functionally, the hypothalamus can be divided into lateral, medial, and periventricular (i.e., third ventricle) areas or zones, with further rostrocaudal subdivisions, many of them with specific functions (e.g., "centers" for feeding, satiety, thermoregulation).

Cranial Nerves I (Olfactory), II (Optic), and III (Oculomotor)—Supratentorial Location

The first two pairs of cranial nerves are not truly cranial nerves but extensions of the brain (telencephalon and diencephalon, respectively).

The first cranial nerve (olfactory nerve) passes from the olfactory nasal mucosa to the anterior medial region of the anterior cranial fossa. In doing so, the fibers pass as olfactory filia through the small foramina of the cribriform plate and reach the olfactory bulbs which gives rise to the olfactory tracts. The olfactory tracts course posteriorly along the cribriform plate and planum sphenoidale and terminate opposite the anterior perforated substance at the olfactory trigone. At this point, the olfactory nerve divides into three striae (or roots). The lateral olfactory stria first passes laterally along the horizontal Sylvian cistern and then medially to terminate in the medial temporal lobe on or near the uncus. The intermediate olfactory stria terminates at the anterior perforated substance, forming a slight elevation called the olfactory tubercle. The medial olfactory stria courses superiorly and medially to reach the subcallosal and precommissural septal regions near the rostrum and genu of the corupus callosum.

The second cranial nerve (optic nerve) consists of the axons of the ganglion cells of the neural retina and arises at the posterior pole of the globe (eyeball) in a region called the lamina cribrosa. The optic nerve then courses posteriorly within the orbit, passes through the optic canal and becomes intracranial. The intracranial optic nerves (prechiasmatic or cisternal segments) lead to the optic chiasm where the medial (nasal) fibers of the optic nerves cross to the contralateral side. The optic tracts extend posteriorly from the chiasm, curve posterolaterally around the cerebral peduncle and divides into two bands. The larger lateral band (most of the fibers) projects to the lateral geniculate body of the thalamus while the smaller medial band extends near the medial geniculate body of the thalamus on the way to the pretectal nuclei. Efferent axons from the lateral geniculate body form the optic radiations, which run as a broad fiber tract to the calcarine fissure.

The third cranial nerve (oculomotor) is formed by the oculomotor nuclear complex proper and the Edinger–Westphal parasympathetic nuclei (located dorsal to the motor nuclei of cranial nerve [CN] III) in the midbrain at the level of the superior colliculus. The combined fascicles run anteriorly extending through the medial longitudinal fasciculus, red nucleus, and substantia nigra to exit the midbrain along the lateral aspect of the interpeduncular cistern (i.e., medial aspect of the cerebral peduncle). They pass between the posterior cerebral and superior cerebellar arteries, medial to cranial nerves IV. Their course extends inferior to the posterior communicating arteries and medial to the free edge of the tentorium cerebelli. After crossing the petroclinoid ligament (Gruber's ligament), they enter the superior aspect of the lateral dura covering the cavernous sinus and exit the intracranial compartment through the superior orbital fissure.

INFRATENTORIAL COMPARTMENT

The midbrain (mesencephalon) passes through the tentorial notch and is the conduit between the supratentorial compartment and the infratentorial compartment (lying in the posterior cranial fossa, caudal to the tentorium cerebelli). The infratentorial compartment hosts the cerebellum, pons, medulla oblongata, and the intracranial segments of the cranial nerves associated with them. Each of the three longitudinal subdivisions of the brainstem is connected to the cerebellum via a pair of cerebellar peduncles: superior (brachium conjunctivum), middle (brachium pontis), and inferior (restiform bodies) cerebellar peduncles, respectively. The superior cerebellar peduncles contain axons that are mainly efferent from the cerebellum, the middle cerebellar peduncles (which are the largest) contain only axons afferent to the cerebellum and the inferior cerebellar peduncles contain mainly axons afferent to the cerebellum.

In addition to the previously-mentioned longitudinal subdivision of the brainstem, it is also useful from an anatomical, functional, and clinical perspective to look at the brainstem as an arrangement of structures from medial to lateral (as discussed with the development and illustrated by the arrangement of cranial nerves) and from posterior to anterior: tectum (found only in the midbrain), tegmentum (composed of gray and white matter), and large white matter structures located more anteriorly (cerebral peduncles for the midbrain, basilar pons for the pons and pyramids for the medulla oblongata).

■ ANTERIOR (VENTRAL) ASPECT OF THE BRAINSTEM

Beginning at the level of the medulla, the ventral surface of the brainstem is remarkable for two longitudinally oriented elevations on each side of the midline representing the medullary pyramids and, lateral to each of them, the inferior olives (containing the inferior olivary nuclei). The hypoglossal nerve emerges as a bundle of nerve filaments from the pre-olivary sulci (separating the medullary pyramids from the inferior olives), while the glossopharyngeal and vagus nerves are attached to the post-olivary sulci.

The pontomedullary junction contains the attachments of three cranial nerves: abducens (cranial nerve VI which arises just off the midline) and the facial (cranial nerve VII) and vestibulocochlear (cranial nerve VIII), which arise laterally from the post-olivary sulcus. The ventral surface of pons is marked by the large and horizontally ridged prominence of the basilar pons (basis pontis) with the sulcus for the basilar artery in the midline and the attachments of the trigeminal nerves (sensory and motor components) more laterally on each side. The middle cerebellar peduncles are located even more laterally and are the only cerebellar peduncles visible on the anterior aspect of the brainstem.

The anterior surface of the mesencephalon is notable for the V-shaped presence of the longitudinally ridged cerebral peduncles (crus cerebri) and the interpeduncular fossa (cistern) between them, where the oculomotor nerves (CNIII) emerge.

If the tentorium cerebelli were removed, the location of uncus (part of the temporal lobe) next to the tentorial notch becomes visible and explains why the midbrain and/or occulomotor nerve(s) are affected in uncal herniations.

■ POSTERIOR (DORSAL) ASPECT OF THE BRAINSTEM

The dorsal aspect of the brainstem (with the cerebellum removed) represents a more complex anatomic organization. All three pairs of cerebellar peduncles are sectioned and seen in this view.

The spinal cord continues cranially to the caudal medulla (closed medulla), showing on each side (from medial to lateral) the gracile and cuneate tubercles. They overlie the nuclei with the same names that contain the secondary neurons of the pathways that convey information about precise touch, pressure, vibration, and conscious position sense from the same side of the body. These secondary neurons receive their information from the axons in the dorsal columns (gracile and cuneate fasciculi) and project their axons via the medial lemniscus to the contralateral ventroposterolateral thalamic nucleus where the tertiary neurons are located. Lateral to the cuneate tubercle is the posterolateral sulcus that separates it from the trigeminal tubercle (also known as the tuberculum cinereum), overlying the spinal trigeminal tract that contains axons of the primary neurons that convey pain, temperature, and crude touch stimuli from the ipsilateral face to the spinal trigeminal nucleus.

The rostral medulla (open medulla) together with the posterior aspect of the pons forms the rhomboid fossa (the floor of the fourth ventricle), with the median sulcus in the middle and the sulcus limitans on each side (showing the limit between the location of motor [medial] and sensory [lateral] nuclei of cranial nerves). The striae medullares runs transversely across the fourth ventricular floor and divides it into the inferior medullary and superior pontine triangles. The vestibular area (overlying the vestibular nuclear complex) forms the most lateral part of the rhomboid fossa as part of both rostral medulla and caudal pons, a position that is consistent with the developmental arrangement of sensory nuclei. The cochlear nuclei have a similar position.

The medullary part of the rhomboid fossa is flanked by the inferior cerebellar peduncles and shows from medial to lateral two prominences: the hypoglossal trigone (overlying the hypoglossal nucleus—cranial nerve XII, which is somatomotor) and the vagal trigone (overlying the dorsal motor nucleus of the vagus nerve—cranial nerve X, which is a parasympathetic nucleus).

The obex resides at the caudal aspect of the medullary triangle and is the conduit for CSF entering the central canal of the spinal cord. Close to the obex and the vagal trigone is the area postrema, one of the circumventricular organs that lacks a tight blood–brain barrier and initiates the vomiting reflex associated with the detection of toxic substances in circulation.

The pontine triangle represents the floor of the fourth ventricle superior to the striae medullares. The symmetrical facial colliculus, located close to the midline, is formed by fibers of the facial nerve—cranial nerve VII looping around the abducens nucleus—cranial nerve VI. Locus (nucleus) ceruleus is located laterally, at the edge of the rhomboid fossa, at mid and rostral pontine levels and contains noradrenergic neurons that project to the entire CNS.

The superior medullary velum connects the right and left superior cerebellar peduncles and is part of the roof of the fourth ventricle. The small para-brachial recess represents an extension of the subarachnoid space (not within the fourth ventricle) and is located laterally between the superior and middle cerebellar peduncles.

The dorsal surface of the mesencephalon is part of the tectum and is characterized by the corpora quadrigemina (formed by the superior and inferior colliculi), which represents the floor of the quadrigeminal plate cistern. The pineal gland which is part of the diencephalon (epithalamus) lies superior to the colliculi. The proximity between the two structures explains why tumors of the pineal gland often result in obstructive hydrocephalus due to compression of the cerebral aqueduct and Parinaud's syndrome (paralysis of upward gaze) secondary to compression of the superior tectum. The trochlear nerves (cranial nerve IV) emerge just caudal to the inferior colliculi.

On each side, the inferior colliculus is connected via the brachium of the inferior colliculus to the medial geniculate body (part of the thalamus, overlying the medial geniculate nucleus). All of these structures are part of the auditory pathway. Similarly, the superior colliculus is connected via the brachium of the superior colliculus with the lateral geniculate body of the thalamus. The superior colliculus is a highly layered structure that receives various types of input (visual, auditory, somatosensory) and is therefore involved in multiple circuits and functions including, but not limited to, control of eye movements, visual reflexes, and visual attention. The center for upward gaze lies close to the superior colliculi and diseases in this region can result in Parinaud's syndrome.

■ CRANIAL NERVES IV THROUGH XII

Cranial nerves IV through X and XII emerge from the brainstem, traverse the subarachnoid space, and exit the intracranial compartment through specified foramina. Although the spinal accessory nerve retains its name as cranial nerve XI, it has been accepted that this nerve is limited to its spinal component (the fibers that were previously considered as the cranial part of this nerve run in fact with the vagus nerve).

Cranial nerve IV (trochlear) is the only cranial nerve to cross the midline and be attached to the dorsal aspect of the brainstem. The nucleus is located just ventral to the periaqueductal gray matter at the level of the inferior colliculus. The fascicular segment passes posterior and caudally in the periaquedutal gray matter, then decussating in the superior medullary velum. It emerges from the contralateral midbrain just caudal to the level of the inferior colliculi, to enter the quadrigeminal plate cistern, and then passes anteriorly between the edges of the tentorial insicura adjacent to the midbrain. It passes between the posterior cerebral and superior cerebellar arteries lateral and inferior to the oculomotor nerves (CN III) and then passes through the lateral dural wall of the cavernous sinus inferior to CN III on its way to the orbit via the superior orbital fissure. Cranial nerve IV is the smallest and has the longest intracranial length (about 7.5 cm) of any cranial nerve.

Cranial nerve V (trigeminal) is the largest nerve of the brainstem and is attached at the transition between the basilar pons and the middle cerebellar peduncle. It consists of a larger (sensory) component and a smaller (motor) component. The nuclei of the trigeminal nerve (three sensory and one motor) are located at various levels of the brainstem along its entire length. The trigeminal nerve extends anteriorly from the medial cerebellopontine angle cistern as the pre-ganglionic segment, and extends into Meckel's cave via the porus trigeminus. The trigeminal (Gasserian) ganglion is a sensory ganglion bathed with CSF in Meckel's cave and accounts for only one tenth of the volume of Meckel's cave. Out of the three divisions of the trigeminal nerve, the mandibular nerve (V3) is the only mixed (sensory and motor) one and exits the middle cranial fossa through the foramen ovale to reach the infratemporal fossa. The ophthalmic nerve (V1) and maxillary nerve (V2) pass anteriorly within the inferior lateral dural wall of the cavernous sinus. V1 then passes anteriorly through the superior orbital fissure to enter the orbit while V2 exits earlier within the cavernous sinus and passes through the foramen rotundum to enter the pterygopalatine fossa.

Cranial nerve VI (abducens nerve) exits the ventral brainstem at the pontomedullary junction, just off the midline. It passes anteriorly and superiorly in the prepontine cistern to enter Dorello's canal posterior to the clivus. This canal is considered to be located between two dural leaves and is felt by some to be a CSF filled invagination into the petroclival dura matter. It courses across the sulcus for the abducens nerve at the petrous apex to enter the cavernous sinus where it lies adjacent to the lateral aspect of the intracavernous internal carotid artery (the closest nerve to the artery in this region). It exits the cavernous sinus to enter the orbit via the superior orbital fissure.

Cranial nerve VII (facial nerve) and VIII (vestibulocochochlear or acustico-vestibular nerve) are attached to the brainstem in the lateral part of the pontomedullary junction (with cranial nerve VIII being the most lateral and posterior of the two). They course through the cerebellopontine angle cistern on their way to the internal auditory (acoustic) canal (meatus). The facial nerve consists of a larger (motor) root and a smaller (sensory) root, also known as the intermediate nerve.

Cranial nerve IX (glossopharyngeal) and X (vagus) emerge from the post-olivary sulcus of the medulla oblongata. Cranial nerve IX passes laterally through the glossopharyngeal meatus to enter pars nervosa of the jugular foramen, while cranial nerve X passes laterally through the vagal meatus to enter pars vascularis of the jugular foramen.

Cranial nerve XI (accessory nerve) arises from the cervical spinal cord between the posterior cervical roots and the denticulate ligament (more ventrally), ascends through the foramen magnum and exits the intracranial compartment through pars vascularis of the jugular foramen. This current concept that CN XI has no cranial contribution in most individuals challenges the more traditional concept that there is a cranial contribution to this nerve via rootlets emerging from the caudal medulla originating in the nucleus ambiguous. These cranial rootlets are now felt to contribute only to CN X.

Cranial nerve XII (hypoglossal) exits the brainstem at the pre-olivary sulcus (between the olive and pyramid) as multiple nerve filaments that converge and then pass laterally to exit the skull through the hypoglossal canal (within the occipital condyle).

Cranial nerves IX–XII enter the carotid sheath after exiting their respective skull base foramina. However, only cranial nerve X (vagus nerve) travels within the carotid sheath for the entire length of the neck.

■ CEREBELLUM

While the anatomic/morphologic descriptions of the cerebellum are organized vertically with divisions into the anterior lobe, the posterior lobe, and the flocculonodular lobes (and has clinical syndromes corresponding to this classification), the functional organization is quite different within the divisions in a transverse, median to lateral framework. Functionally the cerebellum consists of the flocculonodulus (phylogenetically the oldest part, known also as archicerebellum), the vermis and paravermal regions (paleocerebellum), and the cerebellar hemispheres (the newest and largest part, also named neocerebellum). Each of these divisions is vertically associated with different deep cerebellar nuclei and has specific connections (inputs and outputs).

Flocculonodulus is also named the vestibulocerebellum due to its strong connections with the vestibular system as the main inputs originate in both the vestibular nucleus and ganglion and outputs project to the vestibular nuclei either directly or through the fastigial nucleus. Outputs also reach the reticular formation nuclei. The main role of the flocculonodulus is to work together with the vestibular system in maintaining equilibrium of the body and stability of images on the fovea of the retina.

The vermis and paravermal region are known as the spinocerebellum due to the strong input they receive from the spinal cord (via spinocerebellar and cuneocerebellar tracts). It also receives input from the trigeminal and reticular formation nuclei. The vermis projects to the fastigial nucleus, which in turn projects to the vestibular and reticular formation nuclei. The paravermis projects to the interposed nuclei (globose and emboliform) that in turn project via the superior cerebellar peduncles (brachium conjunctivum), mainly to the red nucleus and to a lesser extent to the thalamus. The role of the spinocerebellum is related to control of axial and proximal limb musculature.

The lateral portion of the cerebellar hemisphere is the largest; therefore, it receives its main input via the largest cerebellar peduncle (the middle cerebellar peduncle, also named the brachium pontis) and sends its output to the largest and most lateral of the deep cerebellar nuclei, which is the dentate nucleus. The lateral cerebellar hemisphere (neocerebellum) is also called the cerebrocerebellum or the pontocerebellum, due to its connections with large cortical areas of the contralateral cerebral hemisphere. The main cerebellar input in this circuit is formed by corticopontine fibers that synapse in the pontine nuclei with pontocerebellar fibers that cross the midline and enter the cerebellum via the middle cerebellar peduncle (brachium pontis). The cerebellar output is via the dentate nucleus that projects mainly to the contralateral motor thalamus via the superior cerebellar peduncles (brachium conjunctivum). The fibers of the dentothalamic tract cross the midline in the decussation of the superior cerebellar peduncles, located in the caudal midbrain. Other fibers from the dentate nucleus project to the contralateral red nucleus. The cerebrocerebellum plays important functions in the planning of movement, coordination of the ongoing movements of the distal muscles of the limbs but also in complex functions, such as cognition, spatiotemporal anticipation, motor learning, memory, speech and has influences on visceromotor functions. Lesions affecting one cerebellar hemisphere will result in ipsilateral motor clinical manifestations.

A special role in the cerebellar connections and functions (especially related to motor learning) is played by the inferior olivary nuclei that project their axons as climbing fibers directly to the Purkinje cells in the contralateral cerebellar cortex.

INTRACRANIAL CSF SPACES AND VENTRICLES

Cerebrospinal fluid production and resorption has been previously discussed in this chapter. This section deals with the distribution of CSF intracranially.

The ventricular system is filled with cerebrospinal fluid but also contains choroid plexus (specialized epithelium with capillaries, lacking a blood–brain barrier, which has the capacity to produce cerebrospinal fluid and remove metabolic waste material). Choroid plexus is present in the low cerebellopontine angle cisterns and extends into the fourth ventricle through the foramen of Luschka. It extends along the roof of the fourth ventricle, roof of the third ventricle, through the foramen of Monroe, along the floor of the lateral ventricle, around the atrium/trigone, and along the roof of the temporal horn. Normally, there is no choroid plexus within the aqueduct of Sylvius, frontal horns or occipital horns of the lateral ventricles.

The ventricular system is composed of two lateral ventricles which can be subdivided into the frontal horns, bodies, atria (or trigones), occipital and temporal horns. The lateral ventricles are continuous with a single midline third ventricle via the interventricular foramen of Monroe. Posteriorly, the third ventricle continues via the aqueduct of Sylvius, a single small caliber channel connecting the third ventricle with the fourth ventricle. Cerebrospinal fluid leaves the fourth ventricle via the dorsal midline foramen of Magendie and the lateral recesses, the foramen of Luschka. The lining of the ventricular system consists of a layer of ependymal cells.

The cerebrospinal fluid outside of the ventricular system resides within the subarachnoid space in which it circulates. Cerebrospinal fluid produced within the ventricle exits the fourth ventricle through the dorsal midline aperture called the foramen of Magendie and through lateral apertures called the foramen of Luschka. The CSF normally circulates upward along the convexity surfaces from the basilar cisterns toward the vertex. The primary route for reabsorption into the venous system occurs through specialized structures of the arachnoid called arachnoid (or pacchionian) granulations.

Extraventricular expansions of the subarachnoid spaces are called cisterns or fissures. Many of the cerebral cisterns are named by adjacent structures. For instance, the cistern immediately posterior to the quadrigeminal plate is called the quadrigeminal plate cistern. A large number of cisterns exist including the cisterna magna, the cerebellopontine angle cistern, the perimedullary cistern, the prepontine cistern, the interpeduncular cistern, the perimesencephalic cistern, the crural cistern, the retropulvinar (retrothalamic) cistern, the suprasellar (pentagonal) cistern, the horizontal sylvian cistern, the sylvian fissure, and the interhemispheric fissure.

Color Illustrations of the Human Brain Using 3D Modeling Techniques

ILLUSTRATOR'S (ARTIST'S) STATEMENT

The relationships of the various structures in the human body are inherently complex, and it is my opinion that a full understanding of anatomy is best achieved through studying the structures in multiple dimensions. Classically, this has been achieved through the surgical or laboratory setting and by incorporating information yielded from cross-sectional images and two-dimensional (2D) atlases. This can be daunting and has its own limitations when applied to the brain. For example, an understanding of the surface anatomy of the brain can be particularly challenging to extrapolate from two-dimensional images, and certain structures, such as the cranial nerve nuclei, are only appreciable on the microscopic level. Keeping these factors in mind, the illustrations in this book are meant to be as clear as possible with multiple view points while maintaining a high degree of macroscopic and microscopic accuracy. All of the illustrations presented are derived from 3D models based on real CT and MRI images of the brain and are the culmination of hundreds of hours of work. The process, described on the following page, resulted in anatomically precise 3D scenes that can be manipulated to accommodate any view point. Displayed here in static 2D images, these scenes can also be rendered as full animations, 3D printed, or can be displayed in real time in a fully interactive 360° environment via an online platform.

THE PROCESS

The preliminary 3D model base for the sulcal and gyral anatomy was reconstructed from the same volumetric T1 weighted MRI images seen elsewhere in this book. This was achieved on a dedicated workstation using Freesurfer software imaging analysis suite. The software created segmented 3D mesh data based on the original digital imaging and communications in medicine (DICOM) data. The base model consisted of approximately 1.5 million triangles and was imported into the free and open source 3D animation suite, Blender, where it could be freely manipulated and sculpted. Using integrated picture archiving and communication system (PACS) 3D reconstruction software, a skull model was extracted from high resolution 0.9 mm axial CT images of the head and was also imported into the initial setup. The original cross-sectional images from the MRI were loaded into the scene as background references to ensure accuracy at every step. The cortical surface model was adjusted and refined, the skull model was modified to fit the MRI-derived brain (these models were obtained from two different subjects), and models of the midbrain and cerebellum were painstakingly hand-sculpted. The cranial nerve illustrations were derived from the hand-sculpted models using Boolean operators to segment the midbrain into slices at multiple levels. The cranial nerve nuclei were then modeled and placed into their appropriate locations after comparison with microscopic atlases. Lastly, the cranial nerves themselves were modeled and idealized using vectorized paths based on the heavily T2 weighted images used in this book for reference. All told, these efforts yielded a 3D model of the brain comprised of approximately 2.1 million triangles and 1.1 GB of raw 3D data. Scenes were lit with a custom virtual lighting setup, and multiple "cameras" were placed throughout. The models were custom shaded, textured, and rendered through an unbiased photorealistic graphics processing unit (GPU)-based rendering engine included in the animation suite.

FURTHER INFORMATION

■ FREESURFER

Freesurfer is software used for analysis and visualization of brain data. It was developed at the Martinos Center for Biomedical Imaging by the Laboratory for Computational Neuroimaging. It is free and available for download online.

http://surfer.nmr.mgh.harvard.edu/

■ BLENDER

Blender is a free and open source 3D animation suite. It is cross-platform and runs on Linux, Windows, and Macintosh computers. The software is supported by the nonprofit Blender Foundation, a Dutch public benefit corporation. The software is free and available for download online.

http://www.blender.org/

■ SKETCHFAB

Sketchfab is an online solution for displaying 3D models in an interactive 360° environment. The service includes free accounts for educators and students.

http://www.sketchfab.com/

COLOR ILLUSTRATIONS (FIGURES 2.1–2.18)

■ **SURFACE ANATOMY OF THE BRAIN (FIGURES 2.1–2.7, 2.9–2.10)**

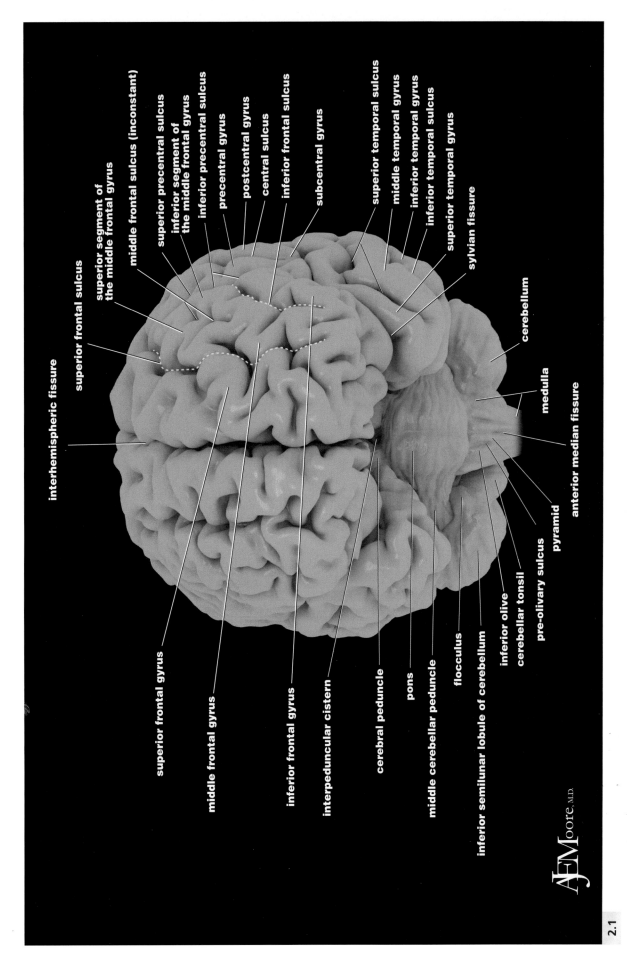

FIGURE 2.1   Gyri and sulci of the cerebrum: anterior view.

2.1

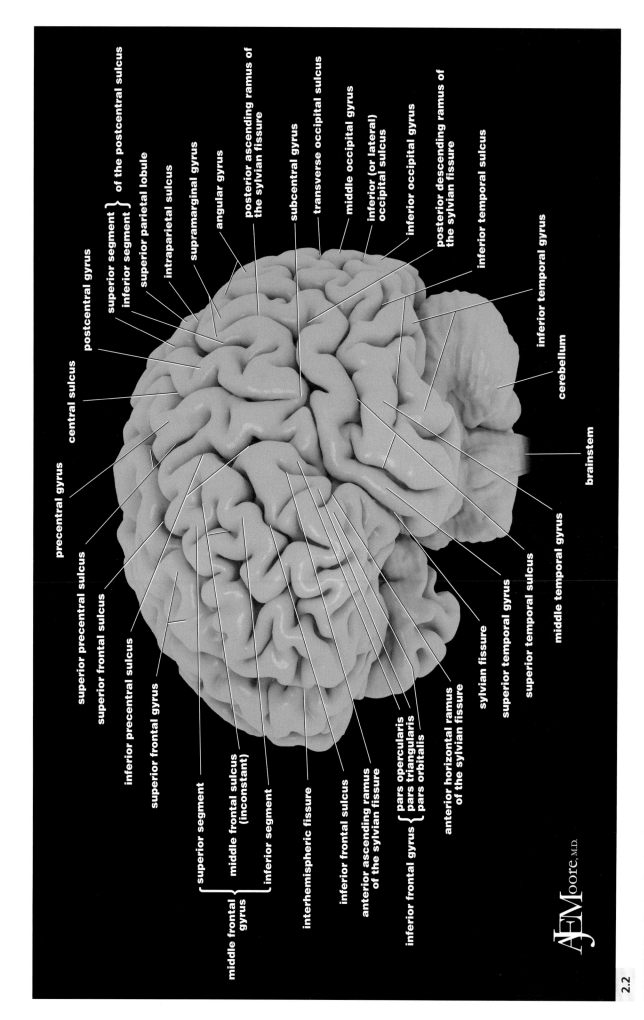

FIGURE 2.2 Gyri and sulci of the cerebrum: anterior oblique view.

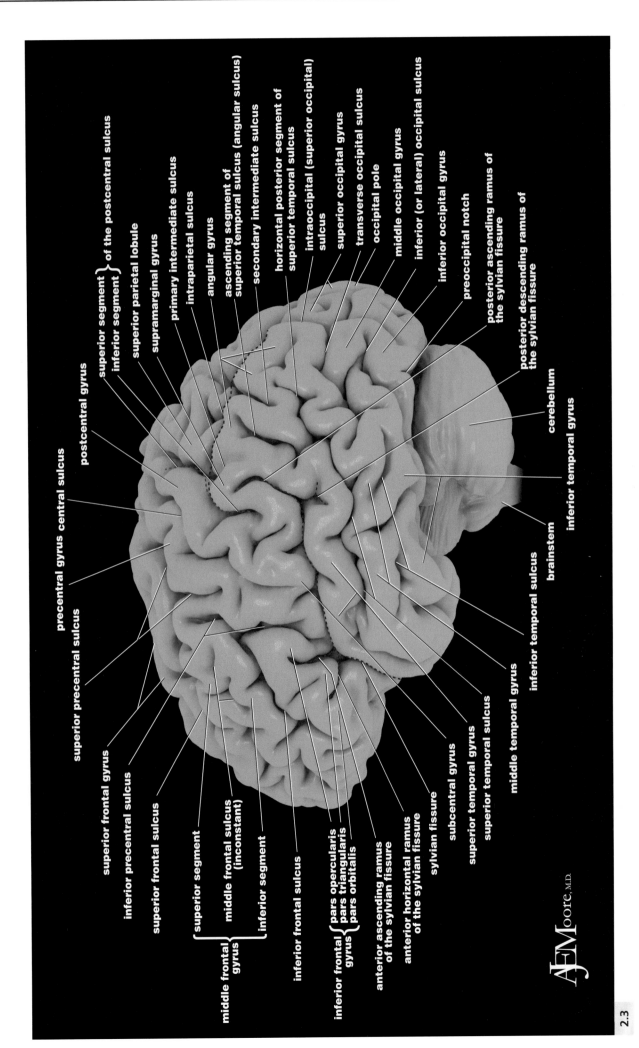

FIGURE 2.3   Gyri and sulci of the cerebrum: lateral view.

2.3

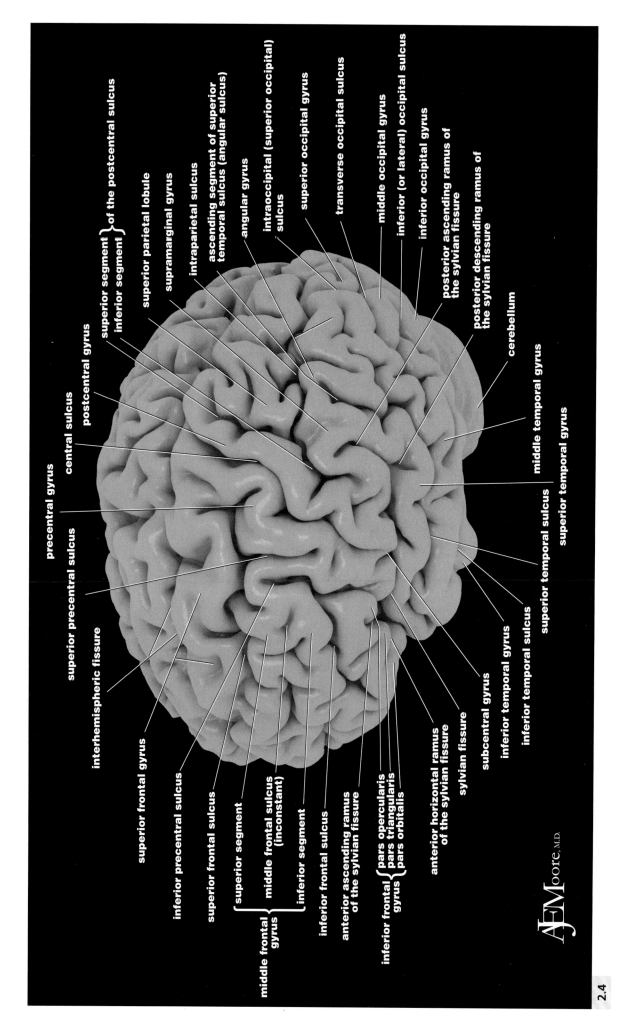

FIGURE 2.4   Gyri and sulci of the cerebrum: superior oblique view.

2.4

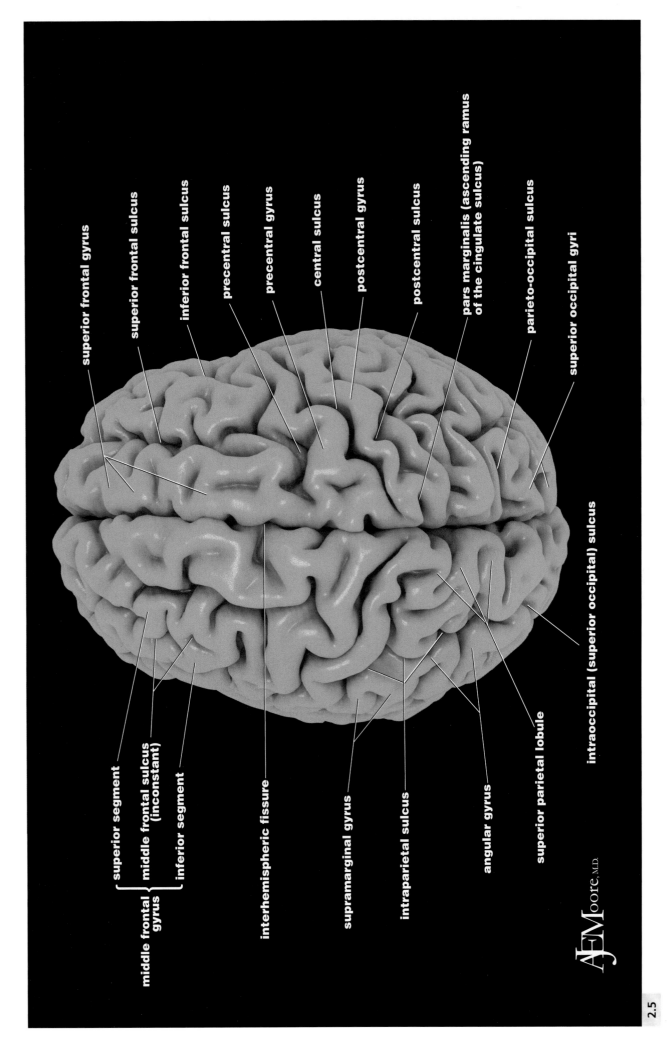

FIGURE 2.5   Gyri and sulci of the cerebrum: superior view.

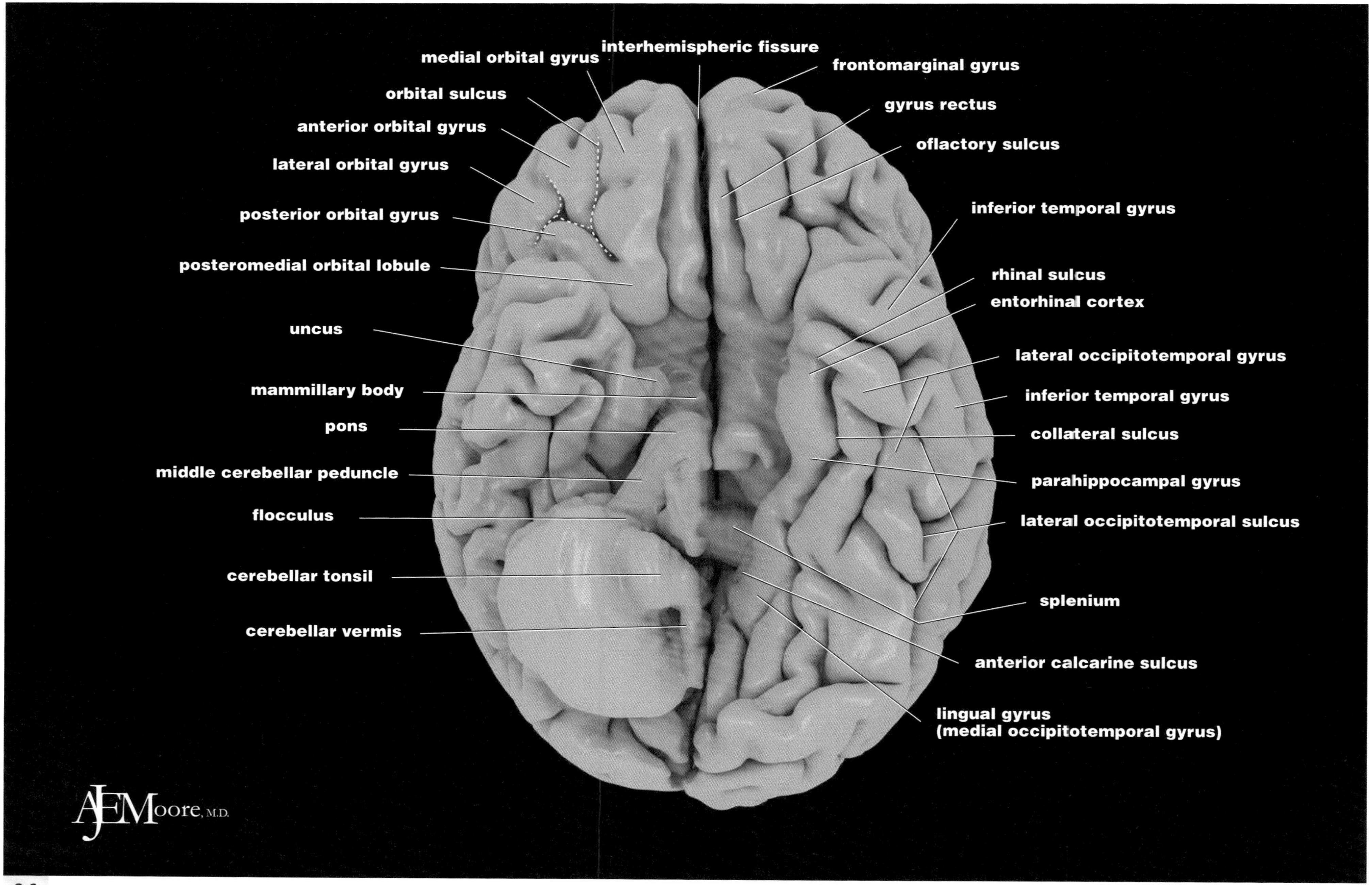

FIGURE 2.6   Gyri and sulci of the cerebrum: interior view.

2.6

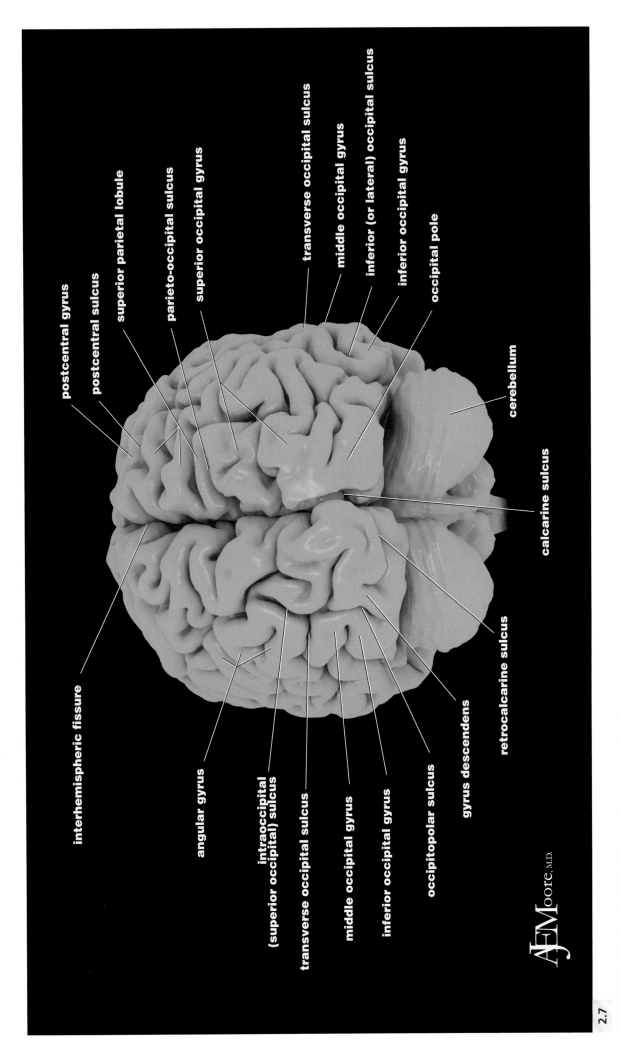

FIGURE 2.7 Gyri and sulci of the cerebrum: posterior view.

■ THE BASAL GANGLIA AND OTHER DEEP STRUCTURES

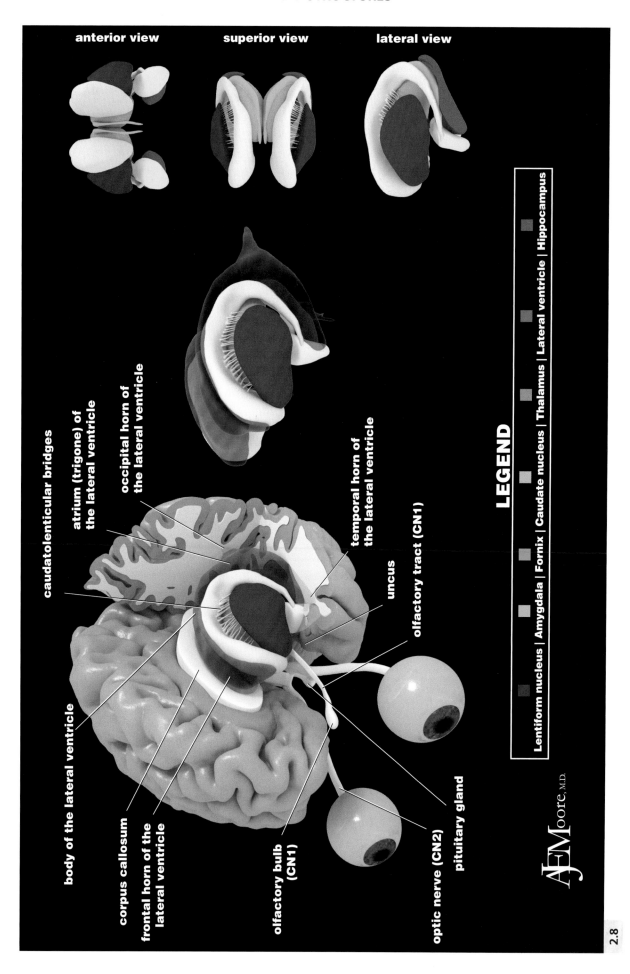

FIGURE 2.8   The basal ganglia.

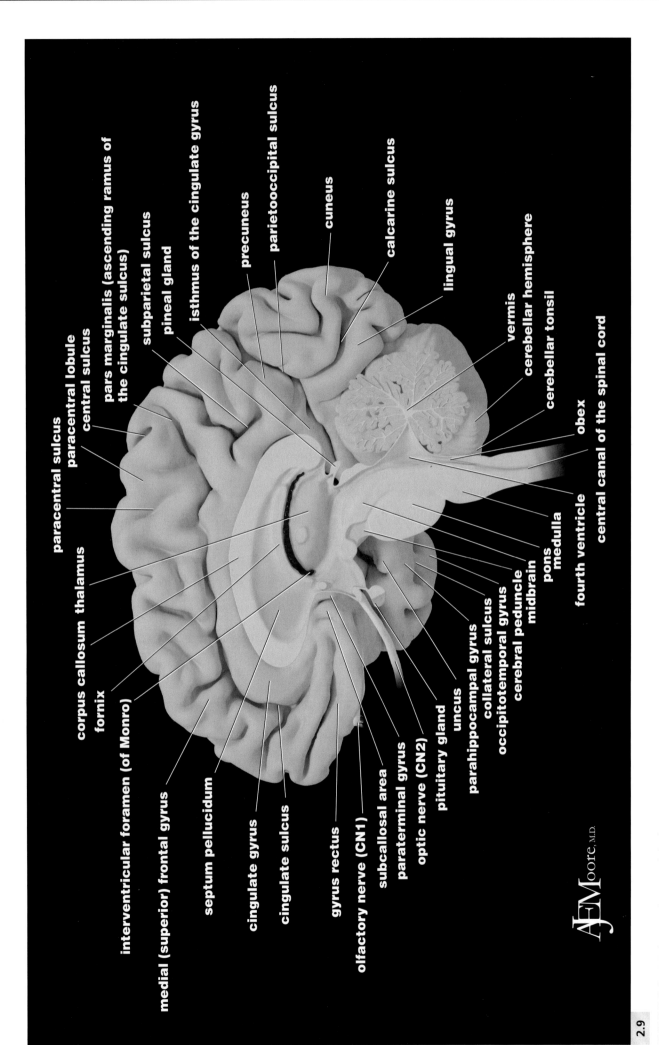

FIGURE 2.9   Midsagittal view of the brain.

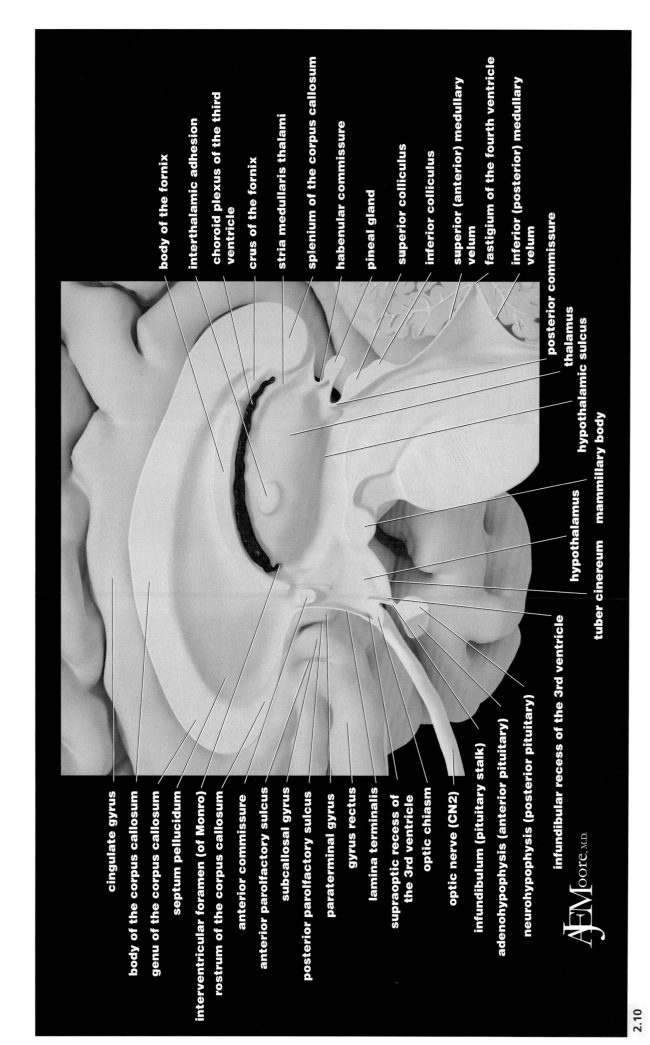

FIGURE 2.10 Midsagittal view of the brain.

2.10

■ THE CRANIAL NERVES (CN) (FIGURES 2.11–2.18)

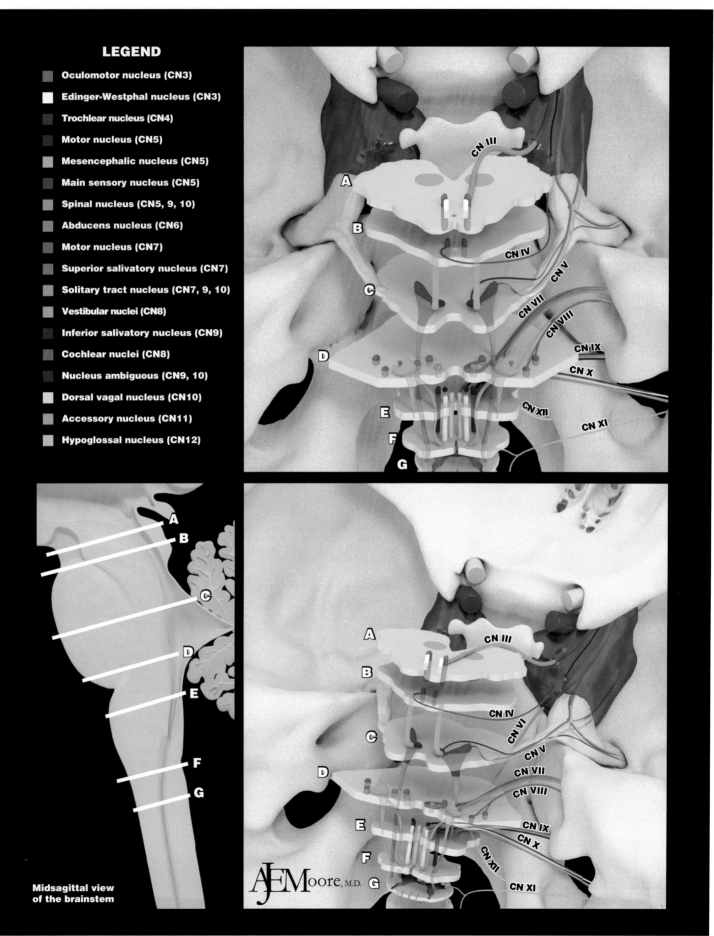

LEGEND

- Oculomotor nucleus (CN3)
- Edinger-Westphal nucleus (CN3)
- Trochlear nucleus (CN4)
- Motor nucleus (CN5)
- Mesencephalic nucleus (CN5)
- Main sensory nucleus (CN5)
- Spinal nucleus (CN5, 9, 10)
- Abducens nucleus (CN6)
- Motor nucleus (CN7)
- Superior salivatory nucleus (CN7)
- Solitary tract nucleus (CN7, 9, 10)
- Vestibular nuclei (CN8)
- Inferior salivatory nucleus (CN9)
- Cochlear nuclei (CN8)
- Nucleus ambiguous (CN9, 10)
- Dorsal vagal nucleus (CN10)
- Accessory nucleus (CN11)
- Hypoglossal nucleus (CN12)

Midsagittal view of the brainstem

AJMoore, M.D.

2.11

FIGURE 2.11   The cranial nerve nuclei.

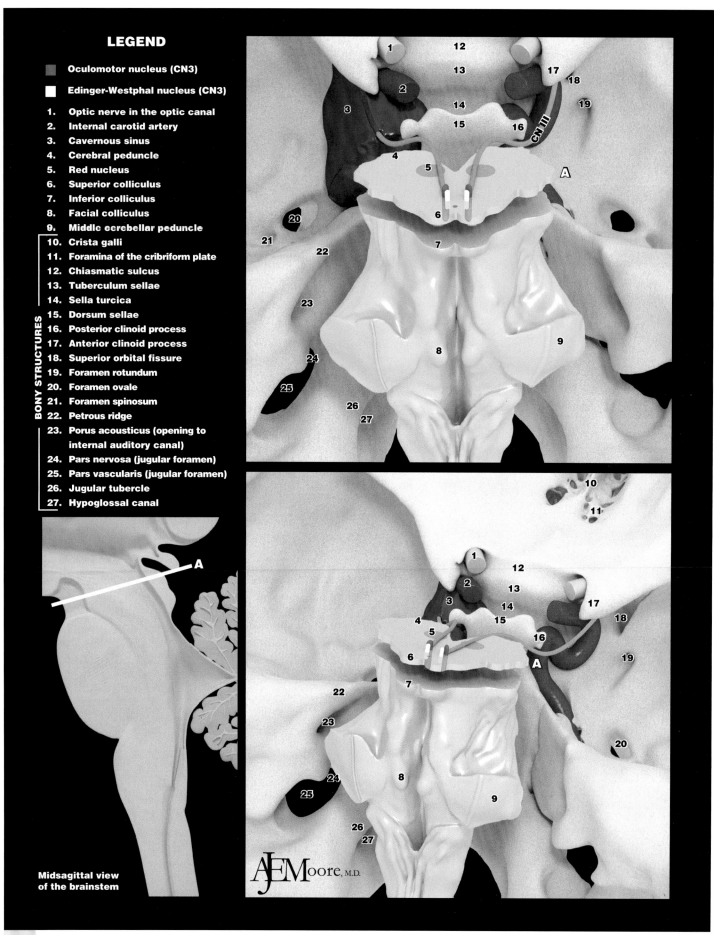

LEGEND

■ **Oculomotor nucleus (CN3)**

□ **Edinger-Westphal nucleus (CN3)**

1. **Optic nerve in the optic canal**
2. **Internal carotid artery**
3. **Cavernous sinus**
4. **Cerebral peduncle**
5. **Red nucleus**
6. **Superior colliculus**
7. **Inferior colliculus**
8. **Facial colliculus**
9. **Middle cerebellar peduncle**

BONY STRUCTURES

10. **Crista galli**
11. **Foramina of the cribriform plate**
12. **Chiasmatic sulcus**
13. **Tuberculum sellae**
14. **Sella turcica**
15. **Dorsum sellae**
16. **Posterior clinoid process**
17. **Anterior clinoid process**
18. **Superior orbital fissure**
19. **Foramen rotundum**
20. **Foramen ovale**
21. **Foramen spinosum**
22. **Petrous ridge**
23. **Porus acousticus (opening to internal auditory canal)**
24. **Pars nervosa (jugular foramen)**
25. **Pars vascularis (jugular foramen)**
26. **Jugular tubercle**
27. **Hypoglossal canal**

Midsagittal view of the brainstem

2.12

FIGURE 2.12 Oculomotor (CN III) nerve.

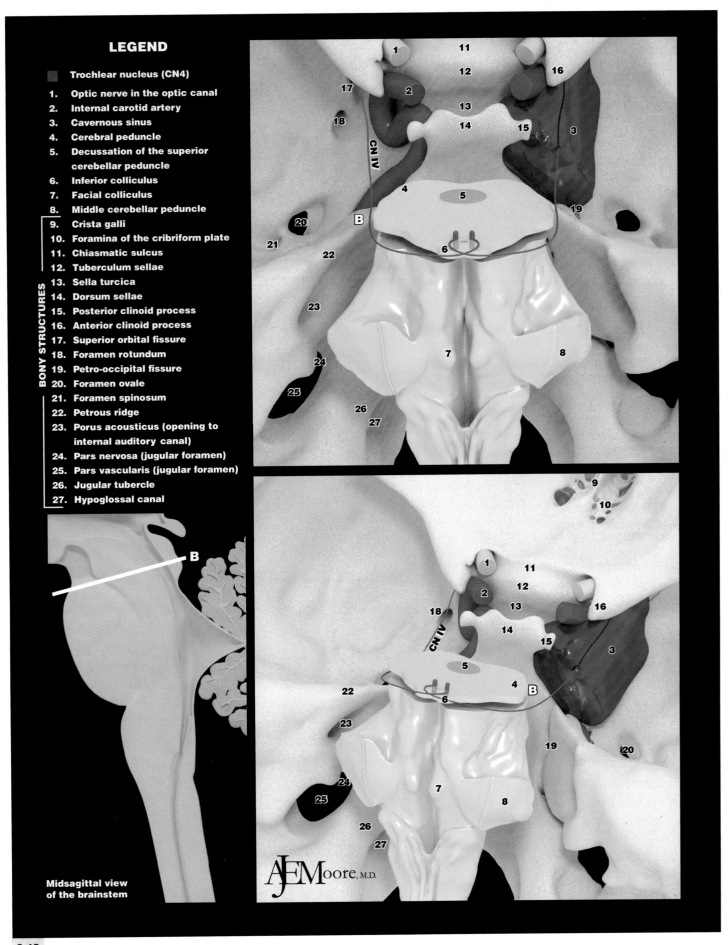

LEGEND

Trochlear nucleus (CN4)

1. Optic nerve in the optic canal
2. Internal carotid artery
3. Cavernous sinus
4. Cerebral peduncle
5. Decussation of the superior cerebellar peduncle
6. Inferior colliculus
7. Facial colliculus
8. Middle cerebellar peduncle

BONY STRUCTURES

9. Crista galli
10. Foramina of the cribriform plate
11. Chiasmatic sulcus
12. Tuberculum sellae
13. Sella turcica
14. Dorsum sellae
15. Posterior clinoid process
16. Anterior clinoid process
17. Superior orbital fissure
18. Foramen rotundum
19. Petro-occipital fissure
20. Foramen ovale
21. Foramen spinosum
22. Petrous ridge
23. Porus acousticus (opening to internal auditory canal)
24. Pars nervosa (jugular foramen)
25. Pars vascularis (jugular foramen)
26. Jugular tubercle
27. Hypoglossal canal

Midsagittal view
of the brainstem

2.13

FIGURE 2.13   Trochlear (CN IV) nerve.

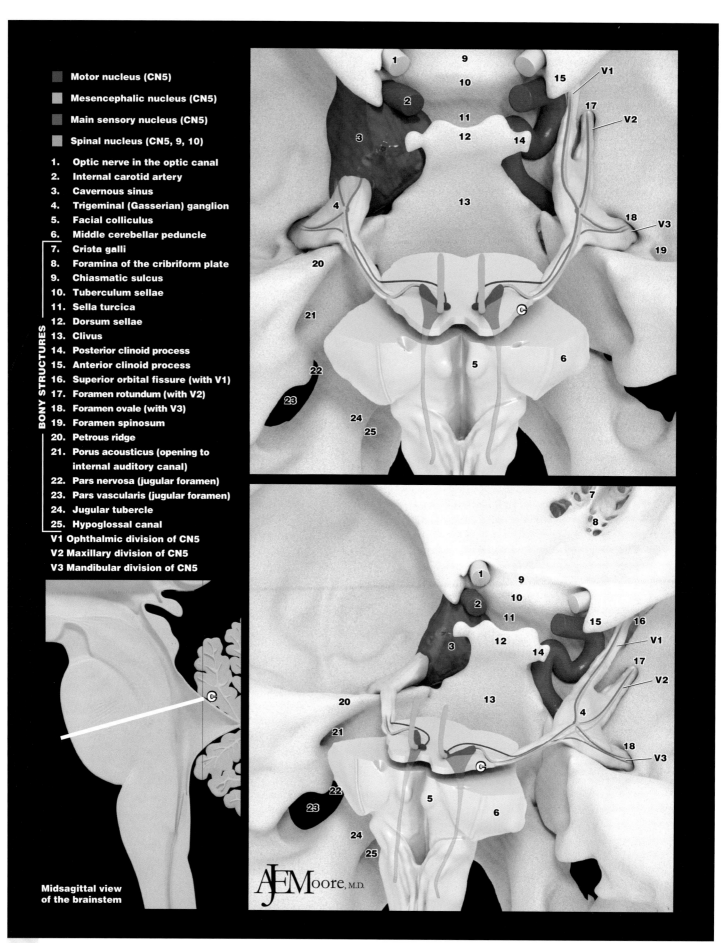

- ■ Motor nucleus (CN5)
- ■ Mesencephalic nucleus (CN5)
- ■ Main sensory nucleus (CN5)
- ■ Spinal nucleus (CN5, 9, 10)

1. Optic nerve in the optic canal
2. Internal carotid artery
3. Cavernous sinus
4. Trigeminal (Gasserian) ganglion
5. Facial colliculus
6. Middle cerebellar peduncle
7. Crista galli
8. Foramina of the cribriform plate
9. Chiasmatic sulcus
10. Tuberculum sellae
11. Sella turcica
12. Dorsum sellae
13. Clivus
14. Posterior clinoid process
15. Anterior clinoid process
16. Superior orbital fissure (with V1)
17. Foramen rotundum (with V2)
18. Foramen ovale (with V3)
19. Foramen spinosum
20. Petrous ridge
21. Porus acousticus (opening to internal auditory canal)
22. Pars nervosa (jugular foramen)
23. Pars vascularis (jugular foramen)
24. Jugular tubercle
25. Hypoglossal canal

V1 Ophthalmic division of CN5
V2 Maxillary division of CN5
V3 Mandibular division of CN5

BONY STRUCTURES

Midsagittal view of the brainstem

AJEMoore, M.D.

2.14

FIGURE 2.14 Trigmeinal (CN V) nerve.

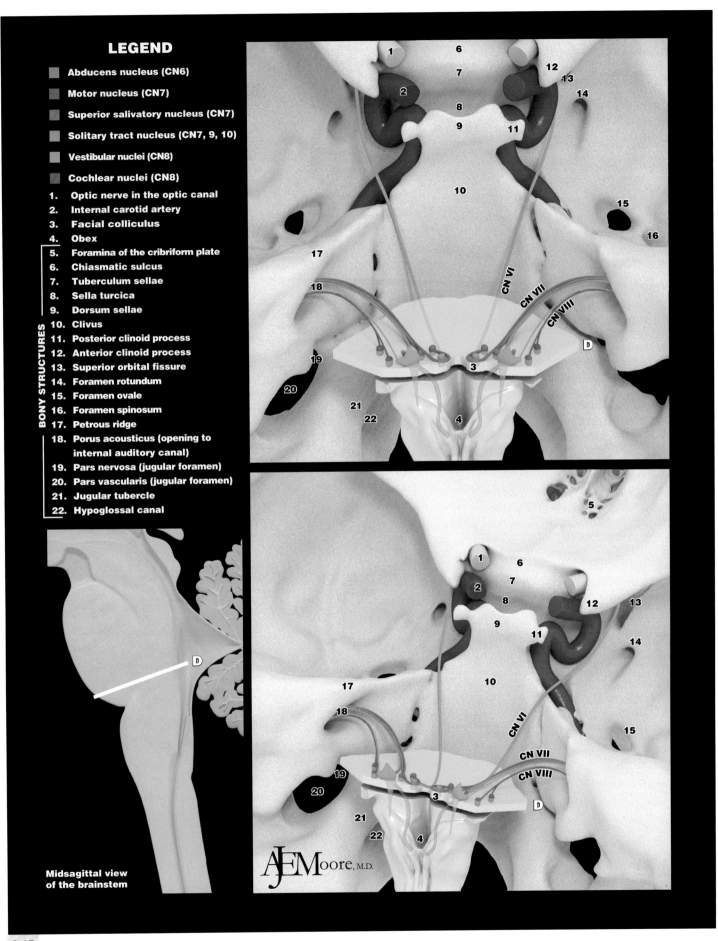

LEGEND

■ Abducens nucleus (CN6)

■ Motor nucleus (CN7)

■ Superior salivatory nucleus (CN7)

■ Solitary tract nucleus (CN7, 9, 10)

■ Vestibular nuclei (CN8)

■ Cochlear nuclei (CN8)

1. Optic nerve in the optic canal
2. Internal carotid artery
3. Facial colliculus
4. Obex
5. Foramina of the cribriform plate
6. Chiasmatic sulcus
7. Tuberculum sellae
8. Sella turcica
9. Dorsum sellae
10. Clivus
11. Posterior clinoid process
12. Anterior clinoid process
13. Superior orbital fissure
14. Foramen rotundum
15. Foramen ovale
16. Foramen spinosum
17. Petrous ridge
18. Porus acousticus (opening to internal auditory canal)
19. Pars nervosa (jugular foramen)
20. Pars vascularis (jugular foramen)
21. Jugular tubercle
22. Hypoglossal canal

BONY STRUCTURES

Midsagittal view of the brainstem

AEMoore, M.D.

2.15

FIGURE 2.15   Abducens (CN VI), facial (CN VII), and vestibulocochlear (CN VIII) nerves.

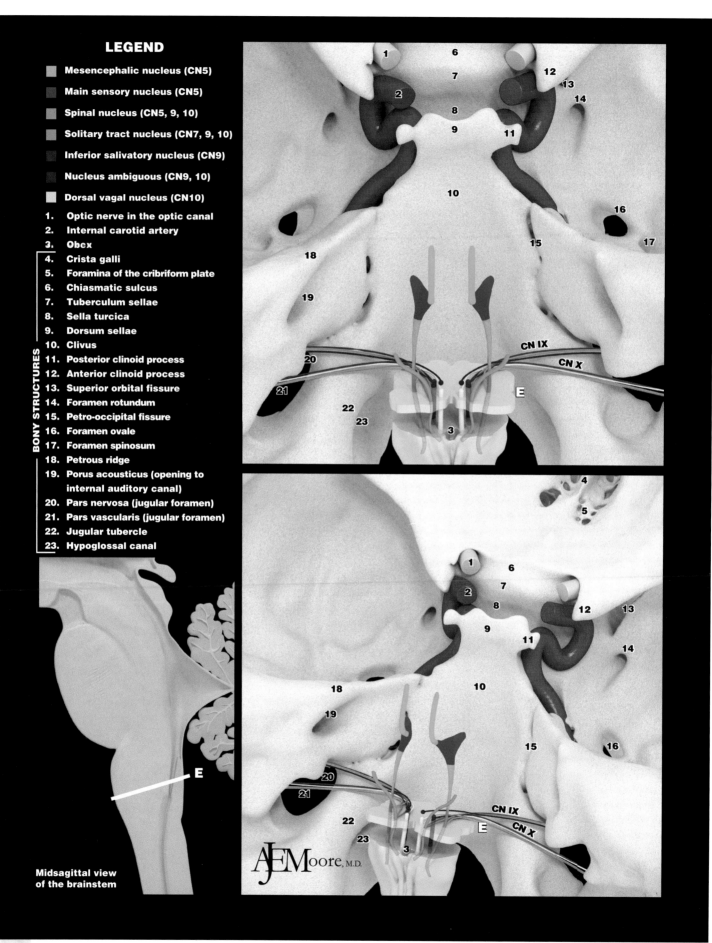

LEGEND

- Mesencephalic nucleus (CN5)
- Main sensory nucleus (CN5)
- Spinal nucleus (CN5, 9, 10)
- Solitary tract nucleus (CN7, 9, 10)
- Inferior salivatory nucleus (CN9)
- Nucleus ambiguous (CN9, 10)
- Dorsal vagal nucleus (CN10)

1. Optic nerve in the optic canal
2. Internal carotid artery
3. Obex

BONY STRUCTURES
4. Crista galli
5. Foramina of the cribriform plate
6. Chiasmatic sulcus
7. Tuberculum sellae
8. Sella turcica
9. Dorsum sellae
10. Clivus
11. Posterior clinoid process
12. Anterior clinoid process
13. Superior orbital fissure
14. Foramen rotundum
15. Petro-occipital fissure
16. Foramen ovale
17. Foramen spinosum
18. Petrous ridge
19. Porus acousticus (opening to internal auditory canal)
20. Pars nervosa (jugular foramen)
21. Pars vascularis (jugular foramen)
22. Jugular tubercle
23. Hypoglossal canal

Midsagittal view of the brainstem

2.16

FIGURE 2.16 Glossopharyngeal (CN IX) and vagus (CN X) nerves.

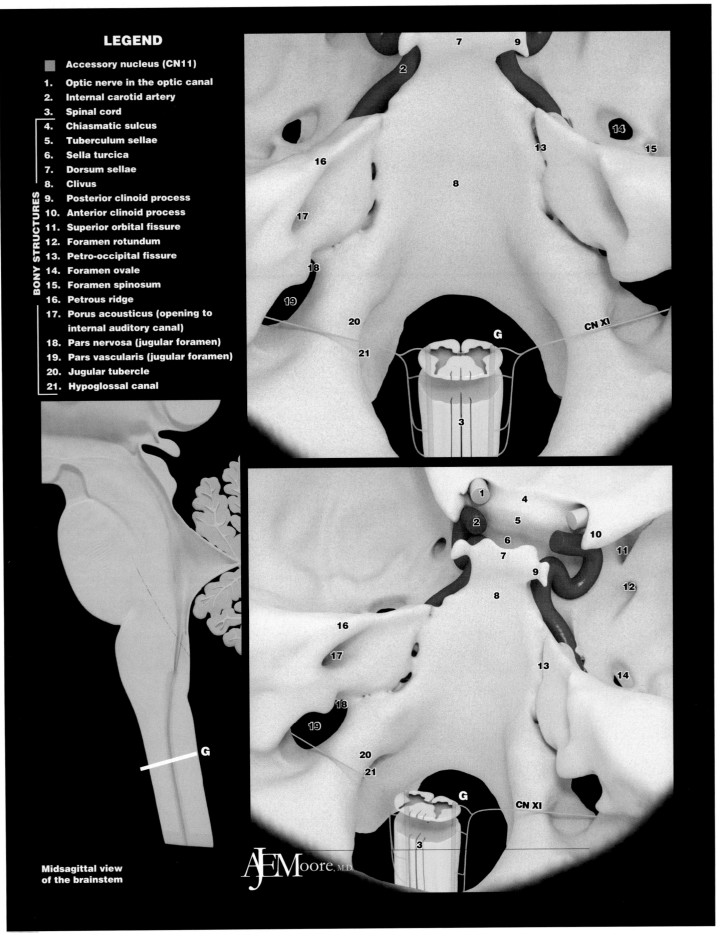

LEGEND

▨ **Accessory nucleus (CN11)**

1. **Optic nerve in the optic canal**
2. **Internal carotid artery**
3. **Spinal cord**

BONY STRUCTURES

4. **Chiasmatic sulcus**
5. **Tuberculum sellae**
6. **Sella turcica**
7. **Dorsum sellae**
8. **Clivus**
9. **Posterior clinoid process**
10. **Anterior clinoid process**
11. **Superior orbital fissure**
12. **Foramen rotundum**
13. **Petro-occipital fissure**
14. **Foramen ovale**
15. **Foramen spinosum**
16. **Petrous ridge**
17. **Porus acousticus (opening to internal auditory canal)**
18. **Pars nervosa (jugular foramen)**
19. **Pars vascularis (jugular foramen)**
20. **Jugular tubercle**
21. **Hypoglossal canal**

Midsagittal view of the brainstem

2.17

FIGURE 2.17   Accessory (CN XI) nerve.

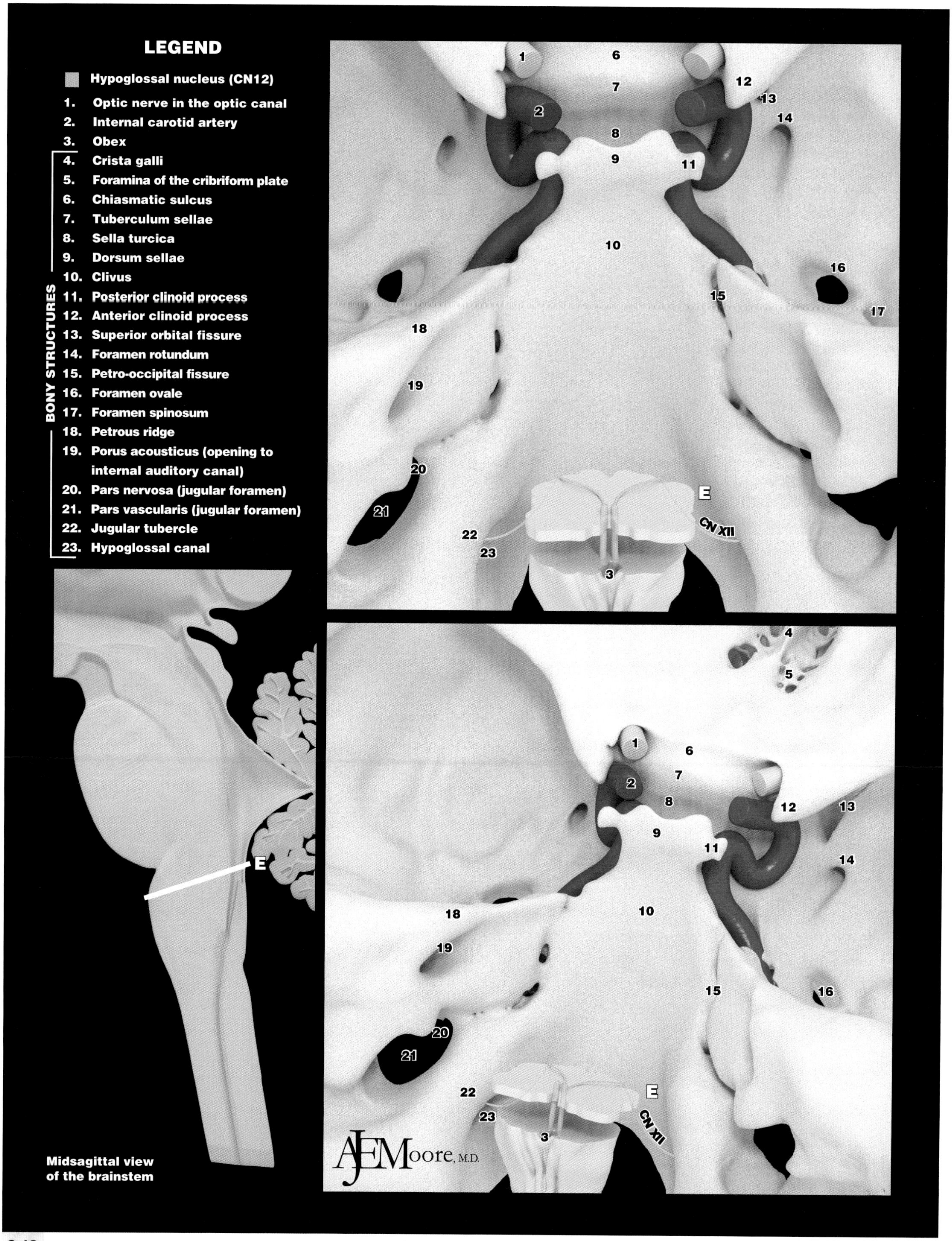

LEGEND

■ **Hypoglossal nucleus (CN12)**

1. **Optic nerve in the optic canal**
2. **Internal carotid artery**
3. **Obex**
4. **Crista galli**
5. **Foramina of the cribriform plate**
6. **Chiasmatic sulcus**
7. **Tuberculum sellae**
8. **Sella turcica**
9. **Dorsum sellae**
10. **Clivus**
11. **Posterior clinoid process**
12. **Anterior clinoid process**
13. **Superior orbital fissure**
14. **Foramen rotundum**
15. **Petro-occipital fissure**
16. **Foramen ovale**
17. **Foramen spinosum**
18. **Petrous ridge**
19. **Porus acousticus (opening to internal auditory canal)**
20. **Pars nervosa (jugular foramen)**
21. **Pars vascularis (jugular foramen)**
22. **Jugular tubercle**
23. **Hypoglossal canal**

BONY STRUCTURES (items 4–23)

Midsagittal view of the brainstem

2.18

FIGURE 2.18 Hypoglossal (CN XII) nerve.

MR Imaging of the Brain

The following MR images are an atlas of the brain in the axial, sagittal, and coronal planes without and with contrast enhancement. The subjects (subject 1—Figures 3.1–3.61 and subject 2—Figures 3.62–3.94) are young adults with no significant past medical history.

3

MRI BRAIN WITHOUT CONTRAST ENHANCEMENT (T1W AND T2W IMAGES)—SUBJECT 1: INTRODUCTION

High resolution, thin section axial, sagittal, and coronal images were obtained without contrast enhancement with T1 and T2 weighting. All of the images are grouped in sets of three, labeled Figures 3.1a–c to 3.61a–c. Figures 3.1a to 3.25a, 3.26a to 3.36a, and 3.37a to 3.61a are extensively labeled axial, sagittal, and coronal T1 weighted images respectively. Figures 3.1b to 3.61b are the same 3 plane T1 weighted images as in 3.1a to 3.61a but without any labeling. Figures 3.1c to 3.61c are sparsely labeled 3 plane T2 weighted images (at similar slice positions as the T1 weighted images) to allow for an unobstructed view and to provide the reader the opportunity to compare with the T1 images. The images are presented from superior (cranial) to inferior (caudal) in the axial plane, from lateral to medial in the sagittal plane and from anterior to posterior in the coronal plane.

Imaging Planes Used for Subject 1:

1. Axial and coronal images were obtained based upon the bicommissural plane (Talairach's AC [anterior commissure]–PC [posterior commissure] line), which is created by a line connecting the top of the anterior commissure with the bottom of the posterior commissure.
   a. Axial images parallel to the AC–PC line were obtained for images 3.1a–c to 3.25a–c.
   b. Coronal images perpendicular to the AC–PC line were obtained for images 3.37a–c to images 3.61a–c.
2. Sagittal Images were obtained in a routine fashion and independent upon the plane of imaging in the axial or coronal planes.

The following are T1 weighted images with reference lines indicating the planes of imaging utilizing the bicommissural line (Talairach's AC–PC line) for Subject 1 non-contrast MRI brain.

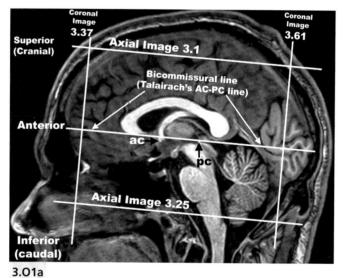

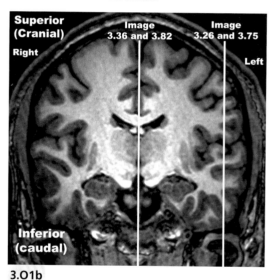

FIGURES 3.0   Orientation 1a and Orientation 1b.

MRI BRAIN WITH CONTRAST ENHANCEMENT (T1W IMAGES)—SUBJECT 2: INTRODUCTION

Thick slab post-contrast T1W images were obtained in the axial (Figures 3.62–3.74), sagittal (Figures 3.75–3.82) and coronal (Figures 3.83–3.94) planes using non-standard axial and coronal imaging planes. The acquisition of these images was not under the supervision of the authors of this text but has been chosen for this atlas because they demonstrate the normally expected appearance of a post-contrast T1W brain MRI. Thicker than typical image slices are presented as they allow for the visualization of structures in a more continuous fashion.

The post-contrast axial images (Figures 3.62–3.74) are presented from caudal (inferior) to cranial (superior). Post-contrast sagittal images (Figures 3.75–3.82) are presented from lateral to medial with the exception that Figure 3.82 is the far lateral image on the subjects other side. Post-contrast coronal images (Figures 3.83–3.94) are presented from anterior to posterior.

MRI BRAIN WITHOUT CONTRAST ENHANCEMENT—SUBJECT 1 (FIGURES 3.1–3.61)

■ AXIAL (FIGURES 3.1–3.25)

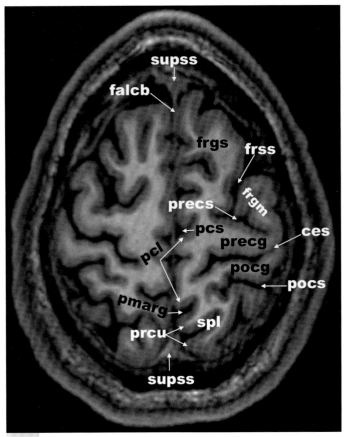

3.1a

3.1b

FIGURES 3.1a–c

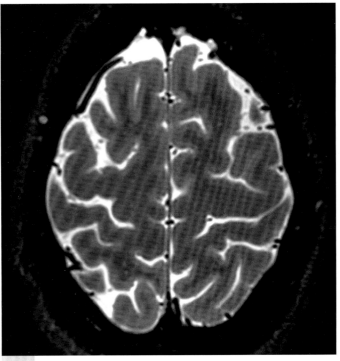

3.1c

KEY	
ces	central sulcus
falcb	falx cerebri
frgm	middle frontal gyrus
frgs	superior frontal gyrus
frss	superior frontal sulcus
pcl	paracentral lobule
pcs	paracentral sulcus
pmarg	pars marginalis (ascending ramus of cingulate sulcus)
pocg	post-central gyrus
pocs	post-central sulcus
prcu	precuneus
precg	pre-central gyrus
precs	pre-central sulcus
spl	superior parietal lobule
supss	superior sagittal sinus

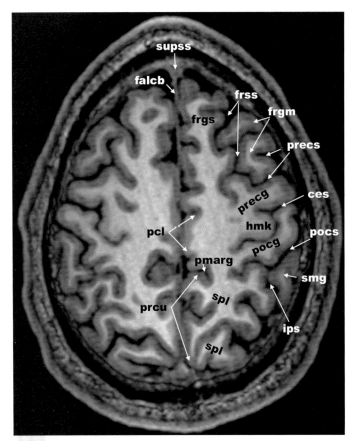

3.2a

3.2b

FIGURES 3.2a–c

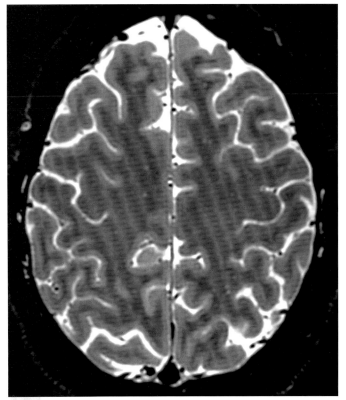

3.2c

KEY

ces	central sulcus
falcb	falx cerebri
frgm	middle frontal gyrus
frgs	superior frontal gyrus
frss	superior frontal sulcus
hmk	hand motor knob
ips	intraparietal sulcus
pcl	paracentral lobule
pmarg	pars marginalis (ascending ramus of cingulate sulcus)
pocg	post-central gyrus
pocs	post-central sulcus
prcu	precuneus
precg	pre-central gyrus
precs	pre-central sulcus
smg	supramarginal gyrus
spl	superior parietal lobule
supss	superior sagittal sinus

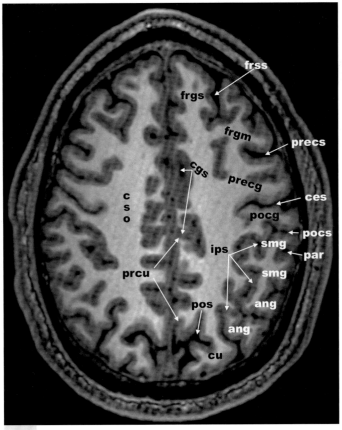

3.3a

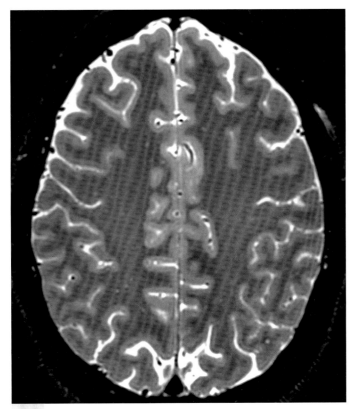

3.3c

3.3b

FIGURES 3.3a–c

KEY

ang	angular gyrus
ces	central sulcus
cgs	cingulate sulcus
cso	centrum semiovale
cu	cuneus
frgm	middle frontal gyrus
frgs	superior frontal gyrus
frss	superior frontal sulcus
ips	intraparietal sulcus
par	posterior ascending ramus of Sylvian fissure
pocg	post-central gyrus
pocs	post-central sulcus
pos	parieto-occipital sulcus
prcu	precuneus
precg	pre-central gyrus
precs	pre-central sulcus
smg	supramarginal gyrus

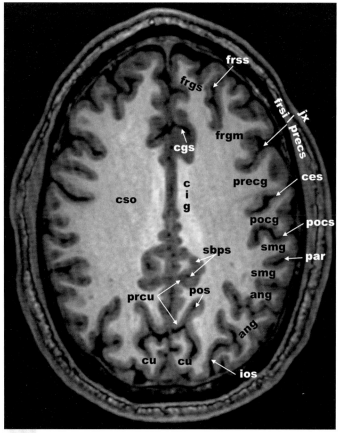

3.4a

3.4b

FIGURES 3.4a–c

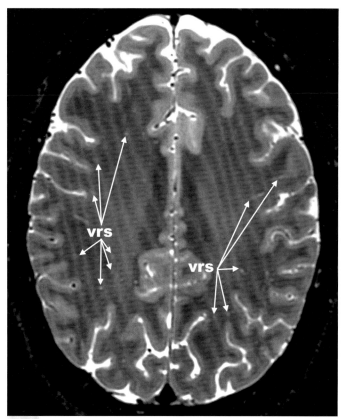

3.4c

KEY

ang	angular gyrus
ces	central sulcus
cgs	cingulate sulcus
cig	cingulate gyrus
cso	centrum semiovale
cu	cuneus
frgm	middle frontal gyrus
frgs	superior frontal gyrus
frsi	inferior frontal sulcus
frss	superior frontal sulcus
ios	intra-occipital sulcus
jx	junction
par	posterior ascending ramus of Sylvian fissure
pocg	post-central gyrus
pocs	post-central sulcus
pos	parieto-occipital sulcus
prcu	precuneus
precg	pre-central gyrus
precs	pre-central sulcus
sbps	subparietal sulcus
smg	supramarginal gyrus
vrs	Virchow-Robin spaces

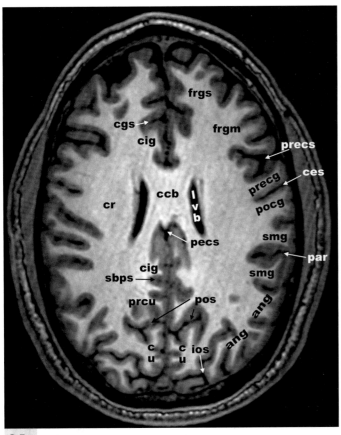

3.5a

3.5b

FIGURES 3.5a–c

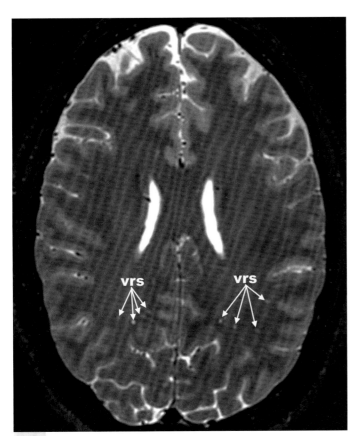

3.5c

KEY	
ang	angular gyrus
ccb	body of corpus callosum
ces	central sulcus
cgs	cingulate sulcus
cig	cingulate gyrus
cr	corona radiata
cu	cuneus
frgm	middle frontal gyrus
frgs	superior frontal gyrus
ios	intra-occipital sulcus
lvb	body of lateral ventricle
par	posterior ascending ramus of Sylvian fissure
pecs	pericallosal cistern (sulcus)
pocg	post-central gyrus
pos	parieto-occipital sulcus
prcu	precuneus
precg	pre-central gyrus
precs	pre-central sulcus
sbps	subparietal sulcus
smg	supramarginal gyrus
vrs	Virchow-Robin spaces

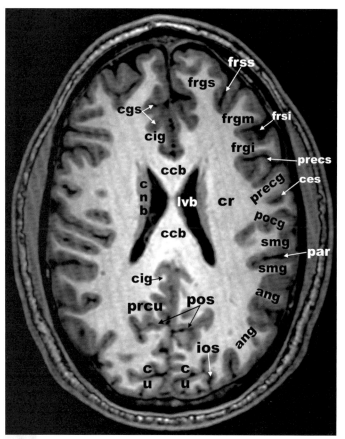

3.6a

3.6b

FIGURES 3.6a–c

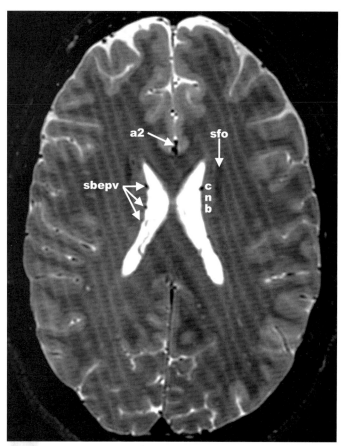

3.6c

KEY

a2	a2 (postcommunicating segment aca)
aca	anterior cerebral artery
ang	angular gyrus
ccb	body of corpus callosum
ces	central sulcus
cgs	cingulate sulcus
cig	cingulate gyrus
cnb	caudate nucleus body
cr	corona radiata
cu	cuneus
frgi	inferior frontal gyrus
frgm	middle frontal gyrus
frgs	superior frontal gyrus
frsi	inferior frontal sulcus
frss	superior frontal sulcus
ios	intra-occipital sulcus
lvb	body of lateral ventricle
par	posterior ascending ramus of Sylvian fissure
pocg	post-central gyrus
pos	parieto-occipital sulcus
prcu	precuneus
precg	pre-central gyrus
precs	pre-central sulcus
sbepv	subependymal veins
sfo	superior fronto-occipital fasciculus
smg	supramarginal gyrus

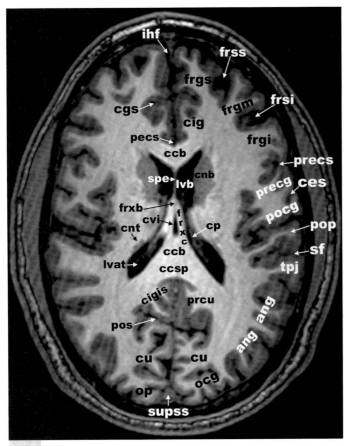

3.7a

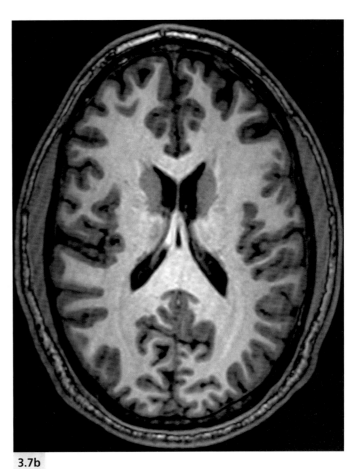

3.7b

FIGURES 3.7a–c

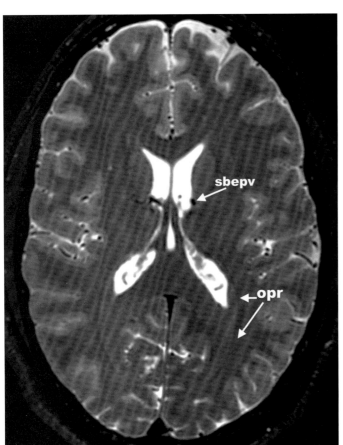

3.7c

KEY	
ang	angular gyrus
ccb	body of corpus callosum
ccsp	splenium of corpus callosum
ces	central sulcus
cgs	cingulate sulcus
cig	cingulate gyrus
cigis	isthmus of cingulate gyrus
cnb	caudate nucleus body
cnt	caudate nucleus tail
cp	choroid plexus
cu	cuneus
cvi	cistern of velum interpositum
frgi	inferior frontal gyrus
frgm	middle frontal gyrus
frgs	superior frontal gyrus
frsi	inferior frontal sulcus
frss	superior frontal sulcus
frxb	body of fornix
frxc	crura of fornix
ihf	interhemispheric fissure
lvat	atrium (trigone) of lateral ventricle
lvb	body of lateral ventricle
ocg	occipital gyri
op	occipital pole
opr	optic radiations
pecs	pericallosal cistern (sulcus)
pocg	post-central gyrus
pop	parietal operculum
pos	parieto-occipital sulcus
prcu	precuneus
precg	pre-central gyrus
precs	pre-central sulcus
sbepv	subependymal veins
sf	Sylvian fissure (lateral sulcus)
spe	septum pellucidum
supss	superior sagittal sinus
tpj	temporal parietal junction

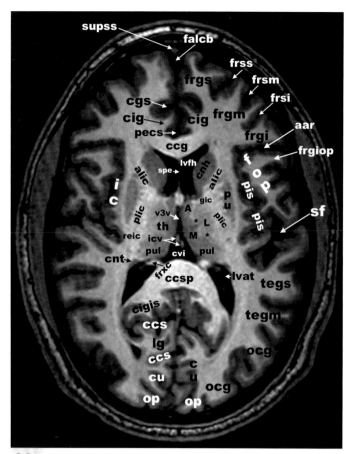

3.8a

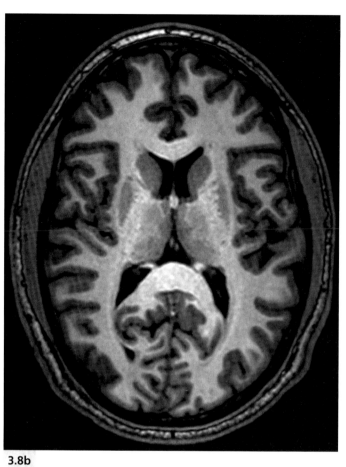

3.8b

FIGURES 3.8a–c

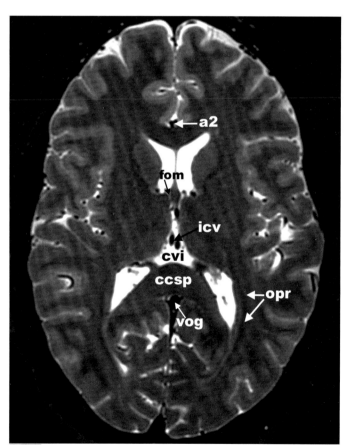

3.8c

KEY

*	internal medullary lamina of thalamus	**frsm**	middle frontal sulcus
A	anterior nuclei of thalamus	**frss**	superior frontal sulcus
		frxc	crura of fornix
L	combined ventral and lateral nuclei of thalamus	**gic**	genu of internal capsule
		ic	insular cortex
M	medial nuclei of thalamus	**icv**	internal cerebral vein
		lg	lingual gyrus (motg)
a2	a2 (postcommunicating segment aca)	**lvat**	atrium (trigone) of lateral ventricle
aar	anterior ascending ramus of Sylvian fissure	**lvfh**	frontal horn of lateral ventricle
aca	anterior cerebral artery	**ocg**	occipital gyri
alic	anterior limb of internal capsule	**op**	occipital pole
		opr	optic radiations
ccg	genu of corpus callosum	**pecs**	pericallosal cistern (sulcus)
ccs	calcarine sulcus		
ccsp	splenium of corpus callosum	**pis**	peri-insular (circular) sulcus
cgs	cingulate sulcus	**plic**	posterior limb of internal capsule
cig	cingulate gyrus		
cigis	isthmus of cingulate gyrus	**pu**	putamen
		pul	pulvinar is part of lateral thalamic nuclear group
cnh	caudate nucleus head		
cnt	caudate nucleus tail	**reic**	retrolenticular internal capsule
cu	cuneus		
cvi	cistern of velum interpositum	**sf**	Sylvian fissure (lateral sulcus)
falcb	falx cerebri		
fom	foramen of Monro	**spe**	septum pellucidum
fop	frontal operculum	**supss**	superior sagittal sinus
frgi	inferior frontal gyrus	**tegm**	middle temporal gyrus
frgiop	pars opercularis of inferior frontal gyrus	**tegs**	superior temporal gyrus
		th	thalamus
frgm	middle frontal gyrus	**v3v**	third ventricle
frgs	superior frontal gyrus	**vog**	vein of Galen
frsi	inferior frontal sulcus		

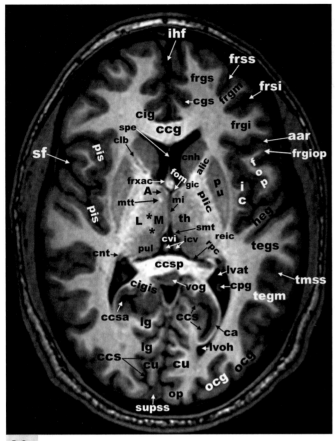

3.9a

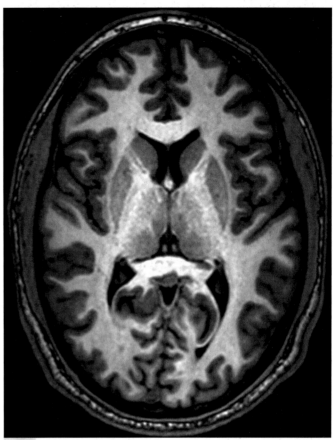

3.9b

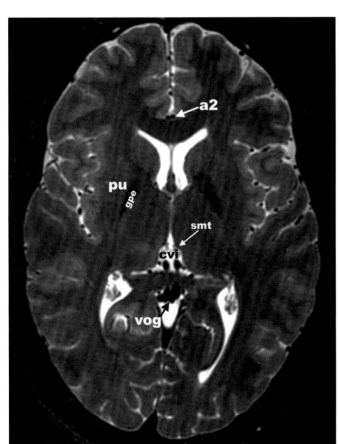

3.9c

FIGURES 3.9a–c

KEY			
*	internal medullary lamina of thalamus	frxac	ascending columns of fornix
A	anterior nuclei of thalamus	gic	genu of internal capsule
L	combined ventral and lateral nuclei of thalamus	gpe	globus pallidus externa
		heg	Heschl's gyrus (transverse temporal gyrus)
M	medial nuclei of thalamus		
a2	a2 (postcommunicating segment aca)	ic	insular cortex
		icv	internal cerebral vein
aar	anterior ascending ramus of Sylvian fissure	ihf	interhemispheric fissure
		lg	lingual gyrus (motg)
aca	anterior cerebral artery	lvat	atrium (trigone) of lateral ventricle
alic	anterior limb of internal capsule		
		lvoh	occipital horn of lateral ventricle
ca	calcar avis		
ccg	genu of corpus callosum	mi	massa intermedia
ccs	calcarine sulcus	mtt	mammilothalamic tract
ccsa	anterior calcarine sulcus	ocg	occipital gyri
ccsp	splenium of corpus callosum	op	occipital pole
		pis	peri-insular (circular) sulcus
cgs	cingulate sulcus		
cig	cingulate gyrus	plic	posterior limb of internal capsule
cigis	isthmus of cingulate gyrus		
		pu	putamen
clb	caudato-lenticular bridges	pul	pulvinar is part of lateral thalamic nuclear group
cnh	caudate nucleus head		
cnt	caudate nucleus tail	reic	retrolenticular internal capsule
cpg	glomus of choroid plexus		
cu	cuneus	rpc	retro-pulvinar (thalamic) cistern (wings of ambient cistern)
cvi	cistern of velum interpositum		
		sf	Sylvian fissure (lateral sulcus)
fom	foramen of Monro		
fop	frontal operculum	smt	stria medullaris thalami
frgi	inferior frontal gyrus	spe	septum pellucidum
frgiop	pars opercularis of inferior frontal gyrus	supss	superior sagittal sinus
		tegm	middle temporal gyrus
frgm	middle frontal gyrus	tegs	superior temporal gyrus
frgs	superior frontal gyrus	th	thalamus
frsi	inferior frontal sulcus	tmss	superior temporal sulcus
frss	superior frontal sulcus	vog	vein of Galen

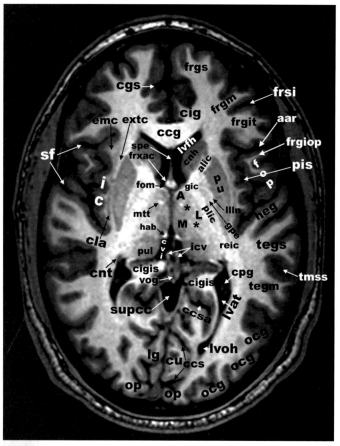

3.10a

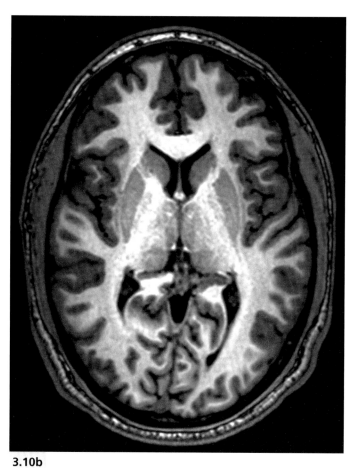

3.10b

FIGURES 3.10a–c

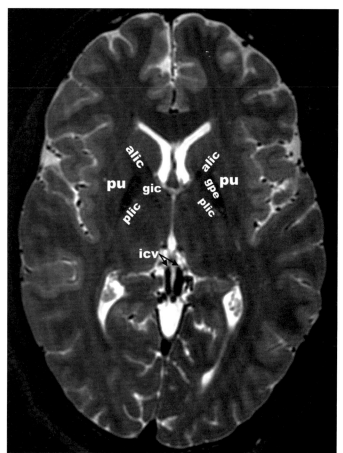

3.10c

KEY

*	internal medullary lamina of thalamus	gic	genu of internal capsule
A	anterior nuclei of thalamus	gpe	globus pallidus externa
		hab	habenular trigone
L	combined ventral and lateral nuclei of thalamus	heg	Heschl's gyrus (transverse temporal gyrus)
M	medial nuclei of thalamus	ic	insular cortex
aar	anterior ascending ramus of Sylvian fissure	icv	internal cerebral vein
alic	anterior limb of internal capsule	lg	lingual gyrus (motg)
		llln	lateral lamina of lenticular nucleus
ccg	genu of corpus callosum	lvat	atrium (trigone) of lateral ventricle
ccs	calcarine sulcus		
ccsa	anterior calcarine sulcus	lvfh	frontal horn of lateral ventricle
cgs	cingulate sulcus		
cig	cingulate gyrus	lvoh	occipital horn of lateral ventricle
cigis	isthmus of cingulate gyrus		
		mtt	mammilothalamic tract
cla	claustrum	ocg	occipital gyri
cnh	caudate nucleus head	op	occipital pole
cnt	caudate nucleus tail	pis	peri-insular (circular) sulcus
cpg	glomus of choroid plexus		
cu	cuneus	plic	posterior limb of internal capsule
cvi	cistern of velum interpositum		
		pu	putamen
emc	extreme capsule	pul	pulvinar is part of lateral thalamic nuclear group
extc	external capsule		
fom	foramen of Monro	reic	retrolenticular internal capsule
fop	frontal operculum		
frgiop	pars opercularis of inferior frontal gyrus	sf	Sylvian fissure (lateral sulcus)
		spe	septum pellucidum
frgit	pars triangularis of inferior frontal gyrus	supcc	supracerebellar cistern
		tegm	middle temporal gyrus
frgm	middle frontal gyrus	tegs	superior temporal gyrus
frgs	superior frontal gyrus	tmss	superior temporal sulcus
frsi	inferior frontal sulcus	vog	vein of Galen
frxac	ascending columns of fornix		

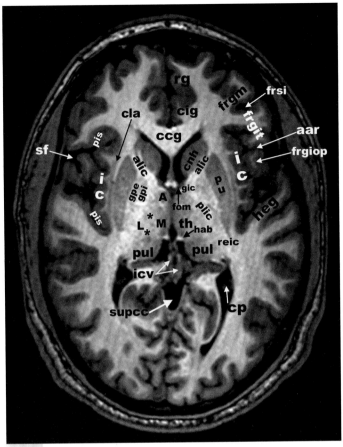

3.11a

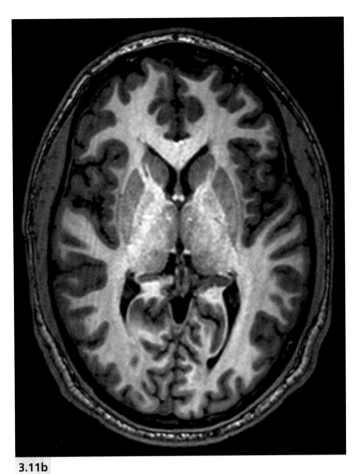

3.11b

FIGURES 3.11a–c

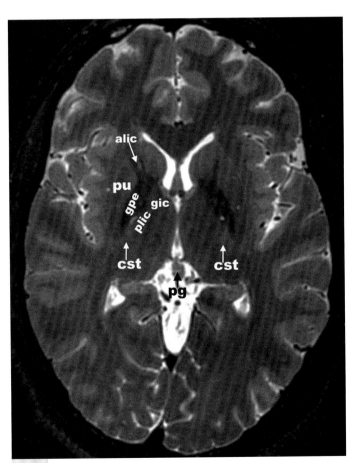

3.11c

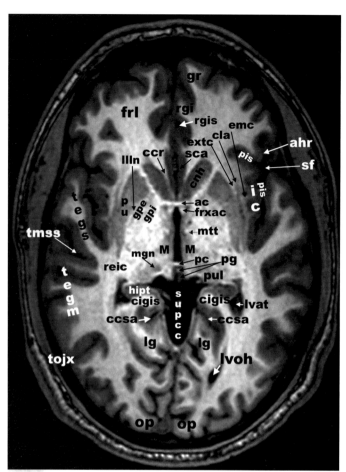

3.12a

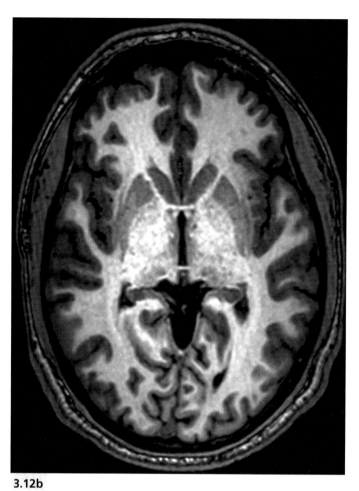

3.12b

FIGURES 3.12a–c

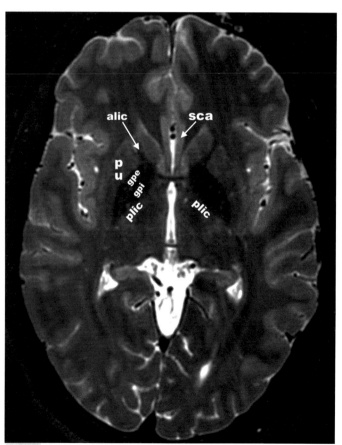

3.12c

KEY

M	medial nuclei of thalamus	lvoh	occipital horn of lateral ventricle
ac	anterior commissure	mgn	medial geniculate
ahr	anterior horizontal ramus of Sylvian fissure	mtt	nucleus mammilothalamic tract
alic	anterior limb of internal capsule	op	occipital pole
		pc	posterior commissure
ccr	rostrum of corpus callosum	pg	pineal gland
		pis	peri-insular (circular)
ccsa	anterior calcarine sulcus		sulcus
cigis	isthmus of cingulate gyrus	plic	posterior limb of internal capsule
cla	claustrum	pu	putamen
cnh	caudate nucleus head	pul	pulvinar is part of lateral thalamic nuclear group
emc	extreme capsule		
extc	external capsule	reic	retrolenticular internal capsule
frl	frontal lobe		
frxac	ascending columns of fornix	rgi	inferior rostral gyrus
		rgis	inferior rostral sulcus
gpe	globus pallidus externa	sca	subcallosal area
gpi	globus pallidus interna	sf	Sylvian fissure (lateral sulcus)
gr	gyrus rectus		
hipt	hippocampal tail	supcc	supracerebellar cistern
ic	insular cortex	tegm	middle temporal gyrus
lg	lingual gyrus (motg)	tegs	superior temporal gyrus
llln	lateral lamina of lenticular nucleus	tmss	superior temporal sulcus
lvat	atrium (trigone) of lateral ventricle	tojx	temporal occipital junction

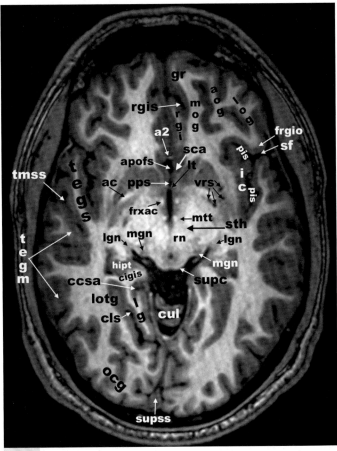

3.13a

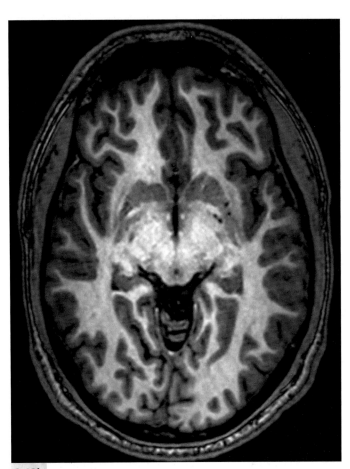

3.13b

FIGURES 3.13a–c

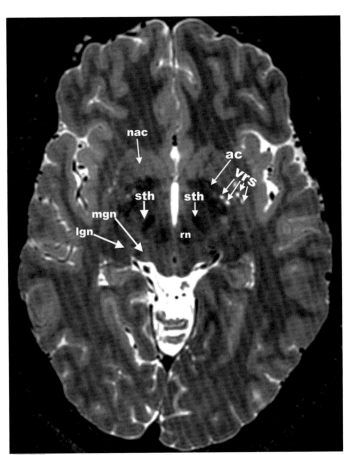

3.13c

KEY			
a2	a2 (postcommunicating segmentaca)	lt	lamina terminalis
ac	anterior commissure	mgn	medial geniculate nucleus
aca	anterior cerebral artery	mog	medial orbital gyrus
aog	anterior orbital gyrus	mtt	mammilothalamic tract
apofs	anterior parolfactory sulcus	nac	nucleus accumbens
		ocg	occipital gyri
ccsa	anterior calcarine sulcus	pis	peri-insular (circular) sulcus
cigis	isthmus of cingulate gyrus	pps	posterior parolfactory sulcus
cls	collateral sulcus	rgi	inferior rostral gyrus
cul	culmen	rgis	inferior rostral sulcus
frgio	pars orbitalis of inferior frontal gyrus	rn	red nucleus
		sca	subcallosal area
frxac	ascending columns of fornix	sf	Sylvian fissure (lateral sulcus)
gr	gyrus rectus	sth	subthalamic nucleus
hipt	hippocampal tail	supc	superior colliculus
ic	insular cortex	supss	superior sagittal sinus
lg	lingual gyrus (motg)	tegm	middle temporal gyrus
lgn	lateral geniculate nucleus	tegs	superior temporal gyrus
log	lateral orbital gyrus	tmss	superior temporal sulcus
lotg	lateral occipital temporal gyrus (lotg)/fusiform gyrus	vrs	Virchow-Robin spaces

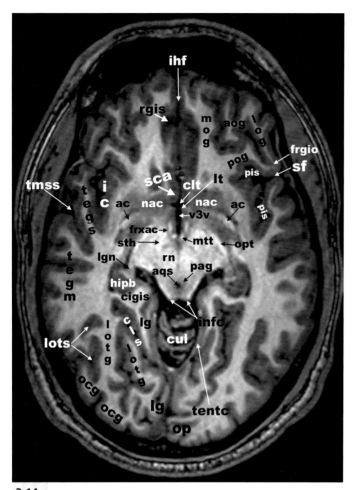

3.14a

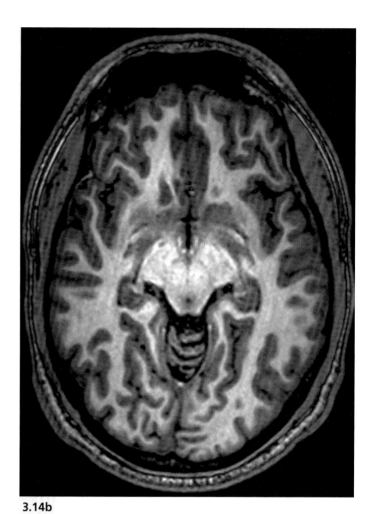

3.14b

FIGURES 3.14a–c

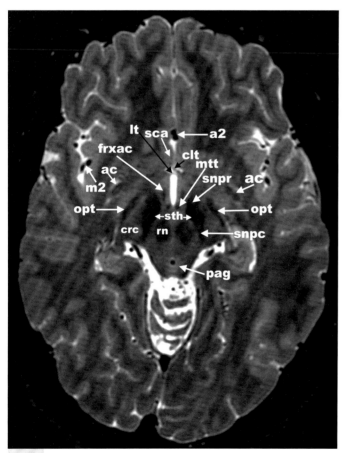

3.14c

KEY

a2	a2 (postcommunicating segment aca)	lt	lamina terminalis
ac	anterior commissure	m2	m2 (Sylvian/insular branches mca)
aca	anterior cerebral artery	mca	middle cerebral artery
aog	anterior orbital gyrus	mog	medial orbital gyrus
aqs	aqueduct of Sylvius	mtt	mammilothalamic tract
cigis	isthmus of cingulate gyrus	nac	nucleus accumbens
cls	collateral sulcus	ocg	occipital gyri
clt	cistern of lamina terminalis	op	occipital pole
		opt	optic tract
crc	crus cerebri	pag	periaqueductal gray matter
cul	culmen (lobules IV and V)	pis	peri-insular (circular) sulcus
frgio	pars orbitalis of inferior frontal gyrus	pog	posterior orbital gyrus
frxac	ascending columns of fornix	rgis	inferior rostral sulcus
		rn	red nucleus
hipb	hippocampal body	sca	subcallosal area
ic	insular cortex	sf	Sylvian fissure (lateral sulcus)
ihf	interhemispheric fissure		
infc	inferior colliculus	snpc	pars compacta of substantia nigra
lg	lingual gyrus (motg)		
lgn	lateral geniculate nucleus	snpr	pars reticulata of substantia nigra
log	lateral orbital gyrus	sth	subthalamic nucleus
lotg	lateral occipital temporal gyrus (lotg)/fusiform gyrus	tegm	middle temporal gyrus
		tegs	superior temporal gyrus
		tentc	tentorium cerebelli
		tmss	superior temporal sulcus
lots	lateral occipital temporal sulcus	v3v	third ventricle

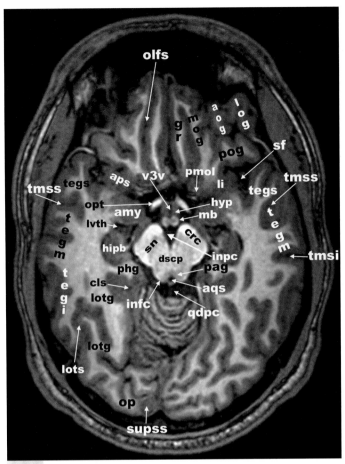

3.15a

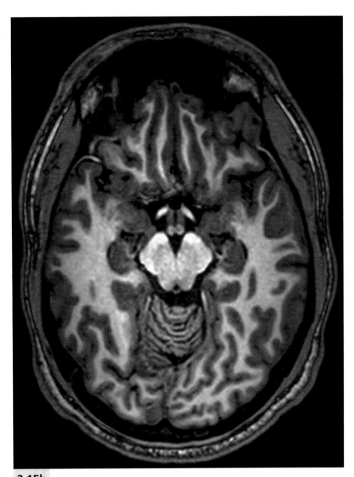

3.15b

FIGURES 3.15a–c

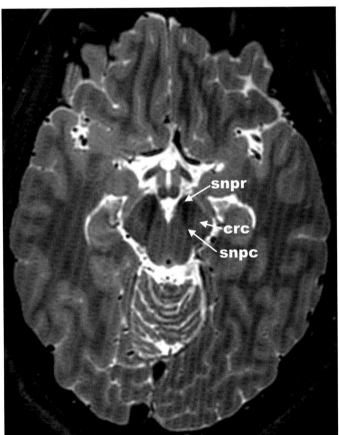

3.15c

KEY			
amy	amygdala	olfs	olfactory sulcus
aog	anterior orbital gyrus	op	occipital pole
aps	anterior perforated substance	opt	optic tract
		pag	periaqueductal gray matter
aqs	aqueduct of Sylvius		
cls	collateral sulcus	phg	parahippocampal gyrus
crc	crus cerebri	pmol	posteromedial orbital lobule
dscp	decussation of superior cerebellar peduncles		
		pog	posterior orbital gyrus
gr	gyrus rectus	qdpc	quadrigeminal plate cistern
hipb	hippocampal body		
hyp	hypothalamus	sf	Sylvian fissure (lateral sulcus)
infc	inferior colliculus		
inpc	interpeduncular cistern	sn	substantia nigra
li	limen insulae	snpc	pars compacta of substantia nigra
log	lateral orbital gyrus		
lotg	lateral occipital temporal gyrus (lotg)/fusiform gyrus	snpr	pars reticulata of substantia nigra
		supss	superior sagittal sinus
lots	lateral occipital temporal sulcus	tegi	inferior temporal gyrus
		tegm	middle temporal gyrus
lvth	temporal horn of lateral ventricle	tegs	superior temporal gyrus
		tmsi	inferior temporal sulcus
mb	mammillary body	tmss	superior temporal sulcus
mog	medial orbital gyrus	v3v	third ventricle

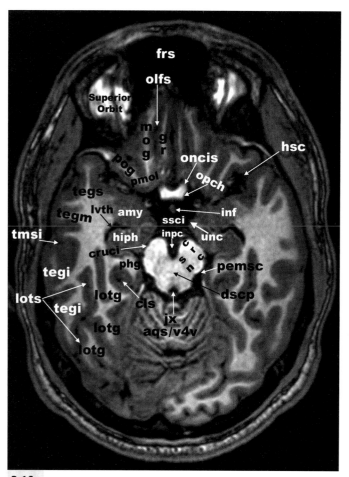

3.16a

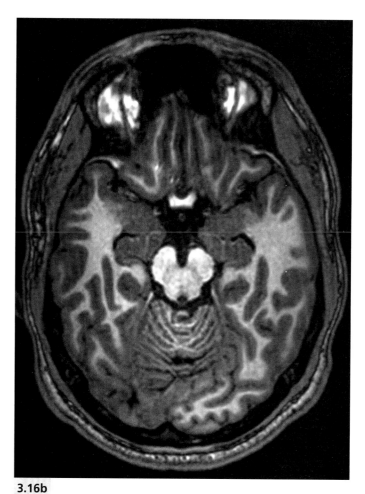

3.16b

FIGURES 3.16a–c

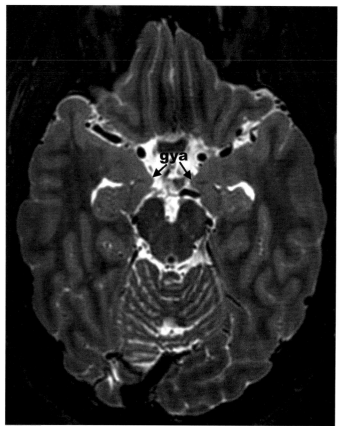

3.16c

KEY

amy	amygdala	mog	medial orbital gyrus
aqs	aqueduct of Sylvius	olfs	olfactory sulcus
cls	collateral sulcus	oncis	cisternal (pre-chiasmatic) segment optic nerve
crc	crus cerebri		
cruci	crural cistern		
dscp	decussation of superior cerebellar peduncles	opch	optic chiasm
		pemsc	perimesencephalic (ambient) cistern
frs	frontal sinus		
gr	gyrus rectus	phg	parahippocampal gyrus
gya	gyrus ambiens	pmol	posteromedial orbital lobule
hiph	hippocampal head		
hsc	horizontal Sylvian cistern (Sylvian fissure)	pog	posterior orbital gyrus
		sn	substantia nigra
inf	infundibulum	ssci	suprasellar cistern
inpc	interpeduncular cistern	tegi	inferior temporal gyrus
jx	junction	tegm	middle temporal gyrus
lotg	lateral occipital temporal gyrus (lotg)/ fusiform gyrus	tegs	superior temporal gyrus
		tmsi	inferior temporal sulcus
		unc	uncus
lots	lateral occipital temporal sulcus	v4v	fourth ventricle
lvth	temporal horn of lateral ventricle		

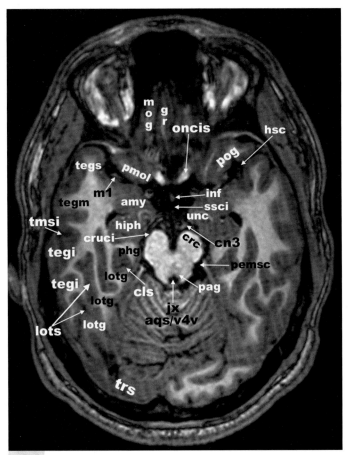

3.17a

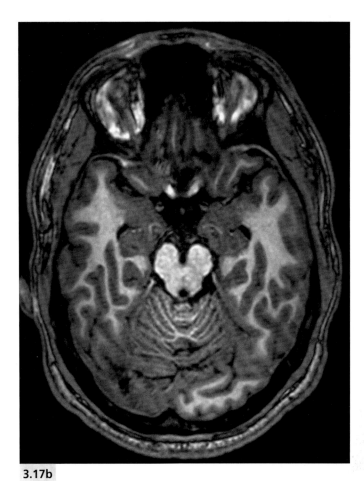

3.17b

FIGURES 3.17a–c

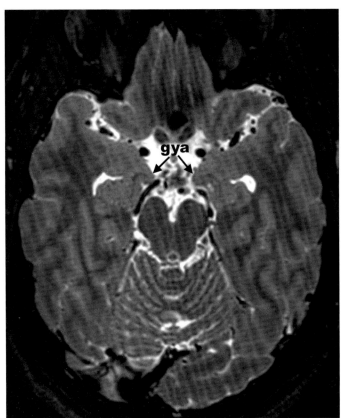

3.17c

KEY			
amy	amygdala	**mog**	medial orbital gyrus
aqs	aqueduct of Sylvius	**oncis**	cisternal (pre-
cls	collateral sulcus		chiasmatic) segment
cn3	oculomotor nerve		optic nerve
crc	crus cerebri	**pag**	periaqueductal gray
cruci	crural cistern		matter
gr	gyrus rectus	**pemsc**	perimesencephalic
gya	gyrus ambiens		(ambient) cistern
hiph	hippocampal head	**phg**	parahippocampal gyrus
hsc	horizontal Sylvian	**pmol**	posteromedial orbital
	cistern (Sylvian fissure)		lobule
inf	infundibulum	**pog**	posterior orbital gyrus
jx	junction	**ssci**	suprasellar cistern
lotg	lateral occipital	**tegi**	inferior temporal gyrus
	temporal gyrus (lotg)/	**tegm**	middle temporal gyrus
	fusiform gyrus	**tegs**	superior temporal gyrus
lots	lateral occipital	**tmsi**	inferior temporal sulcus
	temporal sulcus	**trs**	transverse sinus
m1	m1 (horizontal segment	**unc**	uncus
	mca)	**v4v**	fourth ventricle
mca	middle cerebral artery		

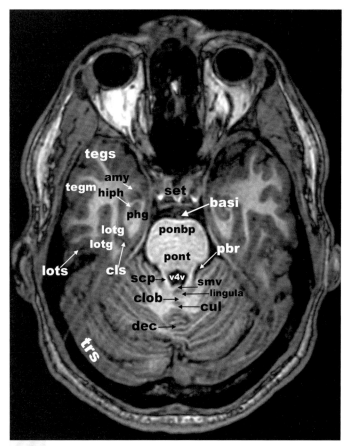

3.18a

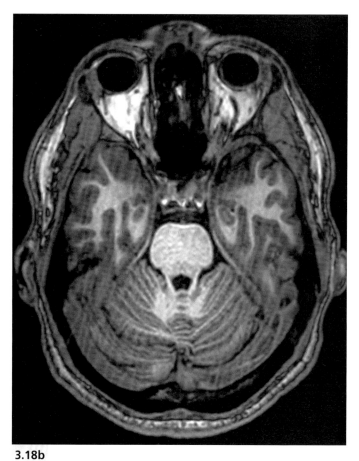

3.18b

FIGURES 3.18a–c

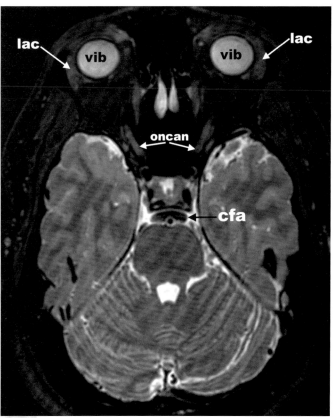

3.18c

KEY

amy	amygdala
basi	basilar artery
cfa	csf flow artifact
clob	central lobule of vermis (lobules II and III)
cls	collateral sulcus
cul	culmen (lobules IV and V)
dec	declive of vermis (lobule VI)
hiph	hippocampal head
lac	lacrimal gland
lingula	lingula of vermis (lobule I)
lotg	lateral occipital temporal gyrus (lotg)/fusiform gyrus
lots	lateral occipital temporal sulcus
oncan	canalicular segment of optic nerve
pbr	para-brachial recess
phg	parahippocampal gyrus
ponbp	basis pontis of pons
pont	tegmentum of pons
scp	superior cerebellar peduncle (brachium conjunctivum)
set	sella turcica
smv	superior/anterior medullary velum
tegm	middle temporal gyrus
tegs	superior temporal gyrus
trs	transverse sinus
v4v	fourth ventricle
vib	vitreous body (chamber) of eye

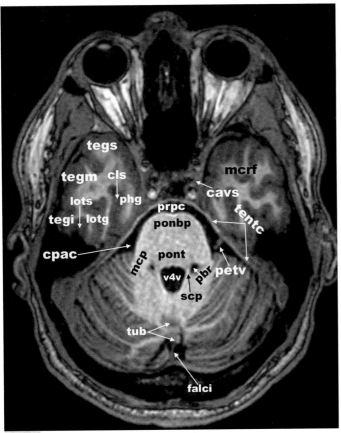

3.19a

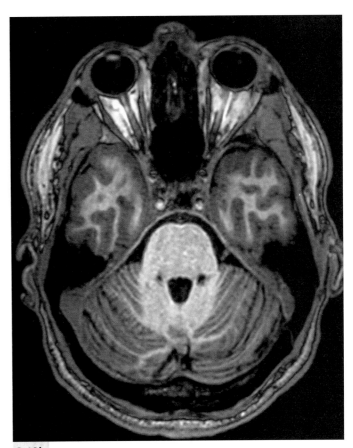

3.19b

FIGURES 3.19a–c

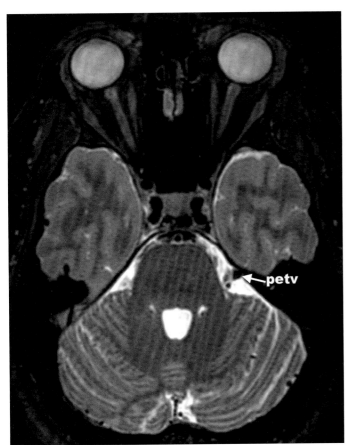

3.19c

KEY

cavs	cavernous sinus
cls	collateral sulcus
cpac	cerebellopontine angle cistern
falci	falx cerebelli
lotg	lateral occipital temporal gyrus (lotg)/fusiform gyrus
lots	lateral occipital temporal sulcus
mcp	middle cerebellar peduncle (brachium pontis)
mcrf	middle cranial fossa
pbr	para-brachial recess
petv	petrosal vein
phg	parahippocampal gyrus
ponbp	basis pontis of pons
pont	tegmentum of pons
prpc	prepontine cistern
scp	superior cerebellar peduncle (brachium conjunctivum)
tegi	inferior temporal gyrus
tegm	middle temporal gyrus
tegs	superior temporal gyrus
tentc	tentorium cerebelli
tub	tuber of vermis (lobule VII)
v4v	fourth ventricle

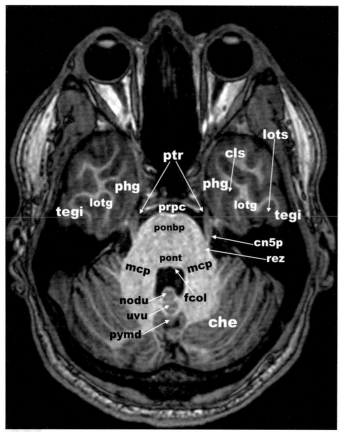

3.20a

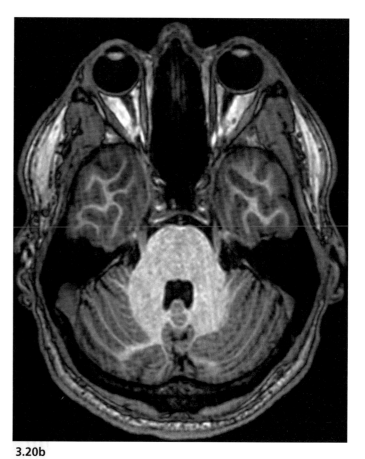

3.20b

FIGURES 3.20a–c

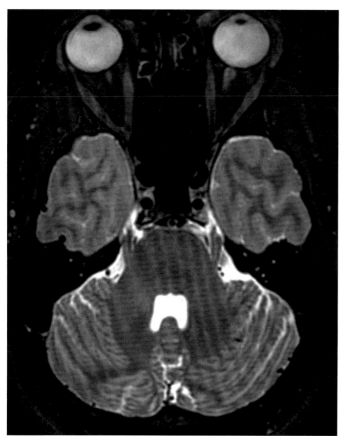

3.20c

KEY

che	cerebellar hemisphere
cls	collateral sulcus
cn5p	pre-ganglionic segment trigeminal nerve
fcol	facial colliculus
lotg	lateral occipital temporal gyrus (lotg)/fusiform gyrus
lots	lateral occipital temporal sulcus
mcp	middle cerebellar peduncle (brachium pontis)
nodu	nodulus of vermis (lobule X)
phg	parahippocampal gyrus
ponbp	basis pontis of pons
pont	tegmentum of pons
prpc	prepontine cistern
ptr	porus trigeminus
pymd	pyramid of vermis (lobule VIII)
rez	root entry zone of trigeminal nerve
tegi	inferior temporal gyrus
uvu	uvula of the vermis (lobule IX)

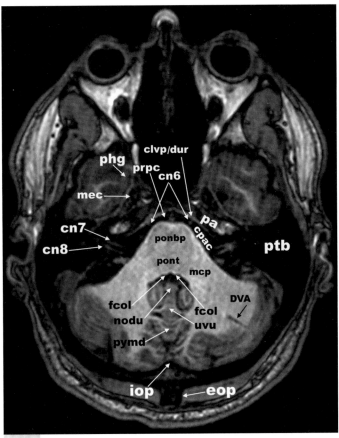

3.21a

3.21b

FIGURES 3.21a–c

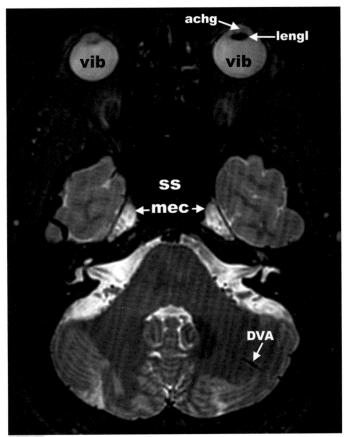

3.21c

KEY

DVA	developmental venous anomaly
achg	anterior chamber of eye
clvp	clival venous plexus
cn6	abducens nerve
cn7	facial nerve
cn8	vestibulocochlear nerve
cpac	cerebellopontine angle cistern
dur	dura (pachymeninges)
eop	external occipital protuberance (inion)
fcol	facial colliculus
iop	internal occipital protuberance
lengl	lens of globe
mcp	middle cerebellar peduncle (brachium pontis)
mec	Meckel's cave
nodu	nodulus of vermis (lobule X)
pa	petrous apex
phg	parahippocampal gyrus
ponbp	basis pontis of pons
pont	tegmentum of pons
prpc	prepontine cistern
ptb	petrous temporal bone
pymd	pyramid of vermis (lobule VIII)
ss	sphenoid sinus
uvu	uvula of the vermis (lobule IX)
vib	vitreous body (chamber) of eye

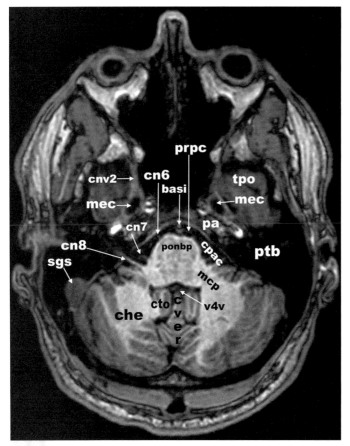

3.22a

3.22b

FIGURES 3.22a–c

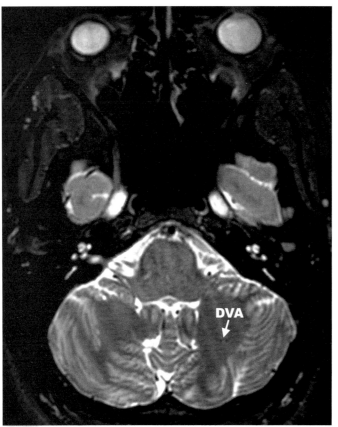

3.22c

KEY

DVA	developmental venous anomaly
basi	basilar artery
che	cerebellar hemisphere
cn6	abducens nerve
cn7	facial nerve
cn8	vestibulocochlear nerve
cnv2	maxillary branch (v2) of trigeminal nerve
cpac	cerebellopontine angle cistern
cto	cerebellar tonsil
cver	cerebellar vermis
mcp	middle cerebellar peduncle (brachium pontis)
mec	Meckel's cave
pa	petrous apex
ponbp	basis pontis of pons
prpc	prepontine cistern
ptb	petrous temporal bone
sgs	sigmoid sinus
tpo	temporal pole
v4v	fourth ventricle

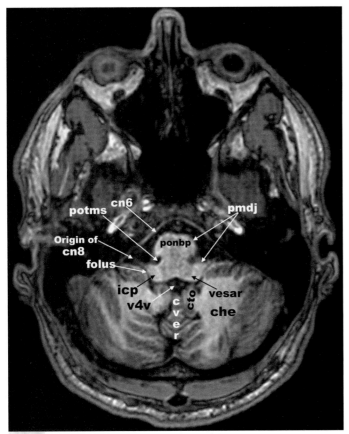

3.23a

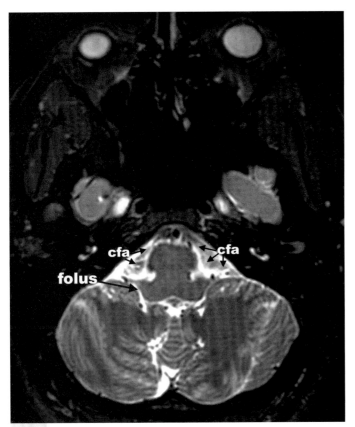

3.23c

3.23b

FIGURES 3.23a–c

KEY

cfa	csf flow artifact
che	cerebellar hemisphere
cn6	abducens nerve
cn8	vestibulocochlear nerve
cto	cerebellar tonsil
cver	cerebellar vermis
folus	foramen of Luschka
icp	inferior cerebellar peduncle (restiform body)
pmdj	ponto-medullary junction
ponbp	basis pontis of pons
potms	pontomedullary sulcus
v4v	fourth ventricle
vesar	vestibular area

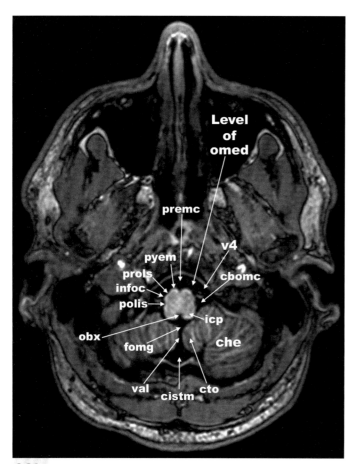

3.24a

3.24b

FIGURES 3.24a–c

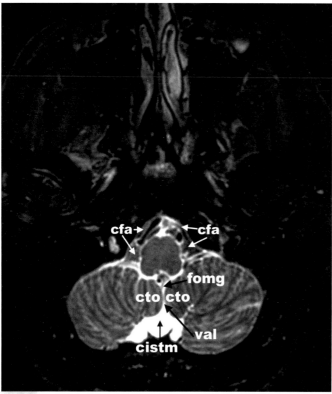

3.24c

KEY

cbomc	cerebellomedullary cistern
cfa	csf flow artifact
che	cerebellar hemisphere
cistm	cisterna magna
cto	cerebellar tonsil
fomg	foramen of Magendie
icp	inferior cerebellar peduncle (restiform body)
infoc	inferior olivary complex
obx	obex
omed	open medulla
polis	post-olivary sulcus
premc	premedullary cistern
prols	pre-olivary sulcus
pyem	pyramidal eminence
v4	v4 intracranial/intradural segment vertebral artery
val	vallecula space

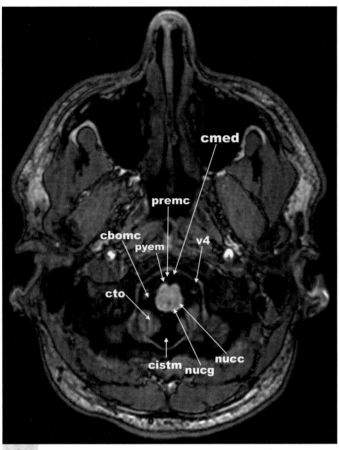

3.25a

3.25b

FIGURES 3.25a–c

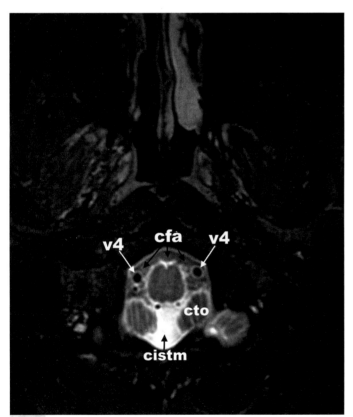

3.25c

KEY

cbomc	cerebellomedullary cistern
cfa	csf flow artifact
cistm	cisterna magna
cmed	closed medulla
cto	cerebellar tonsil
nucc	nucleus cuneatus
nucg	nucleus gracilis
premc	premedullary cistern
pyem	pyramidal eminence
v4	v4 intracranial/intradural segment vertebral artery

■ SAGITTAL (FIGURES 3.26–3.36)

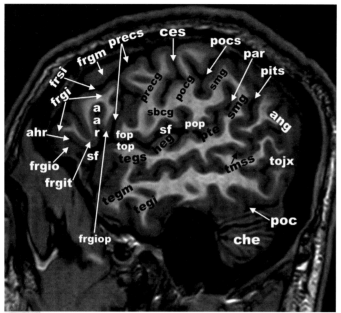

3.26a

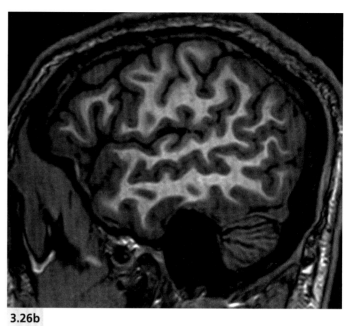

3.26b

FIGURES 3.26a–c

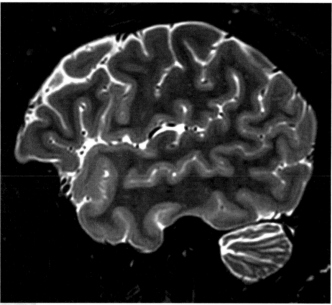

3.26c

KEY

aar	anterior ascending ramus of Sylvian fissure
ahr	anterior horizontal ramus of Sylvian fissure
ang	angular gyrus
ces	central sulcus
che	cerebellar hemisphere
fop	frontal operculum
frgi	inferior frontal gyrus
frgio	pars orbitalis of inferior frontal gyrus
frgiop	pars opercularis of inferior frontal gyrus
frgit	pars triangularis of inferior frontal gyrus
frgm	middle frontal gyrus
frsi	inferior frontal sulcus
heg	Heschl's gyrus (transverse temporal gyrus)
par	posterior ascending ramus of Sylvian fissure
pits	primary intermediate sulcus
poc	pre-occipital notch
pocg	post-central gyrus
pocs	post-central sulcus
pop	parietal operculum
precg	pre-central gyrus
precs	pre-central sulcus
pte	planum temporale
sbcg	subcentral gyrus
sf	Sylvian fissure (lateral sulcus)
smg	supramarginal gyrus
tegi	inferior temporal gyrus
tegm	middle temporal gyrus
tegs	superior temporal gyrus
tmss	superior temporal sulcus
tojx	temporal occipital junction
top	temporal operculum

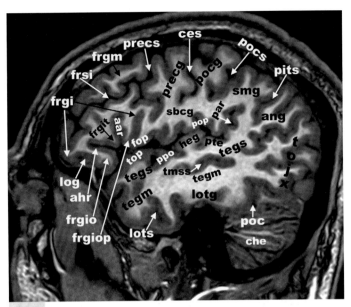

3.27a

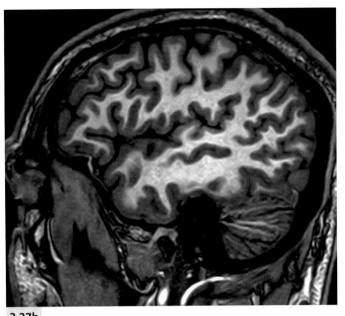

3.27b

FIGURES 3.27a–c

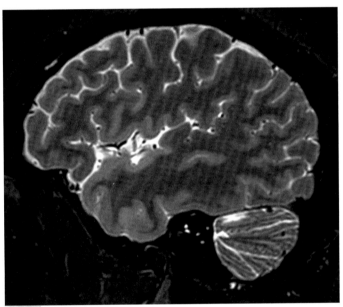

3.27c

KEY

aar	anterior ascending ramus of Sylvian fissure	**lots**	lateral occipital temporal sulcus
ahr	anterior horizontal ramus of Sylvian fissure	**par**	posterior ascending ramus of Sylvian fissure
ang	angular gyrus	**pits**	primary intermediate sulcus
ces	central sulcus		
che	cerebellar hemisphere	**poc**	pre-occipital notch
fop	frontal operculum	**pocg**	post-central gyrus
frgi	inferior frontal gyrus	**pocs**	post-central sulcus
frgio	pars orbitalis of inferior frontal gyrus	**pop**	parietal operculum
		ppo	planum polare
frgiop	pars opercularis of inferior frontal gyrus	**precg**	pre-central gyrus
		precs	pre-central sulcus
frgit	pars triangularis of inferior frontal gyrus	**pte**	planum temporale
		sbcg	subcentral gyrus
frgm	middle frontal gyrus	**smg**	supramarginal gyrus
frsi	inferior frontal sulcus	**tegm**	middle temporal gyrus
heg	Heschl's gyrus (transverse temporal gyrus)	**tegs**	superior temporal gyrus
		tmss	superior temporal sulcus
log	lateral orbital gyrus	**tojx**	temporal occipital junction
lotg	lateral occipital temporal gyrus (lotg)/ fusiform gyrus	**top**	temporal operculum

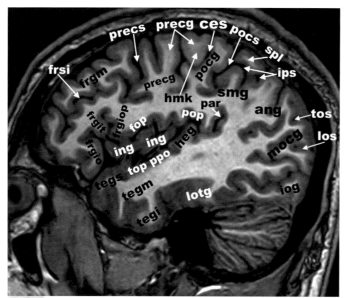

3.28a

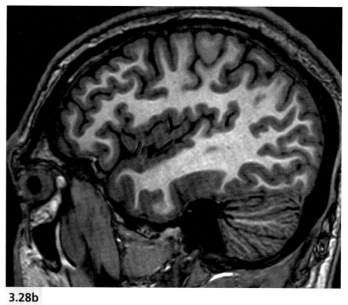

3.28b

FIGURES 3.28a–c

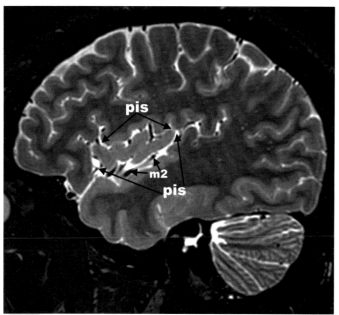

3.28c

KEY

ang	angular gyrus	m2	m2 (Sylvian/insular branches mca)
ces	central sulcus		
fop	frontal operculum	mca	middle cerebral artery
frgio	pars orbitalis of inferior frontal gyrus	mocg	middle occipital gyrus
		par	posterior ascending ramus of Sylvian fissure
frgiop	pars opercularis of inferior frontal gyrus		
		pis	peri-insular (circular) sulcus
frgit	pars triangularis of inferior frontal gyrus		
		pocg	post-central gyrus
frgm	middle frontal gyrus	pocs	post-central sulcus
frsi	inferior frontal sulcus	pop	parietal operculum
heg	Heschl's gyrus (transverse temporal gyrus)	ppo	planum polare
		precg	pre-central gyrus
		precs	pre-central sulcus
hmk	hand motor knob	smg	supramarginal gyrus
ing	insular gyri	spl	superior parietal lobule
iog	inferior occipital gyrus	tegi	inferior temporal gyrus
ips	intraparietal sulcus	tegm	middle temporal gyrus
los	lateral (inferior) occipital sulcus	tegs	superior temporal gyrus
		top	temporal operculum
lotg	lateral occipital temporal gyrus (lotg)/ fusiform gyrus	tos	transverse occipital sulcus

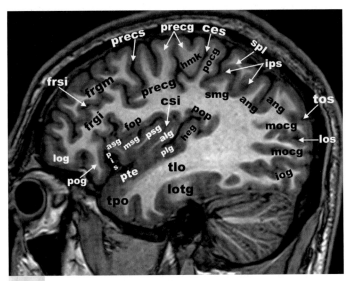

3.29a

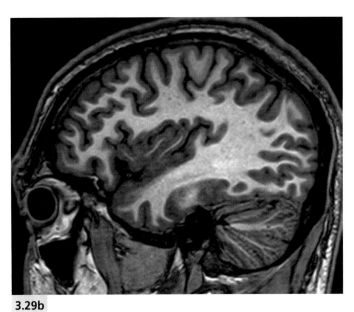

3.29b

FIGURES 3.29a–c

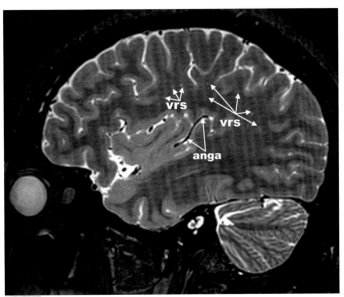

3.29c

KEY			
alg	anterior long insular gyrus	**mocg**	middle occipital gyrus
ang	angular gyrus	**msg**	middle short insular gyrus
anga	angular artery	**pis**	peri-insular (circular) sulcus
asg	anterior short insular gyrus	**plg**	posterior long insular gyrus
ces	central sulcus		
csi	central sulcus of insula	**pocg**	post-central gyrus
fop	frontal operculum	**pog**	posterior orbital gyrus
frgi	inferior frontal gyrus	**pop**	parietal operculum
frgm	middle frontal gyrus	**precg**	pre-central gyrus
frsi	inferior frontal sulcus	**precs**	pre-central sulcus
heg	Heschl's gyrus (transverse temporal gyrus)	**psg**	posterior short insular gyrus
		pte	planum temporale
hmk	hand motor knob	**smg**	supramarginal gyrus
iog	inferior occipital gyrus	**spl**	superior parietal lobule
ips	intraparietal sulcus	**tlo**	temporal lobe
log	lateral orbital gyrus	**tos**	transverse occipital sulcus
los	lateral (inferior) occipital sulcus	**tpo**	temporal pole
		vrs	Virchow-Robin spaces
lotg	lateral occipital temporal gyrus (lotg)/ fusiform gyrus		

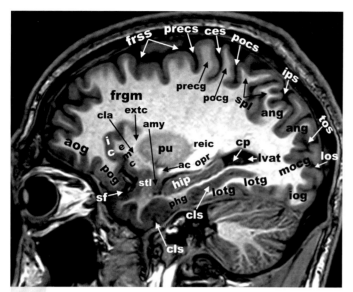

3.30a

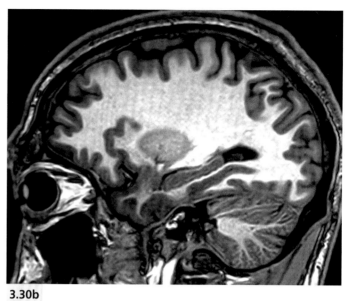

3.30b

FIGURES 3.30a–c

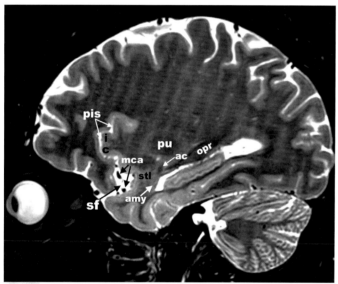

3.30c

KEY

ac	anterior commissure	lvat	atrium (trigone) of
amy	amygdala		lateral ventricle
ang	angular gyrus	mca	middle cerebral artery
aog	anterior orbital gyrus	mocg	middle occipital gyrus
ces	central sulcus	opr	optic radiations
cla	claustrum	phg	parahippocampal gyrus
cls	collateral sulcus	pis	peri-insular (circular)
cp	choroid plexus		sulcus
emc	extreme capsule	pocg	post-central gyrus
extc	external capsule	pocs	post-central sulcus
frgm	middle frontal gyrus	pog	posterior orbital gyrus
frss	superior frontal sulcus	precg	pre-central gyrus
hip	hippocampus	precs	pre-central sulcus
ic	insular cortex	pu	putamen
iog	inferior occipital	reic	retrolenticular internal
	gyrus		capsule
ips	intraparietal sulcus	sf	Sylvian fissure (lateral
los	lateral (inferior)		sulcus)
	occipital sulcus	spl	superior parietal lobule
lotg	lateral occipital	stl	stem of temporal lobe
	temporal gyrus (lotg)/	tos	transverse occipital
	fusiform gyrus		sulcus

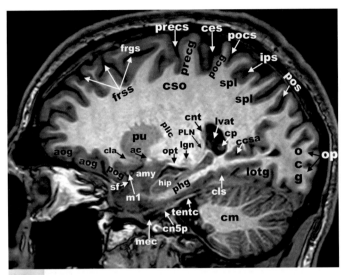

3.31a

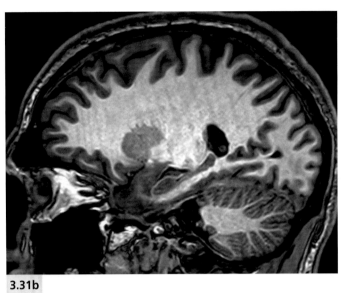

3.31b

FIGURES 3.31a–c

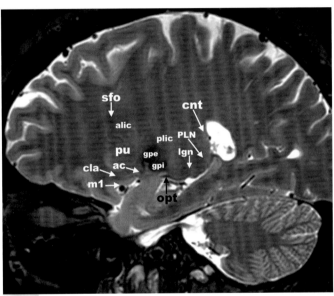

3.31c

KEY

PLN	posterolateral nucleus of thalamus	**lvat**	atrium (trigone) of lateral ventricle
ac	anterior commissure	**m1**	m1 (horizontal segment mca)
alic	anterior limb of internal capsule	**mca**	middle cerebral artery
amy	amygdala	**mec**	Meckel's cave
aog	anterior orbital gyrus	**ocg**	occipital gyri
ccsa	anterior calcarine sulcus	**op**	occipital pole
ces	central sulcus	**opt**	optic tract
cla	claustrum	**phg**	parahippocampal gyrus
cls	collateral sulcus		
cm	corpus medullare	**plic**	posterior limb of internal capsule
cn5p	pre-ganglionic segment trigeminal nerve	**pocg**	post-central gyrus
cnt	caudate nucleus tail	**pocs**	post-central sulcus
cp	choroid plexus	**pog**	posterior orbital gyrus
cso	centrum semiovale	**pos**	parieto-occipital sulcus
frgs	superior frontal gyrus	**precg**	pre-central gyrus
frss	superior frontal sulcus	**precs**	pre-central sulcus
gpe	globus pallidus externa	**pu**	putamen
gpi	globus pallidus interna	**sf**	Sylvian fissure (lateral sulcus)
hip	hippocampus		
ips	intraparietal sulcus	**sfo**	superior fronto-occipital fasciculus
lgn	lateral geniculate nucleus		
		spl	superior parietal lobule
lotg	lateral occipital temporal gyrus (lotg)/ fusiform gyrus	**tentc**	tentorium cerebelli

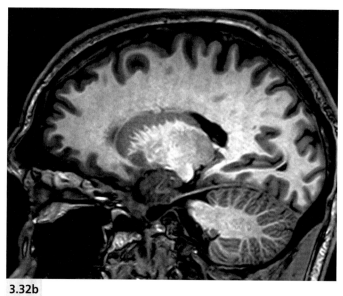

3.32a

3.32b

FIGURES 3.32a–c

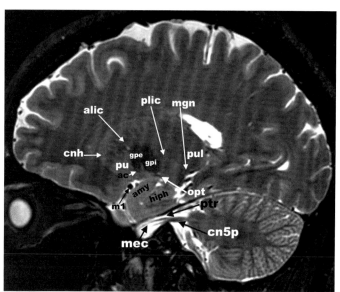

3.32c

KEY

L	combined ventral and lateral nuclei of thalamus	m1	m1 (horizontal segment mca)
ac	anterior commissure	mca	middle cerebral artery
alic	anterior limb of internal capsule	mcp	middle cerebellar peduncle (brachium pontis)
amy	amygdala		
aps	anterior perforated substance	mec	Meckel's cave
		mgn	medial geniculate nucleus
ccsa	anterior calcarine sulcus		
ces	central sulcus	mlln	medial lamina of lenticular nucleus
cigis	isthmus of cingulate gyrus		
		mog	medial orbital gyrus
cm	corpus medullare	ocg	occipital gyri
cn5p	pre-ganglionic segment trigeminal nerve	op	occipital pole
		opt	optic tract
cnb	caudate nucleus body	plic	posterior limb of internal capsule
cnh	caudate nucleus head		
cped	cerebral peduncle	pmol	posteromedial orbital lobule
cu	cuneus		
frgs	superior frontal gyrus	pocg	post-central gyrus
gic	genu of internal capsule	pocs	post-central sulcus
gpe	globus pallidus externa	pos	parieto-occipital sulcus
gpi	globus pallidus interna	precg	pre-central gyrus
hiph	hippocampal head	precs	pre-central sulcus
lg	lingual gyrus (motg)	ptr	porus trigeminus
llln	lateral lamina of lenticular nucleus	pu	putamen
		pul	pulvinar is part of lateral thalamic nuclear group
lvat	atrium (trigone) of lateral ventricle		
		sino	substantia innominata
lvoh	occipital horn of lateral ventricle	spl	superior parietal lobule

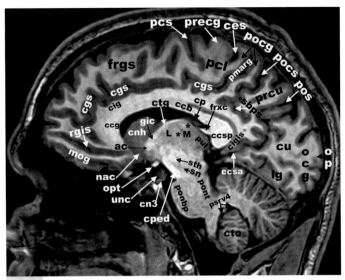

3.33a

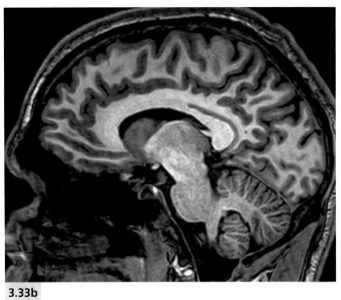

3.33b

FIGURES 3.33a–c

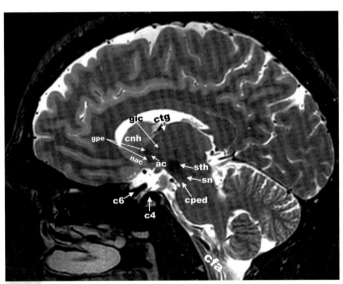

3.33c

KEY

*	internal medullary lamina of thalamus	frxc	crura of fornix
L	combined ventral and lateral nuclei of thalamus	gic	genu of internal capsule
		gpe	globus pallidus externa
M	medial nuclei of thalamus	ica	internal carotid artery
		lg	lingual gyrus (motg)
ac	anterior commissure	mog	medial orbital gyrus
c4	c4 (cavernous segment of ica)	nac	nucleus accumbens
		ocg	occipital gyri
c6	c6 (ophthalmic segment of ica)	op	occipital pole
		opt	optic tract
ccb	body of corpus callosum	pcl	paracentral lobule
		pcs	paracentral sulcus
ccg	genu of corpus callosum	pmarg	pars marginalis (ascending ramus of cingulate sulcus)
ccsa	anterior calcarine sulcus		
		pocg	post-central gyrus
ccsp	splenium of corpus callosum	pocs	post-central sulcus
		ponbp	basis pontis of pons
ces	central sulcus	pont	tegmentum of pons
cfa	csf flow artifact	pos	parieto-occipital sulcus
cgs	cingulate sulcus	prcu	precuneus
cig	cingulate gyrus	precg	pre-central gyrus
cigis	isthmus of cingulate gyrus	psrv4	posterior superior recess of fourth ventricle
cn3	oculomotor nerve		
cnh	caudate nucleus head	pul	pulvinar is part of lateral thalamic nuclear group
cp	choroid plexus		
cped	cerebral peduncle		
ctg	caudo-thalamic groove (notch)	rgis	inferior rostral sulcus
		sbps	subparietal sulcus
cto	cerebellar tonsil	sn	substantia nigra
cu	cuneus	sth	subthalamic nucleus
frgs	superior frontal gyrus	unc	uncus

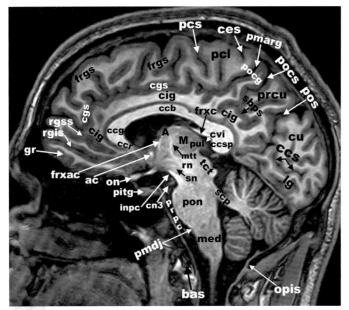

3.34a

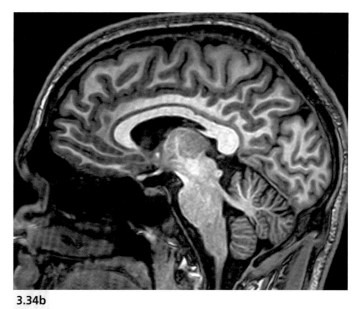

3.34b

FIGURES 3.34a–c

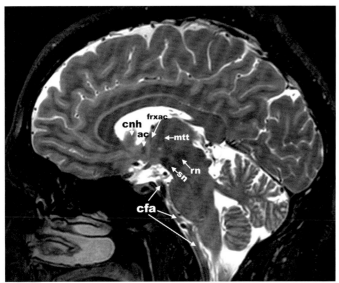

3.34c

KEY

A	anterior nuclei of thalamus		med	medulla
M	medial nuclei of thalamus		mtt	mammilothalamic tract
			on	optic nerve
ac	anterior commissure		opis	opisthion
bas	basion		pcl	paracentral lobule
ccb	body of corpus callosum		pcs	paracentral sulcus
			pitg	pituitary gland
ccg	genu of corpus callosum		pmarg	pars marginalis (ascending ramus of cingulate sulcus)
ccr	rostrum of corpus callosum		pmdj	ponto-medullary junction
ccs	calcarine sulcus		pocg	post-central gyrus
ccsp	splenium of corpus callosum		pocs	post-central sulcus
			pon	pons
ces	central sulcus		pos	parieto-occipital sulcus
cfa	csf flow artifact		prcu	precuneus
cgs	cingulate sulcus		prpc	prepontine cistern
cig	cingulate gyrus		pul	pulvinar is part of lateral thalamic nuclear group
cn3	oculomotor nerve			
cnh	caudate nucleus head			
cu	cuneus		rgis	inferior rostral sulcus
cvi	cistern of velum interpositum		rgss	superior rostral sulcus
			rn	red nucleus
frgs	superior frontal gyrus		sbps	subparietal sulcus
frxac	ascending columns of fornix		scp	superior cerebellar peduncle (brachium conjunctivum)
frxc	crura of fornix			
gr	gyrus rectus		sn	substantia nigra
inpc	interpeduncular cistern		tct	tectum
lg	lingual gyrus (motg)			

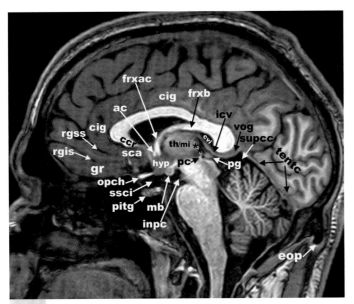

3.35a

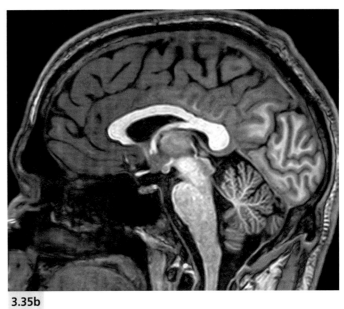

3.35b

FIGURES 3.35a–c

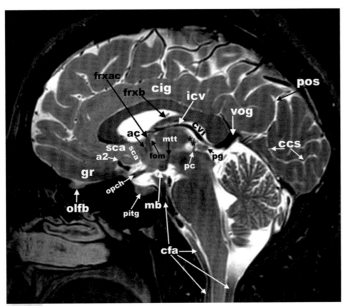

3.35c

KEY			
*	stria medullaris thalami	inpc	interpeduncular cistern
a2	a2 (postcommunicating segment aca)	mb	mammillary body
		mi	massa intermedia
ac	anterior commissure	mtt	mammilothalamic tract
aca	anterior cerebral artery	olfb	olfactory bulb
ccr	rostrum of corpus callosum	opch	optic chiasm
		pc	posterior commissure
ccs	calcarine sulcus	pg	pineal gland
cfa	csf flow artifact	pitg	pituitary gland
cig	cingulate gyrus	pos	parieto-occipital sulcus
cvi	cistern of velum interpositum	rgis	inferior rostral sulcus
		rgss	superior rostral sulcus
eop	external occipital protuberance (inion)	sca	subcallosal area
		ssci	suprasellar cistern
fom	foramen of Monro	supcc	supracerebellar cistern
frxac	ascending columns of fornix	tentc	tentorium cerebelli
		th	thalamus
frxb	body of fornix	vog	vein of Galen
gr	gyrus rectus		
hyp	hypothalamus		
icv	internal cerebral vein		

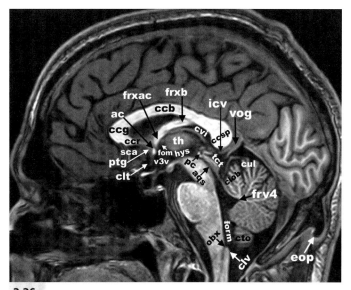

3.36a

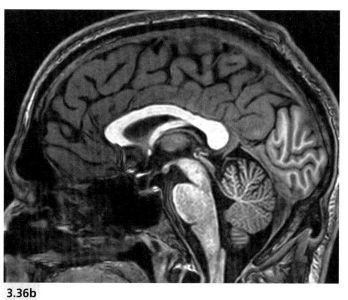

3.36b

FIGURES 3.36a–c

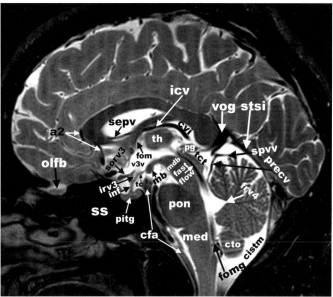

3.36c

KEY

a2	a2 (postcommunicating segment aca)	**hys**	hypothalamic sulcus
aca	anterior cerebral artery	**icv**	internal cerebral vein
aqs	aqueduct of Sylvius	**inf**	infundibulum
ccb	body of corpus callosum	**irv3**	infindibular recess of third ventricle
ccg	genu of corpus callosum	**mb**	mammillary body
ccr	rostrum of corpus callosum	**mdb**	midbrain
		med	medulla
ccsp	splenium of corpus callosum	**obx**	obex
		olfb	olfactory bulb
cfa	csf flow artifact	**pc**	posterior commissure
cistm	cisterna magna	**pg**	pineal gland
clob	central lobule of vermis	**pitg**	pituitary gland
clt	cistern of lamina terminalis	**pon**	pons
		precv	pre-central cerebellar vein
clv	clava		
cto	cerebellar tonsil	**ptg**	paraterminal gyrus
cul	culmen (lobules IV and V)	**sca**	subcallosal area
cvi	cistern of velum interpositum	**sepv**	septal vein
		sorv3	supra-optic recess of third ventricle
eop	external occipital protuberance (inion)	**spvv**	superior vermian vein
fom	foramen of Monro	**ss**	sphenoid sinus
fomg	foramen of Magendie	**stsi**	straight sinus
form	foramen magnum	**tc**	tuber cinereum
frv4	fastigial recess of fourth ventricle	**tct**	tectum
		th	thalamus
frxac	ascending columns of fornix	**v3v**	third ventricle
frxb	body of fornix	**vog**	vein of Galen

■ CORONAL (FIGURES 3.37–3.61)

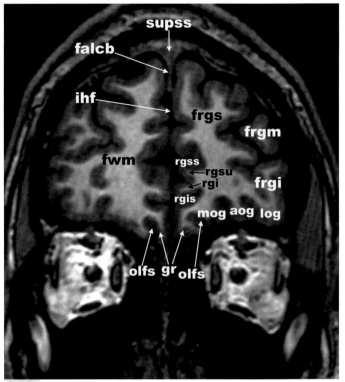

3.37a

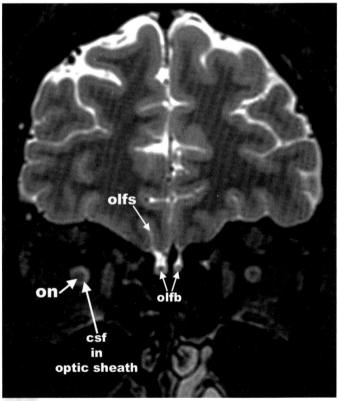

3.37c

3.37b

FIGURES 3.37a–c

KEY	
aog	anterior orbital gyrus
csf	cerebrospinal fluid
falcb	falx cerebri
frgi	inferior frontal gyrus
frgm	middle frontal gyrus
frgs	superior frontal gyrus
fwm	frontal white matter
gr	gyrus rectus
ihf	interhemispheric fissure
log	lateral orbital gyrus
mog	medial orbital gyrus
olfb	olfactory bulb
olfs	olfactory sulcus
on	optic nerve
rgi	inferior rostral gyrus
rgis	inferior rostral sulcus
rgss	superior rostral sulcus
rgsu	superior rostral gyrus
supss	superior sagittal sinus

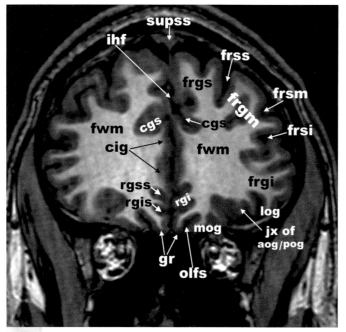

3.38a

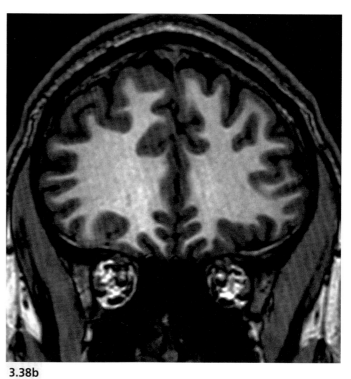

3.38b

FIGURES 3.38a–c

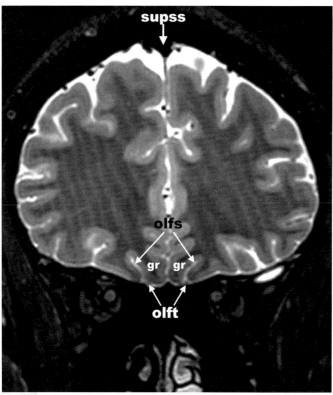

3.38c

KEY

aog	anterior orbital gyrus
cgs	cingulate sulcus
cig	cingulate gyrus
frgi	inferior frontal gyrus
frgm	middle frontal gyrus
frgs	superior frontal gyrus
frsi	inferior frontal sulcus
frsm	middle frontal sulcus
frss	superior frontal sulcus
fwm	frontal white matter
gr	gyrus rectus
ihf	interhemispheric fissure
jx	junction
log	lateral orbital gyrus
mog	medial orbital gyrus
olfs	olfactory sulcus
olft	olfactory tract
pog	posterior orbital gyrus
rgi	inferior rostral gyrus
rgis	inferior rostral sulcus
rgss	superior rostral sulcus
supss	superior sagittal sinus

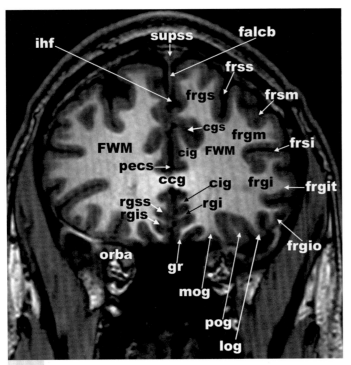

3.39a

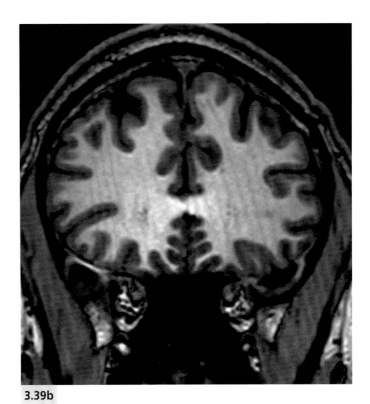

3.39b

FIGURES 3.39a–c

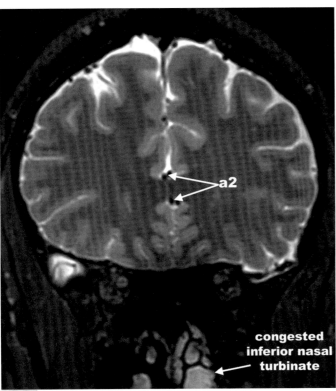

3.39c

KEY

FWM	frontal white matter
a2	a2 (postcommunicating segment aca)
aca	anterior cerebral artery
ccg	genu of corpus callosum
cgs	cingulate sulcus
cig	cingulate gyrus
falcb	falx cerebri
frgi	inferior frontal gyrus
frgio	pars orbitalis of inferior frontal gyrus
frgit	pars triangularis of inferior frontal gyrus
frgm	middle frontal gyrus
frgs	superior frontal gyrus
frsi	inferior frontal sulcus
frsm	middle frontal sulcus
frss	superior frontal sulcus
gr	gyrus rectus
ihf	interhemispheric fissure
log	lateral orbital gyrus
mog	medial orbital gyrus
orba	orbital apex
pecs	pericallosal cistern (sulcus)
pog	posterior orbital gyrus
rgi	inferior rostral gyrus
rgis	inferior rostral sulcus
rgss	superior rostral sulcus
supss	superior sagittal sinus

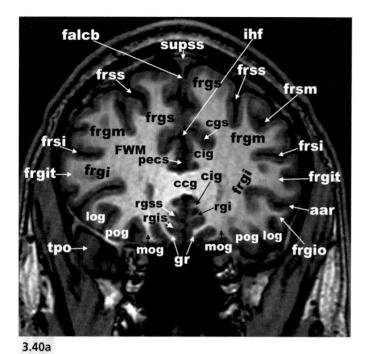

3.40a

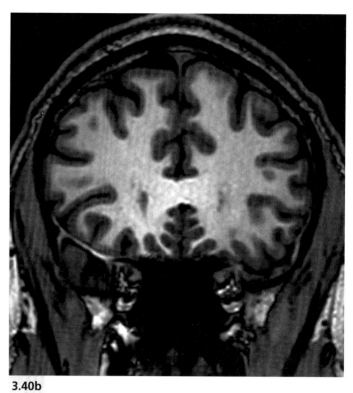

3.40b

FIGURES 3.40a–c

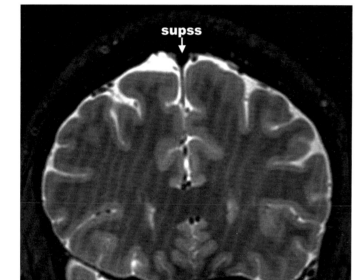

3.40c

KEY

FWM	frontal white matter
aar	anterior ascending ramus of Sylvian fissure
ccg	genu of corpus callosum
cgs	cingulate sulcus
cig	cingulate gyrus
falcb	falx cerebri
frgi	inferior frontal gyrus
frgio	pars orbitalis of inferior frontal gyrus
frgit	pars triangularis of inferior frontal gyrus
frgm	middle frontal gyrus
frgs	superior frontal gyrus
frsi	inferior frontal sulcus
frsm	middle frontal sulcus
frss	superior frontal sulcus
gr	gyrus rectus
ihf	interhemispheric fissure
log	lateral orbital gyrus
mog	medial orbital gyrus
orba	orbital apex
pecs	pericallosal cistern (sulcus)
pog	posterior orbital gyrus
rgi	inferior rostral gyrus
rgis	inferior rostral sulcus
rgss	superior rostral sulcus
supss	superior sagittal sinus
tpo	temporal pole

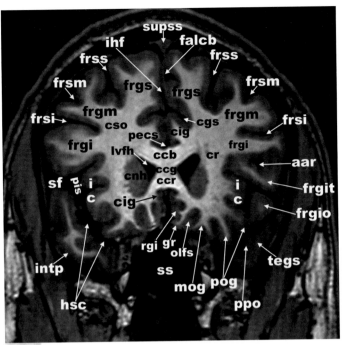

3.41a

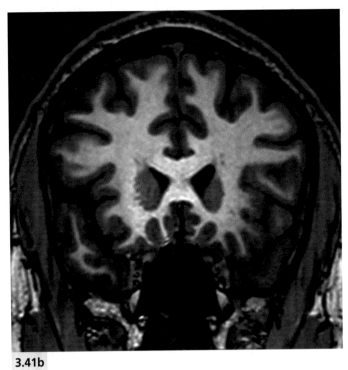

3.41b

FIGURES 3.41a–c

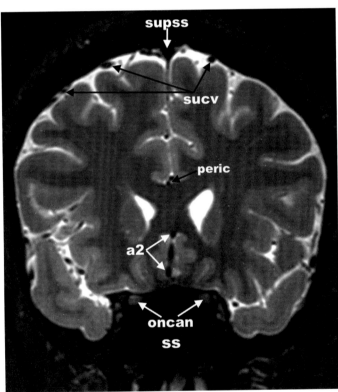

3.41c

KEY			
a2	a2 (postcommunicating segment aca)	**hsc**	horizontal Sylvian cistern (Sylvian fissure)
aar	anterior ascending ramus of Sylvian fissure	**ic**	insular cortex
aca	anterior cerebral artery	**ihf**	interhemispheric fissure
ccb	body of corpus callosum	**intp**	inferior temporal polar region
ccg	genu of corpus callosum	**lvfh**	frontal horn of lateral ventricle
ccr	rostrum of corpus callosum	**mog**	medial orbital gyrus
		olfs	olfactory sulcus
cgs	cingulate sulcus	**oncan**	canalicular segment of optic nerve
cig	cingulate gyrus	**pecs**	pericallosal cistern (sulcus)
cnh	caudate nucleus head		
cr	corona radiata	**peric**	pericallosal branch of aca
cso	centrum semiovale		
falcb	falx cerebri	**pis**	peri-insular (circular) sulcus
frgi	inferior frontal gyrus		
frgio	pars orbitalis of inferior frontal gyrus	**pog**	posterior orbital gyrus
		ppo	planum polare
frgit	pars triangularis of inferior frontal gyrus	**rgi**	inferior rostral gyrus
		sf	Sylvian fissure (lateral sulcus)
frgm	middle frontal gyrus		
frgs	superior frontal gyrus	**ss**	sphenoid sinus
frsi	inferior frontal sulcus	**sucv**	superficial cortical vein(s)
frsm	middle frontal sulcus		
frss	superior frontal sulcus	**supss**	superior sagittal sinus
gr	gyrus rectus	**tegs**	superior temporal gyrus

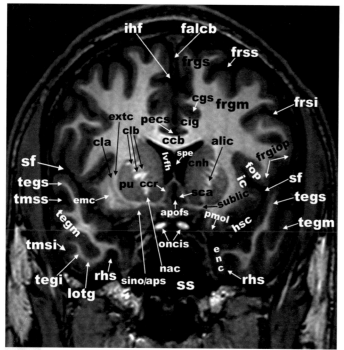

3.42a

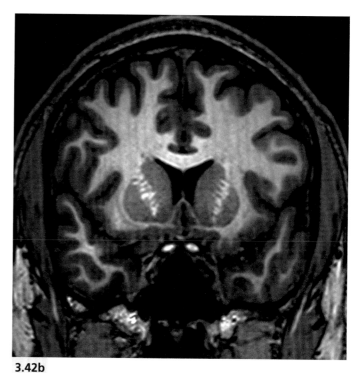

3.42b

FIGURES 3.42a–c

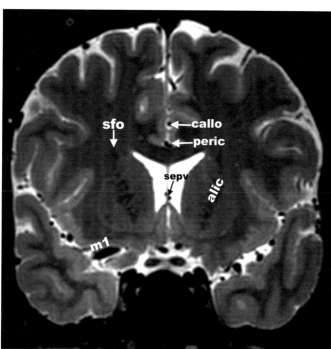

3.42c

KEY

aca	anterior cerebral artery	**lvfh**	frontal horn of lateral ventricle
alic	anterior limb of internal capsule	**m1**	m1 (horizontal segment mca)
apofs	anterior parolfactory sulcus	**mca**	middle cerebral artery
aps	anterior perforated substance	**nac**	nucleus accumbens
callo	callosomarginal branch of aca	**oncis**	cisternal (pre-chiasmatic) segment optic nerve
ccb	body of corpus callosum	**pecs**	pericallosal cistern (sulcus)
ccr	rostrum of corpus callosum	**peric**	pericallosal branch of aca
cgs	cingulate sulcus	**pmol**	posteromedial orbital lobule
cig	cingulate gyrus		
cla	claustrum	**pu**	putamen
clb	caudato-lenticular bridges	**rhs**	rhinal sulcus
		sca	subcallosal area
cnh	caudate nucleus head	**sepv**	septal vein
emc	extreme capsule	**sf**	Sylvian fissure (lateral sulcus)
enc	entorhinal cortex		
extc	external capsule	**sfo**	superior fronto-occipital fasciculus
falcb	falx cerebri		
fop	frontal operculum	**sino**	substantia innominata
frgiop	pars opercularis of inferior frontal gyrus	**spe**	septum pellucidum
		ss	sphenoid sinus
frgm	middle frontal gyrus	**sublic**	sublenticular internal capsule
frgs	superior frontal gyrus		
frsi	inferior frontal sulcus	**tegi**	inferior temporal gyrus
frss	superior frontal sulcus	**tegm**	middle temporal gyrus
hsc	horizontal Sylvian cistern (Sylvian fissure)	**tegs**	superior temporal gyrus
		tmsi	inferior temporal sulcus
		tmss	superior temporal sulcus
ic	insular cortex		
ihf	interhemispheric fissure		
lotg	lateral occipital temporal gyrus (lotg)/ fusiform gyrus		

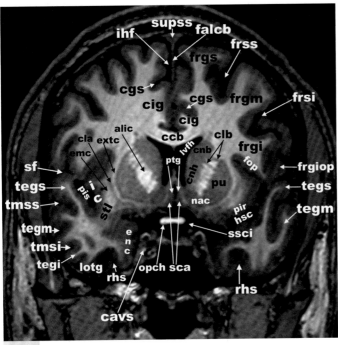

3.43a

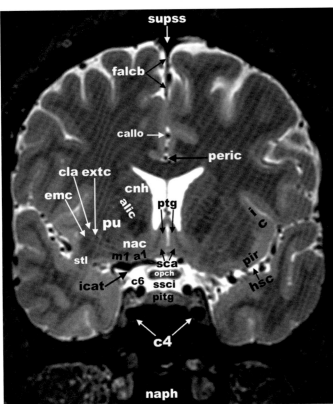

3.43c

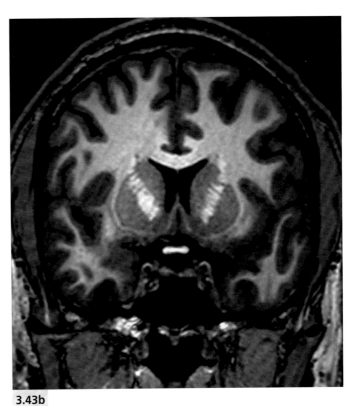

3.43b

FIGURES 3.43a–c

KEY

a1	a1 (precommunicating segment aca)	**icat**	ica terminus/ bifurcation
aca	anterior cerebral artery	**ihf**	interhemispheric fissure
alic	anterior limb of internal capsule	**lotg**	lateral occipital temporal gyrus (lotg)/ fusiform gyrus
c4	c4 (cavernous segment of ica)	**lvfh**	frontal horn of lateral ventricle
c6	c6 (ophthalmic segment of ica)	**m1**	m1 (horizontal segment mca)
callo	callosomarginal branch of aca	**mca**	middle cerebral artery
cavs	cavernous sinus	**nac**	nucleus accumbens
ccb	body of corpus callosum	**naph**	nasopharynx
		opch	optic chiasm
cgs	cingulate sulcus	**peric**	pericallosal branch of aca
cig	cingulate gyrus		
cla	claustrum	**pir**	piriform cortex
clb	caudato-lenticular bridges	**pis**	peri-insular (circular) sulcus
cnb	caudate nucleus body	**pitg**	pituitary gland
cnh	caudate nucleus head	**ptg**	paraterminal gyrus
emc	extreme capsule	**pu**	putamen
enc	entorhinal cortex	**rhs**	rhinal sulcus
extc	external capsule	**sca**	subcallosal area
falcb	falx cerebri	**sf**	Sylvian fissure (lateral sulcus)
fop	frontal operculum		
frgi	inferior frontal gyrus	**ssci**	suprasellar cistern
frgiop	pars opercularis of inferior frontal gyrus	**stl**	stem of temporal lobe
		supss	superior sagittal sinus
frgm	middle frontal gyrus	**tegi**	inferior temporal gyrus
frgs	superior frontal gyrus	**tegm**	middle temporal gyrus
frsi	inferior frontal sulcus	**tegs**	superior temporal gyrus
frss	superior frontal sulcus	**tmsi**	inferior temporal sulcus
hsc	horizontal Sylvian cistern (Sylvian fissure)	**tmss**	superior temporal sulcus
ic	insular cortex		
ica	internal carotid artery		

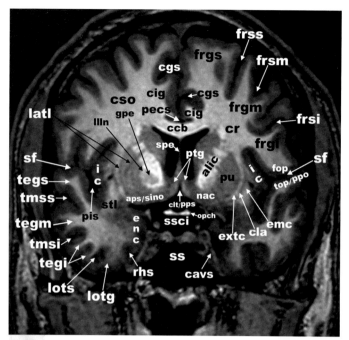

3.44a

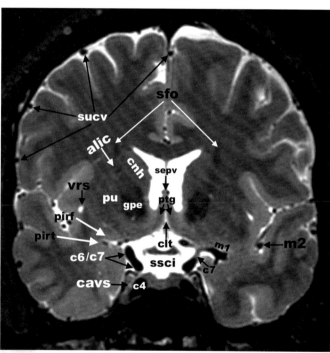

3.44c

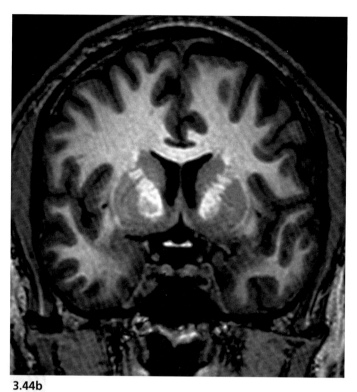

3.44b

FIGURES 3.44a–c

KEY

alic	anterior limb of internal capsule	**m1**	m1 (horizontal segment mca)
aps	anterior perforated substance	**m2**	m2 (Sylvian/insular branches mca)
c4	c4 (cavernous segment of ica)	**mca**	middle cerebral artery
c6	c6 (ophthalmic segment of ica)	**nac**	nucleus accumbens
		opch	optic chiasm
c7	c7 (communicating segment of ica)	**pecs**	pericallosal cistern (sulcus)
cavs	cavernous sinus	**pirf**	piriform cortex, frontal part
ccb	body of corpus callosum	**pirt**	piriform cortex, temporal part
cgs	cingulate sulcus	**pis**	peri-insular (circular) sulcus
cig	cingulate gyrus		
cla	claustrum	**ppo**	planum polare
clt	cistern of lamina terminalis	**pps**	posterior parolfactory sulcus
cnh	caudate nucleus head	**ptg**	paraterminal gyrus
cr	corona radiata	**pu**	putamen
cso	centrum semiovale	**rhs**	rhinal sulcus
emc	extreme capsule	**sepv**	septal vein
enc	entorhinal cortex	**sf**	Sylvian fissure (lateral sulcus)
extc	external capsule		
fop	frontal operculum	**sfo**	superior fronto-occipital fasciculus
frgi	inferior frontal gyrus		
frgm	middle frontal gyrus	**sino**	substantia innominata
frgs	superior frontal gyrus	**spe**	septum pellucidum
frsi	inferior frontal sulcus	**ss**	sphenoid sinus
frsm	middle frontal sulcus	**ssci**	suprasellar cistern
frss	superior frontal sulcus	**stl**	stem of temporal lobe
gpe	globus pallidus externa	**sucv**	superficial cortical vein(s)
ic	insular cortex		
ica	internal carotid artery	**tegi**	inferior temporal gyrus
latl	lateral lenticulostriate arteries	**tegm**	middle temporal gyrus
		tegs	superior temporal gyrus
llln	lateral lamina of lenticular nucleus	**tmsi**	inferior temporal sulcus
		tmss	superior temporal sulcus
lotg	lateral occipital temporal gyrus (lotg)/ fusiform gyrus	**top**	temporal operculum
		vrs	Virchow-Robin spaces
lots	lateral occipital temporal sulcus		

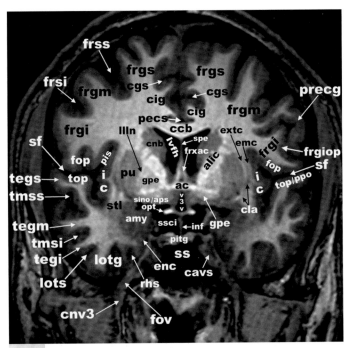

3.45a

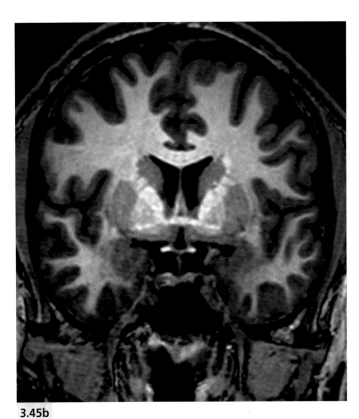

3.45b

FIGURES 3.45a–c

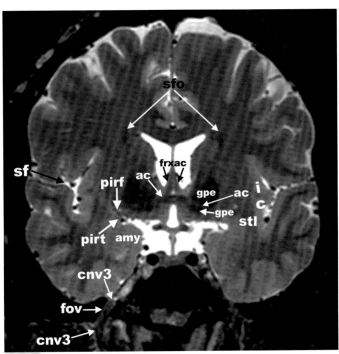

3.45c

KEY

ac	anterior commissure
alic	anterior limb of internal capsule
amy	amygdala
aps	anterior perforated substance
cavs	cavernous sinus
ccb	body of corpus callosum
cgs	cingulate sulcus
cig	cingulate gyrus
cla	claustrum
cnb	caudate nucleus body
cnv3	mandibular division (v3) of trigeminal nerve
emc	extreme capsule
enc	entorhinal cortex
extc	external capsule
fop	frontal operculum
fov	foramen ovale
frgi	inferior frontal gyrus
frgiop	pars opercularis of inferior frontal gyrus
frgm	middle frontal gyrus
frgs	superior frontal gyrus
frsi	inferior frontal sulcus
frss	superior frontal sulcus
frxac	ascending columns of fornix
gpe	globus pallidus externa
ic	insular cortex
inf	infundibulum
llln	lateral lamina of lenticular nucleus
lotg	lateral occipital temporal gyrus (lotg)/ fusiform gyrus

lots	lateral occipital temporal sulcus
lvfh	frontal horn of lateral ventricle
opt	optic tract
pecs	pericallosal cistern (sulcus)
pirf	piriform cortex, frontal part
pirt	piriform cortex, temporal part
pis	peri-insular (circular) sulcus
pitg	pituitary gland
ppo	planum polare
precg	pre-central gyrus
pu	putamen
rhs	rhinal sulcus
sf	Sylvian fissure (lateral sulcus)
sfo	superior fronto-occipital fasciculus
sino	substantia innominata
spe	septum pellucidum
ss	sphenoid sinus
ssci	suprasellar cistern
stl	stem of temporal lobe
tegi	inferior temporal gyrus
tegm	middle temporal gyrus
tegs	superior temporal gyrus
tmsi	inferior temporal sulcus
tmss	superior temporal sulcus
top	temporal operculum
v3v	third ventricle

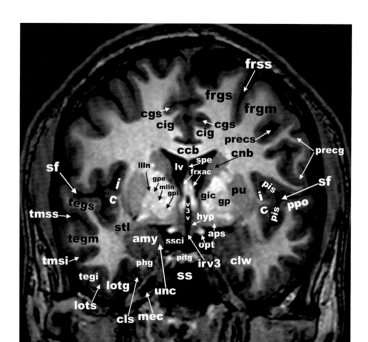

3.46a

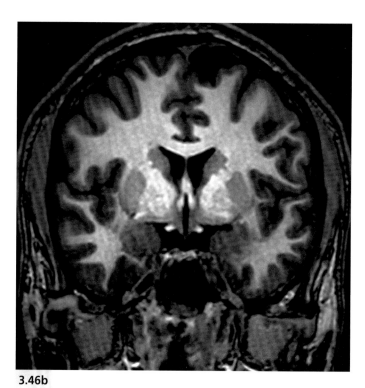

3.46b

FIGURES 3.46a–c

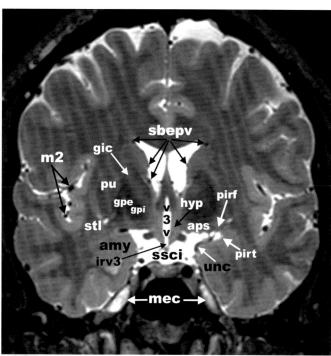

3.46c

KEY

amy	amygdala	mca	middle cerebral artery
aps	anterior perforated substance	mec	Meckel's cave
		mlln	medial lamina of lenticular nucleus
ccb	body of corpus callosum	opt	optic tract
cgs	cingulate sulcus	phg	parahippocampal gyrus
cig	cingulate gyrus	pirf	piriform cortex, frontal part
cls	collateral sulcus		
clw	collateral white matter	pirt	piriform cortex, temporal part
cnb	caudate nucleus body	pis	peri-insular (circular) sulcus
frgm	middle frontal gyrus		
frgs	superior frontal gyrus	pitg	pituitary gland
frss	superior frontal sulcus	ppo	planum polare
frxac	ascending columns of fornix	precg	pre-central gyrus
		precs	pre-central sulcus
gic	genu of internal capsule	pu	putamen
gp	glopus pallidus	sbepv	subependymal veins
gpe	globus pallidus externa	sf	Sylvian fissure (lateral sulcus)
gpi	globus pallidus interna		
hyp	hypothalamus	spe	septum pellucidum
ic	insular cortex	ss	sphenoid sinus
irv3	infindibular recess of third ventricle	ssci	suprasellar cistern
		stl	stem of temporal lobe
llln	lateral lamina of lenticular nucleus	tegi	inferior temporal gyrus
		tegm	middle temporal gyrus
lotg	lateral occipital temporal gyrus (lotg)/ fusiform gyrus	tegs	superior temporal gyrus
		tmsi	inferior temporal sulcus
		tmss	superior temporal sulcus
lots	lateral occipital temporal sulcus		
lv	lateral ventricle	unc	uncus
m2	m2 (Sylvian/insular branches mca)	v3v	third ventricle

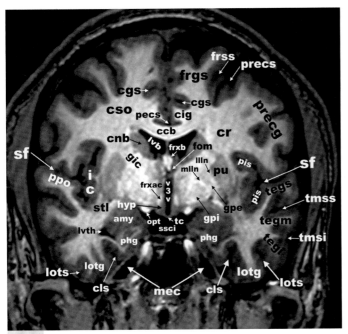

3.47a

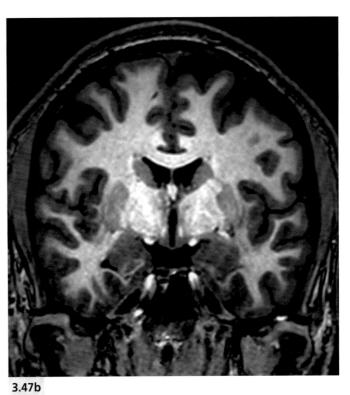

3.47b

FIGURES 3.47a–c

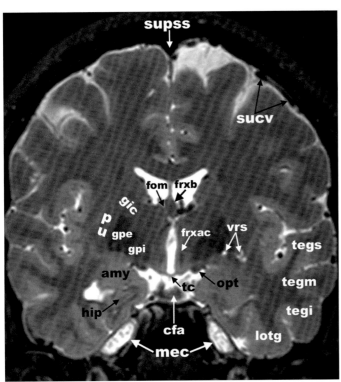

3.47c

KEY			
amy	amygdala	**lvth**	temporal horn of lateral ventricle
ccb	body of corpus callosum		
cfa	csf flow artifact	**mec**	Meckel's cave
cgs	cingulate sulcus	**mlln**	medial lamina of lenticular nucleus
cig	cingulate gyrus		
cls	collateral sulcus	**opt**	optic tract
cnb	caudate nucleus body	**pecs**	pericallosal cistern (sulcus)
cr	corona radiata		
cso	centrum semiovale	**phg**	parahippocampal gyrus
fom	foramen of Monro	**pis**	peri-insular (circular) sulcus
frgs	superior frontal gyrus		
frss	superior frontal sulcus	**ppo**	planum polare
frxac	ascending columns of fornix	**precg**	pre-central gyrus
		precs	pre-central sulcus
frxb	body of fornix	**pu**	putamen
gic	genu of internal capsule	**sf**	Sylvian fissure (lateral sulcus)
		ssci	suprasellar cistern
gpe	globus pallidus externa	**stl**	stem of temporal lobe
		sucv	superficial cortical vein(s)
gpi	globus pallidus interna		
hip	hippocampus	**supss**	superior sagittal sinus
hyp	hypothalamus	**tc**	tuber cinereum
ic	insular cortex	**tegi**	inferior temporal gyrus
llln	lateral lamina of lenticular nucleus	**tegm**	middle temporal gyrus
		tegs	superior temporal gyrus
lotg	lateral occipital temporal gyrus (lotg)/ fusiform gyrus	**tmsi**	inferior temporal sulcus
		tmss	superior temporal sulcus
lots	lateral occipital temporal sulcus	**v3v**	third ventricle
lvb	body of lateral ventricle	**vrs**	Virchow-Robin spaces

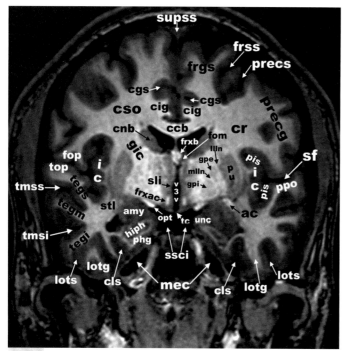

3.48a

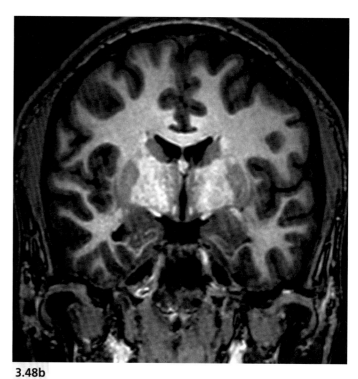

3.48b

FIGURES 3.48a–c

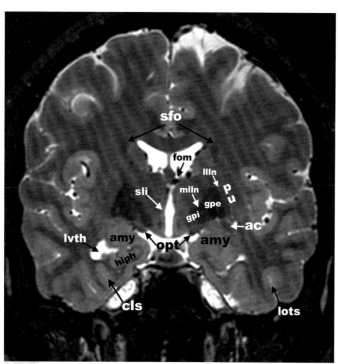

3.48c

KEY

ac	anterior commissure	mec	Meckel's cave
amy	amygdala	mlln	medial lamina of lenticular nucleus
ccb	body of corpus callosum	opt	optic tract
cgs	cingulate sulcus	phg	parahippocampal gyrus
cig	cingulate gyrus	pis	peri-insular (circular) sulcus
cls	collateral sulcus		
cnb	caudate nucleus body	ppo	planum polare
cr	corona radiata	precg	pre-central gyrus
cso	centrum semiovale	precs	pre-central sulcus
fom	foramen of Monro	pu	putamen
fop	frontal operculum	sf	Sylvian fissure (lateral sulcus)
frgs	superior frontal gyrus		
frss	superior frontal sulcus	sfo	superior fronto-occipital fasciculus
frxac	ascending columns of fornix		
		sli	sulcus limitans
frxb	body of fornix	ssci	suprasellar cistern
gic	genu of internal capsule	stl	stem of temporal lobe
gpe	globus pallidus externa	supss	superior sagittal sinus
gpi	globus pallidus interna	tc	tuber cinereum
hiph	hippocampal head	tegi	inferior temporal gyrus
ic	insular cortex	tegm	middle temporal gyrus
llln	lateral lamina of lenticular nucleus	tegs	superior temporal gyrus
		tmsi	inferior temporal sulcus
lotg	lateral occipital temporal gyrus (lotg)/ fusiform gyrus	tmss	superior temporal sulcus
		top	temporal operculum
lots	lateral occipital temporal sulcus	unc	uncus
		v3v	third ventricle
lvth	temporal horn of lateral ventricle		

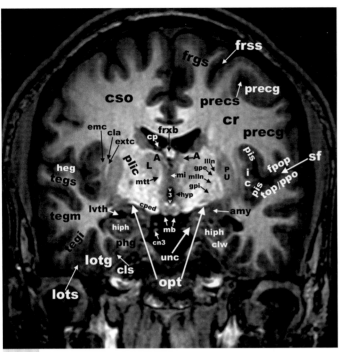

3.49a

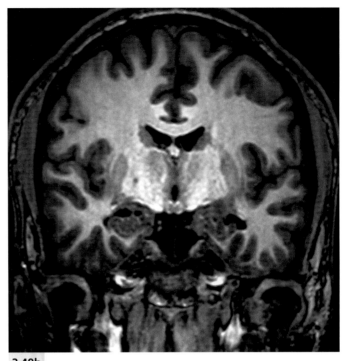

3.49b

FIGURES 3.49a–c

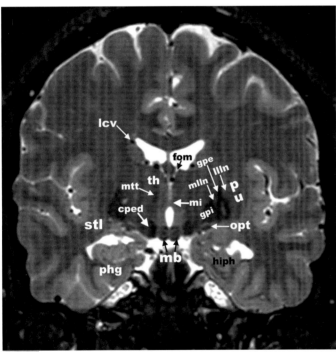

3.49c

KEY			
A	anterior nuclei of thalamus	lotg	lateral occipital temporal gyrus (lotg)/fusiform gyrus
L	combined ventral and lateral nuclei of thalamus	lots	lateral occipital temporal sulcus
amy	amygdala	lvth	temporal horn of lateral ventricle
cla	claustrum		
cls	collateral sulcus	mb	mammillary body
clw	collateral white matter	mi	massa intermedia
cn3	oculomotor nerve	mlln	medial lamina of lenticular nucleus
cp	choroid plexus		
cped	cerebral peduncle	mtt	mammilothalamic tract
cr	corona radiata	opt	optic tract
cso	centrum semiovale	phg	parahippocampal gyrus
emc	extreme capsule	pis	peri-insular (circular) sulcus
extc	external capsule		
fom	foramen of Monro	plic	posterior limb of internal capsule
fpop	fronto-parietal operculum		
		ppo	planum polare
frgs	superior frontal gyrus	precg	pre-central gyrus
frss	superior frontal sulcus	precs	pre-central sulcus
frxb	body of fornix	pu	putamen
gpe	globus pallidus externa	sf	Sylvian fissure (lateral sulcus)
gpi	globus pallidus interna		
heg	Heschl's gyrus (transverse temporal gyrus)	stl	stem of temporal lobe
		tegi	inferior temporal gyrus
		tegm	middle temporal gyrus
hiph	hippocampal head	tegs	superior temporal gyrus
hyp	hypothalamus	th	thalamus
ic	insular cortex	top	temporal operculum
lcv	longitudinal caudate vein	unc	uncus
llln	lateral lamina of lenticular nucleus	v3v	third ventricle

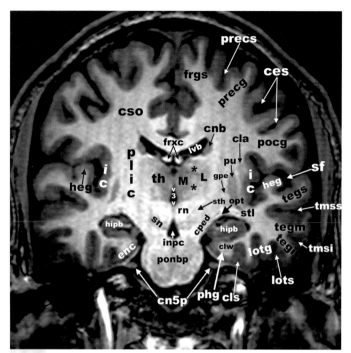

3.50a

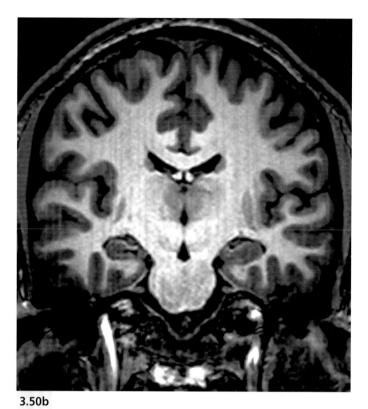

3.50b

3.50a–c

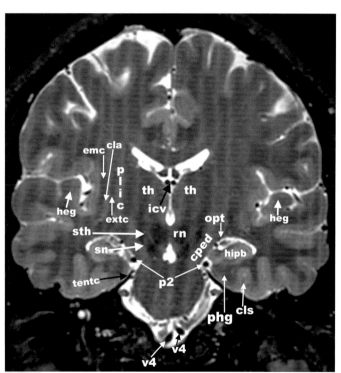

3.50c

KEY

*	internal medullary lamina of thalamus	lvb	body of lateral ventricle
		opt	optic tract
L	combined ventral and lateral nuclei of thalamus	p2	p2 (ambient segment of pca)
M	medial nuclei of thalamus	pca	posterior cerebral artery
ces	central sulcus	phg	parahippocampal gyrus
cla	claustrum	plic	posterior limb of internal capsule
cls	collateral sulcus	pocg	post-central gyrus
clw	collateral white matter	ponbp	basis pontis of pons
cn5p	pre-ganglionic segment trigeminal nerve	precg	pre-central gyrus
		precs	pre-central sulcus
cnb	caudate nucleus body	pu	putamen
cped	cerebral peduncle	rn	red nucleus
cso	centrum semiovale	sf	Sylvian fissure (lateral sulcus)
emc	extreme capsule	sn	substantia nigra
enc	entorhinal cortex	sth	subthalamic nucleus
extc	external capsule	stl	stem of temporal lobe
frgs	superior frontal gyrus	tegi	inferior temporal gyrus
frxc	crura of fornix	tegm	middle temporal gyrus
gpe	globus pallidus externa	tegs	superior temporal gyrus
heg	Heschl's gyrus (transverse temporal gyrus)	tentc	tentorium cerebelli
		th	thalamus
hipb	hippocampal body	tmsi	inferior temporal sulcus
ic	insular cortex	tmss	superior temporal sulcus
icv	internal cerebral vein		
inpc	interpeduncular cistern	v3v	third ventricle
lotg	lateral occipital temporal gyrus (lotg)/ fusiform gyrus	v4	v4 intracranial/ intradural segment vertebral artery
lots	lateral occipital temporal sulcus		

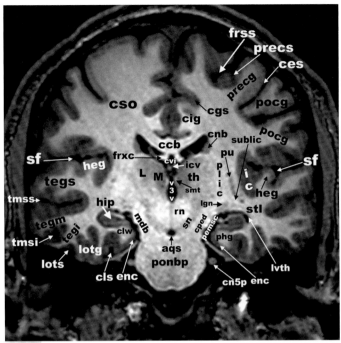

3.51a

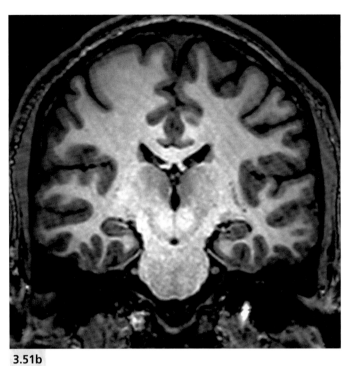

3.51b

FIGURES 3.51a–c

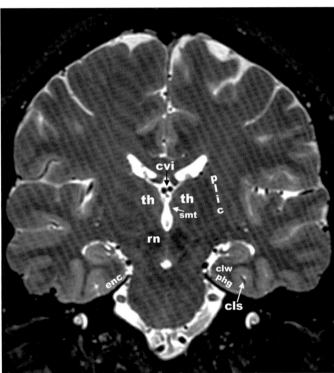

3.51c

KEY			
L	combined ventral and lateral nuclei of thalamus	lots	lateral occipital temporal sulcus
M	medial nuclei of thalamus	lvth	temporal horn of lateral ventricle
aqs	aqueduct of Sylvius	mdb	midbrain
ccb	body of corpus callosum	pemsc	perimesencephalic (ambient) cistern
ces	central sulcus	phg	parahippocampal gyrus
cgs	cingulate sulcus		
cig	cingulate gyrus	plic	posterior limb of internal capsule
cls	collateral sulcus		
clw	collateral white matter	pocg	post-central gyrus
cn5p	pre-ganglionic segment trigeminal nerve	ponbp	basis pontis of pons
		precg	pre-central gyrus
cnb	caudate nucleus body	precs	pre-central sulcus
cped	cerebral peduncle	pu	putamen
cso	centrum semiovale	rn	red nucleus
cvi	cistern of velum interpositum	sf	Sylvian fissure (lateral sulcus)
enc	entorhinal cortex	smt	stria medullaris thalami
frss	superior frontal sulcus	sn	substantia nigra
frxc	crura of fornix	stl	stem of temporal lobe
heg	Heschl's gyrus (transverse temporal gyrus)	sublic	sublenticular internal capsule
		tegi	inferior temporal gyrus
hip	hippocampus	tegm	middle temporal gyrus
ic	insular cortex	tegs	superior temporal gyrus
icv	internal cerebral vein		
lgn	lateral geniculate nucleus	th	thalamus
		tmsi	inferior temporal sulcus
lotg	lateral occipital temporal gyrus (lotg)/ fusiform gyrus	tmss	superior temporal sulcus
		v3v	third ventricle

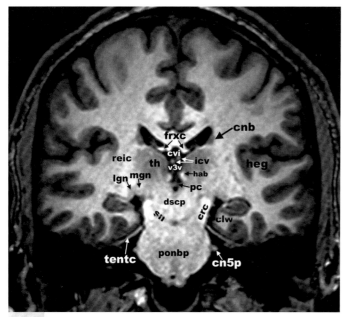

3.52a

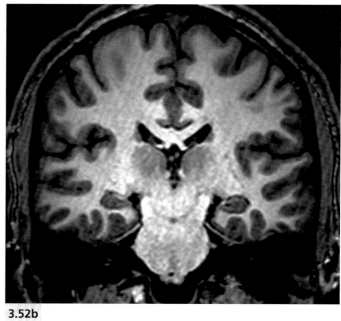

3.52b

FIGURES 3.52a–c

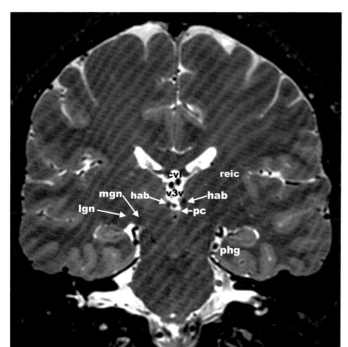

3.52c

KEY

clw	collateral white matter
cn5p	pre-ganglionic segment trigeminal nerve
cnb	caudate nucleus body
crc	crus cerebri
cvi	cistern of velum interpositum
dscp	decussation of superior cerebellar peduncles
frxc	crura of fornix
hab	habenular trigone
heg	Heschl's gyrus (transverse temporal gyrus)
icv	internal cerebral vein
lgn	lateral geniculate nucleus
mgn	medial geniculate nucleus
pc	posterior commissure
phg	parahippocampal gyrus
ponbp	basis pontis of pons
reic	retrolenticular internal capsule
sn	substantia nigra
tentc	tentorium cerebelli
th	thalamus
v3v	third ventricle

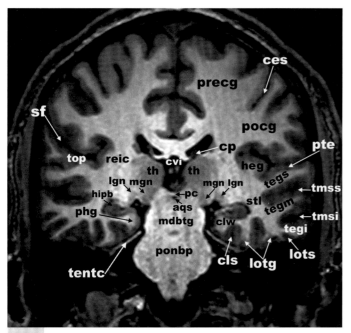

3.53a

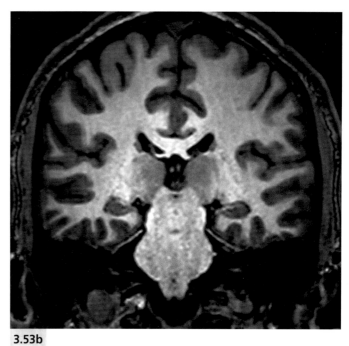

3.53b

FIGURES 3.53a–c

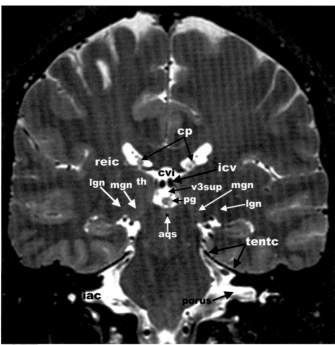

3.53c

KEY

aqs	aqueduct of Sylvius	pg	pineal gland
ces	central sulcus	phg	parahippocampal gyrus
cls	collateral sulcus	pocg	post-central gyrus
clw	collateral white matter	ponbp	basis pontis of pons
cp	choroid plexus	porus	porus acousticus
cvi	cistern of velum interpositum	precg	pre-central gyrus
		pte	planum temporale
heg	Heschl's gyrus (transverse temporal gyrus)	reic	retrolenticular internal capsule
		sf	Sylvian fissure (lateral sulcus)
hipb	hippocampal body		
iac	internal auditory canal	stl	stem of temporal lobe
icv	internal cerebral vein	tegi	inferior temporal gyrus
lgn	lateral geniculate nucleus	tegm	middle temporal gyrus
		tegs	superior temporal gyrus
lotg	lateral occipital temporal gyrus (lotg)/ fusiform gyrus	tentc	tentorium cerebelli
		th	thalamus
lots	lateral occipital temporal sulcus	tmsi	inferior temporal sulcus
		tmss	superior temporal sulcus
mdbtg	tegmentum of midbrain	top	temporal operculum
mgn	medial geniculate nucleus	v3sup	supra-pineal recess of third ventricle
pc	posterior commissure		

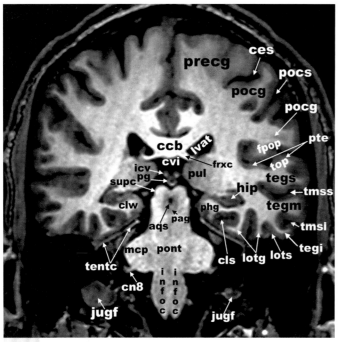

3.54a

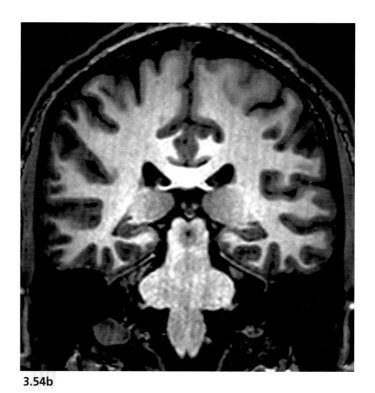

3.54b

FIGURES 3.54a–c

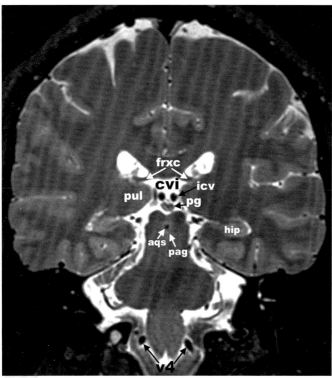

3.54c

KEY

aqs	aqueduct of Sylvius	**pag**	periaqueductal gray matter
ccb	body of corpus callosum		
ces	central sulcus	**pg**	pineal gland
cls	collateral sulcus	**phg**	parahippocampal gyrus
clw	collateral white matter	**pocg**	post-central gyrus
cn8	vestibulocochlear nerve	**pocs**	post-central sulcus
cvi	cistern of velum interpositum	**pont**	tegmentum of pons
		precg	pre-central gyrus
fpop	fronto-parietal operculum	**pte**	planum temporale
		pul	pulvinar is part of lateral thalamic nuclear group
frxc	crura of fornix		
hip	hippocampus		
icv	internal cerebral vein	**supc**	superior colliculus
infoc	inferior olivary complex	**tegi**	inferior temporal gyrus
jugf	jugular foramen	**tegm**	middle temporal gyrus
lotg	lateral occipital temporal gyrus (lotg)/ fusiform gyrus	**tegs**	superior temporal gyrus
		tentc	tentorium cerebelli
		tmsi	inferior temporal sulcus
lots	lateral occipital temporal sulcus	**tmss**	superior temporal sulcus
lvat	atrium (trigone) of lateral ventricle	**top**	temporal operculum
		v4	v4 intracranial/ intradural segment vertebral artery
mcp	middle cerebellar peduncle (brachium pontis)		

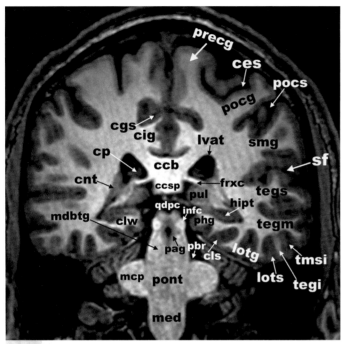

3.55a

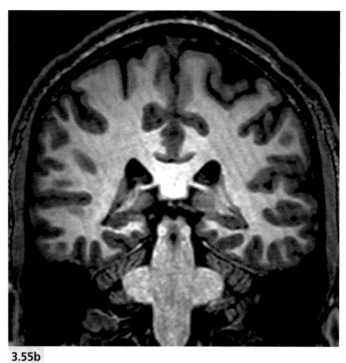

3.55b

FIGURES 3.55a–c

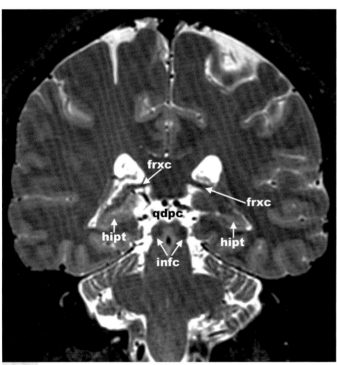

3.55c

KEY

ccb	body of corpus callosum	mdbtg	tegmentum of midbrain
ccsp	splenium of corpus callosum	med	medulla
		pag	periaqueductal gray matter
ces	central sulcus	pbr	para-brachial recess
cgs	cingulate sulcus	phg	parahippocampal gyrus
cig	cingulate gyrus	pocg	post-central gyrus
cls	collateral sulcus	pocs	post-central sulcus
clw	collateral white matter	pont	tegmentum of pons
cnt	caudate nucleus tail	precg	pre-central gyrus
cp	choroid plexus	pul	pulvinar is part of lateral thalamic nuclear group
frxc	crura of fornix		
hipt	hippocampal tail		
infc	inferior colliculus	qdpc	quadrigeminal plate cistern
lotg	lateral occipital temporal gyrus (lotg)/ fusiform gyrus	sf	Sylvian fissure (lateral sulcus)
lots	lateral occipital temporal sulcus	smg	supramarginal gyrus
		tegi	inferior temporal gyrus
lvat	atrium (trigone) of lateral ventricle	tegm	middle temporal gyrus
mcp	middle cerebellar peduncle (brachium pontis)	tegs	superior temporal gyrus
		tmsi	inferior temporal sulcus

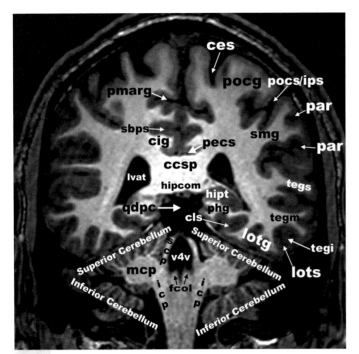

3.56a

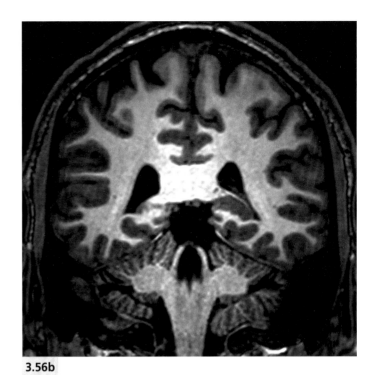

3.56b

FIGURES 3.56a–c

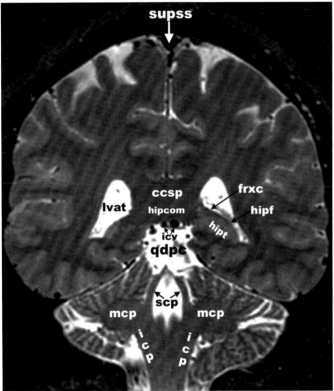

3.56c

KEY

ccsp	splenium of corpus callosum	par	posterior ascending ramus of Sylvian fissure
ces	central sulcus		
cig	cingulate gyrus	pecs	pericallosal cistern (sulcus)
cls	collateral sulcus		
fcol	facial colliculus	phg	parahippocampal gyrus
frxc	crura of fornix	pmarg	pars marginalis (ascending ramus of cingulate sulcus)
hipcom	hippocampal commissure		
hipf	fimbria of hippocampus	pocg	post-central gyrus
hipt	hippocampal tail	pocs	post-central sulcus
icp	inferior cerebellar peduncle (restiform body)	qdpc	quadrigeminal plate cistern
		sbps	subparietal sulcus
icv	internal cerebral vein	scp	superior cerebellar peduncle (brachium conjunctivum)
ips	intraparietal sulcus		
lotg	lateral occipital temporal gyrus (lotg)/ fusiform gyrus		
		smg	supramarginal gyrus
		supss	superior sagittal sinus
lots	lateral occipital temporal sulcus	tegi	inferior temporal gyrus
lvat	atrium (trigone) of lateral ventricle	tegm	middle temporal gyrus
		tegs	superior temporal gyrus
mcp	middle cerebellar peduncle (brachium pontis)	v4v	fourth ventricle

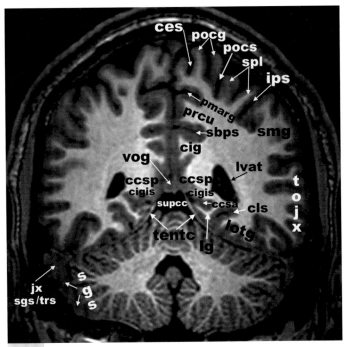

3.57a

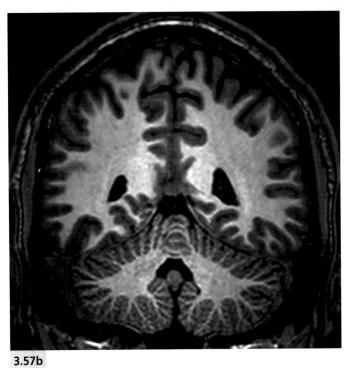

3.57b

FIGURES 3.57a–c

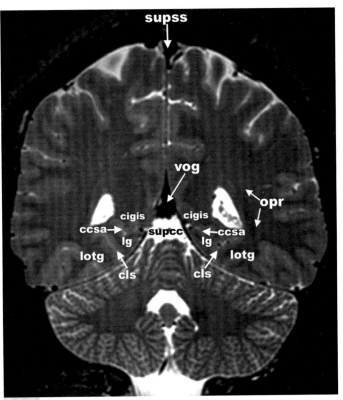

3.57c

KEY			
ccsa	anterior calcarine sulcus	**pmarg**	pars marginalis
ccsp	splenium of corpus		(ascending ramus of
	callosum		cingulate sulcus)
ces	central sulcus	**pocg**	post-central gyrus
cig	cingulate gyrus	**pocs**	post-central sulcus
cigis	isthmus of cingulate	**prcu**	precuneus
	gyrus	**sbps**	subparietal sulcus
cls	collateral sulcus	**sgs**	sigmoid sinus
ips	intraparietal sulcus	**smg**	supramarginal gyrus
jx	junction	**spl**	superior parietal lobule
lg	lingual gyrus (motg)	**supcc**	supracerebellar cistern
lotg	lateral occipital	**supss**	superior sagittal sinus
	temporal gyrus (lotg)/	**tentc**	tentorium cerebelli
	fusiform gyrus	**tojx**	temporal occipital
lvat	atrium (trigone) of		junction
	lateral ventricle	**trs**	transverse sinus
opr	optic radiations	**vog**	vein of Galen

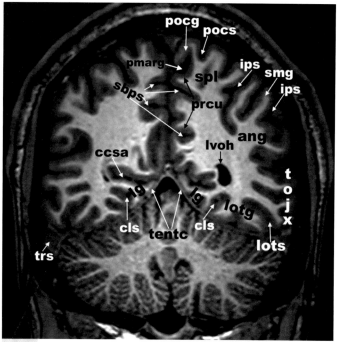

3.58a

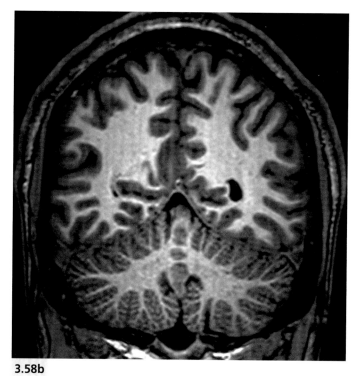

3.58b

FIGURES 3.58a–c

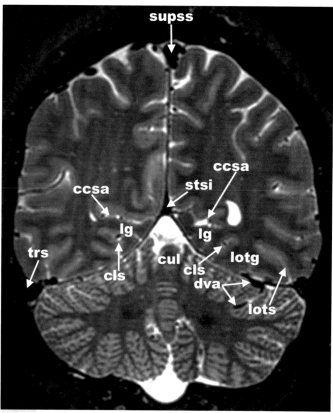

3.58c

KEY

ang	angular gyrus
ccsa	anterior calcarine sulcus
cls	collateral sulcus
cul	culmen (lobules IV and V)
dva	developmental venous anomaly
ips	intraparietal sulcus
lg	lingual gyrus (motg)
lotg	lateral occipital temporal gyrus (lotg)/fusiform gyrus
lots	lateral occipital temporal sulcus
lvoh	occipital horn of lateral ventricle
pmarg	pars marginalis (ascending ramus of cingulate sulcus)
pocg	post-central gyrus
pocs	post-central sulcus
prcu	precuneus
sbps	subparietal sulcus
smg	supramarginal gyrus
spl	superior parietal lobule
stsi	straight sinus
supss	superior sagittal sinus
tentc	tentorium cerebelli
tojx	temporal occipital junction
trs	transverse sinus

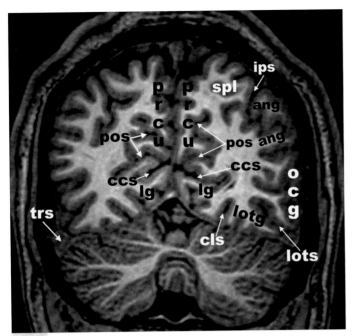

3.59a

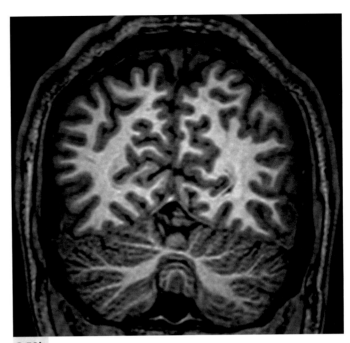

3.59b

FIGURES 3.59a–c

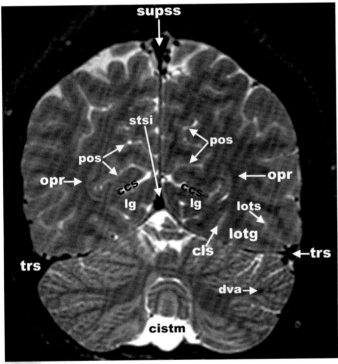

3.59c

KEY	
ang	angular gyrus
ccs	calcarine sulcus
cistm	cisterna magna
cls	collateral sulcus
dva	developmental venous anomaly
ips	intraparietal sulcus
lg	lingual gyrus (motg)
lotg	lateral occipital temporal gyrus (lotg)/fusiform gyrus
lots	lateral occipital temporal sulcus
ocg	occipital gyri
opr	optic radiations
pos	parieto-occipital sulcus
prcu	precuneus
spl	superior parietal lobule
stsi	straight sinus
supss	superior sagittal sinus
trs	transverse sinus

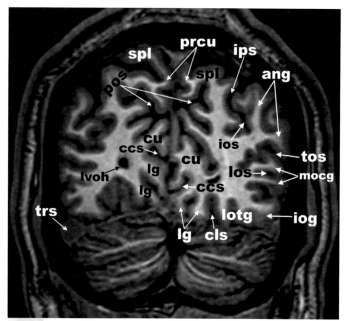

3.60a

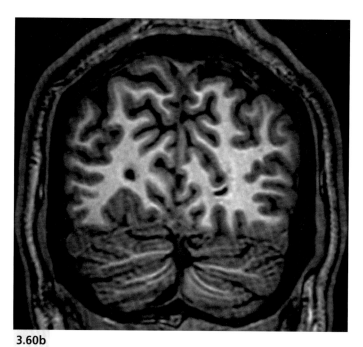

3.60b

FIGURES 3.60a–c

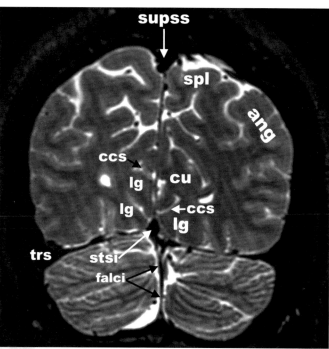

3.60c

KEY

ang	angular gyrus
ccs	calcarine sulcus
cls	collateral sulcus
cu	cuneus
falci	falx cerebelli
iog	inferior occipital gyrus
ios	intra-occipital sulcus
ips	intraparietal sulcus
lg	lingual gyrus (motg)
los	lateral (inferior) occipital sulcus
lotg	lateral occipital temporal gyrus (lotg)/fusiform gyrus
lvoh	occipital horn of lateral ventricle
mocg	middle occipital gyrus
pos	parieto-occipital sulcus
prcu	precuneus
spl	superior parietal lobule
stsi	straight sinus
supss	superior sagittal sinus
tos	transverse occipital sulcus
trs	transverse sinus

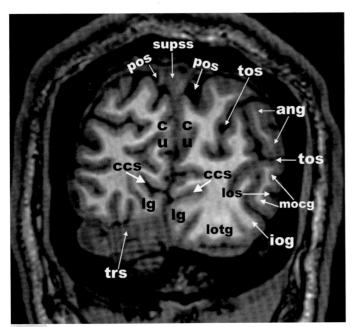

3.61a

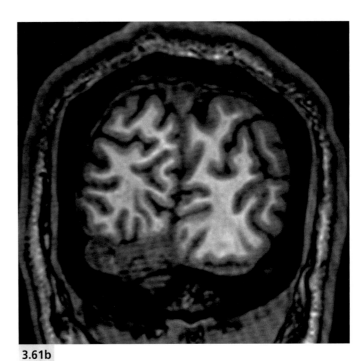

3.61b

FIGURES 3.61a–c

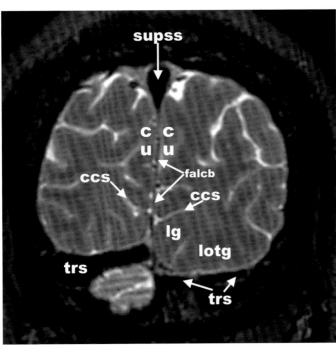

3.61c

KEY

ang	angular gyrus
ccs	calcarine sulcus
cu	cuneus
falcb	falx cerebri
iog	inferior occipital gyrus
lg	lingual gyrus (motg)
los	lateral (inferior) occipital sulcus
lotg	lateral occipital temporal gyrus (lotg)/fusiform gyrus
mocg	middle occipital gyrus
pos	parieto-occipital sulcus
supss	superior sagittal sinus
tos	transverse occipital sulcus
trs	transverse sinus

MRI BRAIN WITH CONTRAST ENHANCEMENT—SUBJECT 2 (FIGURES 3.62–3.94)

■ AXIAL (FIGURES 3.62–3.74)

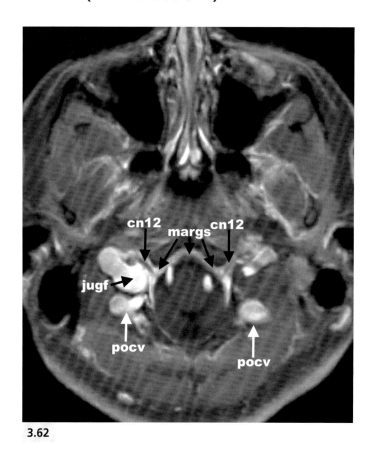

3.62

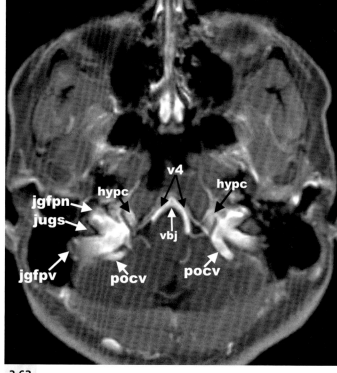

3.63

FIGURES 3.62–3.64

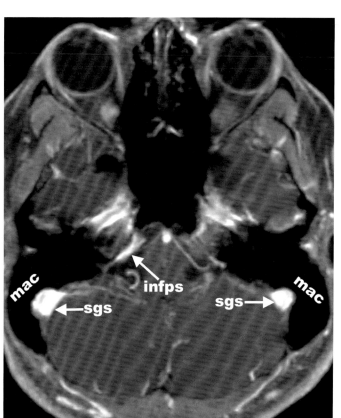

3.64

KEY

cn12	hypoglossal nerve
hypc	hypoglossal canal
infps	inferior petrosal sinus
jgfpn	pars nervosa-jugular foramen
jgfpv	pars vascularis-jugular foramen
jugf	jugular foramen
jugs	jugular spine
mac	mastoid air cells
margs	marginal sinus
pocv	posterior condylar vein
sgs	sigmoid sinus
v4	v4 intracranial/intradural segment vertebral artery
vbj	vertebral basilar junction

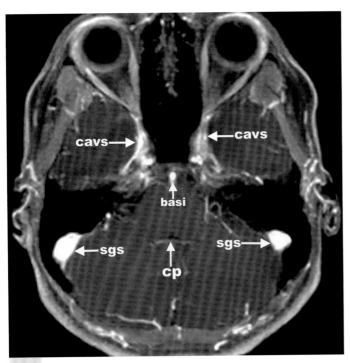

3.65

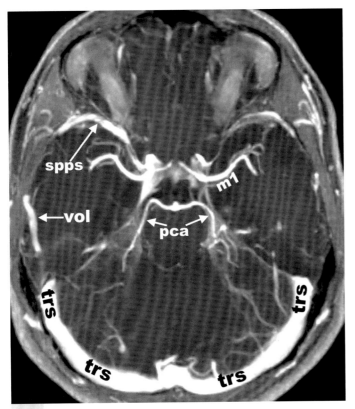

3.67

3.66

FIGURES 3.65–3.67

KEY

basi	basilar artery
c4	c4 (cavernous segment of ica)
cavs	cavernous sinus
clvp	clival venous plexus
cn5p	pre-ganglionic segment trigeminal nerve
cp	choroid plexus
ica	internal carotid artery
m1	m1 (horizontal segment mca)
mca	middle cerebral artery
mec	Meckel's cave
pca	posterior cerebral artery
petv	petrosal vein
ptr	porus trigeminus
sgs	sigmoid sinus
spps	sphenoparietal sinus
trs	transverse sinus
vol	vein of Labbe

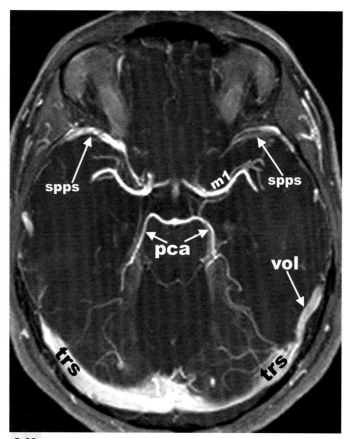

3.68

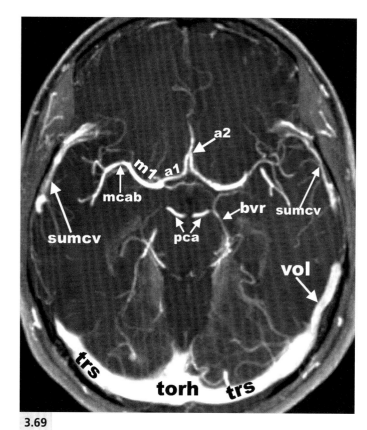

3.69

FIGURES 3.68–3.70

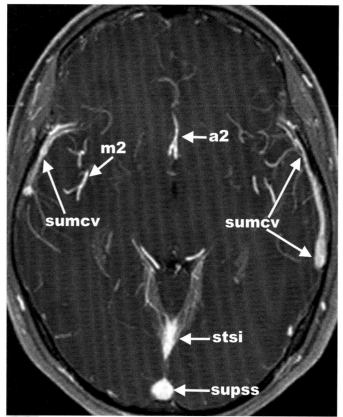

3.70

KEY

a1	a1 (precommunicating segment aca)
a2	a2 (postcommunicating segment aca)
aca	anterior cerebral artery
bvr	basal vein of Rosenthal
m1	m1 (horizontal segment mca)
m2	m2 (Sylvian/insular branches mca)
mca	middle cerebral artery
mcab	mca bifurcation/trifurcation
pca	posterior cerebral artery
spps	sphenoparietal sinus
stsi	straight sinus
sumcv	superficial middle cerebral vein
supss	superior sagittal sinus
torh	torcular herophili (confluence of sinuses)
trs	transverse sinus
vol	vein of Labbe

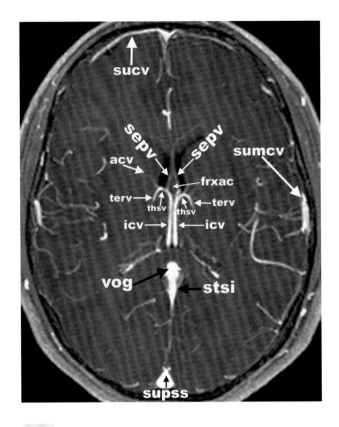

3.71

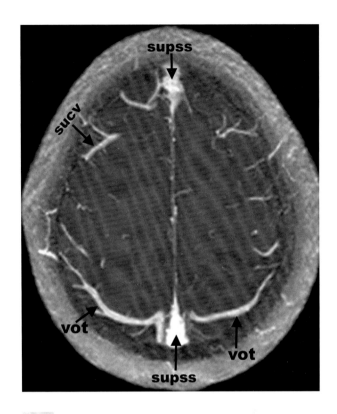

3.72

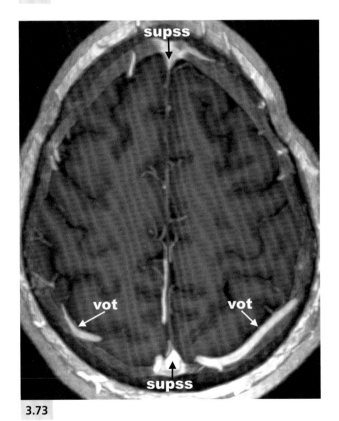

3.73

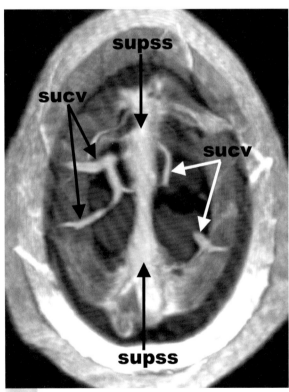

3.74

FIGURES 3.71–3.74

KEY			
acv	anterior caudate vein	**sumcv**	superficial middle cerebral vein
frxac	ascending columns of fornix	**supss**	superior sagittal sinus
icv	internal cerebral vein	**terv**	terminal vein
sepv	septal vein	**thsv**	thalamostriate vein
stsi	straight sinus	**vog**	vein of Galen
sucv	superficial cortical vein(s)	**vot**	vein of Trolard

■ SAGITTAL (FIGURES 3.75–3.82)

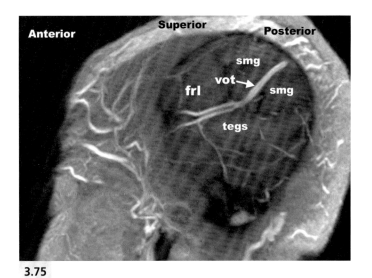

3.75

FIGURES 3.75–3.76

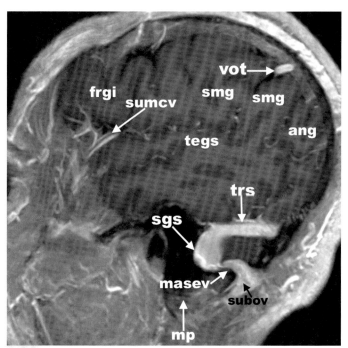

3.76

KEY

ang	angular gyrus
frgi	inferior frontal gyrus
frl	frontal lobe
masev	mastoid emissary vein
mp	mastoid process
sgs	sigmoid sinus
smg	supramarginal gyrus
subov	suboccipital veins
sumcv	superficial middle cerebral vein
tegs	superior temporal gyrus
trs	transverse sinus
vot	vein of Trolard

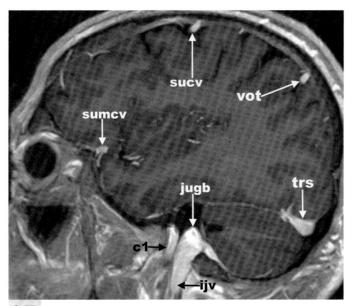

3.77

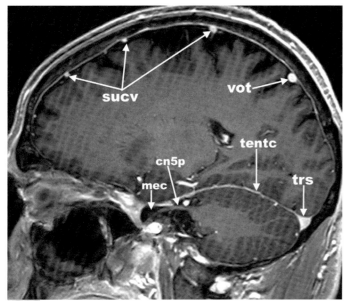

3.79

3.78

FIGURES 3.77–3.79

KEY

c1	c1 (cervical segment ica)
cn5p	pre-ganglionic segment trigeminal nerve
ica	internal carotid artery
ijv	internal jugular vein
jugb	jugular bulb
mec	Meckel's cave
sgs	sigmoid sinus
spps	sphenoparietal sinus
sucv	superficial cortical vein(s)
sumcv	superficial middle cerebral vein
tentc	tentorium cerebelli
trs	transverse sinus
vot	vein of Trolard

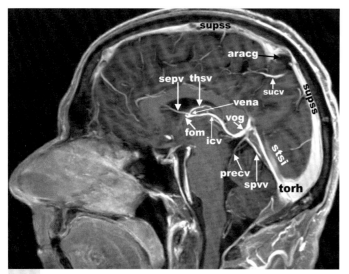

3.80

3.81

FIGURES 3.80–3.82

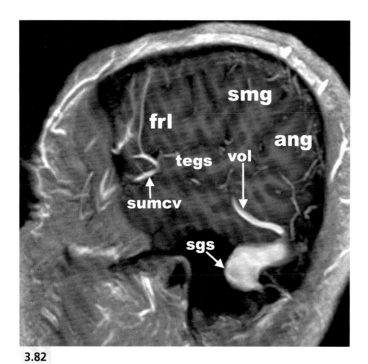

3.82

KEY			
ang	angular gyrus	**smg**	supramarginal gyrus
aracg	arachnoid granulations	**spvv**	superior vermian vein
clvp	clival venous plexus	**stsi**	straight sinus
fom	foramen of Monro	**sucv**	superficial cortical
frl	frontal lobe		vein(s)
icv	internal cerebral	**sumcv**	superficial middle
	vein		cerebral vein
infss	inferior sagittal sinus	**supss**	superior sagittal sinus
inf	infundibulum	**tegs**	superior temporal gyrus
occs	occipital sinus	**thsv**	thalamostriate vein
		torh	torcular herophili
pitg	pituitary gland		(confluence of sinuses)
precv	pre-central cerebellar	**vena**	venous angle
	vein	**vog**	vein of Galen
sepv	septal vein	**vol**	vein of Labbe
sgs	sigmoid sinus		

■ CORONAL (FIGURES 3.83–3.94)

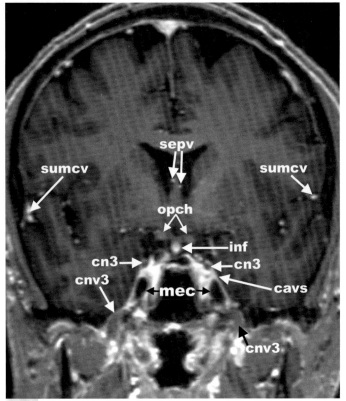

3.83

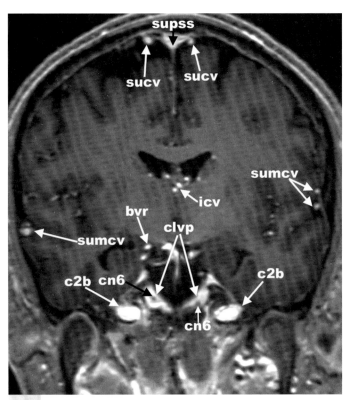

3.85

3.84

FIGURES 3.83–3.85

KEY	
bvr	basal vein of Rosenthal
c2b	c2b (horizontal petrous segment of ica)
cavs	cavernous sinus
clvp	clival venous plexus
cnv3	mandibular division (v3) of trigeminal nerve
cn3	oculomotor nerve
cn6	abducens nerve
ica	internal carotid artery
icv	internal cerebral vein
inf	infundibulum
mec	Meckel's cave
opch	optic chiasm
sepv	septal vein
sucv	superficial cortical vein(s)
sumcv	superficial middle cerebral vein
supss	superior sagittal sinus
thsv	thalamostriate vein

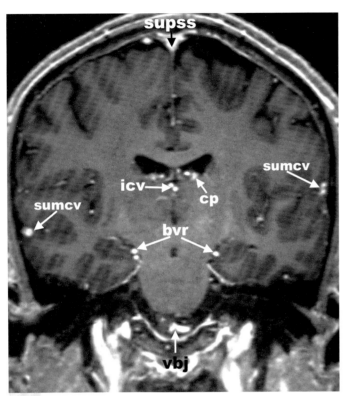

3.86

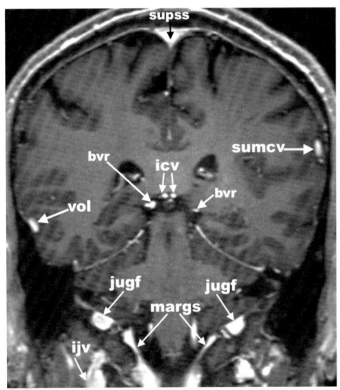

3.88

3.87

FIGURES 3.86–3.88

KEY

bvr	basal vein of Rosenthal
cp	choroid plexus
hypc	hypoglossal canal
icv	internal cerebral vein
ijv	internal jugular vein
jugf	jugular foramen
margs	marginal sinus
sucv	superficial cortical vein(s)
sumcv	superficial middle cerebral vein
supss	superior sagittal sinus
vbj	vertebral basilar junction
vol	vein of Labbe

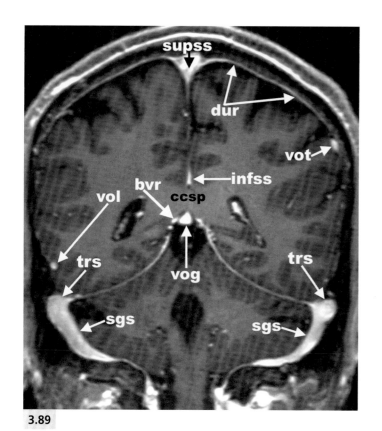

3.89

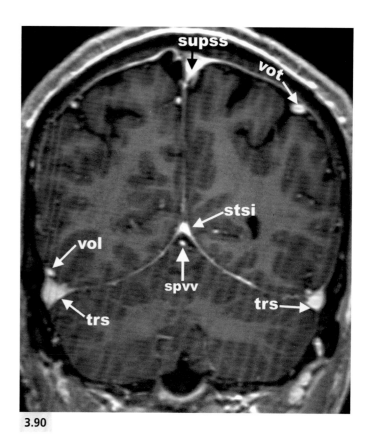

3.90

FIGURES 3.89–3.91

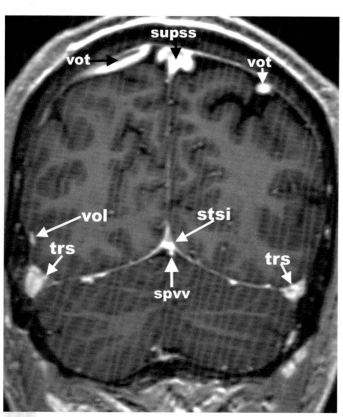

3.91

KEY	
bvr	basal vein of Rosenthal
ccsp	splenium of corpus callosum
dur	dura (pachymeninges)
infss	inferior sagittal sinus
sgs	sigmoid sinus
spvv	superior vermian vein
stsi	straight sinus
supss	superior sagittal sinus
trs	transverse sinus
vog	vein of Galen
vol	vein of Labbe
vot	vein of Trolard

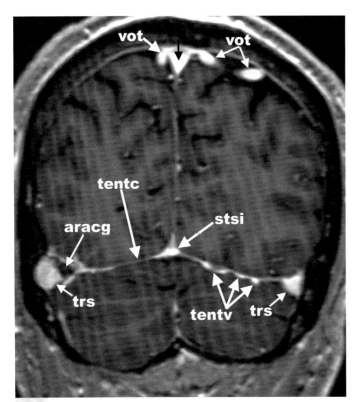

3.92

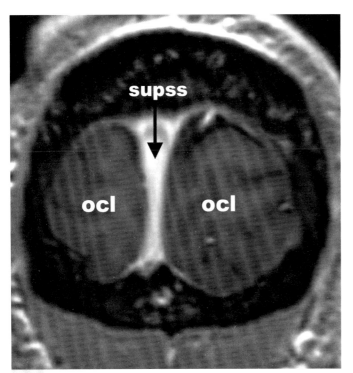

3.93

FIGURES 3.92–3.94

3.94

KEY

aracg	arachnoid granulations
ocl	occipital lobe
stsi	straight sinus
supss	superior sagittal sinus
tentc	tentorium cerebelli
tentv	tentorial vein
torh	torcular herophili (confluence of sinuses)
trs	transverse sinus
vot	vein of Trolard

MR Imaging of the Cerebellum

4

INTRODUCTION

The following MR images are an atlas of the cerebellum. The subject is a healthy, 27-year old male with no significant past medical history.

The first set of images consists of T1 and T2 weighted axial images at similar slice positions. Figures 4.1a–4.10a are T1 weighted images with predominant labeling of the cerebellar vermis. Figures 4.1b–4.10b are similar T1 axial images with predominant labeling of the cerebellar hemispheres. Figures 4.1c–4.10c are T2 weighted axial images at similar slice positions as corresponding T1 weighted images with sparse labeling for comparison purposes. The axial images are presented from superior to inferior.

Figures 4.11a,b–4.19a,b are labeled T1 (a) and very sparsely labeled T2 (b) images of the cerebellum in the sagittal plane presented from medial to lateral for comparison purposes.

Figures 4.20a,b–4.29a,b consist of labeled T1W coronal images (a) and sparsely labeled T2W coronal images (b) for comparison purposes presented from anterior to posterior.

The coronal and axial planes of imaging were obtained parallel and perpendicular to the intercommissural reference plane (Schaltenbrand's line) as indicated in Figure 4.O1, page 112.

Sagittal images were obtained in a routine fashion and independent upon the plane of imaging in the axial or coronal planes.

Historically, there have been multiple schemas of defining and naming the cerebellar anatomy that is a source of much confusion. The labeling of anatomic structures of the vermis and hemispheres of the cerebellum in this atlas will use common names familiar to many in addition to the division of the vermis by roman numerals. This is based upon my readings in *Duvernoy's Atlas of the Human Brain Stem and Cerebellum* (see in Suggested Readings).

The anatomic labeling of the cerebellar vermis and hemispheres in this atlas was based upon software allowing simultaneous visualization of the MRI in three planes with the use of synchronized cross-reference lines.

NOMENCLATURE USED FOR CEREBELLUM

Cerebellar Vermis—Naming of the vermian lobules will be listed in order from the anterior lobe to the flocculonodular lobe. The anterior lobe of the vermis extends from the Lingula to the anterior-superior (primary fissure). The posterior lobe extends from the Declive to the Uvula at the posterolateral fissure. Finally, there is the Nodulus of the vermis, a part of the flocculonodular lobe.

> **Anterior Lobe**
> Lingula (I)
> Central Lobule (II, III)
> Culmen (IV, V)

> *Anterior Superior (primary) Fissure*

> **Posterior Lobe**
> Declive (VI)
> Folium (VII)
> Tuber (VII)
> Pyramid (VIII)
> Uvula (IX)

> *Posterolateral Fissure*

> **Flocculonodular Lobe**
> Nodulus (X)

Cerebellar Hemispheres—Naming of the lobules of the cerebellar hemispheres will also be listed in order from the anterior lobe to the flocculonodular lobe.

> **Anterior Lobe**
> Ala (wing) of the central lobule
> Quadrangular lobule (anterior quadrangular lobule)

> *Anterior-Superior (primary) Fissure*

> **Posterior Lobe**
> Simple lobule (posterior quadrangular lobule)

> *Posterior Superior Fissure*

> Superior Semilunar lobule (Crus I)

> *Great Horizontal Fissure*

> Inferior Semilunar lobule (Crus II)
> Gracile lobule

> *Prepyramidal Fissure*

> Biventral lobule

> *Postpyramidal fissure*

> Tonsil

> *Posterolateral fissure*

> **Flocculonodular lobe**
> Flocculus

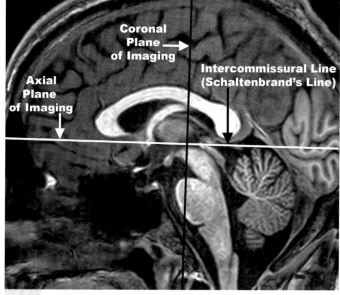

4.01

T1W AND T2W MR IMAGES WITHOUT CONTRAST (FIGURES 4.1–4.29)

■ **AXIAL (FIGURES 4.1a–c TO 4.10a–c)**

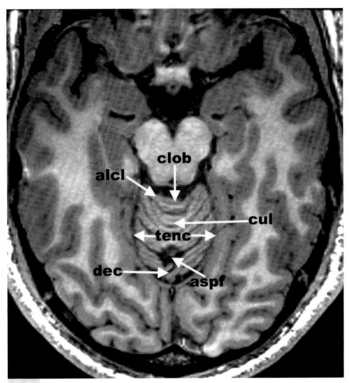

4.1a

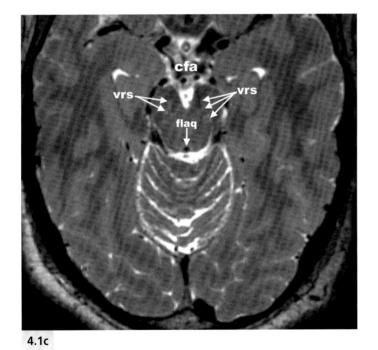

4.1c

4.1b

FIGURES 4.1a–c

KEY	
alcl	ala of central lobule
aqs	aqueduct of Sylvius
aspf	anterior superior (primary) fissure
cfa	csf flow artifact
clob	central lobule (lobules II and III)
cn3	oculomotor nerve
cul	culmen (lobules IV and V)
dec	declive (lobule VI)
flaq	flow void through aqueduct of Sylvius
inf	infundibulum
lamss	lateral mesencephalic sulcus
opch	optic chiasm
quad	quadrangular lobule (anterior quadrangular lobule)
simp	simple lobule (posterior quadrangular lobule)
smv	superior/anterior medullary velum
tenc	tentorial incisura
vrs	Virchow-Robin spaces

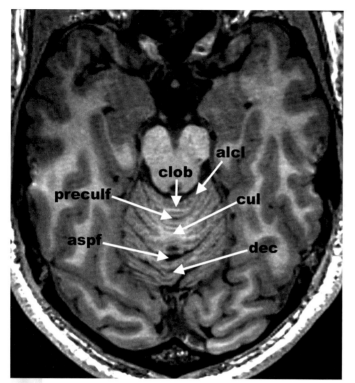

4.2a

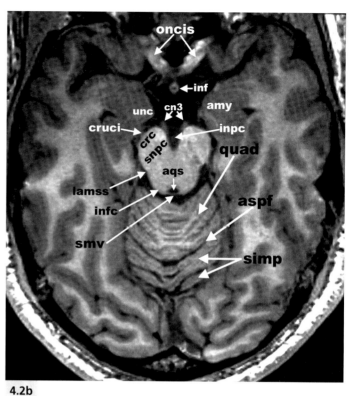

4.2b

FIGURES 4.2a–c

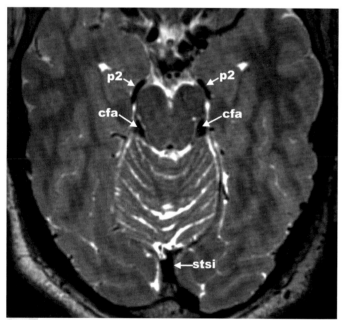

4.2c

KEY

alcl	ala of central lobule
amy	amygdala
aqs	aqueduct of Sylvius
aspf	anterior superior (primary) fissure
cfa	csf flow artifact
clob	central lobule (lobules II and III)
cn3	oculomotor nerve
crc	crus cerebri
cruci	crural cistern
cul	culmen (lobules IV and V)
dec	declive (lobule VI)
inf	infundibulum
infc	inferior colliculus
inpc	interpeduncular cistern
lamss	lateral mesencephalic sulcus
oncis	cisternal (pre-chiasmatic) segment optic nerve
p2	p2 (ambient segment of pca)
pca	posterior cerebral artery
preculf	preculminate fissure
quad	quadrangular lobule (anterior quadrangular lobule)
simp	simple lobule (posterior quadrangular lobule)
smv	superior/anterior medullary velum
snpc	pars compacta of substantia nigra
stsi	straight sinus
unc	uncus

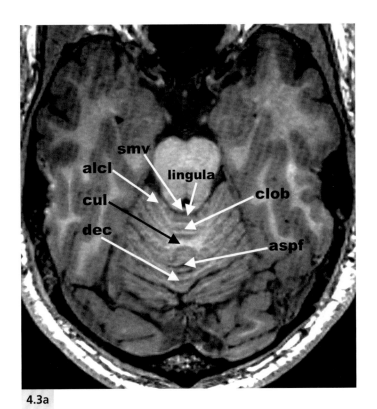

4.3a

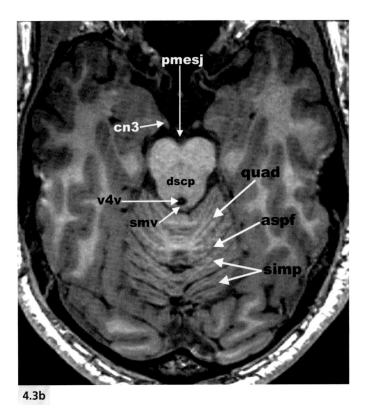

4.3b

FIGURES 4.3a–c

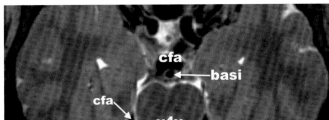

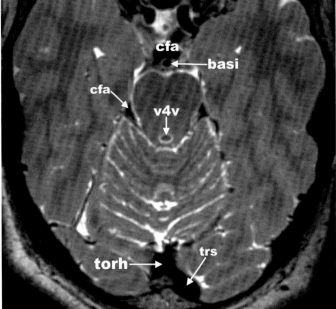

4.3c

KEY

alcl	ala of central lobule
aspf	anterior superior (primary) fissure
basi	basilar artery
cfa	csf flow artifact
clob	central lobule (lobules II and III)
cn3	oculomotor nerve
cul	culmen (lobules IV and V)
dec	declive (lobule VI)
dscp	decussation of superior cerebellar peduncles
lingula	lingula (lobule I)
pmesj	ponto-mesencephalic junction
quad	quadrangular lobule (anterior quadrangular lobule)
simp	simple lobule (posterior quadrangular lobule)
smv	superior/anterior medullary velum
torh	torcular herophili (confluence of sinuses)
trs	transverse sinus
v4v	fourth ventricle

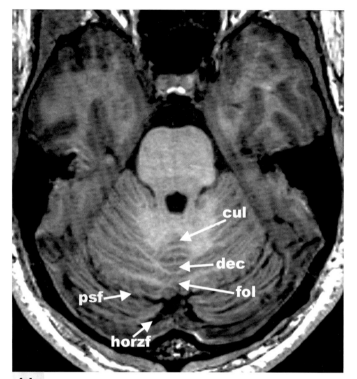

4.4a

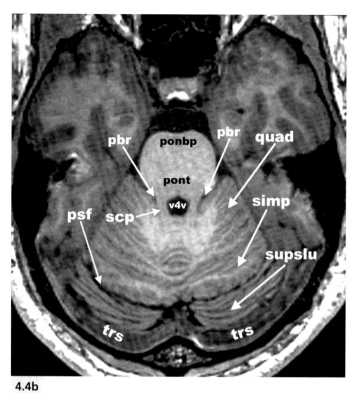

4.4b

FIGURES 4.4a–c

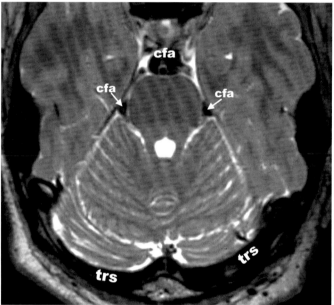

4.4c

KEY

cfa	csf flow artifact
cul	culmen (lobules IV and V)
dec	declive (lobule VI)
fol	folium (lobule VII)
horzf	great horizontal fissure of cerebellum
pbr	para-brachial recess
ponbp	basis pontis of pons
pont	tegmentum of pons
psf	posterior superior fissure of cerebellum
quad	quadrangular lobule (anterior quadrangular lobule)
scp	superior cerebellar peduncle
simp	simple lobule (posterior quadrangular lobule)
supslu	superior semilunar lobule (Crus I)
trs	transverse sinus
v4v	fourth ventricle

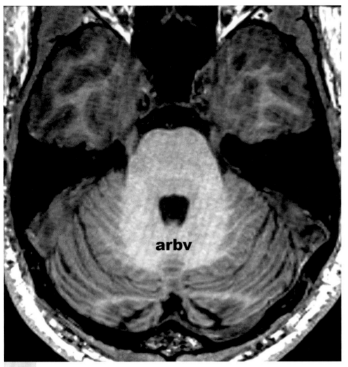

4.5a

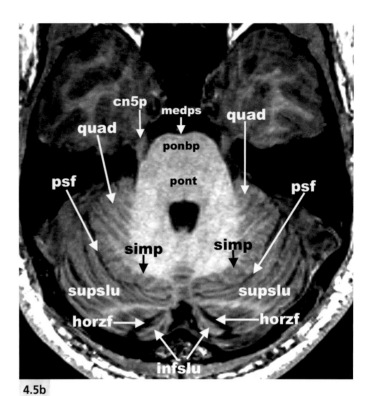

4.5b

FIGURES 4.5a–c

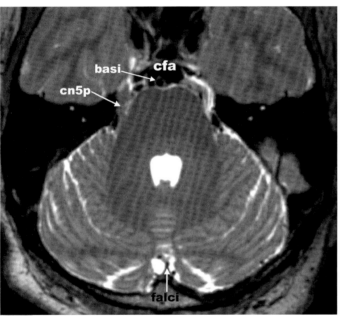

4.5c

KEY

arbv	arbor vitae
basi	basilar artery
cfa	csf flow artifact
cn5p	pre-ganglionic segment trigeminal nerve
falci	falx cerebelli
horzf	great horizontal fissure of cerebellum
infslu	inferior semilunar lobule (Crus II)
medps	median pontine sulcus
ponbp	basis pontis of pons
pont	tegmentum of pons
psf	posterior superior fissure of cerebellum
quad	quadrangular lobule (anterior quadrangular lobule)
simp	simple lobule (posterior quadrangular lobule)
supslu	superior semilunar lobule (Crus I)

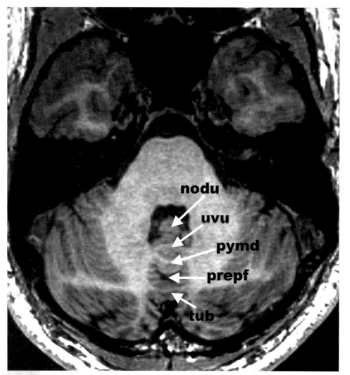

4.6a

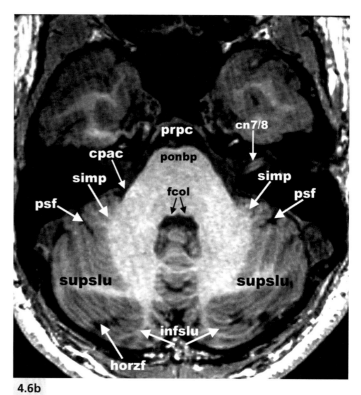

4.6b

FIGURES 4.6a–c

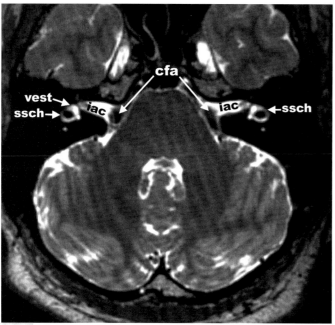

4.6c

KEY

cfa	csf flow artifact
cn7/8	facial and vestibulocochlear nerves
cpac	cerebellopontine angle cistern
fcol	facial colliculus
horzf	great horizontal fissure of cerebellum
iac	internal auditory canal
infslu	inferior semilunar lobule (Crus II)
nodu	nodulus (lobule X)
ponbp	basis pontis of pons
prepf	prepyramidal fissure of cerebellum
prpc	prepontine cistern
psf	posterior superior fissure of cerebellum
pymd	pyramid of the vermis (lobule VIII)
simp	simple lobule (posterior quadrangular lobule)
ssch	horizontal semicircular canal
supslu	superior semilunar lobule (Crus I)
tub	tuber (lobule VII)
uvu	uvula (lobule IX)
vest	vestibule

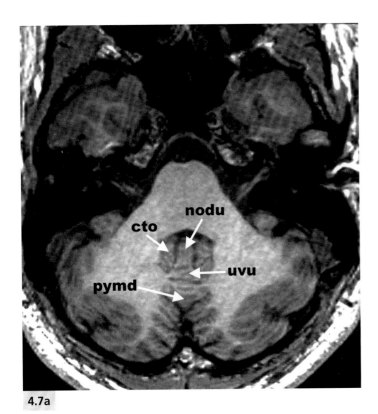

4.7a

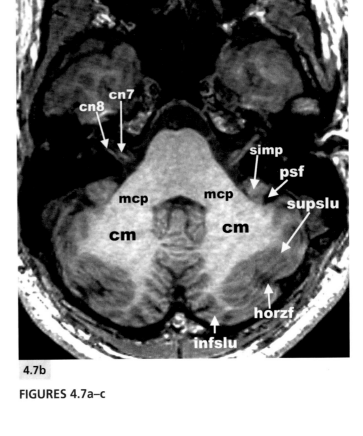

4.7b

FIGURES 4.7a–c

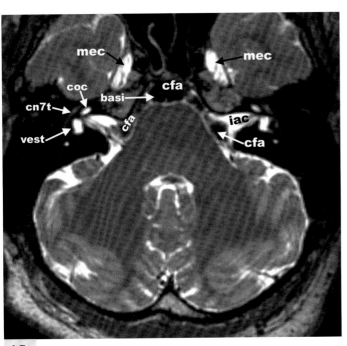

4.7c

KEY	
basi	basilar artery
cfa	csf flow artifact
cm	corpus medullare
cn7	facial nerve
cn7t	tympanic segment of facial nerve
cn8	vestibulocochlear nerve
coc	cochlea
cto	cerebellar tonsil
horzf	great horizontal fissure of cerebellum
iac	internal auditory canal
infslu	inferior semilunar lobule (Crus II)
mcp	middle cerebellar peduncle
mec	Meckel's cave
nodu	nodulus (lobule X)
psf	posterior superior fissure of cerebellum
pymd	pyramid of the vermis (lobule VIII)
simp	simple lobule (posterior quadrangular lobule)
supslu	superior semilunar lobule (Crus I)
uvu	uvula (lobule IX)
vest	vestibule

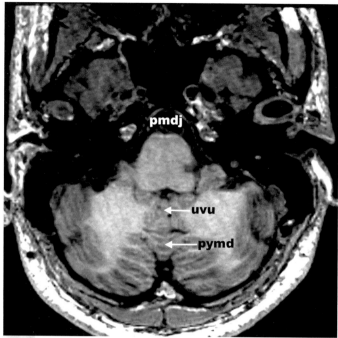

4.8a

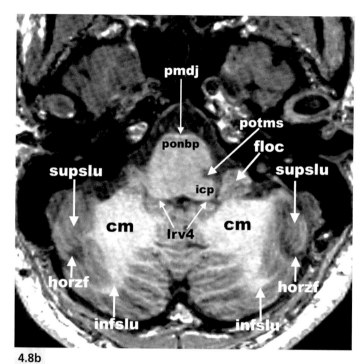

4.8b

FIGURES 4.8a–c

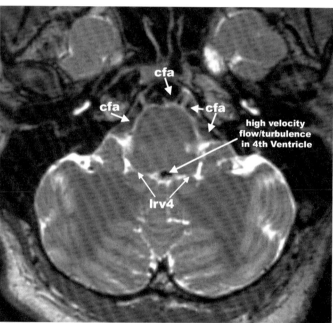

4.8c

KEY

cfa	csf flow artifact
cm	corpus medullare
floc	flocculus
horzf	great horizontal fissure of cerebellum
icp	inferior cerebellar peduncle (restiform body)
infslu	inferior semilunar lobule (Crus II)
lrv4	lateral recess of fourth ventricle
potms	pontomedullary sulcus
pmdj	ponto-medullary junction
ponbp	basis pontis of pons
pymd	pyramid of the vermis (lobule VIII)
supslu	superior semilunar lobule (Crus I)
uvu	uvula (lobule IX)

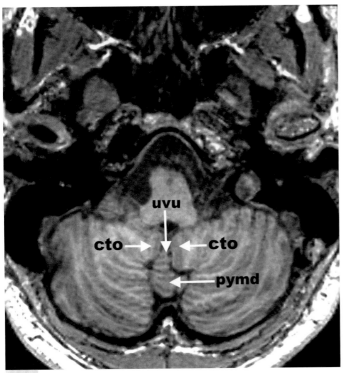

4.9a

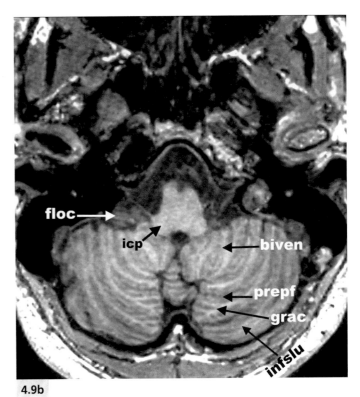

4.9b

FIGURES 4.9a–c

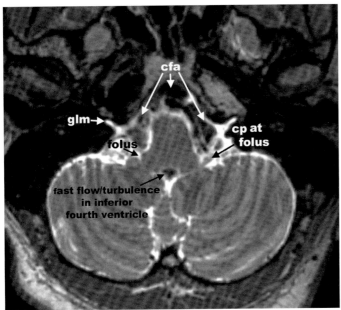

4.9c

KEY

biven	biventral lobule
cfa	csf flow artifact
cp	choroid plexus
cto	cerebellar tonsil
floc	flocculus
folus	foramen of Luschka
glm	glossopharyngeal meatus
grac	gracile lobule
icp	inferior cerebellar peduncle (restiform body)
infslu	inferior semilunar lobule (Crus II)
prepf	prepyramidal fissure of cerebellum
pymd	pyramid of the vermis (lobule VIII)
uvu	uvula (lobule IX)

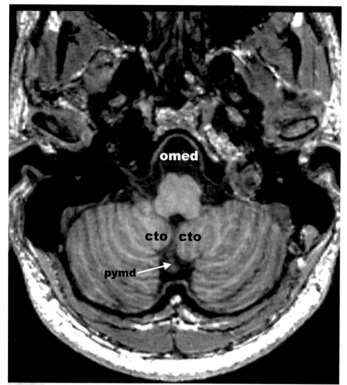

4.10a

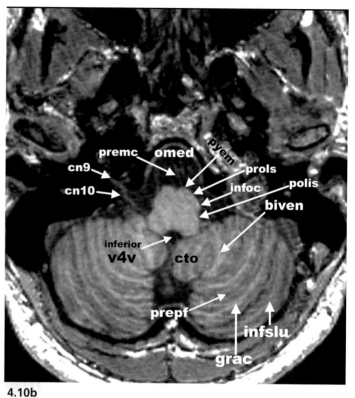

4.10b

FIGURES 4.10a–c

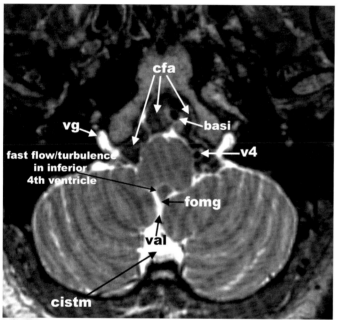

4.10c

KEY

basi	basilar artery
biven	biventral lobule
cfa	csf flow artifact
cistm	cisterna magna
cn9	glossopharyngeal nerve
cn10	vagus nerve
cto	cerebellar tonsil
fomg	foramen of Magendie
grac	gracile lobule
infoc	inferior olivary complex
infslu	inferior semilunar lobule (Crus II)
omed	open medulla
polis	post-olivary sulcus
premc	premedullary cistern
prepf	prepyramidal fissure of cerebellum
prols	pre-olivary sulcus
pyem	pyramidal eminence
pymd	pyramid of the vermis (lobule VIII)
v4	v4 intracranial/intradural segment vertebral artery
v4v	fourth ventricle
val	vallecula space
vg	vagal meatus

■ SAGITTAL (FIGURES 4.11a,b–4.19a,b)

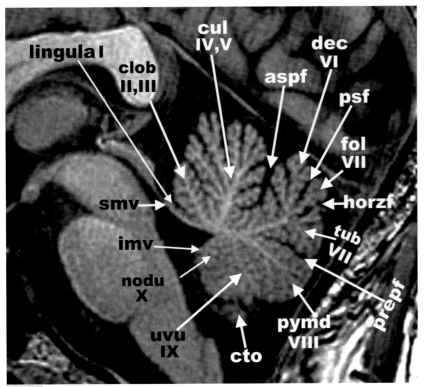

4.11a

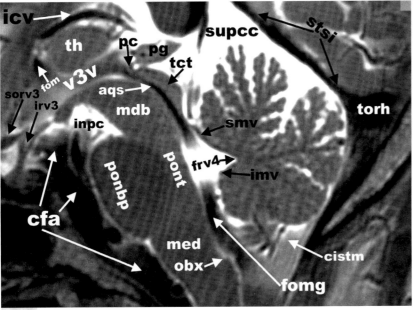

4.11b

FIGURES 4.11a,b

KEY	
aqs	aqueduct of Sylvius
aspf	anterior superior (primary) fissure
cfa	csf flow artifact
cistm	cisterna magna
clob	central lobule (lobules II and III)
cto	cerebellar tonsil
cul	culmen (lobules IV and V)
dec	declive (lobule VI)
fol	folium (lobule VII)
fom	foramen of Monro
fomg	foramen of Magendie
frv4	fastigial recess of fourth ventricle
horzf	great horizontal fissure of cerebellum
icv	internal cerebral vein
imv	inferior/posterior medullary velum
inpc	interpeduncular cistern
irv3	infindibular recess of third ventricle
lingula	lingula (lobule I)
mdb	midbrain
med	medulla
nodu	nodulus (lobule X)
obx	obex
pc	posterior commissure
pg	pineal gland
ponbp	basis pontis of pons
pont	tegmentum of pons
prepf	prepyramidal fissure of cerebellum
psf	posterior superior fissure of cerebellum
pymd	pyramid of the vermis (lobule VIII)
smv	superior/anterior medullary velum
sorv3	supra-optic recess of third ventricle
stsi	straight sinus
supcc	supracerebellar cistern
tct	tectum
th	thalamus
torh	torcular herophili (confluence of sinuses)
tub	tuber (lobule VII)
uvu	uvula (lobule IX)
v3v	third ventricle

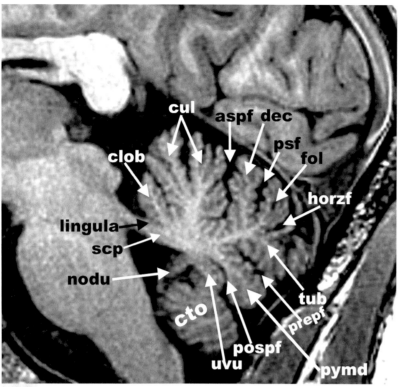

4.12a

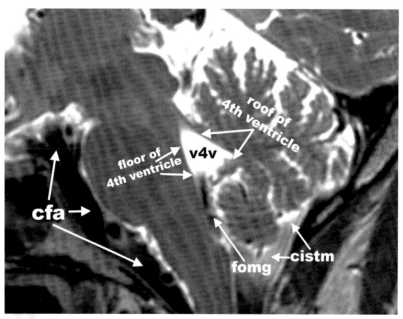

4.12b

FIGURES 4.12a,b

KEY

aspf	anterior superior (primary) fissure
cfa	csf flow artifact
cistm	cisterna magna
clob	central lobule (lobules II and III)
cto	cerebellar tonsil
cul	culmen (lobules IV and V)
dec	declive (lobule VI)
fol	folium (lobule VII)
fomg	foramen of Magendie
horzf	great horizontal fissure of cerebellum
lingula	lingula (lobule I)
nodu	nodulus (lobulc X)
pospf	postpyramidal fissure
prepf	prepyramidal fissure of cerebellum
psf	posterior superior fissure of cerebellum
pymd	pyramid of the vermis (lobule VIII)
scp	superior cerebellar peduncle (brachium conjunctivum)
tub	tuber (lobule VII)
uvu	uvula (lobule IX)
v4v	fourth ventricle

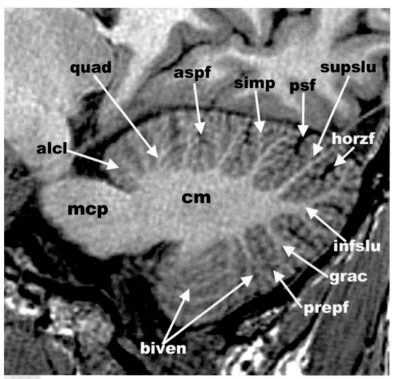

4.13a

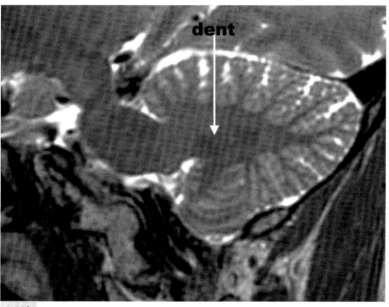

4.13b

FIGURES 4.13a,b

KEY

alcl	ala of central lobule
aspf	anterior superior (primary) fissure
biven	biventral lobule
cm	corpus medullare
dent	dentate nucleus
grac	gracile lobule
horzf	great horizontal fissure of cerebellum
infslu	inferior semilunar lobule (Crus II)
mcp	middle cerebellar peduncle (brachium pontis)
prepf	prepyramidal fissure of cerebellum
psf	posterior superior fissure of cerebellum
quad	quadrangular lobule (anterior quadrangular lobule)
simp	simple lobule (posterior quadrangular lobule)
supslu	superior semilunar lobule (Crus I)

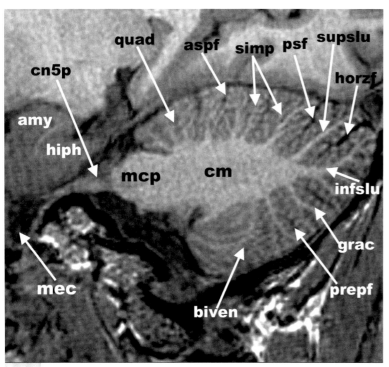

4.14a

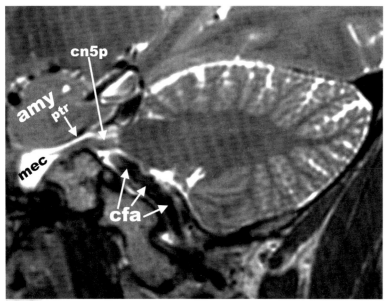

4.14b

FIGURES 4.14a,b

KEY
amy	amygdala
aspf	anterior superior (primary) fissure
biven	biventral lobule
cfa	csf flow artifact
cm	corpus medullare
cn5p	pre-ganglionic segment trigeminal nerve
grac	gracile lobule
hiph	hippocampal head
horzf	great horizontal fissure of cerebellum
infslu	inferior semilunar lobule (Crus II)
mcp	middle cerebellar peduncle (brachium pontis)
mec	Meckel's cave
prepf	prepyramidal fissure of cerebellum
psf	posterior superior fissure of cerebellum
ptr	porus trigeminus
quad	quadrangular lobule (anterior quadrangular lobule)
simp	simple lobule (posterior quadrangular lobule)
supslu	superior semilunar lobule (Crus I)

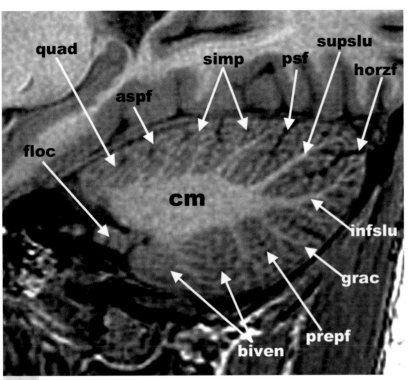

4.15a

FIGURES 4.15a,b

KEY	
aspf	anterior superior (primary) fissure
biven	biventral lobule
cfa	csf flow artifact
cm	corpus medullare
floc	flocculus
grac	gracile lobule
hip	hippocampus
horzf	great horizontal fissure of cerebellum
infslu	inferior semilunar lobule (Crus II)
mec	Meckel's cave
prepf	prepyramidal fissure of cerebellum
psf	posterior superior fissure of cerebellum
quad	quadrangular lobule (anterior quadrangular lobule)
simp	simple lobule (posterior quadrangular lobule)
supslu	superior semilunar lobule (Crus I)

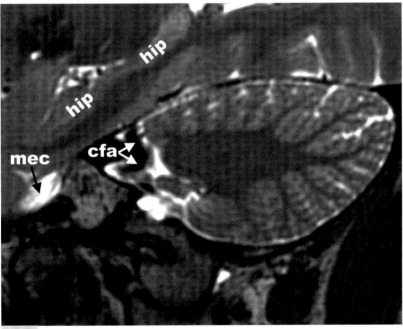

4.15b

FIGURES 4.16a,b

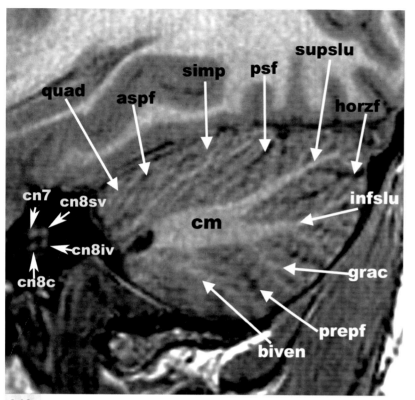

4.16a

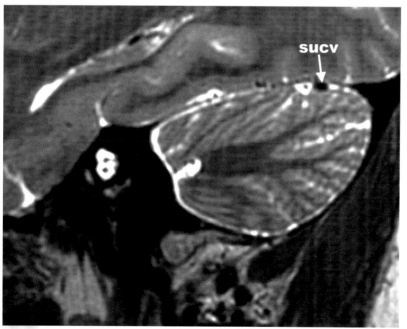

4.16b

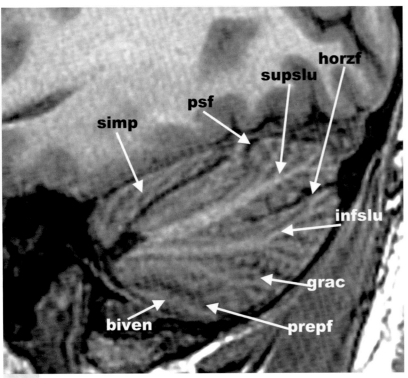

4.17a

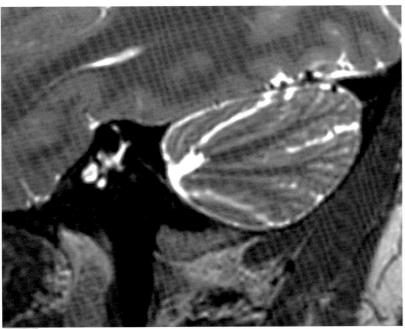

4.17b

FIGURES 4.17a,b

KEY

biven	biventral lobule
grac	gracile lobule
horzf	great horizontal fissure of cerebellum
infslu	inferior semilunar lobule (Crus II)
prepf	prepyramidal fissure of cerebellum
psf	posterior superior fissure of cerebellum
simp	simple lobule (posterior quadrangular lobule)
supslu	superior semilunar lobule (Crus I)

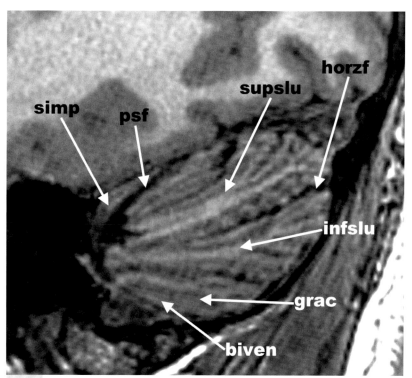

4.18a

FIGURES 4.18a,b

KEY

biven	biventral lobule
grac	gracile lobule
horzf	great horizontal fissure of cerebellum
infslu	inferior semilunar lobule (Crus II)
psf	posterior superior fissure of cerebellum
simp	simple lobule (posterior quadrangular lobule)
supslu	superior semilunar lobule (Crus I)

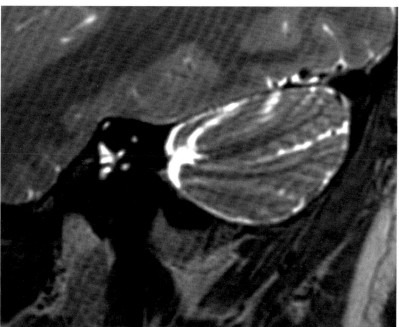

4.18b

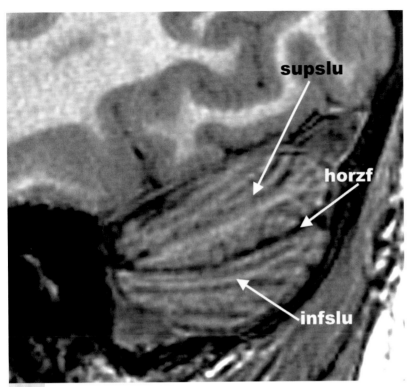

4.19a

FIGURES 4.19a,b

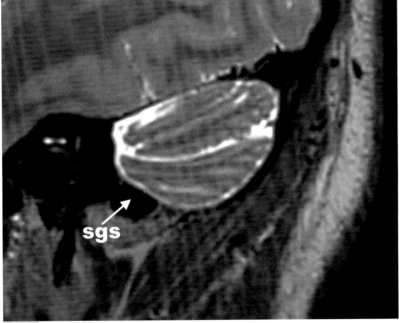

4.19b

■ CORONAL (FIGURES 4.20a,b–4.29a,b)

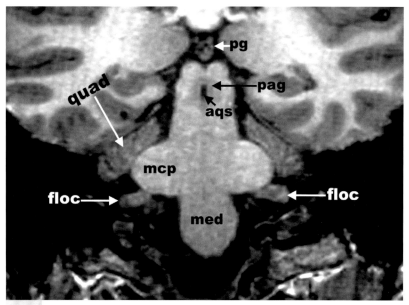

4.20a

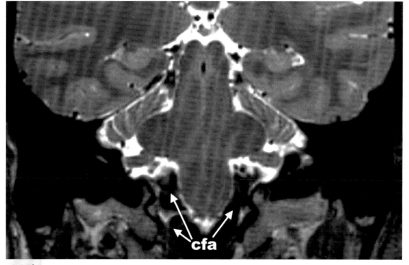

4.20b

FIGURES 4.20a,b

KEY

aqs	aqueduct of Sylvius
cfa	csf flow artifact
floc	flocculus
mcp	middle cerebellar peduncle (brachium pontis)
med	medulla
pag	periaqueductal gray matter
pg	pineal gland
quad	quadrangular lobule (anterior quadrangular lobule)

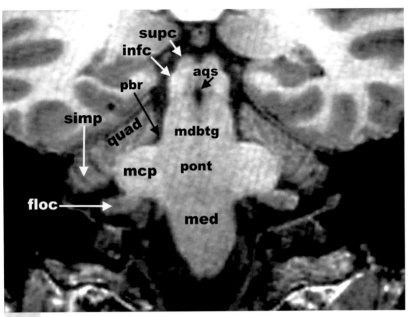

4.21a

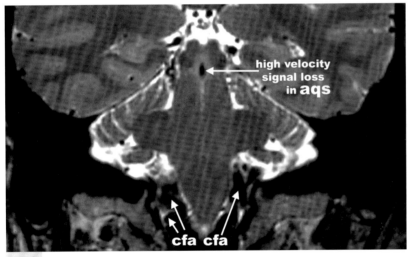

4.21b

FIGURES 4.21a,b

KEY

aqs	aqueduct of Sylvius
cfa	csf flow artifact
floc	flocculus
infc	inferior colliculus
mcp	middle cerebellar peduncle (brachium pontis)
mdbtg	tegmentum of midbrain
med	medulla
pbr	para-brachial recess
pont	tegmentum of pons
quad	quadrangular lobule (anterior quadrangular lobule)
simp	simple lobule (posterior quadrangular lobule)
supc	superior colliculus

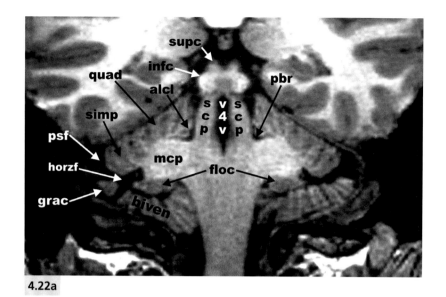

4.22a

4.22b

FIGURES 4.22a,b

KEY

alcl	ala of central lobule
biven	biventral lobule
floc	flocculus
grac	gracile lobule
horzf	great horizontal fissure of cerebellum
infc	inferior colliculus
mcp	middle cerebellar peduncle (brachium pontis)
pbr	para-brachial recess
psf	posterior superior fissure of cerebellum
quad	quadrangular lobule (anterior quadrangular lobule)
scp	superior cerebellar peduncle (brachium conjunctivum)
simp	simple lobule (posterior quadrangular lobule)
supc	superior colliculus
v4v	fourth ventricle

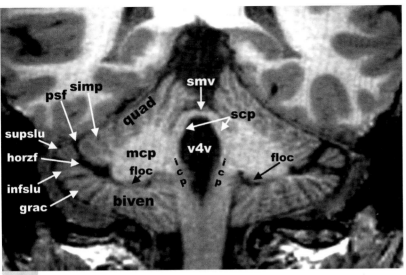

4.23a

FIGURES 4.23a,b

KEY

biven	biventral lobule
floc	flocculus
grac	gracile lobule
horzf	great horizontal fissure of cerebellum
icp	inferior cerebellar peduncle (restiform body)
infslu	inferior semilunar lobule (Crus II)
mcp	middle cerebellar peduncle (brachium pontis)
psf	posterior superior fissure of cerebellum
quad	quadrangular lobule (anterior quadrangular lobule)
scp	superior cerebellar peduncle (brachium conjunctivum)
simp	simple lobule (posterior quadrangular lobule)
smv	superior/anterior medullary velum
supslu	superior semilunar lobule (Crus I)
v4v	fourth ventricle

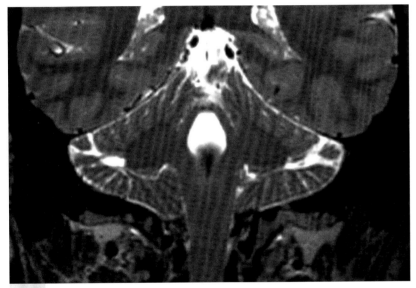

4.23b

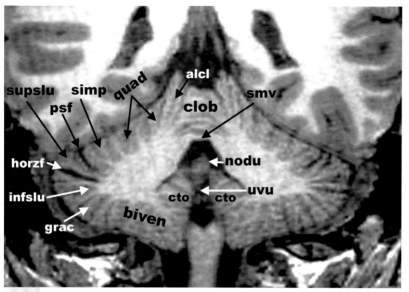

4.24a

FIGURES 4.24a,b

KEY

alcl	ala of central lobule
biven	biventral lobule
clob	central lobule (lobules II and III)
cto	cerebellar tonsil
fomg	foramen of Magendie
grac	gracile lobule
horzf	great horizontal fissure of cerebellum
infslu	inferior semilunar lobule (Crus II)
nodu	nodulus (lobule X)
psf	posterior superior fissure of cerebellum
quad	quadrangular lobule (anterior quadrangular lobule)
simp	simple lobule (posterior quadrangular lobule)
smv	superior/anterior medullary velum
supslu	superior semilunar lobule (Crus I)
uvu	uvula (lobule IX)

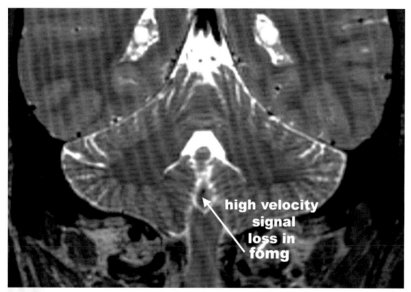

4.24b

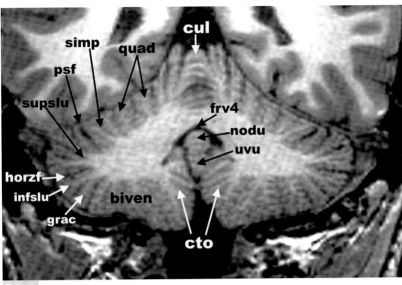

4.25a

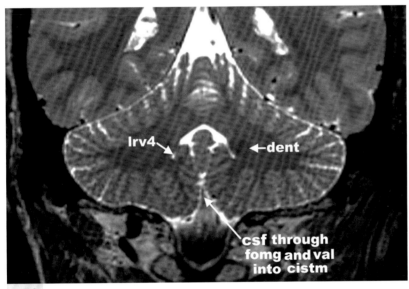

4.25b

FIGURES 4.25a,b

KEY

biven	biventral lobule
cistm	cisterna magna
csf	cerebrospinal fluid
cto	cerebellar tonsil
cul	culmen (lobules IV and V)
dent	dentate nucleus
fomg	foramen of Magendie
frv4	fastigial recess of fourth ventricle
grac	gracile lobule
horzf	great horizontal fissure of cerebellum
infslu	inferior semilunar lobule (Crus II)
lrv4	lateral recess of fourth ventricle
nodu	nodulus (lobule X)
psf	posterior superior fissure of cerebellum
quad	quadrangular lobule (anterior quadrangular lobule)
simp	simple lobule (posterior quadrangular lobule)
supslu	superior semilunar lobule (Crus I)
uvu	uvula (lobule IX)
val	vallecula space

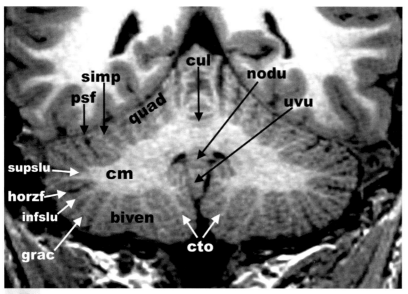

4.26a

FIGURES 4.26a,b

KEY

biven	biventral lobule
cm	corpus medullare
cto	cerebellar tonsil
cul	culmen (lobules IV and V)
grac	gracile lobule
horzf	great horizontal fissure of cerebellum
infslu	inferior semilunar lobule (Crus II)
nodu	nodulus (lobule X)
psf	posterior superior fissure of cerebellum
quad	quadrangular lobule (anterior quadrangular lobule)
simp	simple lobule (posterior quadrangular lobule)
supslu	superior semilunar lobule (Crus I)
uvu	uvula (lobule IX)

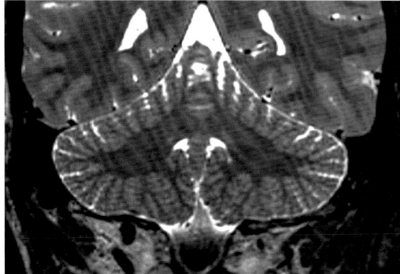

4.26b

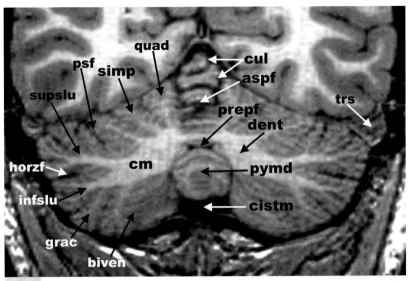

4.27a

FIGURES 4.27a,b

KEY	
aspf	anterior superior (primary) fissure
biven	biventral lobule
cistm	cisterna magna
cm	corpus medullare
cul	culmen (lobules IV and V)
dent	dentate nucleus
grac	gracile lobule
horzf	great horizontal fissure of cerebellum
infslu	inferior semilunar lobule (Crus II)
prepf	prepyramidal fissure of cerebellum
psf	posterior superior fissure of cerebellum
pymd	pyramid of the vermis (lobule VIII)
quad	quadrangular lobule (anterior quadrangular lobule)
simp	simple lobule (posterior quadrangular lobule)
supslu	superior semilunar lobule (Crus I)
trs	transverse sinus

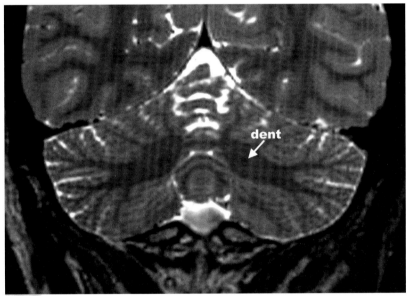

4.27b

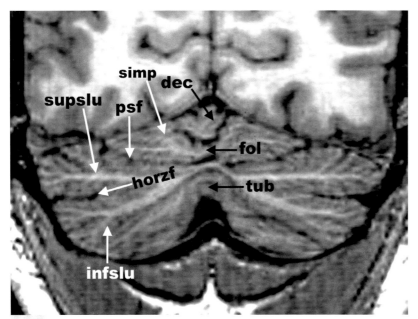

4.28a

FIGURES 4.28a,b

KEY

dec	declive (lobule VI)
fol	folium (lobule VII)
horzf	great horizontal fissure of cerebellum
infslu	inferior semilunar lobule (Crus II)
psf	posterior superior fissure of cerebellum
simp	simple lobule (posterior quadrangular lobule)
supslu	superior semilunar lobule (Crus I)
tub	tuber (lobule VII)

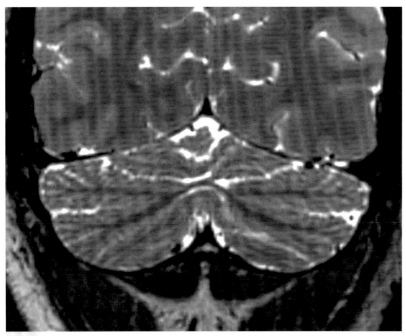

4.28b

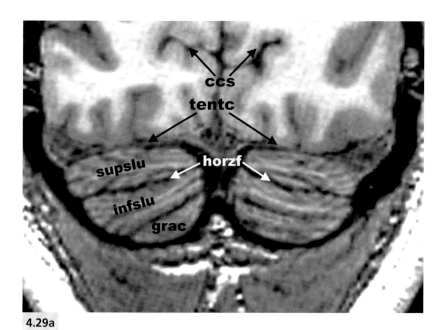

4.29a

FIGURES 4.29a,b

KEY

ccs	calcarine sulcus
falci	falx cerebelli
grac	gracile lobule
horzf	great horizontal fissure of cerebellum
infslu	inferior semilunar lobule (Crus II)
supslu	superior semilunar lobule (Crus I)
tentc	tentorium cerebelli
torh	torcular herophili (confluence of sinuses)

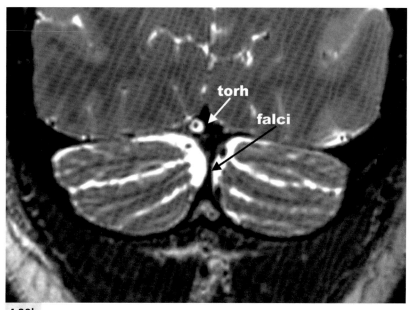

4.29b

MR Imaging of Regional Intracranial Anatomy and Orbits

5

*T*his chapter of the atlas will demonstrate targeted, focused imaging of a variety of interesting, and important anatomic sites that are of particular clinical relevance. It is my hope that these images will enhance your understanding and appreciation for the anatomy demonstrated.

Sites of illustrated anatomy include:

■ PITUITARY GLAND (FIGURES 5.1a–5.5)

Sagittal Plane

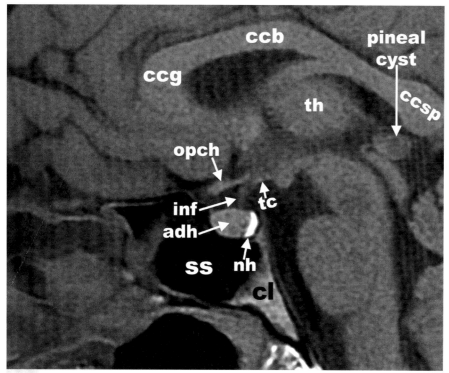

5.1a

FIGURES 5.1a,b–5.4a,b Pre-contrast sagittal (5.1a, 5.2a) and coronal (5.3a, 5.4a) and post-contrast sagittal (5.1b, 5.2b) and coronal (5.3b, 5.4b) T1 weighted (W) images demonstrate normal anatomy of the pituitary gland and surrounding structures.

KEY

adh	adenohypophysis
ccb	body of corpus callosum
ccg	genu of corpus callosum
ccsp	splenium of corpus callosum
cl	clivus
clvp	clival venous plexus
fom	foramen of Monro
icv	internal cerebral vein
inf	infundibulum
mb	mammillary body
nh	neurohypophysis
opch	optic chiasm
sepv	septal vein
sorv3	supra-optic recess of third ventricle
ss	sphenoid sinus
tc	tuber cinereum
th	thalamus

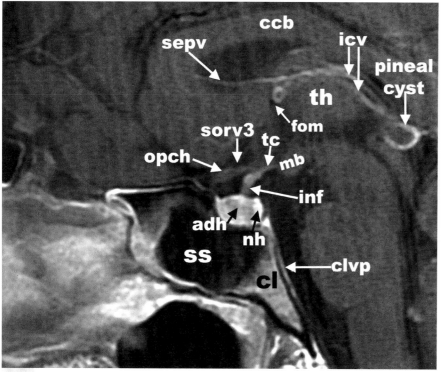

5.1b

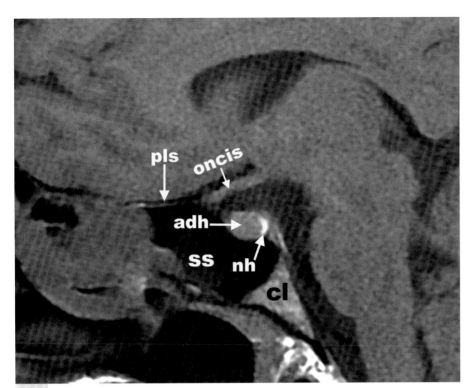

5.2a

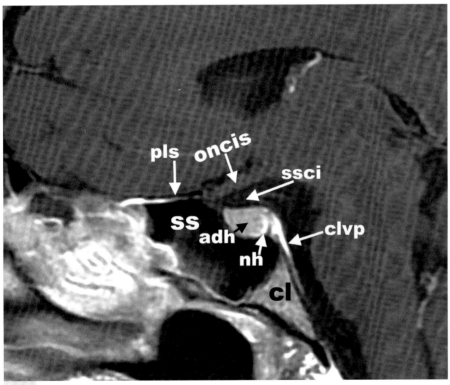

5.2b

FIGURES 5.2a,b

KEY	
adh	adenohypophysis
cl	clivus
clvp	clival venous plexus
nh	neurohypophysis
oncis	cisternal (pre-chiasmatic) segment optic nerve
pls	planum sphenoidale
ss	sphenoid sinus
ssci	suprasellar cistern

Coronal Plane

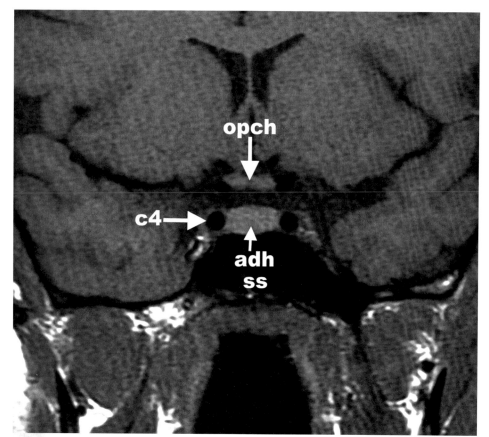

5.3a

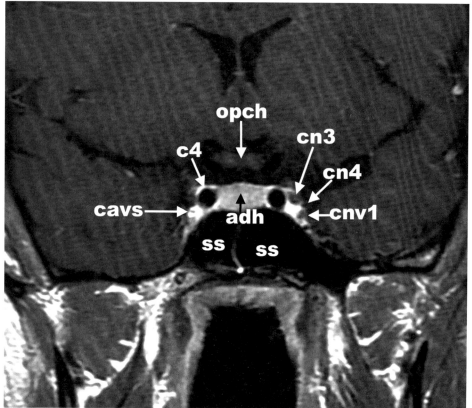

5.3b

FIGURES 5.3a,b

KEY

adh	adenohypophysis
c4	c4 (cavernous segment of ica)
cavs	cavernous sinus
cn3	oculomotor nerve
cn4	trochlear nerve
cnv1	ophthalmic branch (v1) of trigeminal nerve
ica	internal carotid artery
opch	optic chiasm
ss	sphenoid sinus

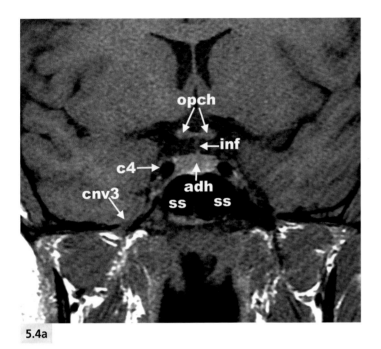

5.4a

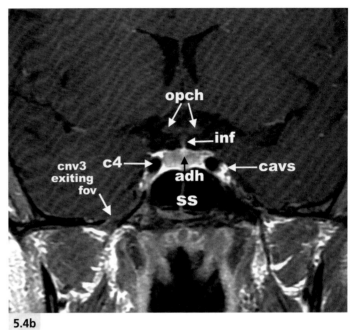

5.4b

FIGURES 5.4a,b

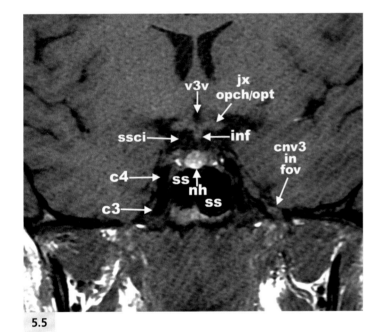

5.5

FIGURE 5.5   Non-contrast T1W coronal image through the sella/parasellar region at the posterior aspect of the sella turcica shows the normal increased signal of the neurohypophysis.

KEY

adh	adenohypophysis
c3	c3 (lacerum segment of ica)
c4	c4 (cavernous segment of ica)
cavs	cavernous sinus
cnv3	mandibular division (v3) of trigeminal nerve
fov	foramen ovale
ica	internal carotid artery
inf	infundibulum
jx	junction
nh	neurohypophysis
opch	optic chiasm
opt	optic tract
ss	sphenoid sinus
ssci	suprasellar cistern
v3v	third ventricle

■ ORBITS (FIGURES 5.6–5.33)

Axial Plane

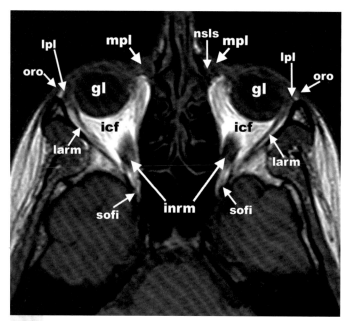

5.6

FIGURES 5.6–5.10   Normal appearance of the orbits and peri-orbital structures on unenhanced axial T1W images without fat suppression from inferior (5.6) to superior (5.10).

KEY

acl	anterior clinoid process
c6	c6 (ophthalmic segment of ica)
ecf	extraconal orbital fat
elid	orbicularis oculi/eyelid
gl	globe
ica	internal carotid artery
icf	intraconal orbital fat
inrm	inferior rectus muscle
laco	orbital portion of lacrimal gland
lacp	palpebral portion of lacrimal gland
larm	lateral rectus muscle
lengl	lens of globe
lpl	lateral palpebral ligament
merm	medial rectus muscle
mpl	medial palpebral ligament
nsls	nasolacrimal saccule
oncan	canalicular segment of optic nerve
onorb	orbital segment optic nerve
onsc	optic nerve/sheath complex
oro	orbicularis oculi muscle
scr	3 ocular coats of eye (sclera, choroid, retina)
sofi	superior orbital fissure
supob	superior oblique muscle
vib	vitreous body (chamber) of eye

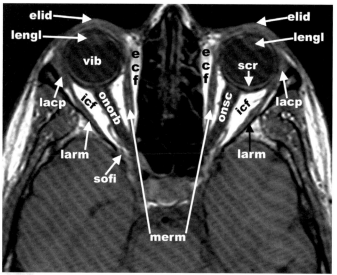

5.7

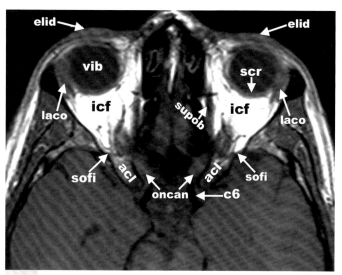

5.8

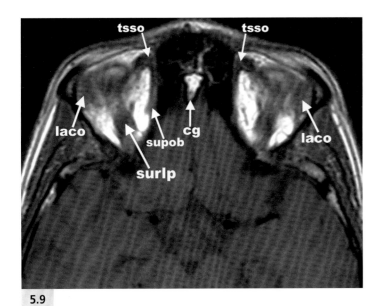

5.9

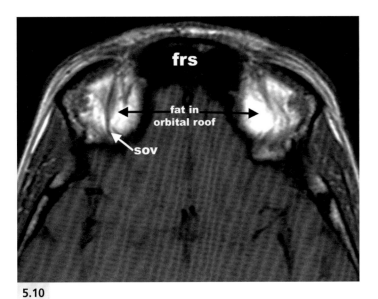

5.10

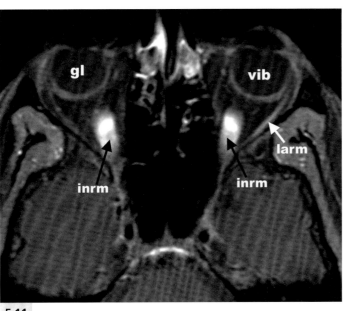

5.11

KEY

cg	crista galli
frs	frontal sinus
gl	globe
inrm	inferior rectus muscle
laco	orbital portion of lacrimal gland
larm	lateral rectus muscle
sov	superior ophthalmic vein
supob	superior oblique muscle
surlp	superior rectus/levator palpebrae muscle
tsso	trochlear sling of superior oblique muscle
vib	vitreous body (chamber) of eye

FIGURES 5.11–5.15   Normal appearance of the orbits and peri-orbital structures on fat suppressed post-contrast T1W axial images from inferior (5.11) to superior (5.15). Two white asterisks in Figure 5.12 indicate technical artifacts.

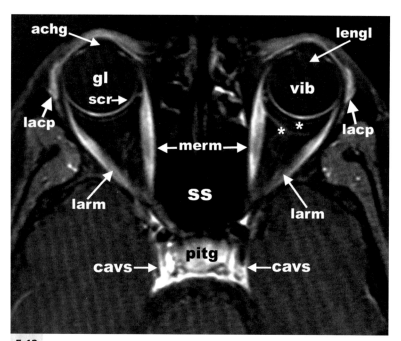

5.12

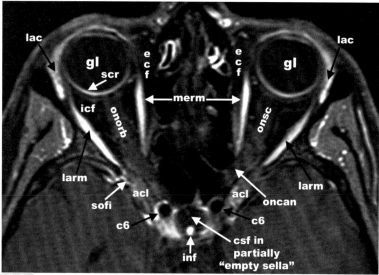

5.13

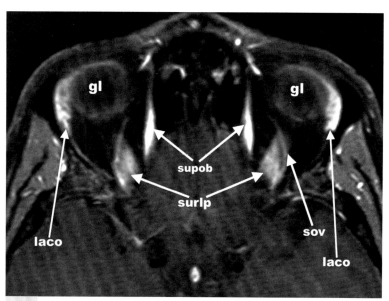

5.14

FIGURES 5.12–5.14

KEY

achg	anterior chamber of eye
acl	anterior clinoid process
c6	c6 (ophthalmic segment of ica)
cavs	cavernous sinus
csf	cerebrospinal fluid
ecf	extraconal orbital fat
gl	globe
ica	internal carotid artery
icf	intraconal orbital fat
inf	infundibulum
lac	lacrimal gland
laco	orbital portion of lacrimal gland
lacp	palpebral portion of lacrimal gland
larm	lateral rectus muscle
lengl	lens of globe
merm	medial rectus muscle
oncan	canalicular segment of optic nerve
onorb	orbital segment optic nerve
onsc	optic nerve/sheath complex
pitg	pituitary gland
scr	3 ocular coats of eye (sclera, choroid, retina)
sofi	superior orbital fissure
sov	superior ophthalmic vein
ss	sphenoid sinus
supob	superior oblique muscle
surlp	superior rectus/levator palpebrae muscle
vib	vitreous body (chamber) of eye

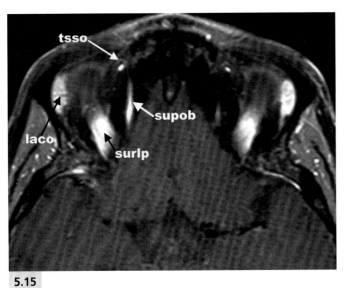

5.15

FIGURE 5.15

Coronal Plane

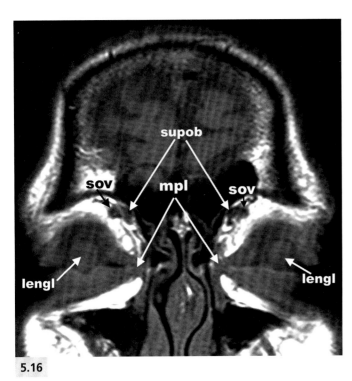

5.16

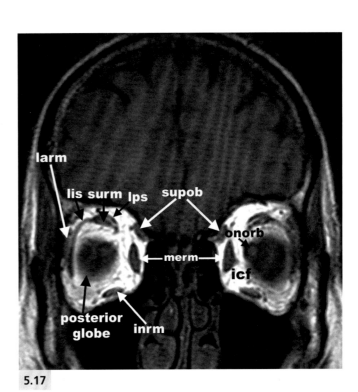

5.17

FIGURES 5.16–5.22   Normal appearance of the orbits and peri-orbital structures on unenhanced T1W coronal images without fat suppression from anterior (5.16) to posterior (5.22).

KEY

icf	intraconal orbital fat
inrm	inferior rectus muscle
laco	orbital portion of lacrimal gland
larm	lateral rectus muscle
lengl	lens of globe
lis	lateral intermuscular septum
lps	levator palpebrae superioris
merm	medial rectus muscle
mpl	medial palpebral ligament
onorb	orbital segment optic nerve
sov	superior ophthalmic vein
supob	superior oblique muscle
surlp	superior rectus/levator palpebrae muscle
surm	superior rectus muscle
tsso	trochlear sling of superior oblique muscle

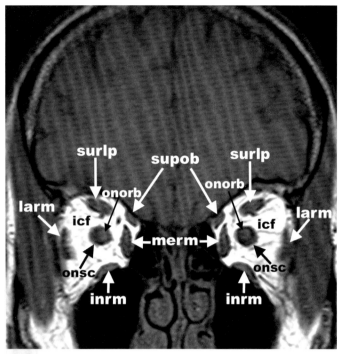

5.18

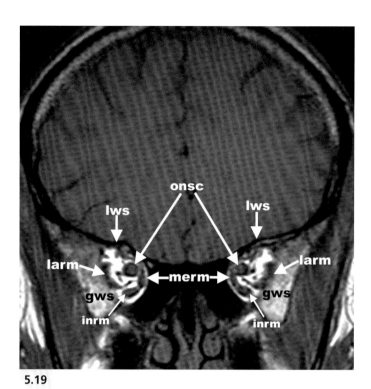

5.19

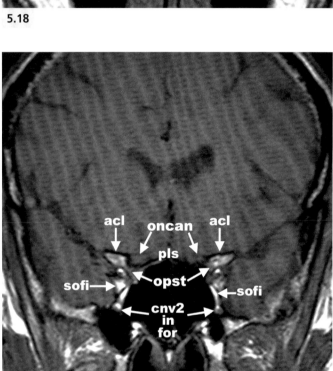

5.20

FIGURES 5.18–5.20

KEY

acl	anterior clinoid process
cnv2	maxillary branch (v2) of trigeminal nerve
for	foramen rotundem
gws	greater wing of the sphenoid bone
icf	intraconal orbital fat
inrm	inferior rectus muscle
larm	lateral rectus muscle
lws	lesser wing of the sphenoid bone
merm	medial rectus muscle
onorb	orbital segment optic nerve
oncan	canalicular segment of optic nerve
onsc	optic nerve/sheath complex
opst	optic strut
pls	planum sphenoidale
sofi	superior orbital fissure
supob	superior oblique muscle
surlp	superior rectus/levator palpebrae muscle

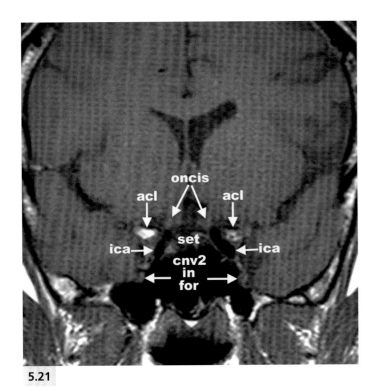

5.21

FIGURE 5.21

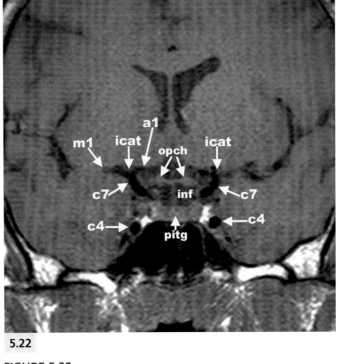

5.22

FIGURE 5.22

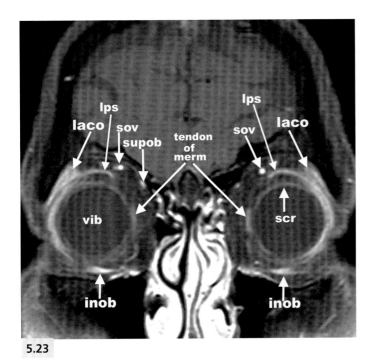

5.23

FIGURES 5.23–5.26   Normal appearance of the orbits and peri-orbital structures on fat suppressed post-contrast T1W coronal images from anterior (5.23) to posterior (5.26).

KEY

a1	a1 (precommunicating segment aca)
aca	anterior cerebral artery
acl	anterior clinoid process
c4	c4 (cavernous segment of ica)
c7	c7 (communicating segment of ica)
cnv2	maxillary branch (v2) of trigeminal nerve
for	foramen rotundem
ica	internal carotid artery
icat	ica terminus/bifurcation
inf	infundibulum
inob	inferior oblique muscle
laco	orbital portion of lacrimal gland
lps	levator palpebrae superioris
m1	m1 (horizontal segment mca)
mca	middle cerebral artery
merm	medial rectus muscle
oncis	cisternal (pre-chiasmatic) segment optic nerve
opch	optic chiasm
pitg	pituitary gland
scr	3 ocular coats of eye (sclera, choroid, retina)
set	sella turcica
sov	superior ophthalmic vein
supob	superior oblique muscle
vib	vitreous body (chamber) of eye

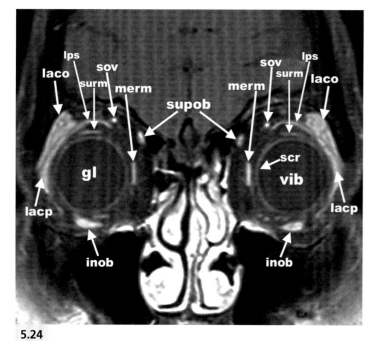

5.24

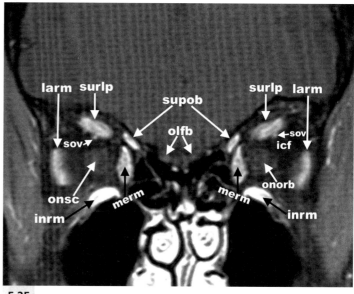

5.25

FIGURES 5.24–5.26

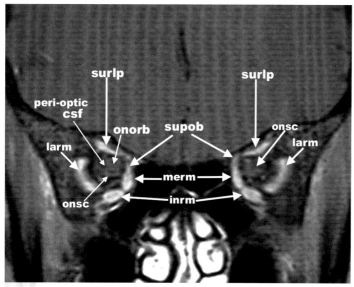

5.26

KEY

csf	cerebrospinal fluid
gl	globe
icf	intraconal orbital fat
inob	inferior oblique muscle
inrm	inferior rectus muscle
laco	orbital portion of lacrimal gland
lacp	palpebral portion of lacrimal gland
larm	lateral rectus muscle
lps	levator palpebrae superioris
merm	medial rectus muscle
olfb	olfactory bulb
onorb	orbital segment optic nerve
onsc	optic nerve/sheath complex
scr	3 ocular coats of eye (sclera, choroid, retina)
sov	superior ophthalmic vein
supob	superior oblique muscle
surlp	superior rectus/levator palpebrae muscle
surm	superior rectus muscle
vib	vitreous body (chamber) of eye

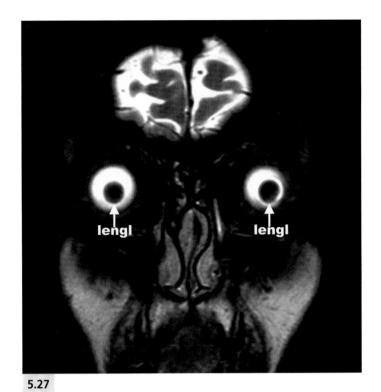

5.27

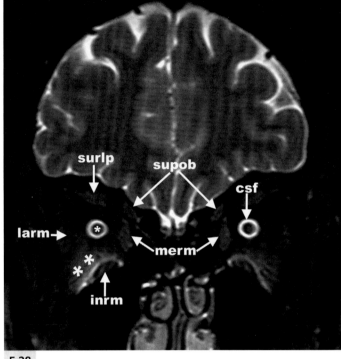

5.28

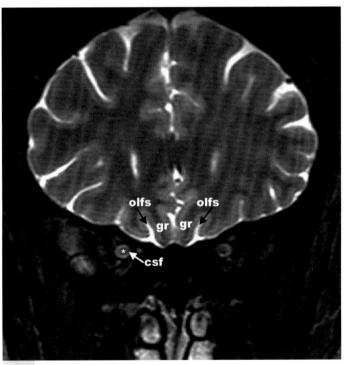

5.29

FIGURES 5.27–5.33 Normal appearance of the orbits and peri-orbital structures on fat suppressed T2W coronal images from anterior (5.27) to posterior (5.33). Single white asterisk in Figures 5.28 and 5.29 represents the optic nerve. Double white asterisks in Figure 5.28 indicate technical artifacts related to fat suppression.

KEY

csf	cerebrospinal fluid
gr	gyrus rectus
inrm	inferior rectus muscle
larm	lateral rectus muscle
lengl	lens of globe
merm	medial rectus muscle
olfs	olfactory sulcus
supob	superior oblique muscle
surlp	superior rectus/levator palpebrae muscle

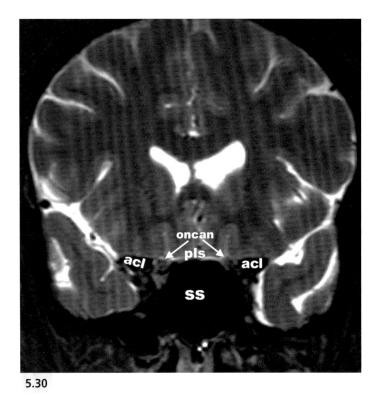

5.30

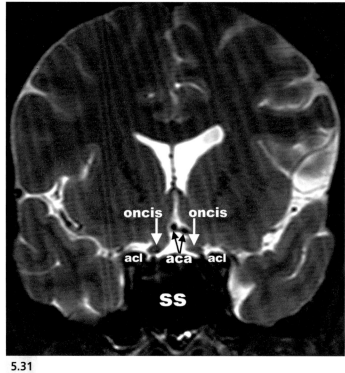

5.31

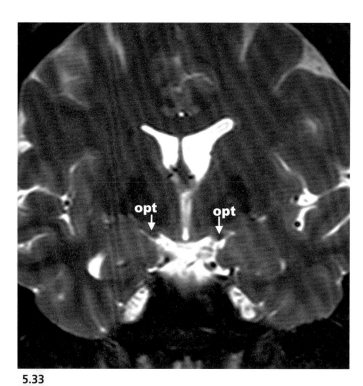

5.33

5.32

FIGURES 5.30–5.33

KEY

aca	anterior cerebral artery
acl	anterior clinoid process
oncan	canalicular segment of optic nerve
oncis	cisternal (pre-chiasmatic) segment optic nerve
opch	optic chiasm
opt	optic tract
pls	planum sphenoidale
ss	sphenoid sinus

■ LILIEQUIST'S MEMBRANE (FIGURES 5.34–5.40)

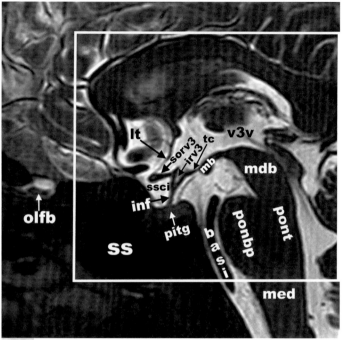

5.34

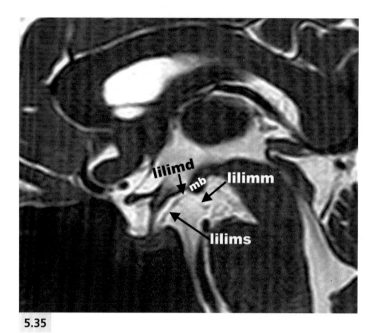

5.35

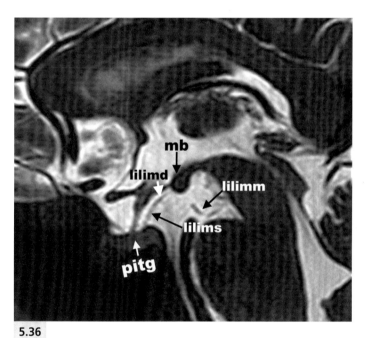

5.36

FIGURES 5.34–5.40 Heavily T2W sagittal (5.34–5.36), axial (5.37–5.39), and coronal (5.40) images demonstrate the normal appearance of Liliequist's membrane.

KEY

basi	basilar artery	**med**	medulla
inf	infundibulum	**olfb**	olfactory bulb (cn1)
irv3	infindibular recess of third ventricle	**pitg**	pituitary gland
lilimd	diencephalic segment of Liliequist's membrane	**ponbp**	basis pontis of pons
		pont	tegmentum of pons
lilimm	mesencephalic segment of Liliequist's membrane	**sorv3**	supra-optic recess of third ventricle
		ss	sphenoid sinus
lilims	sellar segment of Liliequist's membrane	**ssci**	suprasellar cistern
lt	lamina terminalis	**tc**	tuber cinereum
mb	mammillary body	**v3v**	third ventricle
mdb	midbrain		

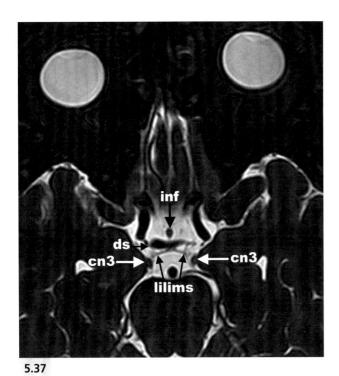

5.37

FIGURES 5.37–5.38

KEY

cn3	oculomotor nerve
ds	dorsum sellae
inf	infundibulum
lilims	sellar segment of Liliequist's membrane

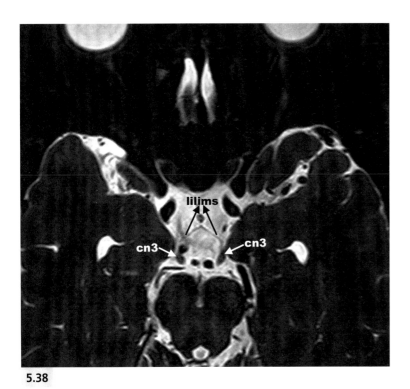

5.38

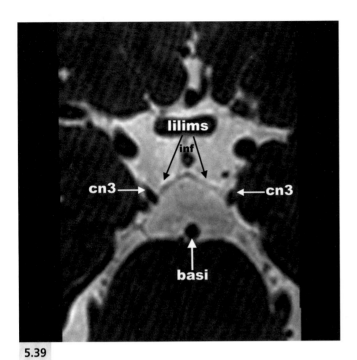

5.39

FIGURE 5.39–5.40

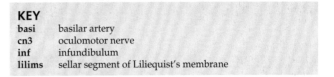

KEY

basi	basilar artery
cn3	oculomotor nerve
inf	infundibulum
lilims	sellar segment of Liliequist's membrane

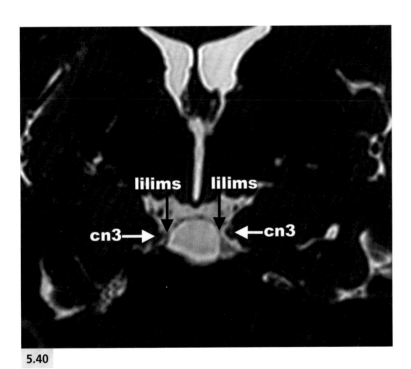

5.40

■ HIPPOCAMPAL FORMATION (FIGURES 5.41–5.80)

Coronal Plane

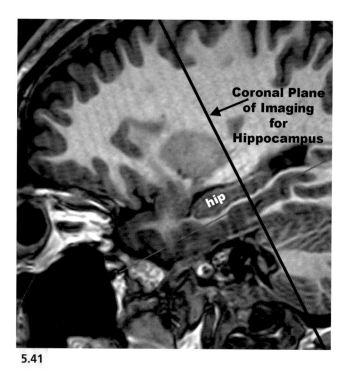

5.41

FIGURE 5.41 Sagittal T1W orientation image shows the plane of coronal images perpendicular to the long axis of the hippocampus.

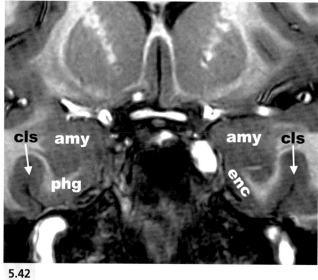

5.42

FIGURES 5.42–5.54 Normal coronal T1W images (5.42–5.48) and T2W images (5.49–5.54) of the hippocampal formations/medial temporal lobes from anterior to posterior.

5.43

KEY	
ac	anterior commissure
amy	amygdala
cls	collateral sulcus
clw	collateral white matter
cn3	oculomotor nerve
cn5p	pre-ganglionic segment trigeminal nerve
cn7	facial nerve
cn8	vestibulocochlear nerve
enc	entorhinal cortex
frxac	ascending columns of fornix
gpe	globus pallidus externa
hip	hippocampus
hiph	hippocampal head
llln	lateral lamina of lenticular nucleus
mb	mammillary body
opt	optic tract
phg	parahippocampal gyrus
ponbp	basis pontis of pons
pu	putamen
pyem	pyramidal eminence
ssci	suprasellar cistern
unc	uncus
v3v	third ventricle

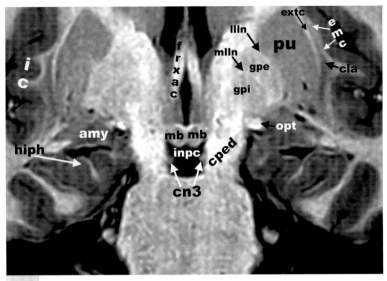

5.44

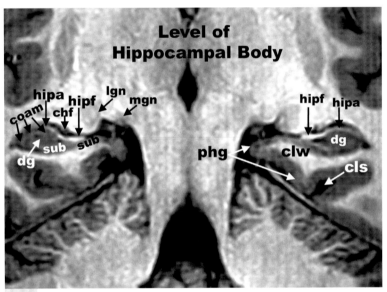

5.45

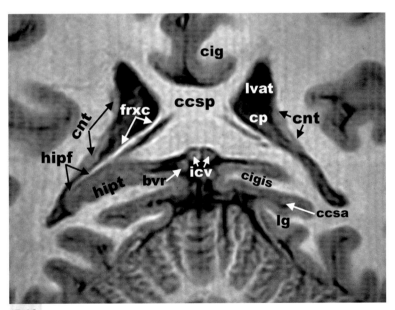

5.46

FIGURES 5.44–5.46

KEY	
amy	amygdala
bvr	basal vein of Rosenthal
ccsa	anterior calcarine sulcus
ccsp	splenium of corpus callosum
chf	choroidal fissure
cig	cingulate gyrus
cigis	isthmus of cingulate gyrus
cla	claustrum
cls	collateral sulcus
clw	collateral white matter
cn3	oculomotor nerve
cnt	caudate nucleus tail
coam	cornu ammonis
cp	choroid plexus
cped	cerebral peduncle
dg	dentate gyrus
emc	extreme capsule
extc	external capsule
frxac	ascending columns of fornix
frxc	crura of fornix
gpe	globus pallidus externa
gpi	globus pallidus interna
hipa	alveus of hippocampus
hipf	fimbria of hippocampus
hiph	hippocampal head
hipt	hippocampal tail
ic	insular cortex
icv	internal cerebral vein
inpc	interpeduncular cistern
lg	lingual gyrus (motg)
lgn	lateral geniculate nucleus
llln	lateral lamina of lenticular nucleus
lvat	atrium (trigone) of lateral ventricle
mb	mammillary body
mgn	medial geniculate nucleus
mlln	medial lamina of lenticular nucleus
opt	optic tract
phg	parahippocampal gyrus
pu	putamen
sub	subiculum

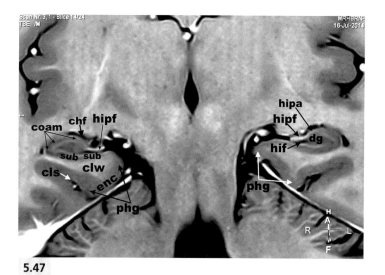

5.47

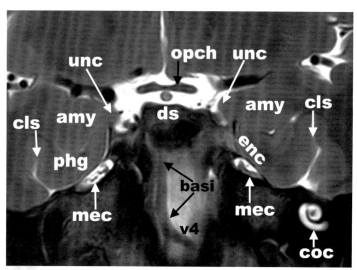

5.49

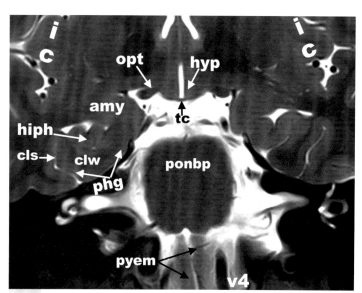

5.50

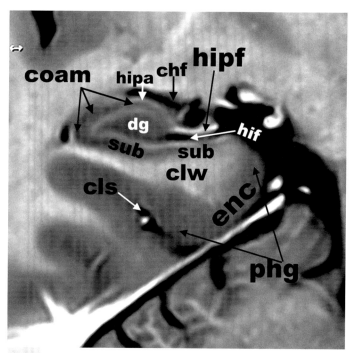

5.48

FIGURES 5.47–5.50

KEY

amy	amygdala
basi	basilar artery
chf	choroidal fissure
cls	collateral sulcus
clw	collateral white matter
coam	cornu ammonis
coc	cochlea
dg	dentate gyrus
ds	dorsum sellae
enc	entorhinal cortex
hif	hippocampal fissure
hipa	alveus of hippocampus
hipf	fimbria of hippocampus
hiph	hippocampal head
hyp	hypothalamus
ic	insular cortex
mec	Meckel's cave
opch	optic chiasm
opt	optic tract
phg	parahippocampal gyrus
ponbp	basis pontis of pons
pyem	pyramidal eminence
sub	subiculum
tc	tuber cinereum
unc	uncus
v4	v4 intracranial/intradural segment vertebral artery

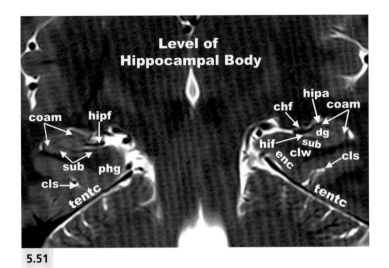

5.51

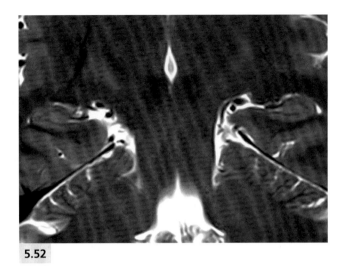

5.52

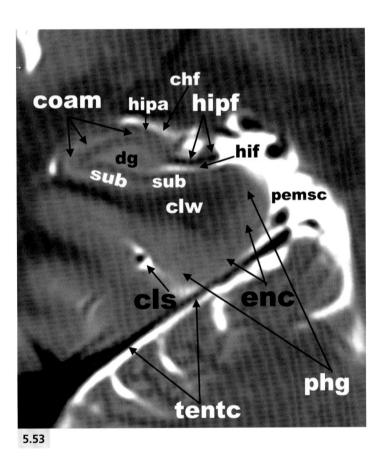

5.53

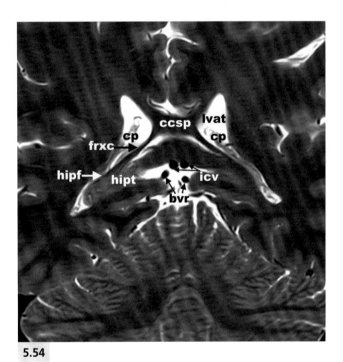

5.54

FIGURES 5.51–5.54

KEY	
bvr	basal vein of Rosenthal
ccsp	splenium of corpus callosum
chf	choroidal fissure
cls	collateral sulcus
clw	collateral white matter
coam	cornu ammonis
cp	choroid plexus
dg	dentate gyrus
enc	entorhinal cortex
frxc	crura of fornix
hif	hippocampal fissure (sulcus)
hipa	alveus of hippocampus
hipf	fimbria of hippocampus
hipt	hippocampal tail
icv	internal cerebral vein
lvat	atrium (trigone) of lateral ventricle
pemsc	perimesencephalic (ambient) cistern
phg	parahippocampal gyrus
sub	subiculum
tentc	tentorium cerebelli

Axial Plane

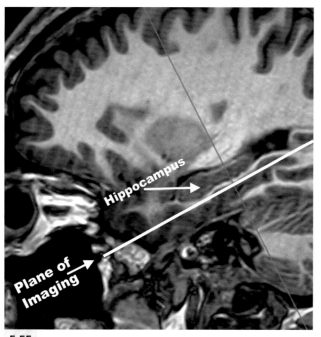

5.55

FIGURE 5.55 Sagittal T1W orientation image shows the plane of axial images (thick white line) parallel to the long axis of the hippocampus used to acquire Figures 5.56–5.69.

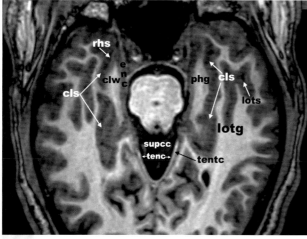

5.56

FIGURES 5.56–5.62 Normal axial T1W images of the hippocampal formations/medial temporal lobes from inferior (caudal) to superior (cranial).

KEY

cls	collateral sulcus
clw	collateral white matter
cruci	crural cistern
enc	entorhinal cortex
hipb	hippocampal body
hiph	hippocampal head
inpc	interpeduncular cistern
lamss	lateral mesencephalic sulcus
lotg	lateral occipital temporal gyrus (lotg)/fusiform gyrus
lots	lateral occipital temporal sulcus
pemsc	perimesencephalic (ambient) cistern
phg	parahippocampal gyrus
rhs	rhinal sulcus
ss	sphenoid sinus
sub	subiculum
supcc	supracerebellar cistern
tenc	tentorial incisura
tentc	tentorium cerebelli

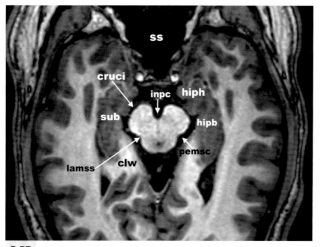

5.57

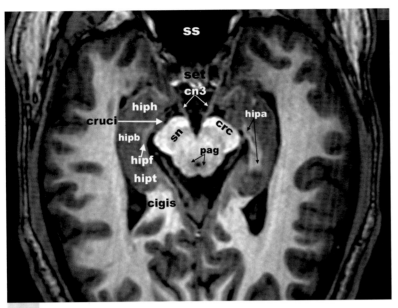

5.58

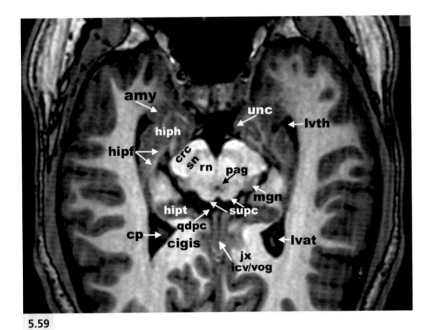

5.59

FIGURES 5.58–5.59

KEY

amy	amygdala
cigis	isthmus of cingulate gyrus
cn3	oculomotor nerve
cp	choroid plexus
crc	crus cerebri
cruci	crural cistern
hipa	alveus of hippocampus
hipb	hippocampal body
hipf	fimbria of hippocampus
hiph	hippocampal head
hipt	hippocampal tail
icv	internal cerebral vein
jx	junction
lvat	atrium (trigone) of lateral ventricle
lvth	temporal horn of lateral ventricle
mgn	medial geniculate nucleus
pag	periaqueductal gray matter
qdpc	quadrigeminal plate cistern
rn	red nucleus
set	sella turcica
sn	substantia nigra
ss	sphenoid sinus
supc	superior colliculus
unc	uncus
vog	vein of Galen

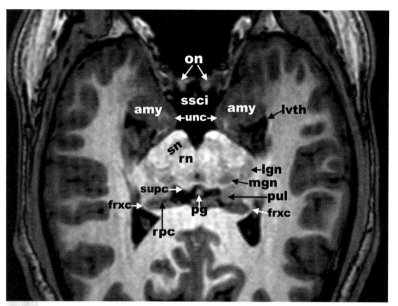

5.60

FIGURES 5.60–5.62

KEY

ac	anterior commissure
acl	anterior clinoid process
amy	amygdala
ccsp	splenium of corpus callosum
cla	claustrum
cnt	caudate nucleus tail
cvi	cistern of velum interpositum
frxac	ascending columns of fornix
frxc	crura of fornix
hab	habenular trigone
hyp	hypothalamus
ica	internal carotid artery
icv	internal cerebral vein
inpc	interpeduncular cistern
irv3	infindibular recess of third ventricle
lgn	lateral geniculate nucleus
lvat	atrium (trigone) of lateral ventricle
lvth	temporal horn of lateral ventricle
mb	mammillary body
mgn	medial geniculate nucleus
mtt	mammilothalamic tract
on	optic nerve
oncis	cisternal (pre-chiasmatic) segment optic nerve
opch	optic chiasm
opt	optic tract
pc	posterior commissure
pg	pineal gland
pmol	posteromedial orbital lobule
pu	putamen
pul	pulvinar is part of lateral thalamic nuclear group
rn	red nucleus
rpc	retro-pulvinar (thalamic) cistern (wings of ambient cistern)
sn	substantia nigra
ss	sphenoid sinus
ssci	suprasellar cistern
sth	subthalamic nucleus
stl	stem of temporal lobe
supc	superior colliculus
tc	tuber cinereum
unc	uncus
v3v	third ventricle

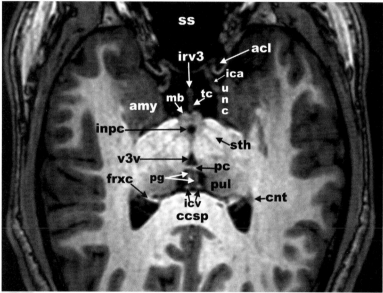

5.61

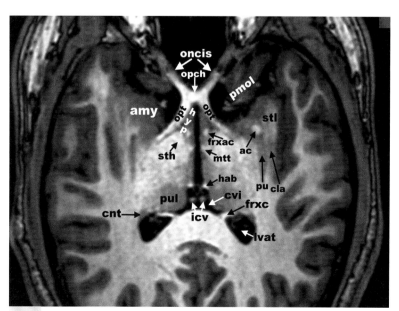

5.62

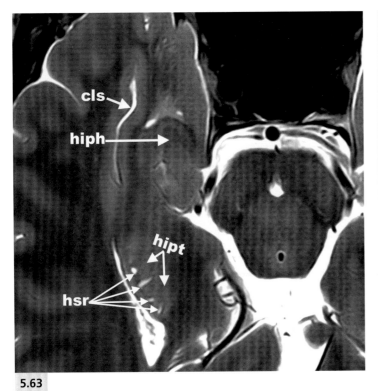

5.63

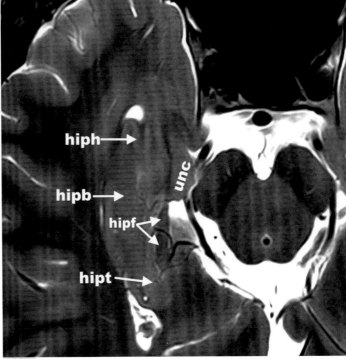

5.64

FIGURES 5.63–5.69   Normal axial T2W images of the hippocampal formations/medial temporal lobes from inferior (caudal) to superior (cranial).

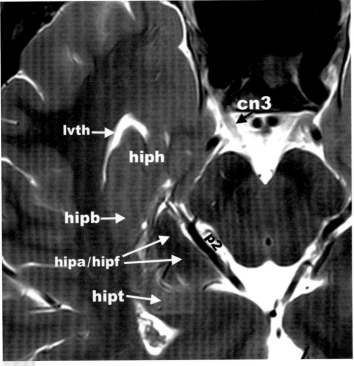

5.65

KEY

cls	collateral sulcus
cn3	oculomotor nerve
hipa	alveus of hippocampus
hipb	hippocampal body
hipf	fimbria of hippocampus
hiph	hippocampal head
hipt	hippocampal tail
hsr	hippocampal sulcal remnants
lvth	temporal horn of lateral ventricle
p2	p2 (ambient segment of pca)
pca	posterior cerebral artery
unc	uncus

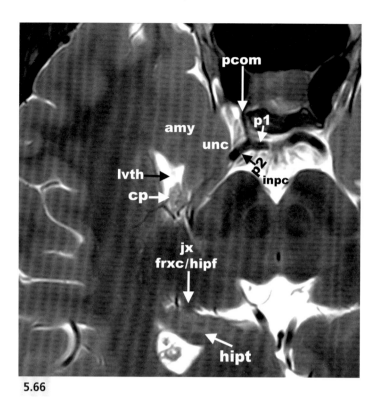

5.66

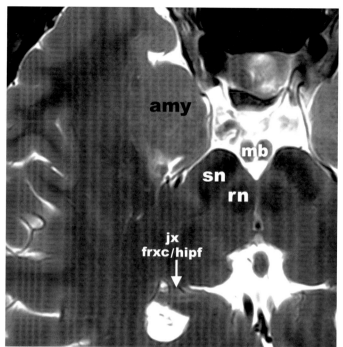

5.67

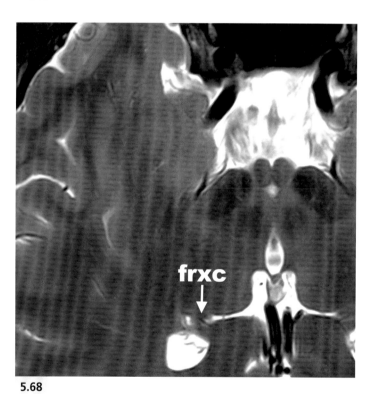

5.68

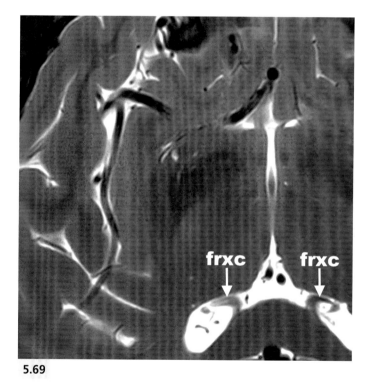

5.69

FIGURES 5.66–5.69

KEY

amy	amygdala	p1	p1 (precommunicating/ mesencephalic segment pca)
cp	choroid plexus		
frxc	crura of fornix		
hipf	fimbria of hippocampus	p2	p2 (ambient segment of pca)
hipt	hippocampal tail		
inpc	interpeduncular cistern	pca	posterior cerebral artery
jx	junction	pcom	posterior communicating artery
lvth	temporal horn of lateral ventricle	rn	red nucleus
		sn	substantia nigra
mb	mammillary body	unc	uncus

Sagittal Plane

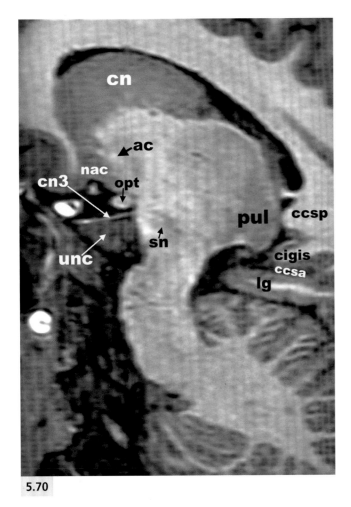

5.70

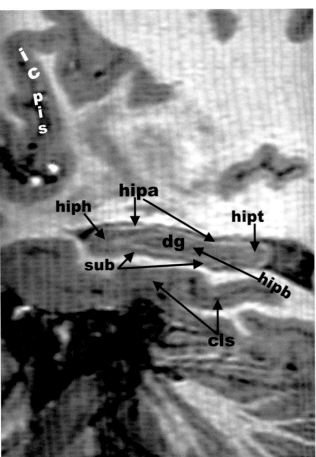

5.72

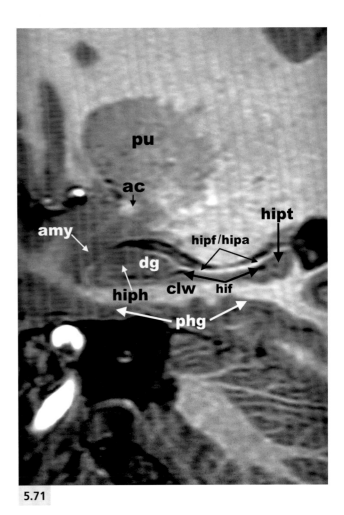

5.71

FIGURES 5.70–5.72   Normal sagittal T1W images of the hippocampal formations/medial temporal lobes from medial to lateral.

KEY

ac	anterior commissure	**hipf**	fimbria of hippocampus
amy	amygdala	**hiph**	hippocampal head
ccsa	anterior calcarine sulcus	**hipt**	hippocampal tail
		ic	insular cortex
ccsp	splenium of corpus callosum	**lg**	lingual gyrus (motg)
		nac	nucleus accumbens
cigis	isthmus of cingulate gyrus	**opt**	optic tract
		phg	parahippocampal gyrus
cls	collateral sulcus	**pis**	peri-insular (circular) sulcus
clw	collateral white matter		
cn3	oculomotor nerve	**pul**	pulvinar is part of lateral thalamic nuclear group
cn	caudate nucleus		
dg	dentate gyrus		
hif	hippocampal fissure (sulcus)	**pu**	putamen
		sn	substantia nigra
hipa	alveus of hippocampus	**sub**	subiculum
hipb	hippocampal body	**unc**	uncus

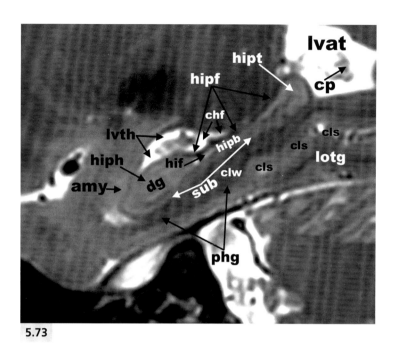

5.73

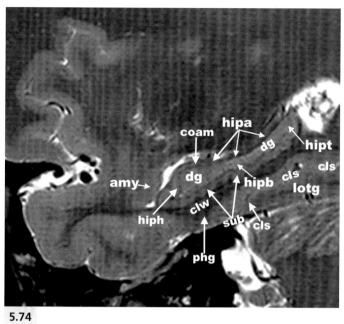

5.74

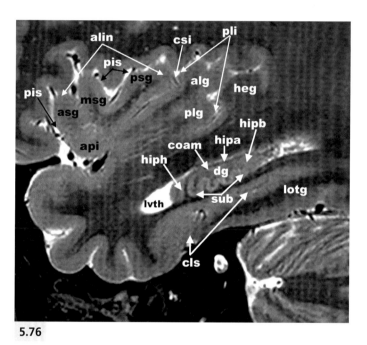

5.75

5.76

FIGURES 5.73–5.76 Normal sagittal T2W images of the hippocampal formations/medial temporal lobes from medial to lateral.

KEY

alg	anterior long insular gyrus	**hipf**	fimbria of hippocampus
alin	anterior lobule of insula	**hiph**	hippocampal head
amy	amygdala	**hipt**	hippocampal tail
api	apex of insula	**lotg**	lateral occipital temporal gyrus (lotg)/fusiform gyrus
asg	anterior short insular gyrus		
chf	choroidal fissure	**lvat**	atrium (trigone) of lateral ventricle
cls	collateral sulcus		
clw	collateral white matter	**lvth**	temporal horn of lateral ventricle
coam	cornu ammonis		
cp	choroid plexus	**msg**	middle short insular gyrus
csi	central sulcus of insula	**phg**	parahippocampal gyrus
dg	dentate gyrus	**pis**	peri-insular (circular) sulcus
heg	Heschl's gyrus (transverse temporal gyrus)	**plg**	posterior long insular gyrus
		pli	posterior lobule of insula
hif	hippocampal fissure (sulcus)	**psg**	posterior short insular gyrus
hipa	alveus of hippocampus	**sub**	subiculum
hipb	hippocampal body		

Sagittal Oblique Plane, Fimbria to Crura of Fornix

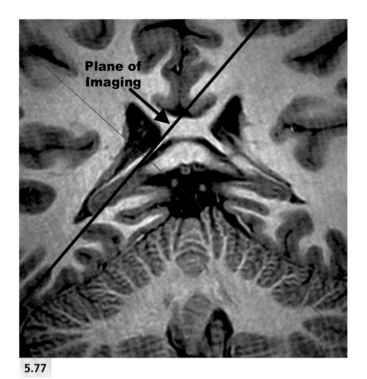

5.77

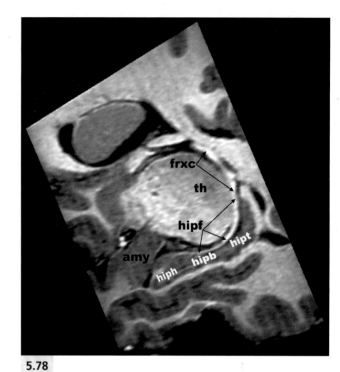

5.78

FIGURES 5.77–5.80

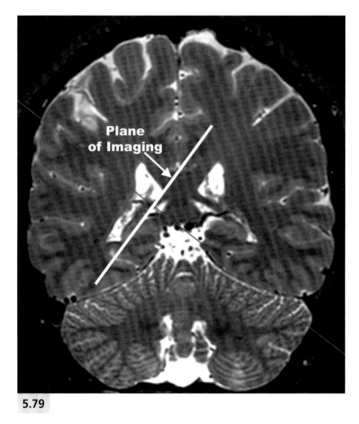

5.79

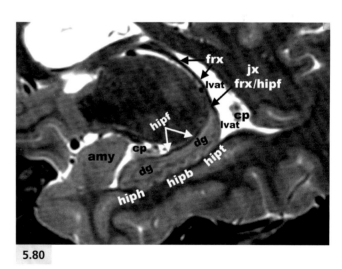

5.80

FIGURES 5.77–5.80c   Orientation coronal images with plane of imaging (T1W = 5.77 and T2W = 5.79) and corresponding sagittal oblique T1W (5.78) and T2W (5.80) images demonstrating the anatomic connection between the crura of the fornix and the fimbria of the hippocampus. Figures 5.80a–c are coronal T1W = 5.80a,b and axial T1W = 5.80c images demonstrating the hippocampal commissure.

KEY

amy	amygdala	hiph	hippocampal head
cp	choroid plexus	hipt	hippocampal tail
dg	dentate gyrus	jx	junction
frx	fornix	lvat	atrium (trigone) of lateral
frxc	crura of fornix		ventricle
hipb	hippocampal body	th	thalamus
hipf	fimbria of hippocampus		

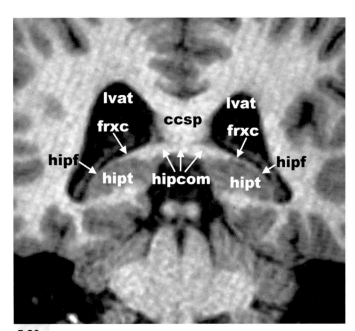

5.80a

FIGURE 5.80a

KEY

ccsp	splenium of corpus callosum
frxc	crura of fornix
hipcom	hippocampal commissure
hipf	fimbria of hippocampus
hipt	hippocampal tail
lvat	atrium (trigone) of lateral ventricle

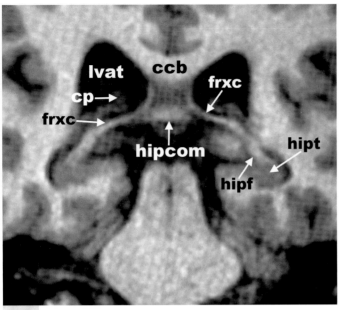

5.80b

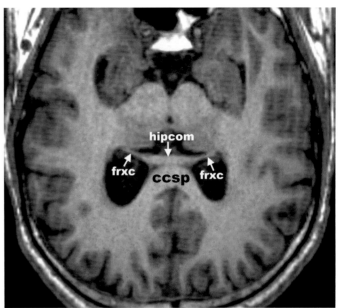

5.80c

FIGURES 5.80b,c

KEY

ccb	body of corpus callosum
ccsp	splenium of corpus callosum
cp	choroid plexus
frxc	crura of fornix
hipcom	hippocampal commissure
hipf	fimbria of hippocampus
hipt	hippocampal tail
lvat	atrium (trigone) of lateral ventricle

■ H-SHAPED ORBITAL FRONTAL SULCI (FIGURES 5.81–5.86)

Axial Plane

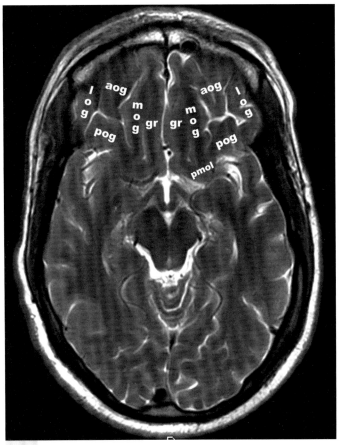

5.81

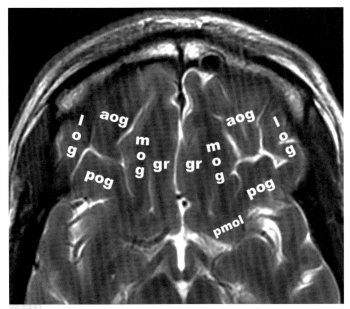

5.82

FIGURES 5.81–5.86 Axial T2W (5.81–5.83) and T1W (5.84–5.86) images demonstrate the normal arrangement of the orbital frontal gyri. The asterisks in Figures 5.83, 5.85, and 5.86 indicate the "H" shaped sulci creating this configuration.

KEY

aog	anterior orbital gyrus
gr	gyrus rectus
log	lateral orbital gyrus
mog	medial orbital gyrus
pmol	posteromedial orbital lobule
pog	posterior orbital gyrus

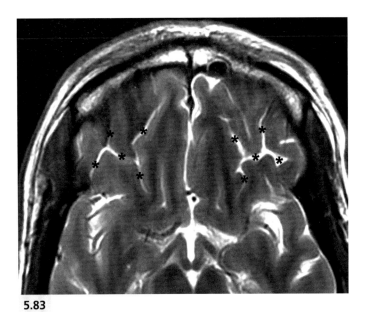

5.83

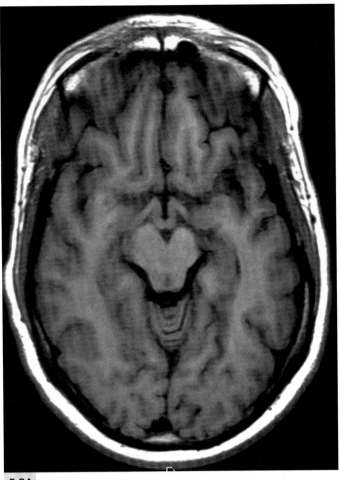

5.84

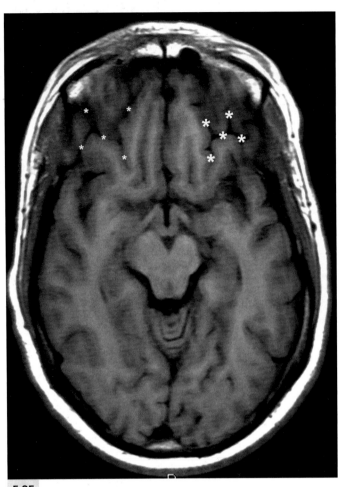

5.85

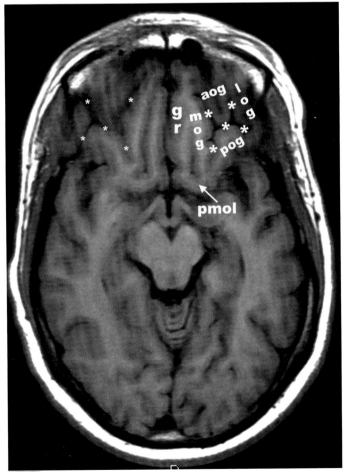

5.86

FIGURES 5.84–5.86

KEY	
aog	anterior orbital gyrus
gr	gyrus rectus
log	lateral orbital gyrus
mog	medial orbital gyrus
pmol	posteromedial orbital lobule
pog	posterior orbital gyrus

■ INSULAR ANATOMY (FIGURES 5.87–5.90)

Sagittal Plane

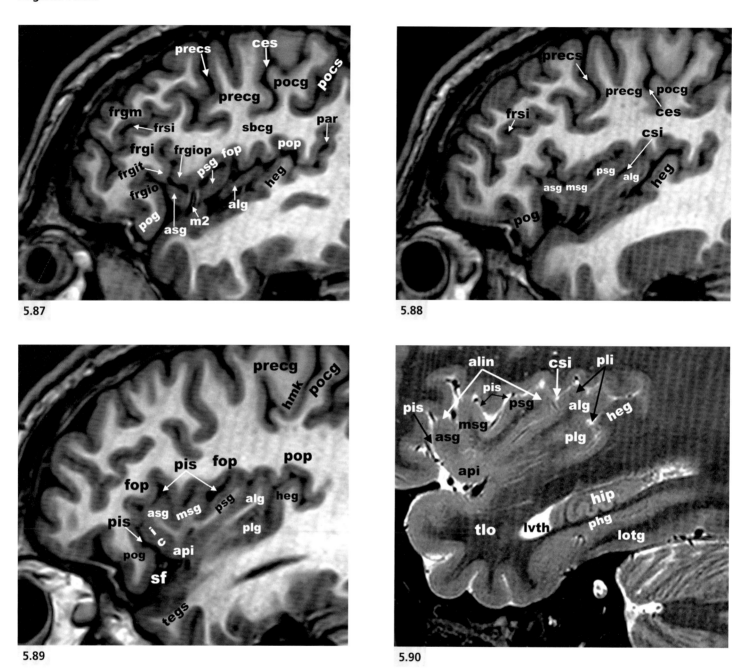

FIGURES 5.87–5.90 Normal anatomy of the insular region from lateral to medial on T1W sagittal images (5.87–5.89) and a T2W (5.90) sagittal image.

KEY

alg	anterior long insular gyrus	heg	Heschl's gyrus (transverse temporal gyrus)
alin	anterior lobule of insula		
api	apex of insula	hip	hippocampus
asg	anterior short insular gyrus	hmk	hand motor knob
ces	central sulcus	ic	insular cortex
csi	central sulcus of insula	lotg	lateral occipital temporal gyrus (lotg)/fusiform gyrus
fop	frontal operculum		
frgi	inferior frontal gyrus	lvth	temporal horn of lateral ventricle
frgio	pars orbitalis of inferior frontal gyrus		
		m2	m2 (Sylvian/insular branches mca)
frgiop	pars opercularis of inferior frontal gyrus		
		mca	middle cerebral artery
frgit	pars triangularis of inferior frontal gyrus	msg	middle short insular gyrus
		par	posterior ascending ramus of Sylvian fissure
frgm	middle frontal gyrus		
frsi	inferior frontal sulcus	phg	parahippocampal gyrus

pis	peri-insular (circular) sulcus
plg	posterior long insular gyrus
pli	posterior lobule of insula
pocg	post-central gyrus
pocs	post-central sulcus
pog	posterior orbital gyrus
pop	parietal operculum
precg	pre-central gyrus
precs	pre-central sulcus
psg	posterior short insular gyrus
sbcg	subcentral gyrus
sf	Sylvian fissure (lateral sulcus)
tegs	superior temporal gyrus
tlo	temporal lobe

■ SUBTHALAMIC NUCLEUS (FIGURES 5.91–5.108)

Coronal Plane

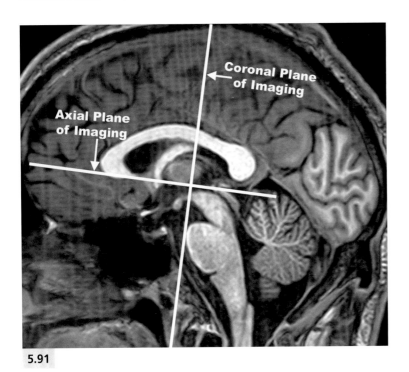

5.91

FIGURE 5.91   Sagittal orientation reference image.

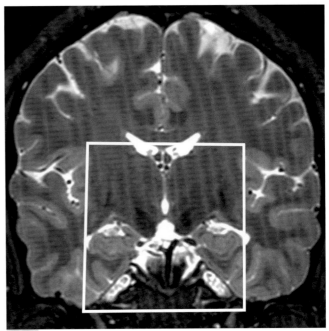

5.92

FIGURES 5.91–5.108   Normal subthalamic nucleus on coronal T2W images (5.92–5.96) from posterior to anterior, on axial T2W images (5.97–5.99), on coronal T1W images (5.100, 5.101), on axial T1W images (5.102–5.104), on sagittal T2W images (5.105–5.107) medial to lateral and on a sagittal T1W image (5.108).

KEY
cped	cerebral peduncle
rn	red nucleus
sn	substantia nigra

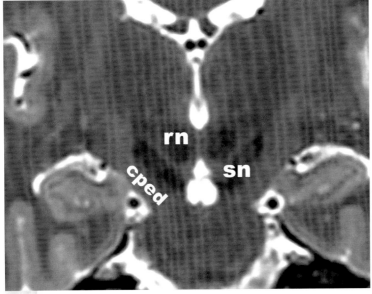

5.93

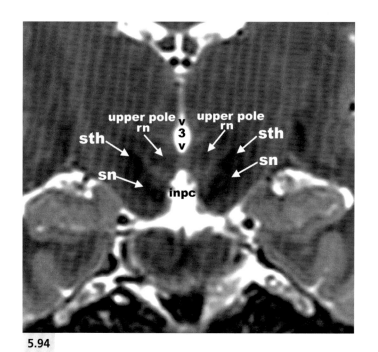

5.94

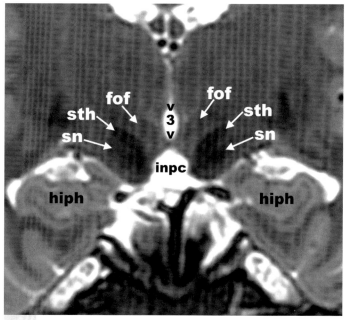

5.95

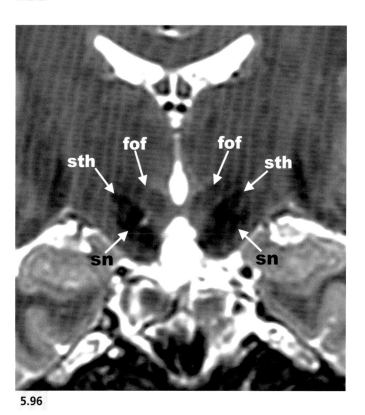

5.96

FIGURES 5.94–5.96

KEY

fof	fields of Forel
hiph	hippocampal head
inpc	interpeduncular cistern
rn	red nucleus
sn	substantia nigra
sth	subthalamic nucleus
v3v	third ventricle

Axial Plane

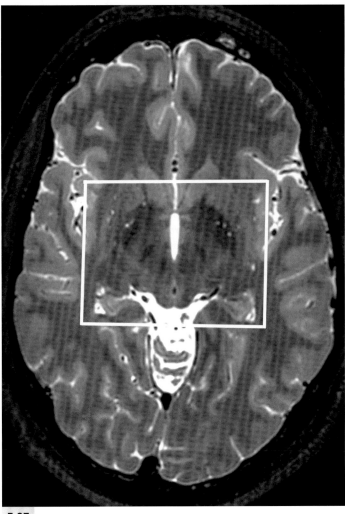

5.97

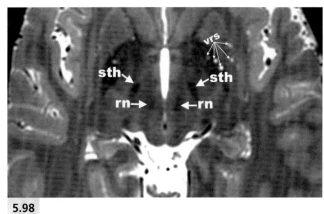

5.98

FIGURES 5.97–5.99

KEY	
frxac	ascending columns of fornix
mtt	mammilothalamic tract
rn	red nucleus
sth	subthalamic nucleus
vrs	Virchow-Robin spaces

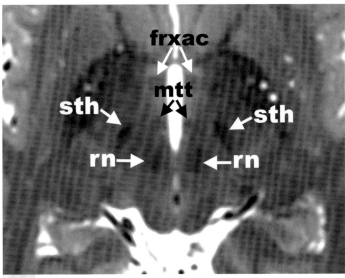

5.99

Coronal Plane

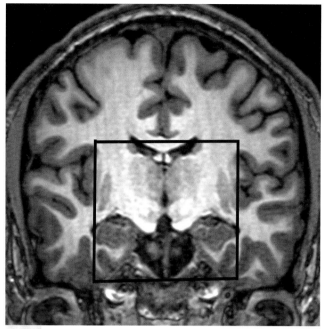

5.100

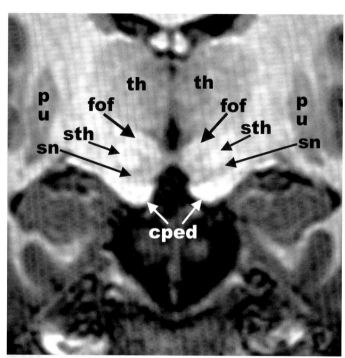

5.101

FIGURES 5.100–5.101

KEY

cped	cerebral peduncle
fof	fields of Forelc
pu	putamen
sn	substantia nigra
sth	subthalamic nucleus
th	thalamus

Axial Plane

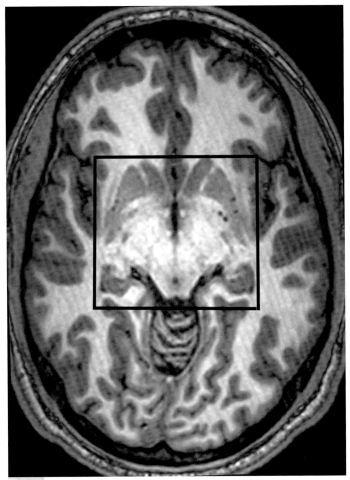

5.102

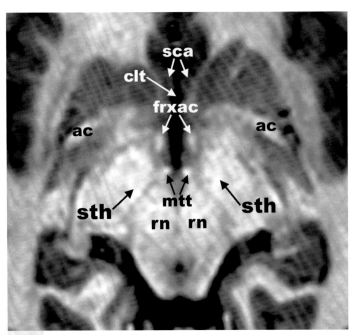

5.103

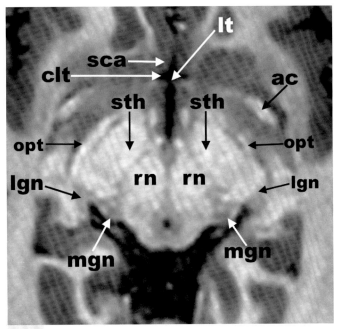

5.104

KEY	
ac	anterior commissure
clt	cistern of lamina terminalis
frxac	ascending columns of fornix
lgn	lateral geniculate nucleus
lt	lamina terminalis
mgn	medial geniculate nucleus
mtt	mammilothalamic tract
opt	optic tract
rn	red nucleus
sca	subcallosal area
sth	subthalamic nucleus

FIGURES 5.102–5.104

Sagittal Plane

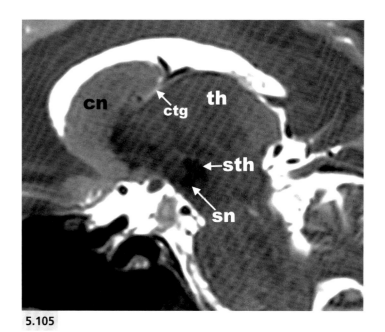

5.105

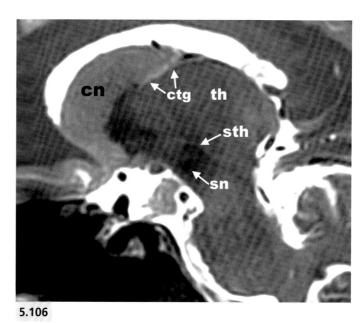

5.106

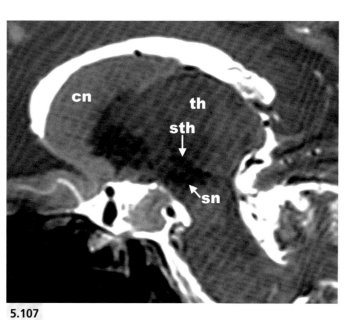

5.107

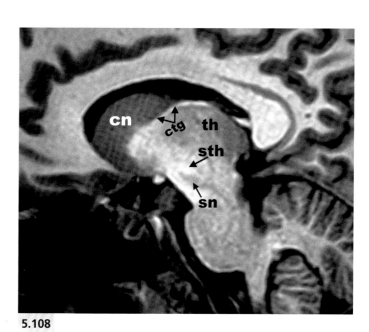

5.108

FIGURES 5.105–5.108

KEY

cn	caudate nucleus
ctg	caudo-thalamic groove (notch)
sn	substantia nigra
sth	subthalamic nucleus
th	thalamus

■ SUBCALLOSAL REGION (FIGURES 5.109–5.113)

Sagittal Plane

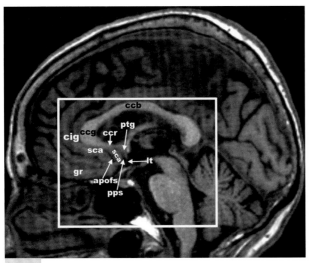

5.109

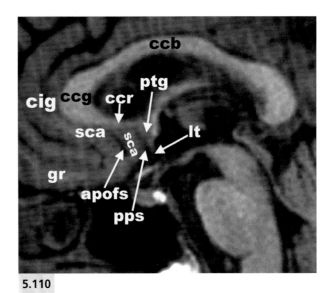

5.110

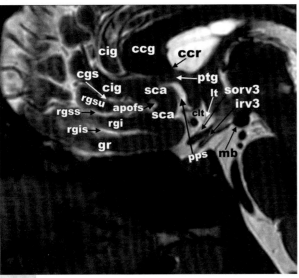

5.111

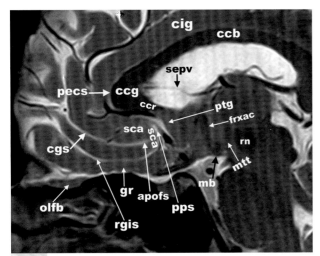

5.113

5.112

KEY

apofs	anterior parolfactory sulcus	mtt	mammilothalamic tract
aqs	aqueduct of Sylvius	olfb	olfactory bulb (cn1)
ccb	body of corpus callosum	pc	posterior commissure
ccg	genu of corpus callosum	pecs	pericallosal cistern (sulcus)
ccr	rostrum of corpus callosum	pitg	pituitary gland
cgs	cingulate sulcus	pps	posterior parolfactory sulcus
cig	cingulate gyrus	ptg	paraterminal gyrus
clt	cistern of lamina terminalis	rgi	inferior rostral gyrus
		rgis	inferior rostral sulcus
frxac	ascending columns of fornix	rgss	superior rostral sulcus
		rgsu	superior rostral gyrus
frxb	body of fornix	rn	red nucleus
gr	gyrus rectus	sca	subcallosal area
icv	internal cerebral vein	sepv	septal vein
irv3	infindibular recess of third ventricle	sorv3	supra-optic recess of third ventricle
lt	lamina terminalis	tct	tectum
mb	mammillary body		

FIGURES 5.109–5.113 Sagittal T1 (5.109, 5.110), and T2W (2 different subjects, 5.111 and 5.112, 5.113) images demonstrating normal anatomy of the subcallosal area.

(*continued*)

■ INTERNAL AUDITORY CANALS (IAC) (FIGURES 5.114a–i)

Axial Plane

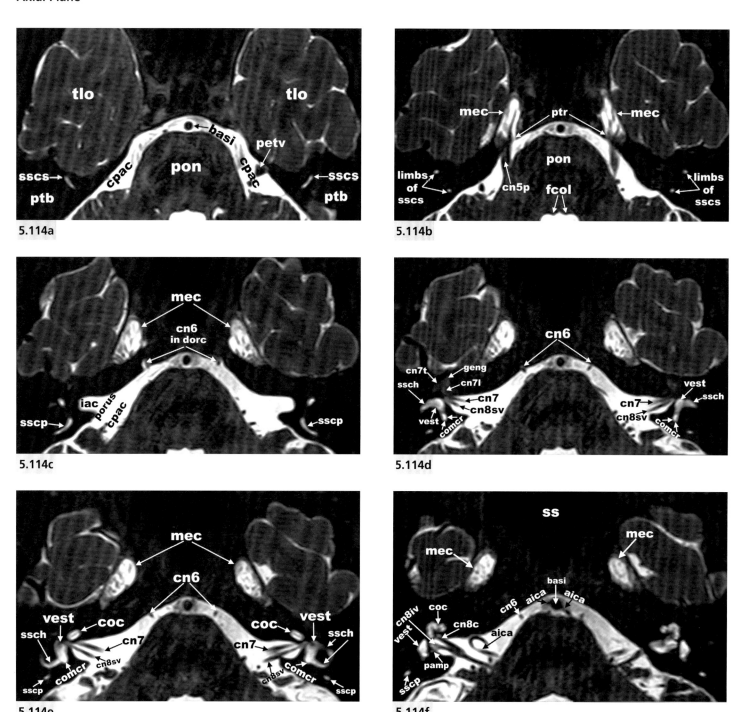

FIGURES 5.114a–g Normal heavily T2W axial images targeted to the region of the cerebellopontine angle cistern and IACs from superior to inferior.

KEY

aica	anterior inferior cerebellar artery	**coc**	cochlea	**porus**	porus acousticus
basi	basilar artery	**comcr**	common crus	**ptb**	petrous temporal bone
cn5p	pre-ganglionic segment trigeminal nerve	**cpac**	cerebellopontine angle cistern	**ptr**	porus trigeminus
		dorc	Dorello's canal	**ss**	sphenoid sinus
cn6	abducens nerve	**fcol**	facial colliculus	**ssch**	horizontal semicircular canal
cn7	facial nerve	**geng**	geniculate ganglion	**sscp**	posterior semicircular canal
cn7l	labyrinthine segment facial nerve	**iac**	internal auditory canal	**sscs**	superior semicircular canal
cn7t	tympanic segment of facial nerve	**mec**	Meckel's cave	**tlo**	temporal lobe
cn8c	cochlear nerve	**pamp**	posterior ampullary nerve	**vest**	vestibule
cn8iv	inferior division of vestibular nerve	**petv**	petrosal vein		
cn8sv	superior division of vestibular nerve	**pon**	pons		

(continued)

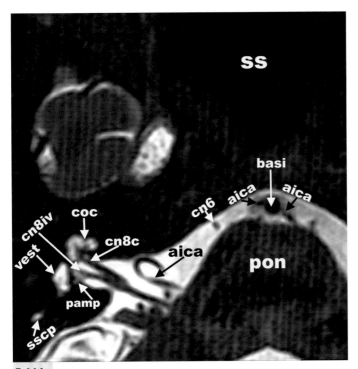

KEY

aica	anterior inferior cerebellar artery
basi	basilar artery
cn6	abducens nerve
cn8c	cochlear nerve
cn8iv	inferior division of vestibular nerve
coc	cochlea
pamp	posterior ampullary nerve
pon	pons
ss	sphenoid sinus
sscp	posterior semicircular canal
sscs	superior semicircular canal
vest	vestibule

FIGURE 5.114g

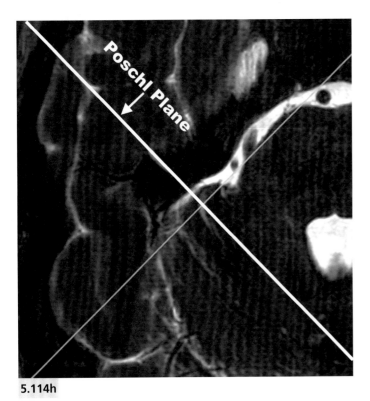

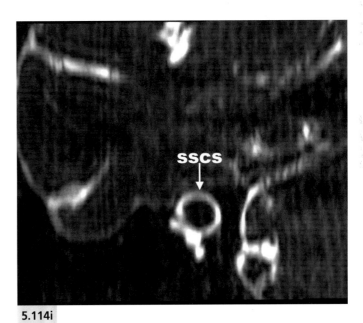

FIGURES 5.114h,i   Axial T2W image with orientation reference line along Poschl's plane (thick white arrow in 5.114h) and the normal T2W reformat (5.114i) along Poschl's plane showing a normal superior semicircular canal.

■ VIRCHOW–ROBIN SPACES (FIGURES 5.115–5.117)

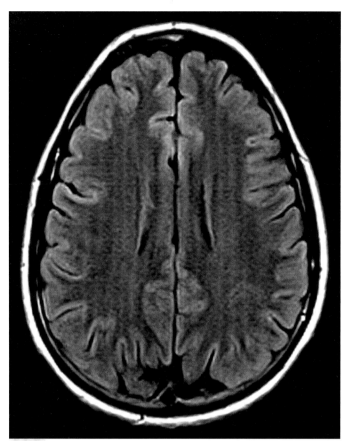

5.115

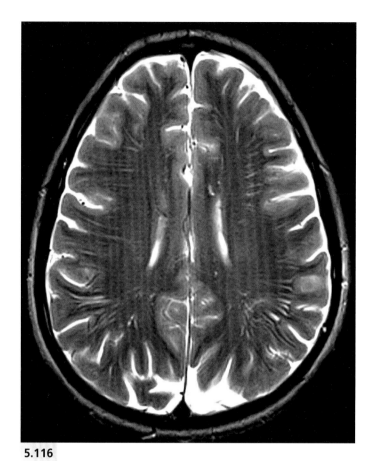

5.116

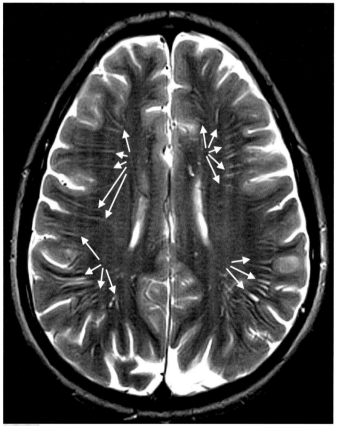

5.117

FIGURES 5.115–5.117 Normal axial T2 FLAIR (fluid attenuated inversion recovery) image (5.115) and axial T2W fast spin echo (FSE) images (5.116, 5.117) demonstrate the typical appearance of Virchow–Robin spaces (arrows in 5.117).

The Cranial Nerves

6

*T*he first section of this chapter consists of cadaver dissections with the brain removed from the cranial vault with preservation of the cisternal segments of the CN (cranial nerves) and their relationships to the dural surfaces and skull base foramina. These images provide a different perspective and allow one to integrate the imaging appearance to that of a human prosection. The images to follow will demonstrate the CN in a multiplanar format, some of which are not done on routine clinical exams but were obtained specifically for this atlas to illustrate the nerves to best advantage. These additional views could be used to tailor specific MR protocols if appropriate for the clinical question to be answered.

The illustrations provided by Dr. Moore in Chapter 2 beautifully illustrate the CN from their nuclear origins to their exit through their respective foramina. Those illustrations, along with the cadaver specimens and the imaging of the CN to follow should truly enhance your knowledge of this anatomy through this multimodality approach.

CADAVER DISSECTIONS REVEALING THE CRANIAL NERVES (CN) (FIGURES 6.1–6.4)

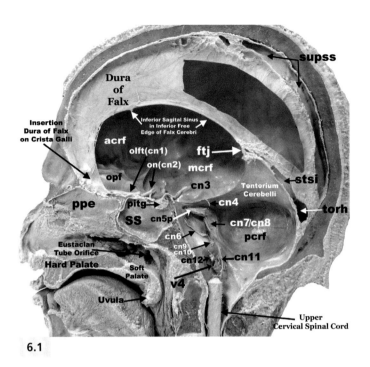

6.1

KEY

acrf	anterior cranial fossa
bas	basion
cl	clivus
cn3	oculomotor nerve
cn4	trochlear nerve
cn5p	pre-ganglionic segment trigeminal nerve
cn6	abducens nerve
cn7	facial nerve
cn8	vestibulocochlear nerve
cn9	glossopharyngeal nerve
cn10	vagus nerve
cn11	accessory nerve
cn12	hypoglossal nerve
eop	external occipital protuberance (inion)
ftj	falco-tentorial junction
mcrf	middle cranial fossa
olft (cn1)	olfactory tract
on (cn2)	optic nerve
opf	orbital plate of frontal bone
opis	opisthion
pcrf	posterior cranial fossa
pitg	pituitary gland
ppe	perpendicular plate of ethmoid
ss	sphenoid sinus
stsi	straight sinus
supss	superior sagittal sinus
torh	torcular herophili (confluence of sinuses)
v4	v4 intracranial/intradural segment vertebral artery

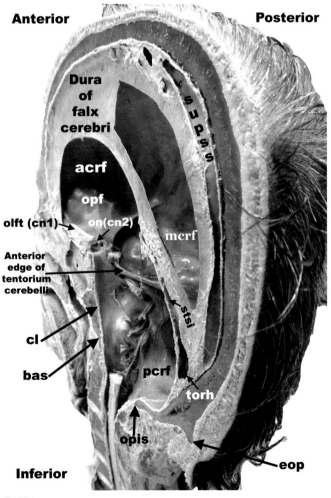

6.2

FIGURES 6.1–6.4 Lateral (6.1), steep lateral oblique (6.2) and magnified lateral (6.3, 6.4) photographs of a cadaveric specimen of the head sectioned through the mid sagittal plane.

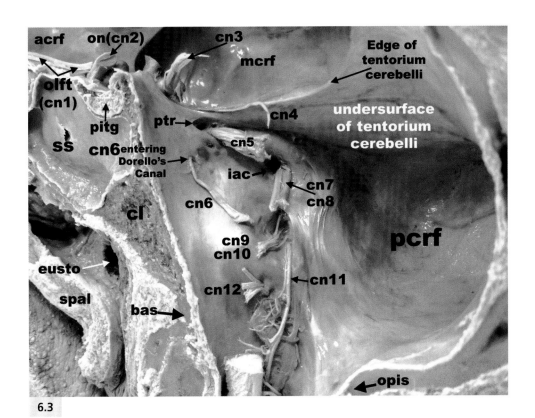

6.3

FIGURES 6.2–6.3

KEY

acrf	anterior cranial fossa
bas	basion
cl	clivus
cn3	oculomotor nerve
cn4	trochlear nerve
cn5	trigeminal nerve
cn6	abducens nerve
cn7	facial nerve
cn8	vestibulocochlear nerve
cn9	glossopharyngeal nerve
cn10	vagus nerve
cn11	accessory nerve
cn12	hypoglossal nerve
ds	dorsum sellae
eusto	eustachian tube orifice
iac	internal auditory canal
jugf	jugular foramen
mcrf	middle cranial fossa
olft (cn1)	olfactory tract
on (cn2)	optic nerve
opis	opisthion
pcrf	posterior cranial fossa
pitg	pituitary gland
ptr	porus trigeminus
spal	soft palate
ss	sphenoid sinus
tentc	tentorium cerebelli

6.4

CN IN CAVERNOUS SINUS (FIGURES 6.5–6.7)

Coronal Plane

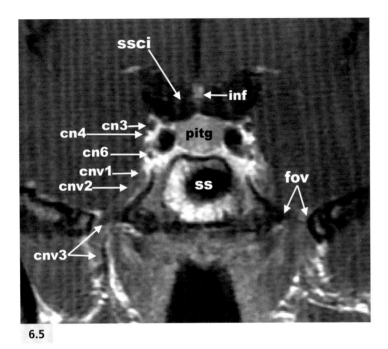

6.5

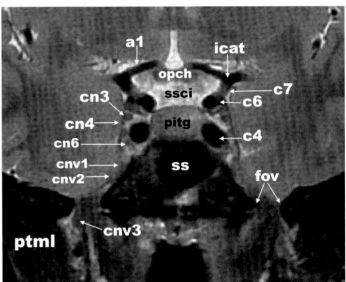

6.6

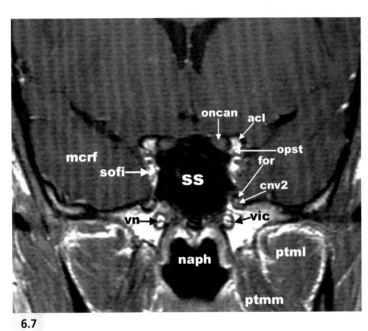

6.7

FIGURES 6.5–6.7 Figure 6.5 (contrast enhanced coronal T1W image) and figure 6.6 (coronal T2W image) are small field of view images targeted to the sella/parasellar region demonstrating normal anatomy. Figure 6.7 is a contrast enhanced coronal T1W image just anterior to the cavernous sinus in the region of the superior orbital fissures.

KEY

a1	a1 (precommunicating segment aca)
acl	anterior clinoid process
aca	anterior cerebral artery
c4	c4 (cavernous segment of ica)
c6	c6 (ophthalmic segment of ica)
c7	c7 (communicating segment of ica)
cn3	oculomotor nerve
cn4	trochlear nerve
cn6	abducens nerve
cnv1	ophthalmic branch (v1) of trigeminal nerve
cnv2	maxillary branch (v2) of trigeminal nerve
cnv3	mandibular division (v3) of trigeminal nerve
for	foramen rotundem
fov	foramen ovale
ica	internal carotid artery
icat	ica terminus/bifurcation
inf	infundibulum
mcrf	middle cranial fossa
naph	nasopharynx
oncan	canalicular segment of optic nerve
opch	optic chiasm
opst	optic strut
pitg	pituitary gland
ptml	lateral pterygoid muscle
ptmm	medial pterygoid muscle
sofi	superior orbital fissure
ss	sphenoid sinus
ssci	suprasellar cistern
vic	vidian canal
vn	vidian nerve

CRANIAL NERVES I–XII

■ CN I (1)—OLFACTORY NERVE (FIGURES 6.8a–c)

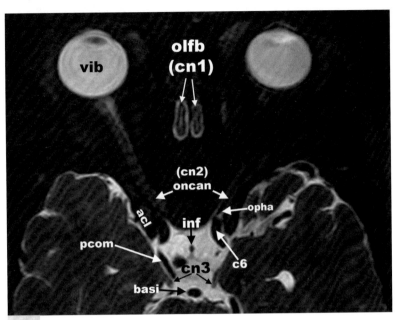

6.8a

FIGURES 6.8a–c Figures 6.8a,b and c are heavily T2W axial (6.8a), coronal (6.8b) and sagittal oblique (6.8c) views which demonstrate a normal appearance of the olfactory bulbs and tract.

KEY

acl	anterior clinoid process
basi	basilar artery
c6	c6 (ophthalmic segment of ica)
cn3	oculomotor nerve
gr	gyrus rectus
ica	internal carotid artery
inf	infundibulum
mog	medial orbital gyrus
olfb (cn1)	olfactory bulb
olfs	olfactory sulcus
olft (cn1)	olfactory tract
on (cn2)	optic nerve
oncan	canalicular segment of optic nerve
opha	ophthalmic artery
pcom	posterior communicating artery
pitg	pituitary gland
ponbp	basis pontis of pons
pont	tegmentum of pons
potms	pontomedullary sulcus
prpc	prepontine cistern
vib	vitreous body (chamber) of eye

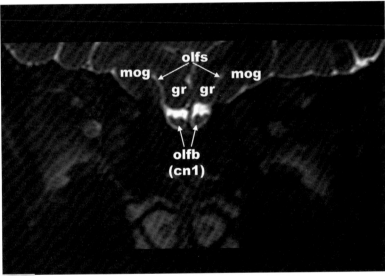

6.8b

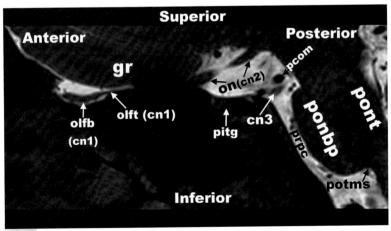

6.8c

■ CN II (2)—OPTIC NERVE (FIGURES 6.9a–j)

CN II (2)—Axial Plane

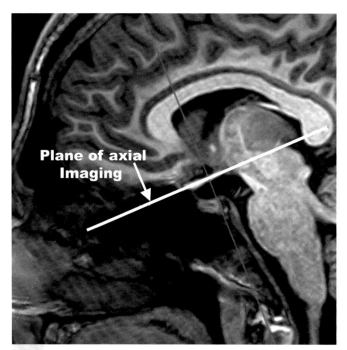

6.9a

FIGURE 6.9a A sagittal T1W orientation reference image indicating the axial plane of imaging.

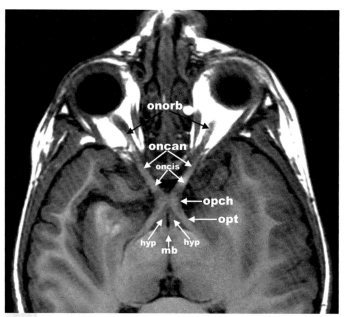

6.9b

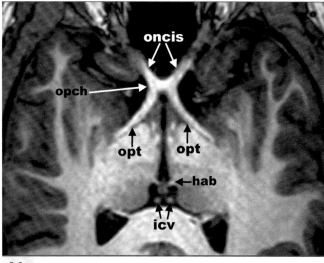

6.9c

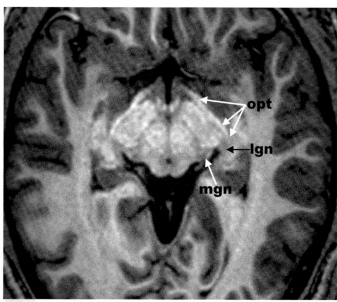

6.9d

FIGURES 6.9b–h Normal axial T1W (6.9b–6.9e) and T2W (6.9f–6.9h) images of the optic nerves, chiasm, tract and lateral geniculate nuclei.

KEY

hab	habenular trigone
hyp	hypothalamus
icv	internal cerebral vein
lgn	lateral geniculate nucleus
mb	mammillary body
mgn	medial geniculate nucleus
oncan	canalicular segment of optic nerve
oncis	cisternal (pre-chiasmatic) segment optic nerve
onorb	orbital segment optic nerve
opch	optic chiasm
opt	optic tract

(*continued*)

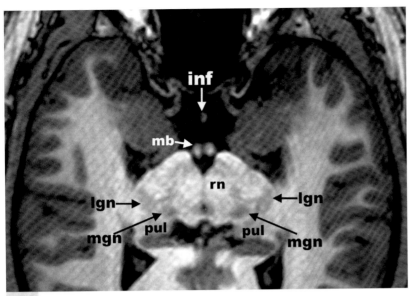

6.9e

FIGURES 6.9e–6.9g

KEY

achg	anterior chamber of eye
acl	anterior clinoid process
c6	c6 (ophthalmic segment of ica)
ica	internal carotid artery
inf	infundibulum
larm	lateral rectus muscle
lengl	lens of globe
lgn	lateral geniculate nucleus
m1	m1 (horizontal segment mca)
mb	mammillary body
mca	middle cerebral artery
merm	medial rectus muscle
mgn	medial geniculate nucleus
oncan	canalicular segment of optic nerve
oncis	cisternal (pre-chiasmatic) segment optic nerve
onorb	orbital segment optic nerve
opch	optic chiasm
opha	ophthalmic artery
opt	optic tract
pul	pulvinar is part of lateral thalamic nuclear group
rn	red nucleus
sn	substantia nigra
ss	sphenoid sinus
v3v	third ventricle
vib	vitreous body (chamber) of eye

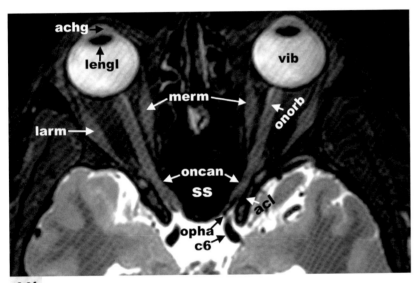

6.9f

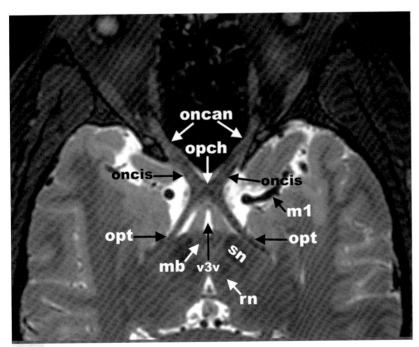

6.9g

(continued)

FIGURE 6.9h

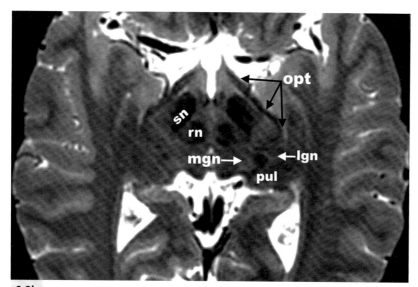

6.9h

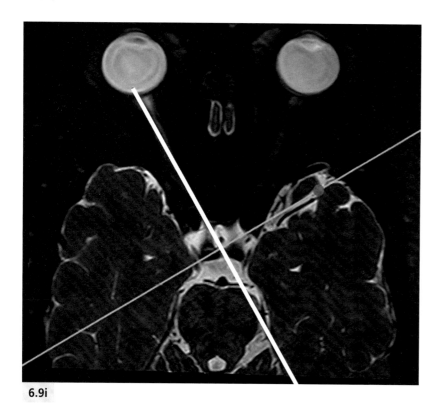

6.9i

FIGURES 6.9i,j 6.9j demonstrates a normal T2W sagittal oblique image (prescribed from the axial reference image—Figure 6.9i) demonstrating the entire optic nerve from the globe to the optic chiasm.

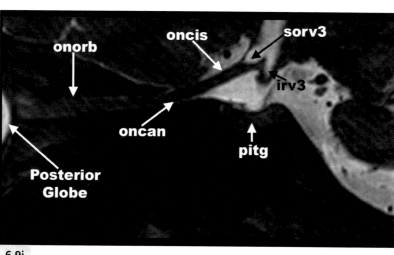

6.9j

■ CN III (3)—OCULOMOTOR NERVE (FIGURES 6.10a–i)

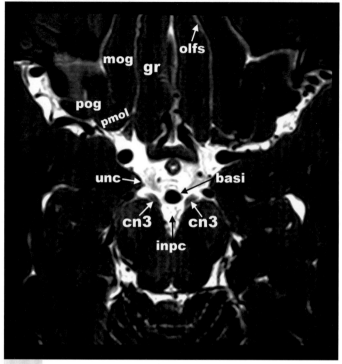

6.10a

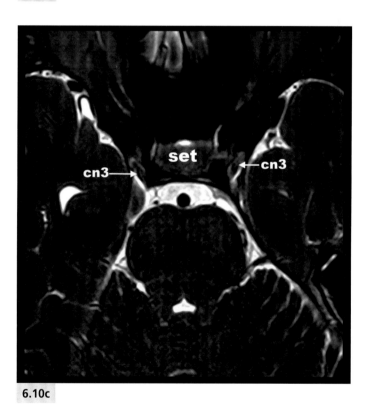

6.10b

FIGURES 6.10a–i   Normal heavily T2 weighted axial (6.10a–6.10d), coronal (6.10e–6.10h) and sagittal (6.10i) images demonstrating the oculomotor nerves from the brainstem to the cavernous sinus.

6.10c

KEY	
acl	anterior clinoid process
basi	basilar artery
c6	c6 (ophthalmic segment of ica)
cn3	oculomotor nerve
ds	dorsum sellae
gr	gyrus rectus
ica	internal carotid artery
inf	infundibulum
inpc	interpeduncular cistern
mog	medial orbital gyrus
olfs	olfactory sulcus
oncan	canalicular segment of optic nerve
opha	ophthalmic artery
pcom	posterior communicating artery
pmol	posteromedial orbital lobule
pog	posterior orbital gyrus
set	sella turcica
unc	uncus

(continued)

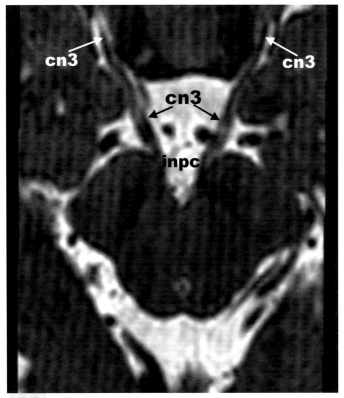

6.10d

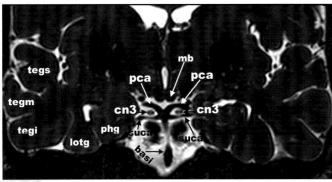

6.10f

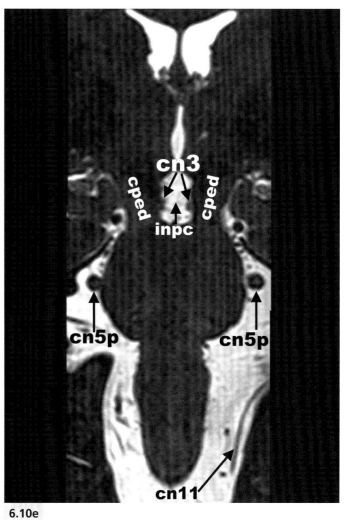

6.10e

FIGURES 6.10d–f

KEY

basi	basilar artery
cn11	accessory nerve
cn3	oculomotor nerve
cn5p	pre-ganglionic segment trigeminal nerve
cped	cerebral peduncle
inpc	interpeduncular cistern
lotg	lateral occipital temporal gyrus (lotg)/fusiform gyrus
mb	mammillary body
pca	posterior cerebral artery
phg	parahippocampal gyrus
suca	superior cerebellar artery
tegi	inferior temporal gyrus
tegm	middle temporal gyrus
tegs	superior temporal gyrus

(continued)

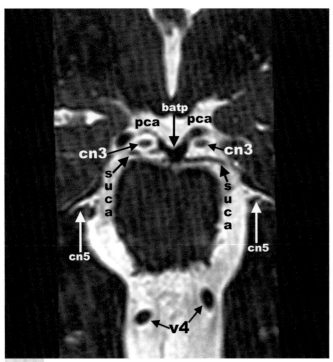

6.10g

FIGURES 6.10g–i

KEY

batp	basilar artery tip
c4	c4 (cavernous segment of ica)
cavs	cavernous sinus
cn3	oculomotor nerve
cn5	trigeminal nerve entering Meckel's cave
csf	cerebrospinal fluid
ds	dorsum sellae
ica	internal carotid artery
inf	infundibulum
inpc	interpeduncular cistern
mdb	midbrain
opch	optic chiasm
pca	posterior cerebral artery
pitg	pituitary gland
ponbp	basis pontis of pons
pont	tegmentum of pons
prpc	prepontine cistern
sorv3	supra-optic recess of third ventricle
ss	sphenoid sinus
ssci	suprasellar cistern
suca	superior cerebellar artery
unc	uncus
v4	v4 intracranial/intradural segment vertebral artery

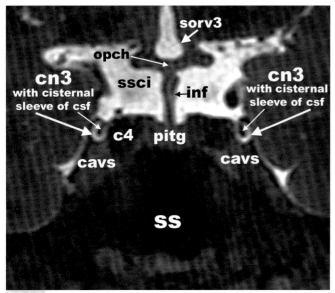

6.10h

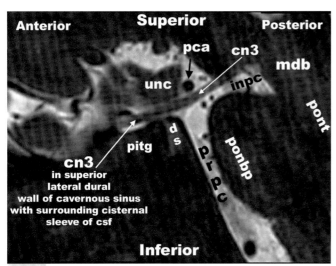

6.10i

■ CN IV (4)—TROCHLEAR NERVE (FIGURES 6.11a–c)

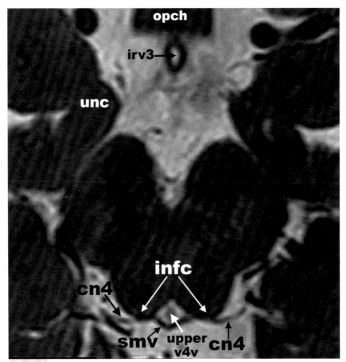

6.11a

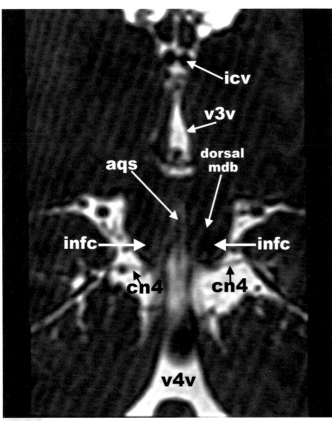

6.11c

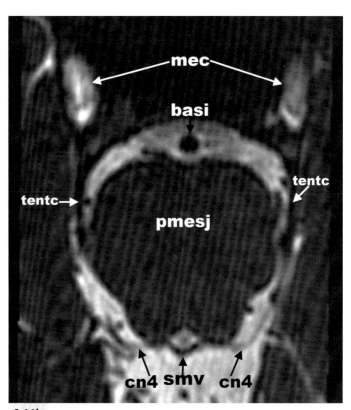

6.11b

FIGURES 6.11a–c Normal magnified T2 axial (6.11a,b) and coronal (6.11c) images demonstrate CN IV emerging from the dorsal midbrain just caudal/inferior to the inferior colliculi.

KEY

aqs	aqueduct of Sylvius
basi	basilar artery
cn4	trochlear nerve
icv	internal cerebral vein
infc	inferior colliculus
irv3	infindibular recess of third ventricle
mdb	midbrain
mec	Meckel's cave
opch	optic chiasm
pmesj	ponto-mesencephalic junction
smv	superior/anterior medullary velum
tentc	tentorium cerebelli
unc	uncus
v3v	third ventricle
v4v	fourth ventricle

■ **CN V (5)—TRIGEMINAL NERVE (FIGURES 6.12a–z)**

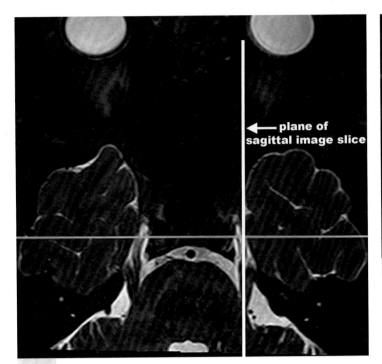

6.12a

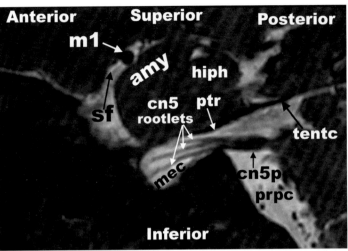

6.12b

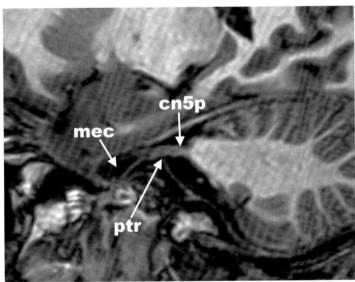

6.12c

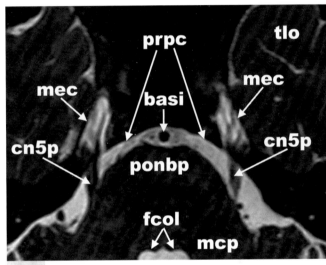

6.12d

FIGURES 6.12a–k Normal sagittal T2W (6.12a,b), and T1W (6.12c) images, normal axial T2W (6.12d) and T1W (6.12e–g), and normal coronal T1W (6.12h–k) images of the trigeminal nerve from its brainstem exit to Meckel's cave.

KEY

amy	amygdala
basi	basilar artery
cn5	trigeminal nerve
cn5p	pre-ganglionic segment trigeminal nerve
fcol	facial colliculus
hiph	hippocampal head
m1	m1 (horizontal segment mca)
mca	middle cerebral artery
mcp	middle cerebellar peduncle (brachium pontis)
mec	Meckel's cave
ponbp	basis pontis of pons
prpc	prepontine cistern
ptr	porus trigeminus
sf	Sylvian fissure (lateral sulcus)
tentc	tentorium cerebelli
tlo	temporal lobe

(continued)

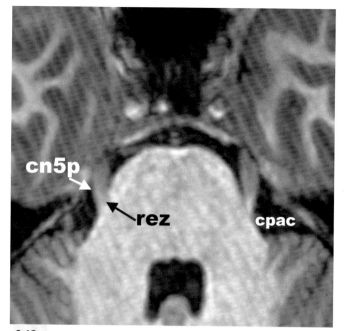

6.12e

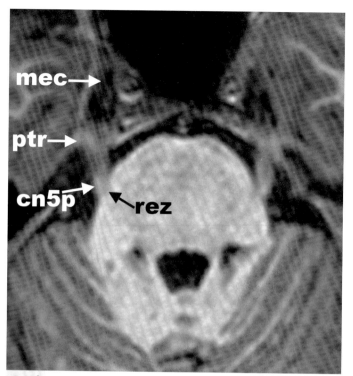

6.12f

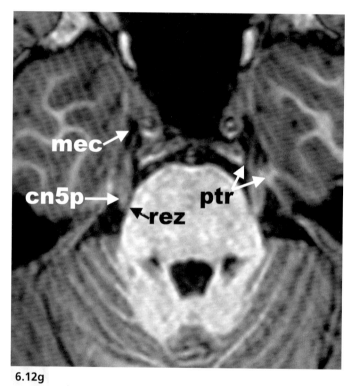

6.12g

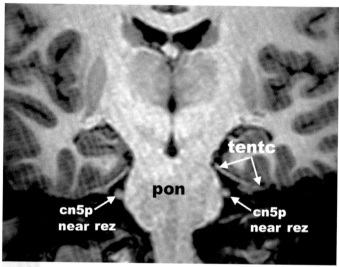

6.12h

FIGURES 6.12e–i

KEY

cn5p	pre-ganglionic segment trigeminal nerve
cpac	cerebellopontine angle cistern
mec	Meckel's cave
pon	pons
ptr	porus trigeminus
rez	root entry zone of trigeminal nerve
tentc	tentorium cerebelli

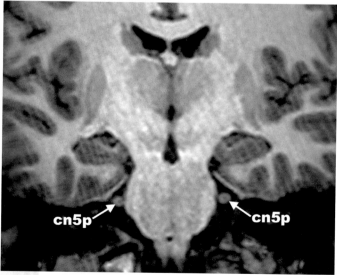

6.12i

(*continued*)

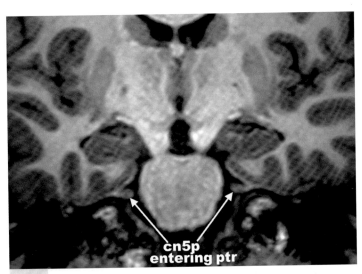

6.12j

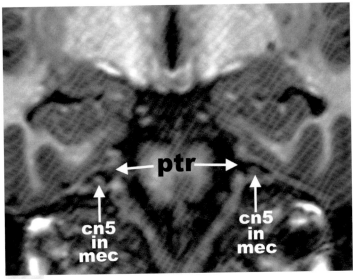

6.12k

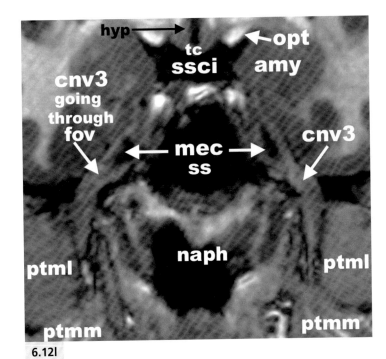

6.12l

FIGURES 6.12j,k

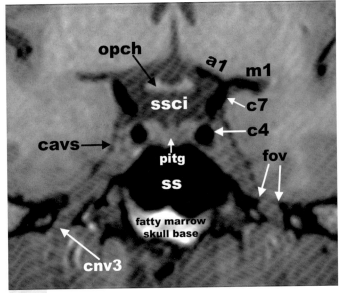

6.12m

FIGURES 6.12l–m   l,m are normal magnified T1W coronal images of the cavernous sinus region and proximal third divisions (V3) of CN V.

(continued)

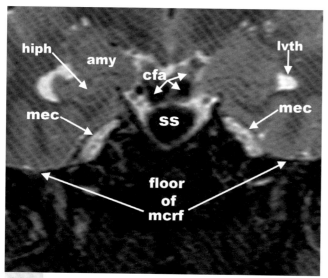

6.12n

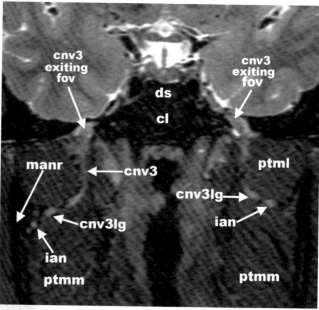

6.12o

FIGURES 6.12n–p   Normal fat suppressed coronal T2W images from Meckel's cave (6.12n) to distal sensory branches (inferior alveolar and lingual nerves) of the third division of CN V (6.12o,p). Note the dural ectasia of the root sheath surrounding V2 in the right (on viewer's left) foramen rotundem in figure 6.12p.

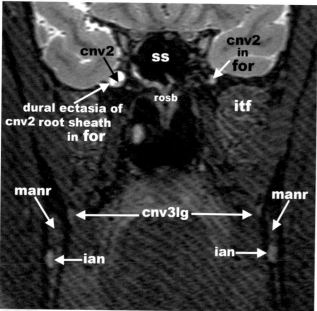

6.12p

KEY

amy	amygdala
cfa	csf flow artifact
cl	clivus
cnv2	maxillary branch (v2) of trigeminal nerve
cnv3	mandibular division (v3) of trigeminal nerve
cnv3lg	lingual nerve (branch of v3)
ds	dorsum sellae
for	foramen rotundem
fov	foramen ovale
hiph	hippocampal head
ian	inferior alveolar nerve (branch of cnv3)
itf	infratemporal fossa
lvth	temporal horn of lateral ventricle
manr	ramus of mandible
mcrf	middle cranial fossa
mec	Meckel's cave
ptml	lateral pterygoid muscle
ptmm	medial pterygoid muscle
rosb	rostrum of sphenoid bone
ss	sphenoid sinus

(continued)

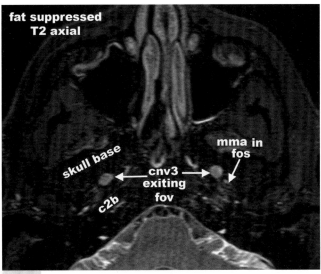

6.12q

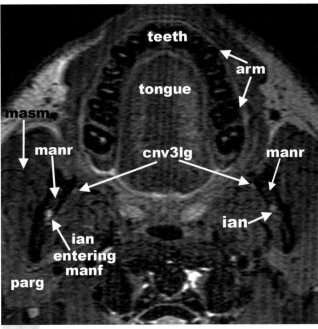

6.12s

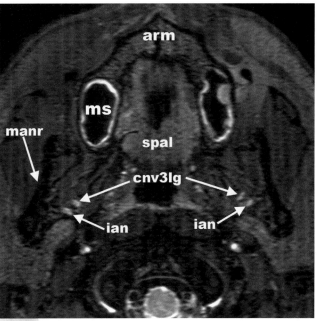

6.12r

FIGURES 6.12q–s   Normal fat suppressed axial T2W images of V3 from the skull base into the masticator spaces where the inferior alveolar and lingual nerves are seen.

KEY

arm	alveolar ridge of maxilla
c2b	c2b (horizontal petrous segment of ica)
cnv3	mandibular division (v3) of trigeminal nerve
cnv3lg	lingual nerve (branch of v3)
fos	foramen spinosum
fov	foramen ovale
ian	inferior alveolar nerve (branch of cnv3)
ica	internal carotid artery
manf	mandibular foramen
manr	ramus of mandible
masm	masseter muscle
mma	middle meningeal artery
ms	maxillary sinus
parg	parotid gland
spal	soft palate

(continued)

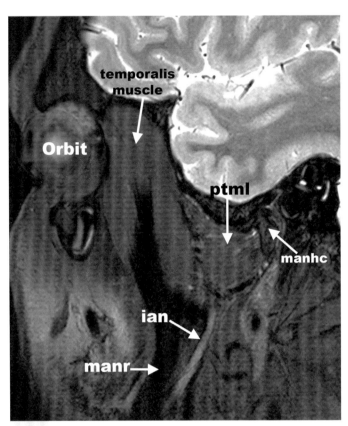

6.12t

FIGURE 6.12t Normal fat suppressed T2 sagittal image of the inferior alveolar nerve entering the mandibular ramus via the mandibular foramen.

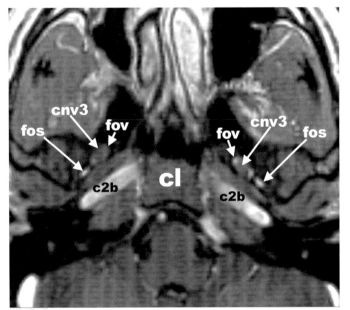

6.12u

FIGURE 6.12u Normal fat suppressed axial contrast enhanced T1W image through the skull base. Normal perineural arteriovenous plexus (enhancement) surrounds V3 in foramen ovale.

KEY

c2b	c2b (horizontal petrous segment of ica)
cl	clivus
cnv3	mandibular division (v3) of trigeminal nerve
fos	foramen spinosum
fov	foramen ovale
ian	inferior alveolar nerve (branch of cnv3)
ica	internal carotid artery
manhc	head of mandibular condyle
manr	ramus of mandible
ptml	lateral pterygoid muscle

(*continued*)

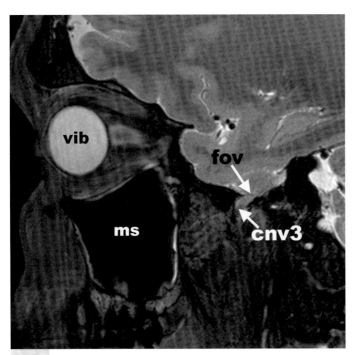

6.12v

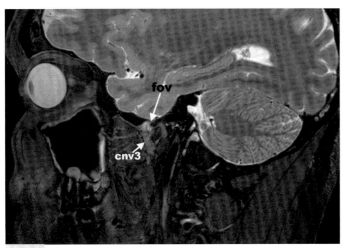

6.12w

FIGURES 6.12v–w   Normal sagittal fat suppressed T2W images showing V3 exiting the middle cranial fossa through foramen ovale and entering the masticator space.

KEY

cnv3	mandibular division (v3) of trigeminal nerve
fov	foramen ovale
ms	maxillary sinus
vib	vitreous body (chamber) of eye

(continued)

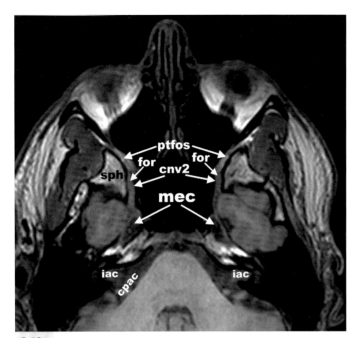

6.12x

FIGURES 6.12x–y Normal T1W axial (6.12x) and sagittal (6.12y) images demonstrate the second division (V2/maxillary) of CN V extending from Meckel's cave into the pterygopalatine fossa.

KEY

cn5p	pre-ganglionic segment trigeminal nerve
cnv2	maxillary branch (v2) of trigeminal nerve
cpac	cerebellopontine angle cistern
for	foramen rotundem
iac	internal auditory canal
mec	Meckel's cave
ptfos	pterygopalatine fossa
sph	sphenoid bone

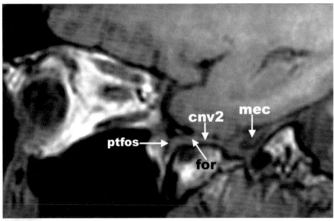

6.12y

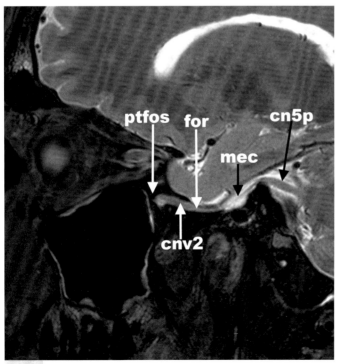

6.12z

FIGURE 6.12z Normal fat suppressed sagittal T2W image showing the trigeminal nerve from the cerebellopontine angle cistern through the course of V2 within the pterygopalatine fossa.

■ CN VI (6)—ABDUCENS NERVE (FIGURES 6.13a–6.14c); CN VII (7)—FACIAL NERVE (FIGURES 6.13a,b, 6.14a–n, AND 6.14p); AND CN VIII (8)—VESTIBULOCOCHLEAR NERVE (FIGURES 6.13a,b, 6.14a–c, AND 6.14g–p)

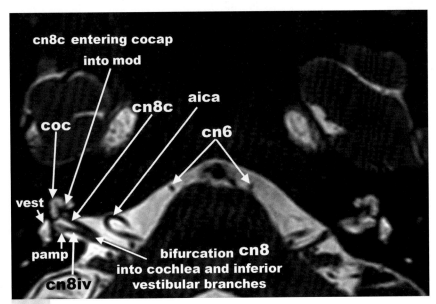

6.13a

FIGURES 6.13a–e Normal T2W axial (6.13a,b,c) and sagittal oblique (6.13d,e) images demonstrate the course of CN VI from the brainstem through Dorello's canal.

KEY

aica	anterior inferior cerebellar artery
basi	basilar artery
cn6	abducens nerve
cn7	facial nerve
cn8	vestibulocochlear nerve
cn8c	cochlear nerve
cn8iv	inferior division of vestibular nerve
cn8sv	superior division of vestibular nerve
coc	cochlea
cocap	cochlear aperture
cpac	cerebellopontine angle cistern
dorc	Dorello's canal
fcol	facial colliculus
iac	internal auditory canal
mec	Meckel's cave
mod	modiolus
pamp	posterior ampullary nerve
pon	pons
prpc	prepontine cistern
porus	porus acousticus
ssch	horizontal semicircular canal
sscp	posterior semicircular canal
tlo	temporal lobe
vest	vestibule

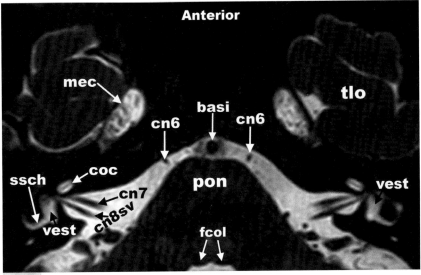

6.13b

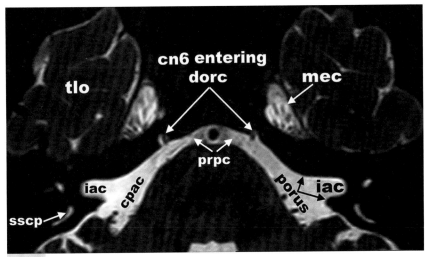

6.13c

(continued)

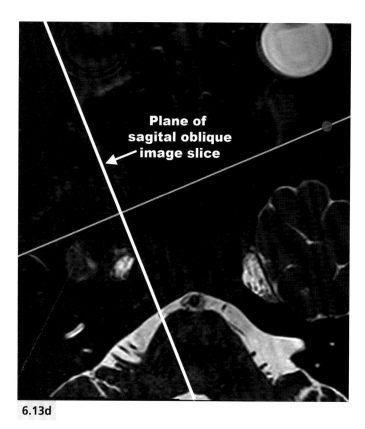

6.13d

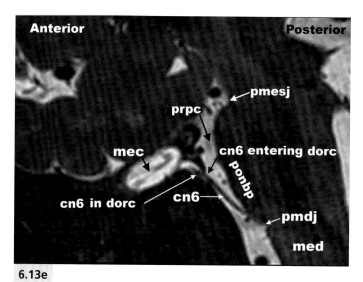

6.13e

FIGURES 6.13d,e

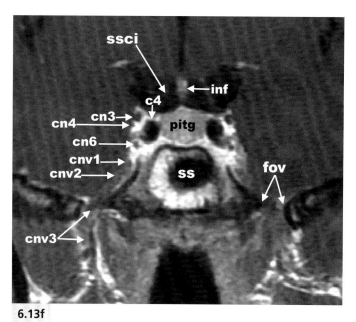

6.13f

KEY

c4	c4 (cavernous segment of ica)
cn3	oculomotor nerve
cn4	trochlear nerve
cn6	abducens nerve
cnv1	ophthalmic branch (v1) of trigeminal nerve
cnv2	maxillary branch (v2) of trigeminal nerve
cnv3	mandibular division (v3) of trigeminal nerve
dorc	Dorello's canal
fov	foramen ovale
ica	internal carotid artery
inf	infundibulum
mec	Meckel's cave
med	medulla
pitg	pituitary gland
pmdj	ponto-medullary junction
pmesj	ponto-mesencephalic junction
ponbp	basis pontis of pons
prpc	prepontine cistern
ss	sphenoid sinus
ssci	suprasellar cistern

FIGURE 6.13f Contrast enhanced coronal T1W image through the cavernous sinus shows the close proximity of CN VI to the cavernous internal carotid artery (c4).

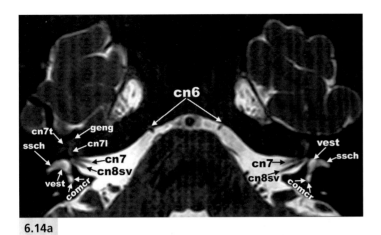

6.14a

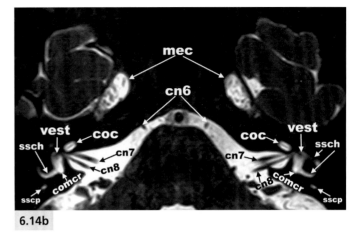

6.14b

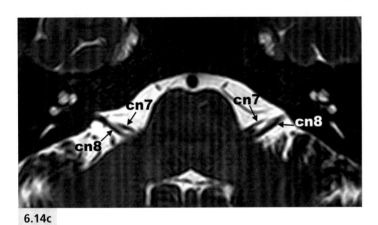

6.14c

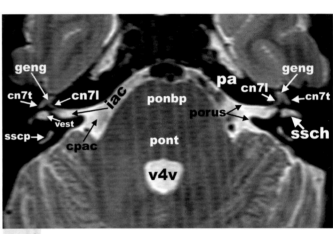

6.14d

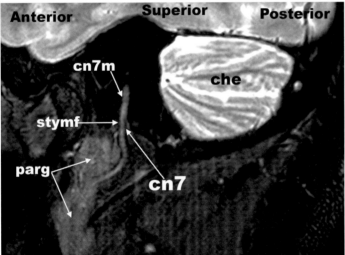

6.14e

KEY

che	cerebellar hemisphere
cn6	abducens nerve
cn7	facial nerve
cn7l	labyrinthine segment facial nerve
cn7m	mastoid segment facial nerve
cn7t	tympanic segment of facial nerve
cn8	vestibulocochlear nerve
cn8sv	superior division of vestibular nerve
coc	cochlea
comcr	common crus
cpac	cerebellopontine angle cistern
geng	geniculate ganglion
iac	internal auditory canal
mec	Meckel's cave
pa	petrous apex
parg	parotid gland
ponbp	basis pontis of pons
pont	tegmentum of pons
porus	porus acousticus
ssch	horizontal semicircular canal
sscp	posterior semicircular canal
stymf	stylomastoid foramen
v4v	fourth ventricle
vest	vestibule

FIGURES 6.14a–e Axial images of 2 different subjects (6.14a,b,c subject 1 and 6.14d subject 2) show the normal appearance of CN VII and VIII. Different T2W MR pulse sequences were used for subject 1 and 2 accounting for the different appearances. Figure 6.14e, a sagittal T2W image of subject 2 shows the mastoid segment of CN VII exiting the stylomastoid foramen and entering the parotid gland.

(continued)

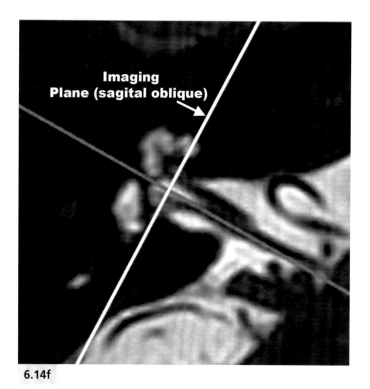

6.14f

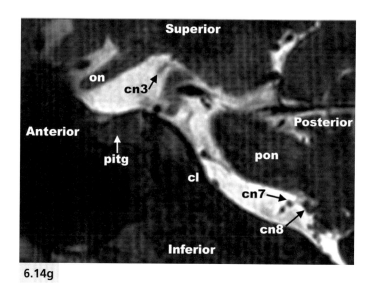

6.14g

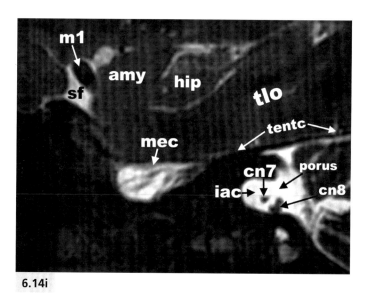

6.14h

6.14i

FIGURES 6.14f–l Normal sagittal oblique T2W images from medial to lateral (6.14f–l) clearly demonstrate CN VII and VIII extending from the brainstem to the inner ear structures.

KEY

amy	amygdala	**mec**	Meckel's cave
cl	clivus	**on**	optic nerve
cn3	oculomotor nerve	**pitg**	pituitary gland
cn5	trigeminal nerve	**pon**	pons
cn7	facial nerve	**porus**	porus acousticus
cn8	vestibulocochlear nerve	**ptr**	porus trigeminus
hip	hippocampus	**sf**	Sylvian fissure (lateral sulcus)
iac	internal auditory canal	**tentc**	tentorium cerebelli
m1	m1 (horizontal segment mca)	**tlo**	temporal lobe
mca	middle cerebral artery		

(continued)

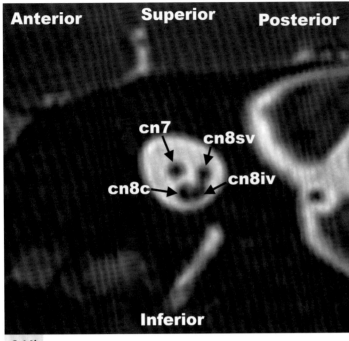

6.14j

Anterior   Superior   Posterior

Inferior

6.14k

FIGURES 6.14j–l

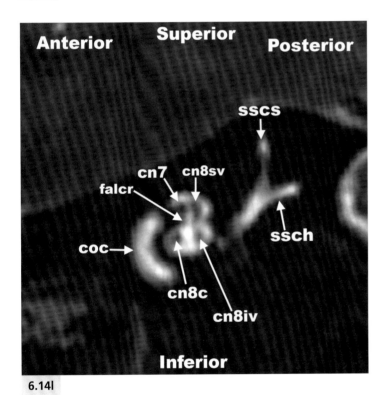

6.14l

KEY

cn7	facial nerve
cn8c	cochlear nerve
cn8iv	inferior division of vestibular nerve
cn8sv	superior division of vestibular nerve
coc	cochlea
falcr	falciform crest
ssch	horizontal semicircular canal
sscs	superior semicircular canal

(*continued*)

■ CN IX (9)—GLOSSOPHARYNGEAL NERVE (FIGURES 6.14o, 6.15, AND 6.18)

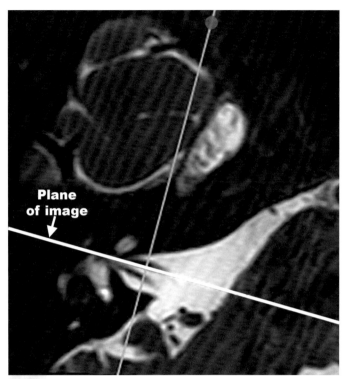

6.14m

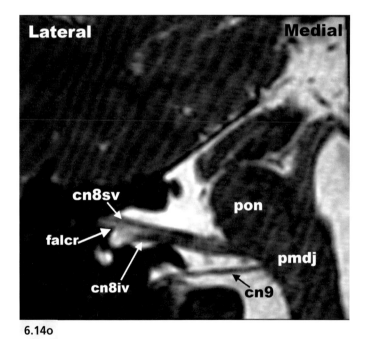

6.14o

6.14n

FIGURES 6.14m–o Coronal oblique T2W image (6.14o) demonstrating CN IX from the pontomedullary junction to the jugular foramen. Also note CN VII and VIII (6.14m,n,o).

KEY

cn7	facial nerve
cn8c	cochlear nerve
cn8iv	inferior division of vestibular nerve
cn8sv	superior division of vestibular nerve
cn9	glossopharyngeal nerve
cocap	cochlear aperture
falcr	falciform crest
pmdj	ponto-medullary junction
pon	pons

(continued)

CN VII (7) Facial to CN XI (11) Accessory Nerves

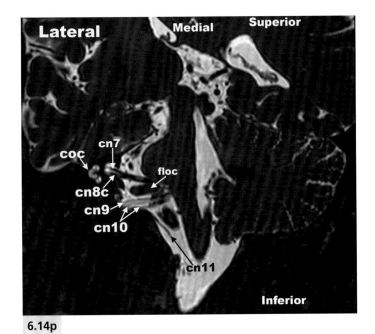

6.14p

FIGURE 6.14p Complex angle coronal oblique T2W image demonstrating CN VII through CN X1.

■ CN X (10)—VAGUS NERVE (FIGURES 6.16 AND 6.18)

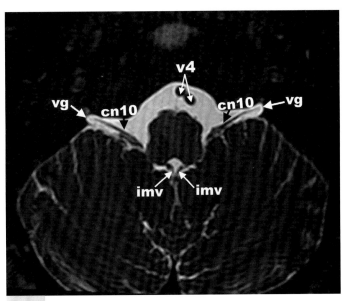

6.16

CN IX (9) Glossopharyngeal Nerve

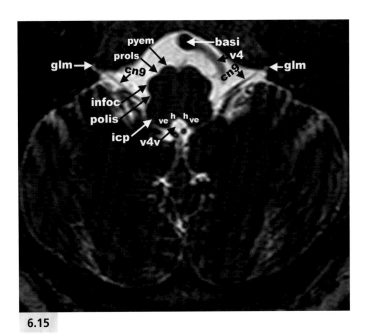

6.15

FIGURES 6.15–16 Normal axial T2W images of CN IX (6.15) and X (6.16).

KEY	
basi	basilar artery
cn10	vagus nerve
cn11	accessory nerve
cn7	facial nerve
cn8c	cochlear nerve
cn9	glossopharyngeal nerve
coc	cochlea
floc	flocculus
glm	glossopharyngeal meatus
h	hypoglossal eminence
icp	inferior cerebellar peduncle (restiform body)
imv	inferior/posterior medullary velum
infoc	inferior olivary complex
polis	post-olivary sulcus
prols	pre-olivary sulcus
pyem	pyramidal eminence
v4	v4 intracranial/intradural segment vertebral artery
v4v	fourth ventricle
ve	vagal eminence
vg	vagal meatus

■ CN XI (11)—ACCESSORY NERVE (FIGURES 6.17, 6.18, AND 6.19a)

CN VII (7) Facial to CN XI (11) Accessory Nerves

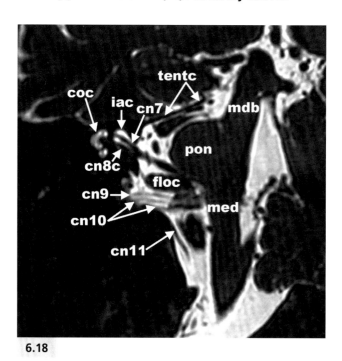

6.17

6.18

FIGURES 6.17–18 Normal T2W axial and complex coronal oblique images demonstrating CN XI (6.17) and CN VII-XI (6.18).

■ CN XII (12)—HYPOGLOSSAL NERVE (FIGURES 6.19a,b)

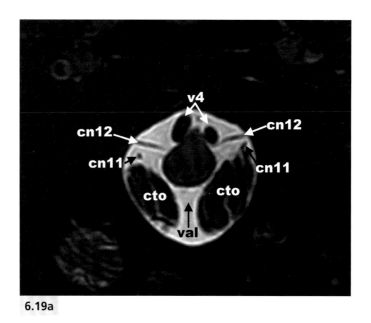

6.19a

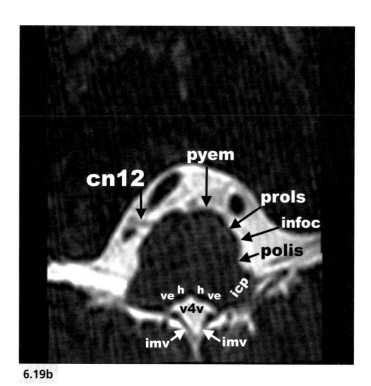

6.19b

FIGURES 6.19a,b Normal T2W axial images of CN XII arising from the pre-olivary sulcus and extending towards the hypoglossal canals. Note the accessory nerves (CN XI) on image 6.19a.

KEY					
cn10	vagus nerve	h	hypoglossal eminence	pon	pons
cn11	accessory nerve	iac	internal auditory canal	prols	pre-olivary sulcus
cn12	hypoglossal nerve	icp	inferior cerebellar peduncle (restiform	pyem	pyramidal eminence
cn7	facial nerve		body)	tentc	tentorium cerebelli
cn8c	cochlear nerve	imv	inferior/posterior medullary velum	v4v	fourth ventricle
cn9	glossopharyngeal nerve	infoc	inferior olivary complex	v4	v4 intracranial/intradural segment
coc	cochlea	mdb	midbrain		vertebral artery
cto	cerebellar tonsil	med	medulla	val	vallecula space
floc	flocculus	polis	post-olivary sulcus	ve	vagal eminence

Advanced MRI Techniques

7

INTRODUCTION TO ADVANCED MRI TECHNIQUES

An up-to-date atlas of the human brain would not be complete without the inclusion of some of the advanced MR techniques now available for clinical use. These techniques have made a significant impact in our abilities to not only diagnose certain disease processes but to have a positive impact in our ability to advise our neurological/neurosurgical colleagues.

Evaluation of brain lesions with spectroscopy can often help in differentiating neoplastic processes from non-neoplastic lesions, which can otherwise appear as non-specific space occupying lesions. The results of MR spectroscopy can also help us to predict the biologic behavior/aggressiveness of a known brain tumor. High-grade neoplasms often demonstrate marked increase in choline (Cho) concentrations relative to N-acetylaspartate (NAA) as well as increased lipid (Lip) and lactate (Lac). The complete absence of NAA within a brain tumor and the absence of abnormal metabolites in non-enhancing increased T2 signal surrounding a well-circumscribed enhancing mass are suggestive of a metastatic lesion from an extracranial site.

Tumors demonstrating diffusion restriction (though DWI—diffusion weighted imaging is not included in this atlas) tend to have high nuclear/cytoplasmic ratios indicating highly cellular, aggressive/malignant masses. This is often seen with primitive neuroectodermal tumors (PNET), high-grade gliomas (such as glioblastoma and anaplastic astrocytoma), and in lymphoma. Preoperative use of MR perfusion (not illustrated in this atlas but similar in principle as CT perfusion which is illustrated in Chapter 8) can often provide details allowing us to suggest high yield sites for biopsy (regions of increased CBV—cerebral blood volume).

fMRI and DTI with generation of color DTI maps and diffusion tractography can have significant impact on how a tumor is resected. fMRI allows us to localize language, motor function, and other regions of the brain involved with eloquent functions and determine the location of a cerebral lesion relative to these important functional regions. This crucial information allows the neurosurgeon to plan a safer resection or partial resection. DTI maps and tractography can help us determine whether a certain tract is destroyed or infiltrated with tumor or merely displaced by a mass. In the latter instance we can tell the neurosurgeon how the tract is displaced and where the tract is located relative to the mass, again providing information to the neurosurgeon, which may allow a safer resection.

SWI, another recently introduced advanced MR technique now provides MR pulse sequences which are highly sensitive to the presence of substances which distort the local magnetic field such as hemorrhage and calcification when other sequences are unable to produce a similar effect. This can be helpful in the diagnosis of traumatic brain injury, cerebral amyloidosis and in patients with certain vascular malformations.

SWI (SUSCEPTIBILITY WEIGHTED IMAGING): INTRODUCTION

SWI is a valuable clinical MR sequence to image the brain. It is a flow-compensated, 3D, T2* weighted MR sequence with high spatial resolution which also uses phase and magnitude information to achieve tissue contrast by exploiting differences in magnetic susceptibility of various tissues. Susceptibility refers to the degree to which a certain material becomes magnetic when placed in a static magnetic field, such as an MRI scanner. Substances are classified as paramagnetic, diamagnetic or ferromagnetic. This indicates whether a specific substance increases the local magnetic field (paramagnetic), decreases the local magnetic field (diamagnetic), or concentrates and greatly increases the local magnetic field and retains magnetism after the external magnetic field is removed (ferromagnetic). The alteration of the local magnetic field by these substances results in magnetic field inhomogeneities, which decreases tissue signal as a result of dephasing of protons. This technique is particularly sensitive to the presence of deoxygenated blood, hemosiderin, ferritin and calcium. As a result, SWI images can be used to visualize the vascular system, particularly the venous system, intracranial hemorrhage of varying ages from acute to remote, calcifications and iron deposition. Clinical indications for SWI include evaluation of traumatic brain injury (diffuse axonal injury), stroke (infarction), neurodegenerative processes, multiple sclerosis, vascular malformations (including cavernous malformations, developmental venous anomalies and capillary telangietasias), dural sinus thrombosis, and the detection of intratumoral calcification and hemorrhage.

■ SWI IMAGES (FIGURES 7.1a–7.1h)

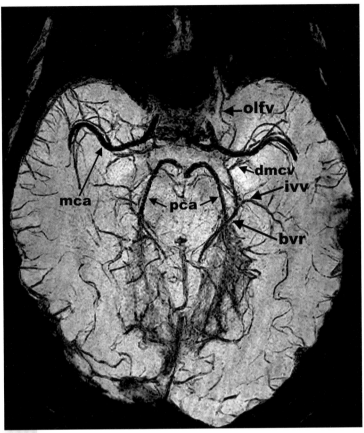

7.1a

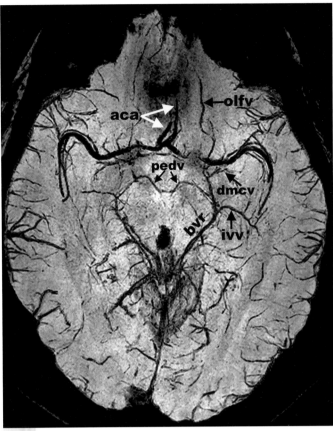

7.1b

FIGURES 7.1a–e   Normal SWI axial images of subject 1 beautifully demonstrating the venous anatomy. There is also visualization of the arterial system.

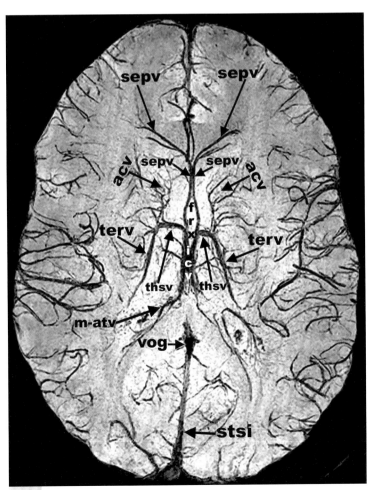

7.1c

KEY

aca	anterior cerebral artery
acv	anterior caudate vein
bvr	basal vein of Rosenthal
dmcv	deep middle cerebral vein
frx	fornix
icv	internal cerebral vein
ivv	inferior ventricular vein
m-atv	medial atrial vein
mca	middle cerebral artery
olfv	olfactory vein
pca	posterior cerebral artery
pedv	peduncular vein
sepv	septal vein
stsi	straight sinus
terv	terminal vein
thsv	thalamostriate vein
vog	vein of Galen

(continued)

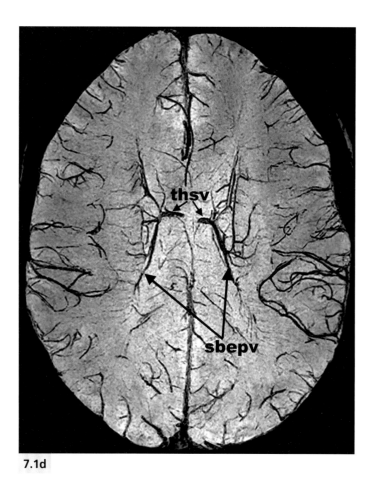

7.1d

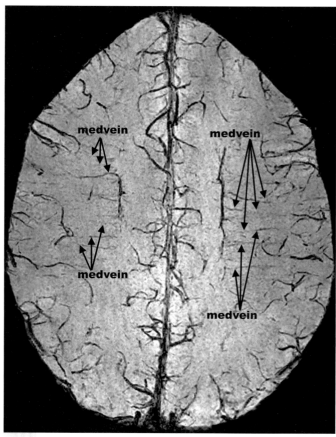

7.1e

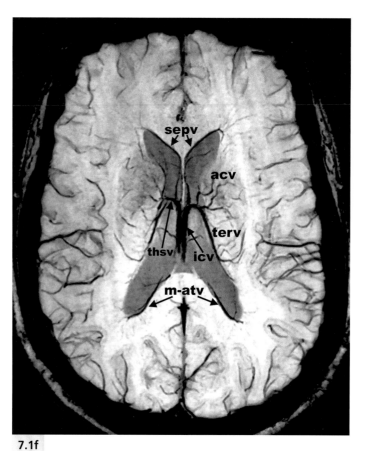

7.1f

KEY

acv	anterior caudate vein
icv	internal cerebral vein
m-atv	medial atrial vein
medvein	medullary vein(s)
sbepv	subependymal veins
sepv	septal vein
terv	terminal vein
thsv	thalamostriate vein

FIGURES 7.1f–h Normal SWI axial images in subject 2 were obtained on an MRI unit with lower magnetic field strength and using a different imaging protocol accounting for the different appearances of the images between subject 1 and 2. Asterisk in figure 7.1h indicates the vein of Galen

(continued)

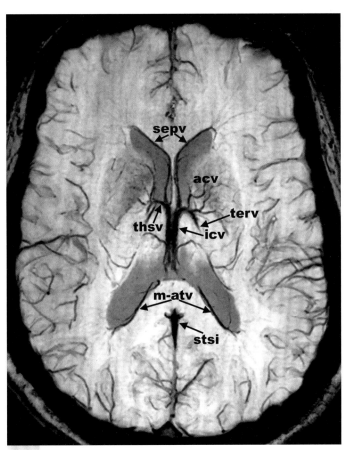

7.1g

FIGURES 7.1g,h

KEY

acv	anterior caudate vein
icv	internal cerebral vein
m-atv	medial atrial vein
sepv	septal vein
stsi	straight sinus
terv	terminal vein
thsv	thalamostriate vein
thv	thalamic vein(s)

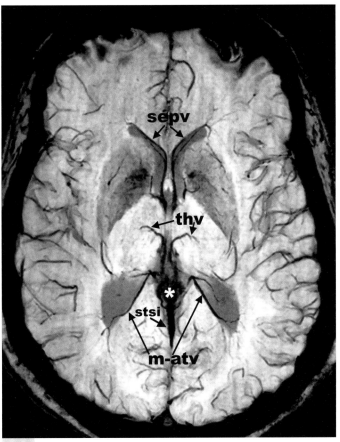

7.1h

fMRI (FUNCTIONAL MRI): INTRODUCTION

One of the advanced MRI techniques now in widespread use is fMRI. A wide variety of neurologic/neurosurgical disorders and psychiatric disorders now routinely use this technique in their armamentarium. One such indication is for the preoperative planning of brain tumor resection. It is imperative that the neurosurgeon be aware of where eloquent regions of the brain are located in relation to the tumor, which will be removed. "Eloquence" of brain tissue means that if direct injury to a certain region of the brain occurs this will result in a neurologic deficit. While we can reliably discuss the location of a brain mass in terms of its anatomic position, routine morphologic MR imaging does not provide details regarding the precise organization of brain function from individual to individual. The German anatomist Korbinian Brodmann described the general organization of higher cortical function as it relates to brain anatomy in maps published in 1909. We now know, however, that there is much variation to this general schema. Canadian neurosurgeon Wilder Penfield was another pioneer in his work on mapping the functional regions in the brain through electrical cortical stimulation.

fMRI provides a non-invasive way of investigating the functional organization of the brain. The MR technique most widely used to visualize brain function employs the *BOLD* effect to generate contrast, which stands for Blood Oxygen Level-Dependent contrast. This technique assumes that, during a functional task (of which there are many, such as finger tapping, word generation, or listening to stories), there is an increase in neuronal activation in the regions of the brain responsible for these tasks. We also know that the increased neuronal activity is accompanied by increased blood flow to the region of the brain where this neuronal activation is occurring. This phenomenon is referred to as neurovascular coupling. Increased blood flow will result in more oxygenated blood (oxyhemoglobin) in this region relative to the concentration of deoxygenated blood (deoxyhemoglobin), compared with unstimulated regions of the brain. This increase in oxyhemoglobin (which is diamagnetic) leads to a slight increase in the local MR signal. This occurs because there is less signal reduction due to decreased deoxyhemoglobin (which is paramagnetic). Deoxyhemoglobin acts to decrease MR signal by creating very small magnetic field gradients within and around blood vessels causing dephasing of stimulated protons and shortening the T2* relaxation. This increases the signal intensity detected by the MR scanner on T2*-weighted images at sites of brain activation. During an fMRI task, data is collected from a series of imaging volumes in rapid succession using a fast gradient echo sequence, such as echo-planar imaging which is highly sensitive to changes in T2*. Subsequent post-processing of the time-series of images visualizes the local increase and decrease of signal intensity in various locations in the brain. After the acquisition of an additional high-resolution anatomic MR image (typically a 3D volume T1 weighted image), this amplified increase in BOLD-based MR signal is mapped onto the anatomy of the brain, producing the fMRI images.

The following images are just but a few examples of how the fMRI data is presented for clinical use.

■ fMRI IMAGES (FIGURES 7.2a–7.9d)

a. Bilateral Finger Tapping

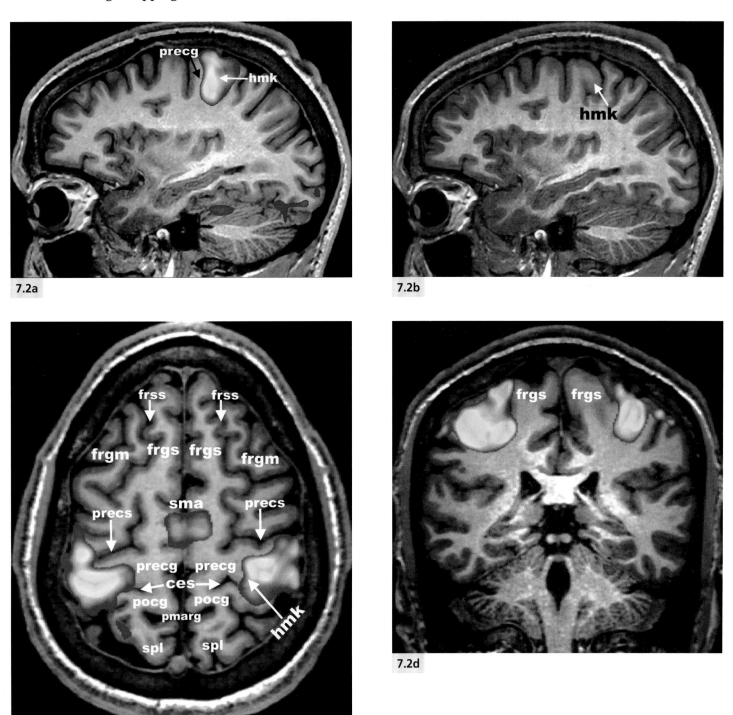

FIGURES 7.2a–d Sagittal (7.2a,b), axial (7.2c) and coronal (7.2d) images were generated from an fMRI study utilizing a bilateral finger-tapping paradigm. Areas of BOLD activation have been overlaid on a structural 3D volume T1 weighted sequence (7.2b). Normally expected brain activation is seen bilaterally in the hand motor knob (hmk) regions of the pre-central gyri (primary motor area), which straddles the central sulcus extending into the post-central gyri. BOLD activation in both supplementary motor regions (SMA) is seen. A small amount of BOLD activation is also seen in the superior cerebellum (normal finding).

KEY

ces	central sulcus	hmk	hand motor knob			precg	pre-central gyrus
frgm	middle frontal gyrus	pmarg	pars marginalis (ascending			precs	pre-central sulcus
frgs	superior frontal gyrus		ramus of cingulate sulcus)			sma	supplementary motor area
frss	superior frontal sulcus	pocg	post-central gyrus			spl	superior parietal lobule

b. Sensory Paradigm With Technologist Stroking Subjects Right Fingers With Abrasive Sponge

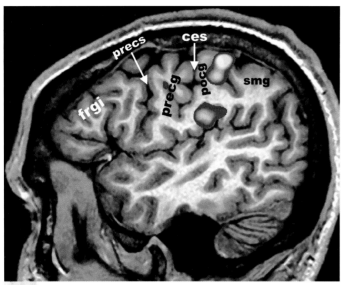

7.3a

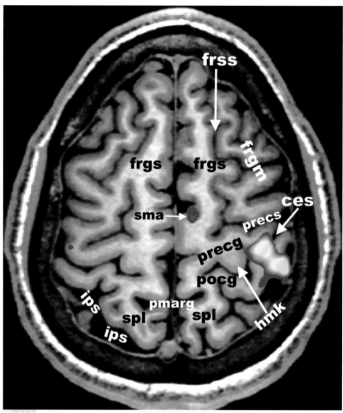

7.3b

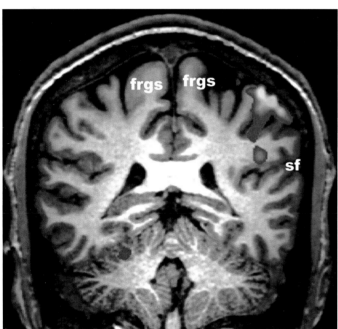

7.3c

FIGURES 7.3a–c Sagittal (7.3a), axial (7.3b) and coronal (7.3c) fMRI images show BOLD activation in the pre and post central gyri of the left cerebral hemisphere, minimal activation in the left SMA and along the superior right cerebellum. These areas of activation are normally expected.

KEY

ces	central sulcus	pocg	post-central gyrus
frgi	inferior frontal gyrus	precg	pre-central gyrus
frgm	middle frontal gyrus	precs	pre-central sulcus
frgs	superior frontal gyrus	sf	Sylvian fissure (lateral
frss	superior frontal sulcus		sulcus)
hmk	hand motor knob	sma	supplementary motor
ips	intraparietal sulcus		area
pmarg	pars marginalis	smg	supramarginal gyrus
	(ascending ramus of	spl	superior parietal lobule
	cingulate sulcus)		

c. **Bilateral Finger Tapping (Motor) and Right Finger Stroking (Sensory) Both Overlaid on the Same Structural T1 Images**

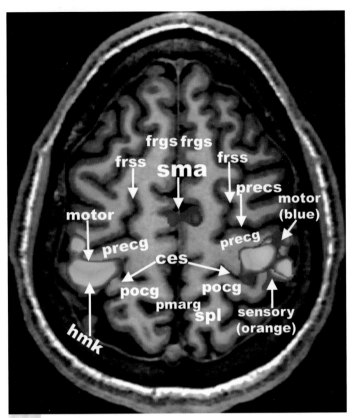

7.4a

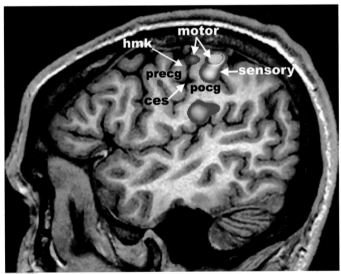

7.4c

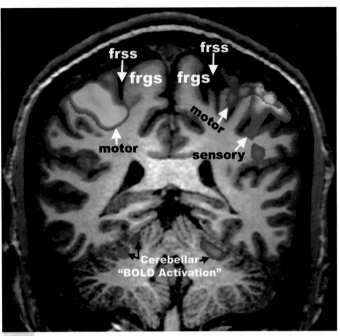

7.4b

FIGURES 7.4a–c Axial (7.4a), coronal (7.4b) and sagittal (7.4c). BOLD activation of both paradigms was previously described in Figures 7.2 and 7.3. Note the normal brain activation along both superior cerebellar hemispheres on the coronal image (figure 7.4b) during the bilateral motor task and only along the right superior cerebellum on the unilateral sensory task (right finger stroking).

KEY	
ces	central sulcus
frgs	superior frontal gyrus
frss	superior frontal sulcus
hmk	hand motor knob
pmarg	pars marginalis (ascending ramus of cingulate sulcus)
pocg	post-central gyrus
precg	pre-central gyrus
precs	pre-central sulcus
sma	supplementary motor area
spl	superior parietal lobule

d. Lip Smacking Task

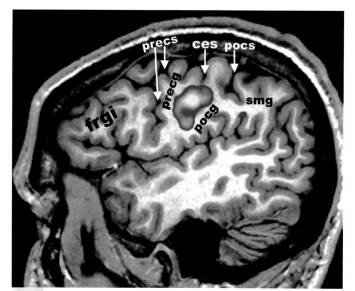

7.5a

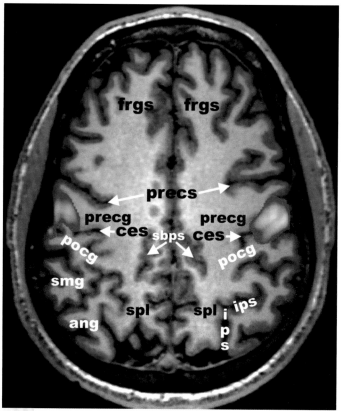

7.5b

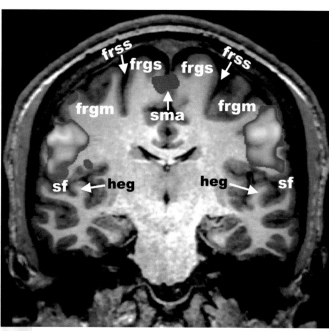

7.5c

FIGURES 7.5a–c Figures 7.5a-sagittal, 7.5b-axial and 7.5c-coronal images. This task is inherently bilateral in nature and involves having the patient smack their lips. It generates BOLD activation straddling the central sulcus, predominantly involving the posterior pre-central gyrus and some of the anterior post-central gyrus. Also present is brain activation of the supplementary motor area (sma) bilaterally. Note that the BOLD activation is located more inferiorly over the lateral convexity surfaces of the cerebral hemispheres compared with the finger-tapping task. This is consistent with our understanding of the motor homunculus.

KEY			
ang	angular gyrus	**pocs**	post-central sulcus
ces	central sulcus	**precg**	pre-central gyrus
frgi	inferior frontal gyrus	**precs**	pre-central sulcus
frgm	middle frontal gyrus	**sbps**	subparietal sulcus
frgs	superior frontal gyrus	**sf**	Sylvian fissure (lateral sulcus)
frss	superior frontal sulcus		
heg	Heschl's gyrus (transverse temporal gyrus)	**sma**	supplementary motor area
		smg	supramarginal gyrus
ips	intraparietal sulcus	**spl**	superior parietal lobule
pocg	post-central gyrus		

e.   **Toe/Foot Motor Task**

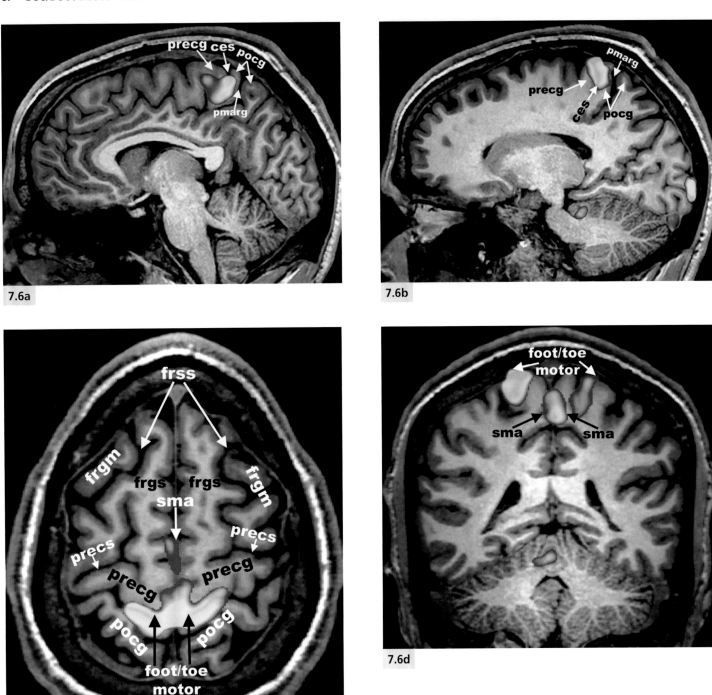

FIGURES 7.6a–d   Figures 7.6a,b-sagittal, 7.6c-axial and 7.6d-coronal images. These images demonstrate normal BOLD activation along the superior medial aspects of both cerebral hemispheres involving the pre and post central gyri, the motor SMA regions and minimally along the superior cerebellum. Note the more superior and medial position of brain activation compared with that generated from finger and lip motor paradigms. Again this is consistent with our understanding of the motor homunculus.

KEY

ces	central sulcus	frss	superior frontal sulcus	precg	pre-central gyrus
frgm	middle frontal gyrus	pmarg	pars marginalis (ascending ramus of cingulate sulcus)	precs	pre-central sulcus
frgs	superior frontal gyrus	pocg	post-central gyrus	sma	supplementary motor area

f. Passive Listening

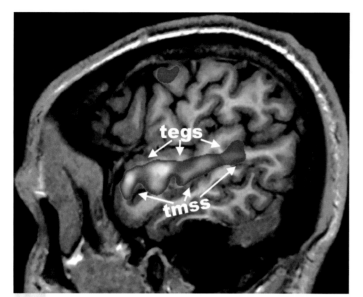

7.7a

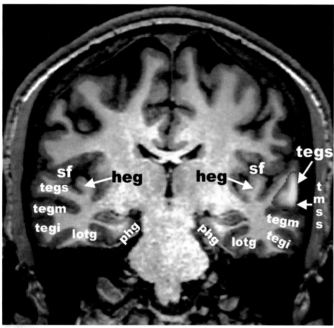

7.7c

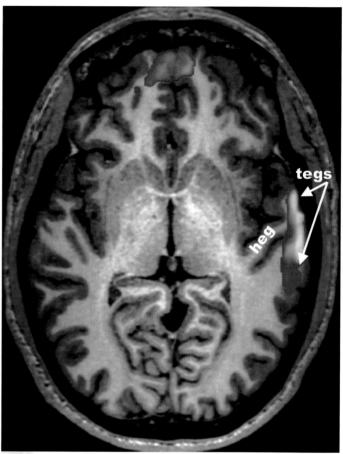

7.7b

FIGURES 7.7a–c   Figures 7.7a-sagittal left, 7.7b-axial and 7.7c-coronal images. These images demonstrate that this language task strongly localizes to the left cerebral hemisphere, predominantly along the left superior temporal gyrus, involving the auditory cortex and extending prominently along the superior temporal gyrus to the anterior left temporal lobe. The regions of activation more posteriorly in the left superior temporal gyrus is consistent with activation in Wernicke's region.

KEY

heg	Heschl's gyrus (transverse temporal gyrus)	sf	Sylvian fissure (lateral sulcus)
lotg	lateral occipital temporal gyrus (lotg)/fusiform gyrus	tegi	inferior temporal gyrus
		tegm	middle temporal gyrus
		tegs	superior temporal gyrus
phg	parahippocampal gyrus	tmss	superior temporal sulcus

g. Word Generation

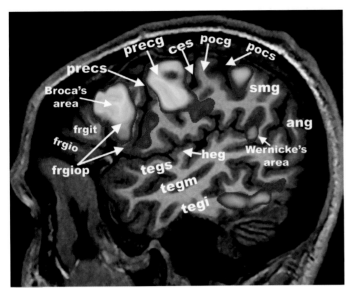

7.8a

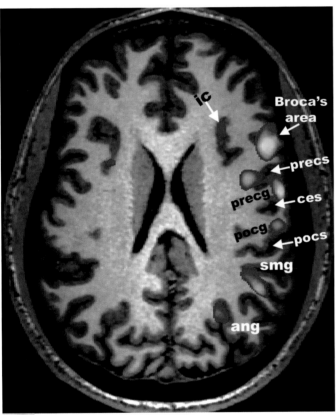

7.8c

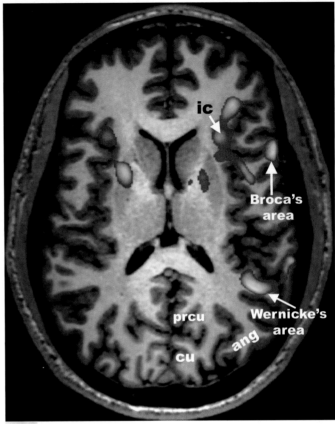

7.8b

FIGURES 7.8a–e Figures 7.8a-sagittal, 7.8b,c-axial, 7.8d,e-coronal. This language task strongly localizes to the left cerebral hemisphere. There is BOLD activation involving the left inferior frontal gyrus (pars opercularis and posterior pars triangularis) representing Broca's area. BOLD activation is also present in Wernicke's area more posteriorly in the region of the posterior left superior temporal gyrus and additional activation in the left parietal lobe. Also note brain activation along the anterior left insula.

KEY

ang	angular gyrus
ces	central sulcus
cu	cuneus
frgio	pars orbitalis of inferior frontal gyrus
frgiop	pars opercularis of inferior frontal gyrus
frgit	pars triangularis of inferior frontal gyrus
heg	Heschl's gyrus (transverse temporal gyrus)
ic	insular cortex
pocg	post-central gyrus
pocs	post-central sulcus
prcu	precuneus
precg	pre-central gyrus
precs	pre-central sulcus
smg	supramarginal gyrus
tegi	inferior temporal gyrus
tegm	middle temporal gyrus
tegs	superior temporal gyrus

(*continued*)

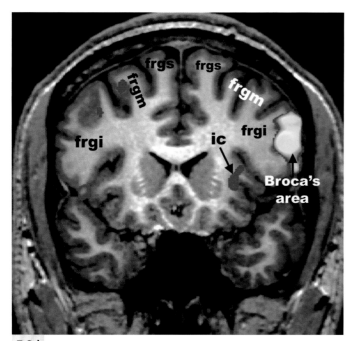

7.8d

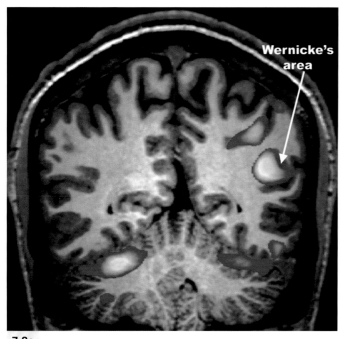

7.8e

FIGURES 7.8d,e

KEY

frgi	inferior frontal gyrus
frgm	middle frontal gyrus
frgs	superior frontal gyrus
ic	insular cortex

h. Visual Checkerboard

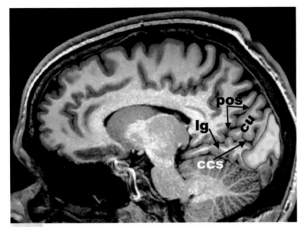

7.9a

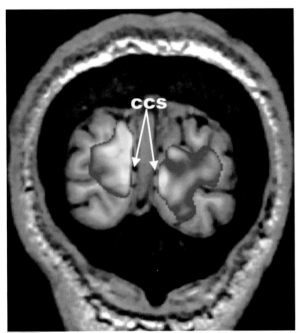

7.9b

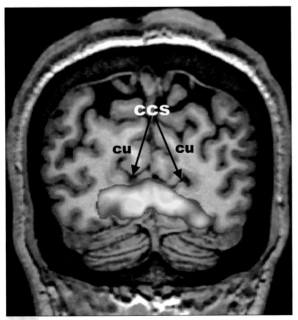

7.9c

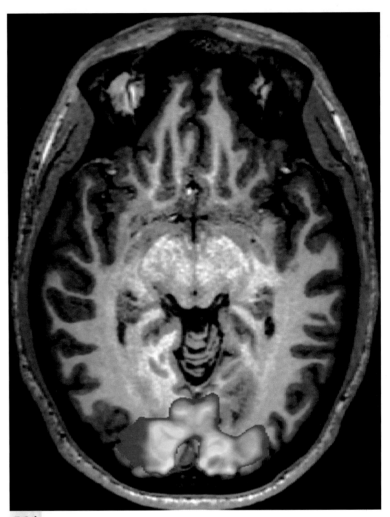

7.9d

FIGURES 7.9a–d Figures 7.9a-sagittal, 7.9b,c-coronal and 7.9d-axial images. Presentation of a checkerboard flashing at a frequency of 7 Hertz to the subject during the "task on" period shows strong bold activation in the region of the visual cortices and surrounding occipital lobes.

KEY

ccs	calcarine sulcus
cu	cuneus
lg	lingual gyrus (motg)
pos	parieto-occipital sulcus

DTI (DIFFUSION TENSOR IMAGING): INTRODUCTION

The white matter of the brain is comprised of multiple directionally-oriented bundles of axons comprising various white matter tracts. These bundles of fiber tracts are invisible to us on routine T1 and T2 weighted MRI images of the brain. An advanced imaging technique in MRI called DTI (Diffusion Tensor Imaging) now allows us to visualize these white matter tracts indirectly using a technique that looks at the diffusion of water protons within the substance of the brain. We know from the principle of Brownian movement that if a drop of ink were placed in a container of water the ink would diffuse equally in all directions. If, however, within the container of water, plates of impermeable material were placed in various directions, the droplet of ink would not diffuse equally in all directions but preferentially in the direction parallel to the plates of this impermeable material. Similarly we can infer the directionality and therefore the pathways of white matter tracts in the brain by looking at the ability of protons to diffuse in various directions. The structured arrangement of the white matter tracts facilitates movement of water parallel to the direction of the tracts and water movement is impeded perpendicular to the tracts. The preferential diffusion of protons *along* the trajectory (parallel) of fiber tracts relative to diffusion *across* the fiber tracts is called anisotropy. Isotropy is the term given when water moves with equal ease in all directions. Diffusion is isotropic both in fluid-filled regions (e.g., ventricles) and in tissues with structure that is not well organized, such as the cerebral gray matter. In the former case, diffusion is not restricted because of the lack of cell membranes and other structures; in the latter case, diffusion is restricted principally via cell membranes, but it is restricted equally in all directions.

The images that follow represent:

1. *Fractional Anisotropy (FA) maps* that depict in a black/white gray scale the magnitude of diffusion anisotropy in the different regions of the brain.
2. *Color directional maps* in the sagittal (from the side), axial (cross sectional), and coronal (from the front) planes. These maps are essentially FA maps, where image brightness indicates the magnitude of anisotropy, color-coded to show the principal direction of diffusion. In voxels containing fiber tracts oriented in one primary direction, the color will indicate that direction parallel to the fiber.
3. *Tractography* that depicts the directional information of individual white matter tracts. Tractograms generally consist of a structural image overlain with a set of tract(s). It is important to note that these tracts only represent a probability for actual fiber bundles to exist within an anatomical region, but *they do not correspond to actual fiber bundles directly.*

By convention tracts traveling in the transverse (right-left) direction are shown in red on color-coded FA maps, those traveling in the anterior to posterior (front to back) direction are green and those traveling in the cranial caudal (superior to inferior) direction blue. If a tract runs obliquely to the standard directions their color represents a combination of the three standard colors.

There are 3 main categories of white matter tracts in the brain:

1. *Commissural tracts* connect similar cortical areas between both cerebral hemispheres. Examples are the corpus callosum, the anterior and posterior commissures and the habenular commissure.
2. *Projection tracts* connect various cortical areas to deep nuclei, brain stem, cerebellum, and the spinal cord. Examples are the corticothalamic, corticobulbar, corticospinal, corticopontine, and geniculocalcarine (optic) tracts.
3. *Association tracts* connect cortical regions in each cerebral hemisphere. Examples are the cingulum, superior and inferior fronto-occipital fasciculi, the temporal-occipital fasciculus (inferior longitudinal fasciculus), the superior longitudinal fasciculus, and the uncinate fasciculus.

■ DTI IMAGES (FIGURES 7.10a–7.13i)

FA (Fractional Anisotropy) Maps

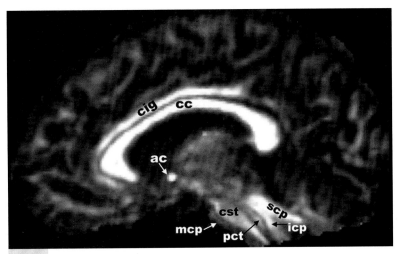

7.10a

FIGURES 7.10a–f Figures 7.10a–f, represent gray scale fractional anisotropy (FA) maps of a normal subject. 7.10a-sagittal, 7.10b,c, d-axial and 7.10e,f-coronal images. Note the darker regions, particularly within the cortex and deep gray matter nuclei, which indicate low FA yielding very low or no preferential diffusion of protons. The bright (whiter areas) have high FA indicating a structured, organized region in which there is preferential diffusion of protons in certain directions due to the inherent underlying structure.

KEY	
ac	anterior commissure
acr	anterior corona radiata
atr	anterior thalamic radiations
cc	corpus callosum
cig	cingulate gyrus (cingulum)
cigh	cingulum (hippocampal part)
cped	cerebral peduncle
cpt	corticopontine tract
cst	corticospinal tract
ctt	central tegmental tract
hipf	fimbria of hippocampus
icp	inferior cerebellar peduncle
ifo	inferior fronto-occipital fasciculus
ilf	inferior longitudinal fasciculus
mcp	middle cerebellar peduncle
ml	medial lemniscus
pct	pontine crossing tract
scp	superior cerebellar peduncle
uf	uncinate fasciculus

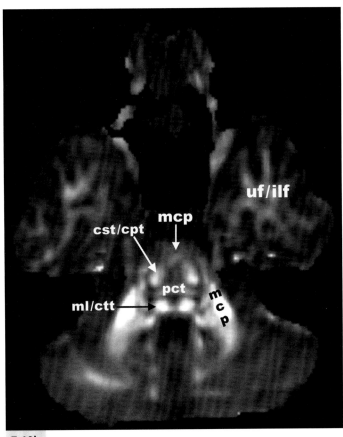

7.10b

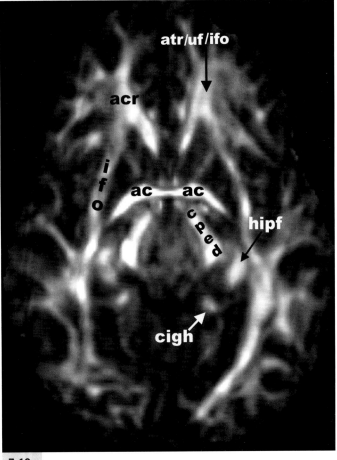

7.10c

(*continued*)

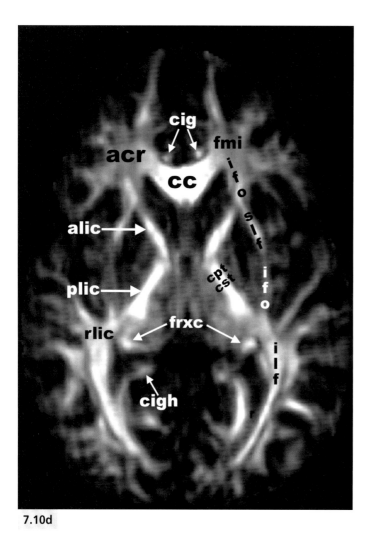

7.10d

KEY

ac	anterior commissure
acr	anterior corona radiata
alic	anterior limb of internal capsule
atr	anterior thalamic radiations
cc	corpus callosum
ccb	corpus callosum body
cig	cingulate gyrus (cingulum)
cigh	cingulum (hippocampal part)
cped	cerebral peduncle
cpt	corticopontine tract
cst	corticospinal tract
fmi	forceps minor
frxac	ascending columns of fornix
frxb	body of fornix
frxc	crura of fornix
ifo	inferior fronto-occipital fasciculus
ilf	inferior longitudinal fasciculus
mcp	middle cerebellar peduncle
ot	optic tract
plic	posterior limb internal capsule
rlic	retrolenticular internal capsule
scr	superior corona radiata
sfo	superior fronto-occipital fasciculus
slf	superior longitudinal fasciculus

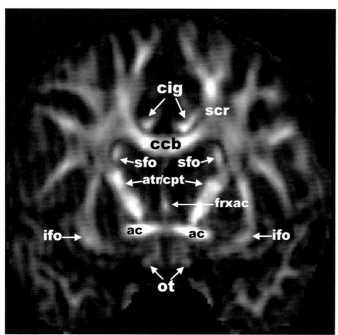

7.10e

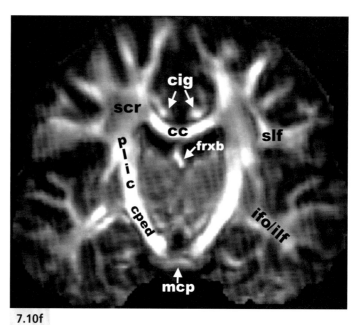

7.10f

FIGURES 7.10d–f

Sagittal Plane

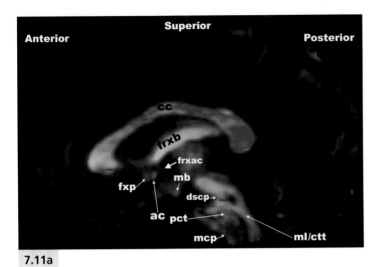

7.11a

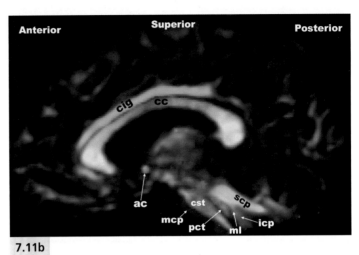

7.11b

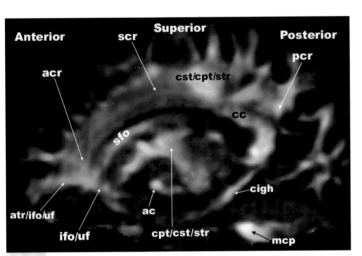

7.11c

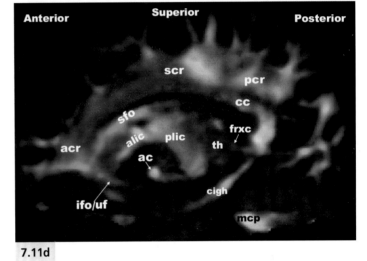

7.11d

FIGURES 7.11a–7.13i Sagittal (7.11a–g), axial (7.12a–g) and coronal (7.13a–7.13i) images demonstrate labeled, normal color DTI images in 3 planes. As noted in the brief introduction to DTI, directionality by convention is color-coded and brightness to the degree of FA.

KEY

ac	anterior commissure
acr	anterior corona radiata
alic	anterior limb of internal capsule
atr	anterior thalamic radiations
cc	corpus callosum
cig	cingulate gyrus (cingulum)
cigh	cingulum (hippocampal part)
cpt	corticopontine tract
cst	corticospinal tract
ctt	central tegmental tract
dscp	decussation of superior cerebellar peduncle
frxac	ascending columns of fornix
frxb	body of fornix
frxc	crura of fornix
fxp	precommissural branch of fornix
icp	inferior cerebellar peduncle
ifo	inferior fronto-occipital fasciculus
mb	mammillary body
mcp	middle cerebellar peduncle
ml	medial lemniscus
pcr	posterior corona radiata
pct	pontine crossing tract
plic	posterior limb internal capsule
scp	superior cerebellar peduncle
scr	superior corona radiata
sfo	superior fronto-occipital fasciculus
str	superior thalamic radiations
th	thalamus
uf	uncinate fasciculus

(continued)

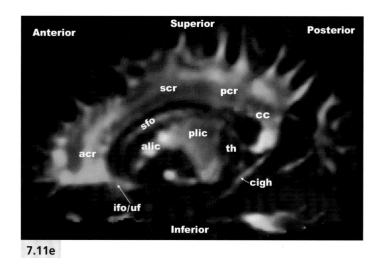

7.11e

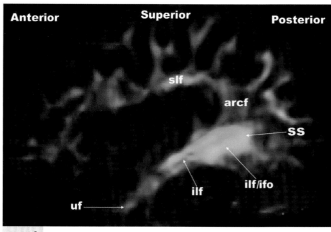

7.11f

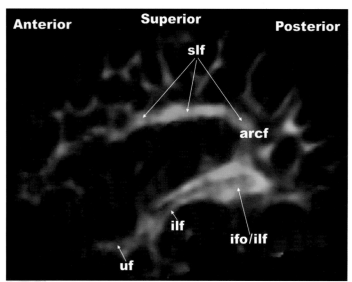

7.11g

FIGURES 7.11e–g

KEY

acr	anterior corona radiata
alic	anterior limb of internal capsule
arcf	arcuate fasciculus
cc	corpus callosum
cigh	cingulum (hippocampal part)
ifo	inferior fronto-occipital fasciculus
ilf	inferior longitudinal fasciculus
pcr	posterior corona radiata
plic	posterior limb internal capsule
scr	superior corona radiata
sfo	superior fronto-occipital fasciculus
slf	superior longitudinal fasciculus
ss	sagittal stratum
th	thalamus
uf	uncinate fasciculus

Axial Plane

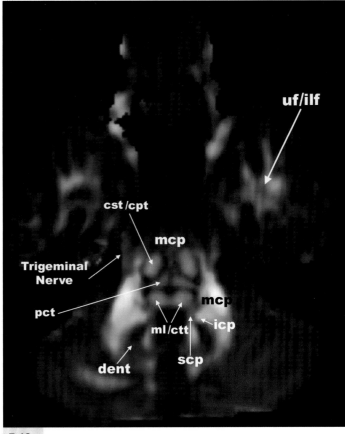

7.12a

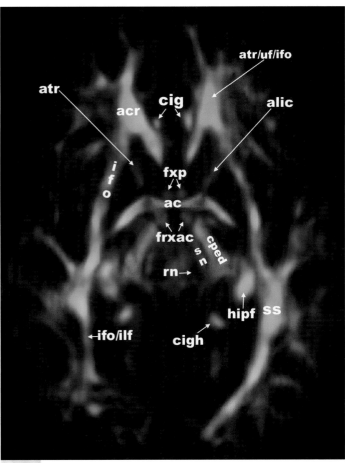

7.12c

FIGURES 7.12a–c

KEY			
ac	anterior commissure	**hipf**	fimbria of hippocampus
acr	anterior corona radiata	**icp**	inferior cerebellar peduncle
alic	anterior limb of internal capsule	**ifo**	inferior fronto-occipital fasciculus
atr	anterior thalamic radiations	**ilf**	inferior longitudinal fasciculus
cc	corpus callosum	**mcp**	middle cerebellar peduncle
cig	cingulate gyrus (cingulum)	**ml**	medial lemniscus
cigh	cingulum (hippocampal part)	**pag**	periaqueductal gray matter
cped	cerebral peduncle	**pct**	pontine crossing tract
cpt	corticopontine tract	**rn**	red nucleus
cs	corticospinal fibers in cerebral peduncle	**scp**	superior cerebellar peduncle
cst	corticospinal tract	**sn**	substantia nigra
ctt	central tegmental tract	**ss**	sagittal stratum
dent	dentate nucleus	**tpo**	temporoparieto-occipital fibers in cerebral peduncle
fp	frontopontine fibers in cerebral peduncle		
frxac	column of fornix	**uf**	uncinate fasciculus
fxp	precommissural branch of fornix	**vta**	ventral tegmental area

(continued)

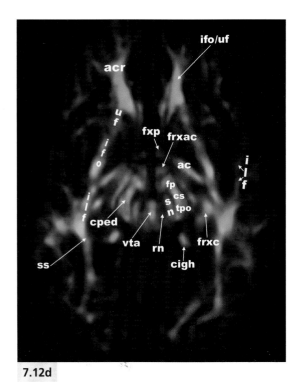

7.12d

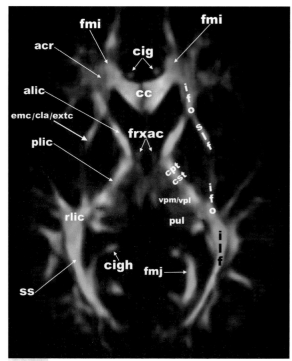

7.12e

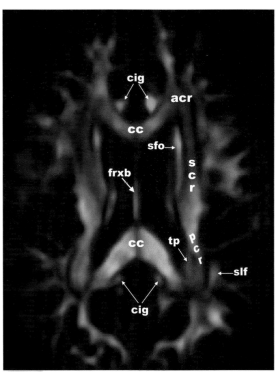

7.12f

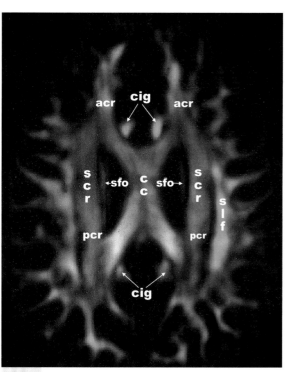

7.12g

FIGURES 7.12d–g

KEY

ac	anterior commissure	**fmi**	forceps minor	**scr**	superior corona radiata
acr	anterior corona radiata	**frxac**	ascending columns of fornix	**sfo**	superior fronto-occipital fasciculus
alic	anterior limb of internal capsule	**frxb**	body of fornix	**slf**	superior longitudinal fasciculus
cc	corpus callosum	**frxc**	crura of fornix	**sn**	substantia nigra
cig	cingulate gyrus (cingulum)	**fxp**	precommissural branch of fornix	**ss**	sagittal stratum
cigh	cingulum (hippocampal part)	**fp**	frontopontine fibers in cerebral peduncle	**tp**	tapetum
cla	claustrum	**ifo**	inferior fronto-occipital fasciculus	**tpo**	temporoparieto-occipital fibers in
cped	cerebral peduncle	**ilf**	inferior longitudinal fasciculus		cerebral peduncle
cpt	corticopontine tract	**pcr**	posterior corona radiata	**uf**	uncinate fasciculus
cs	corticospinal fibers in cerebral peduncle	**plic**	posterior limb internal capsule	**vpm/vpl**	ventroposterior medialis/
cst	corticospinal tract	**pul**	pulvinar of thalamus		ventroposterior lateralis thalamus
extc	external capsule	**rn**	red nucleus	**vta**	ventral tegmental area
emc	extreme capsule	**rlic**	retrolenticular internal capsule		

Coronal Plane

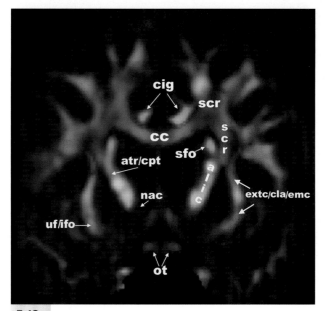

7.13a

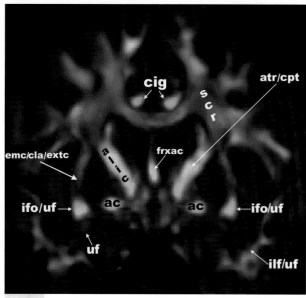

7.13b

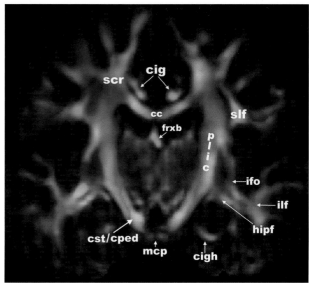

7.13c

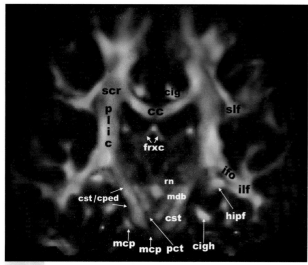

7.13d

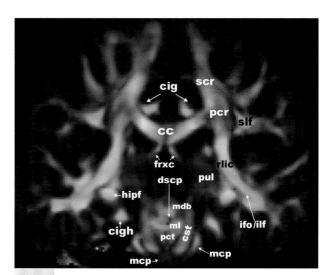

7.13e

FIGURES 7.13a–e

KEY			
ac	anterior commissure	**hipf**	fimbria of hippocampus
alic	anterior limb of internal capsule	**ifo**	inferior fronto-occipital fasciculus
atr	anterior thalamic radiations	**ilf**	inferior longitudinal fasciculus
cc	corpus callosum	**mcp**	middle cerebellar peduncle
cig	cingulate gyrus (cingulum)	**mdb**	midbrain
cigh	cingulum (hippocampal part)	**ml**	medial lemniscus
		nac	nucleus accumbens
cla	claustrum	**ot**	optic tract
cped	cerebral peduncle	**pcr**	posterior corona radiata
cpt	corticopontine tract	**pct**	pontine crossing tract
cst	corticospinal tract	**plic**	posterior limb internal capsule
dscp	decussation of superior cerebellar peduncles	**pul**	pulvinar of thalamus
		rlic	retrolenticular internal capsule
emc	extreme capsule	**rn**	red nucleus
extc	external capsule	**scr**	superior corona radiata
frxac	ascending columns of fornix	**sfo**	superior fronto-occipital fasciculus
frxb	body of fornix		
frxc	crura of fornix	**slf**	superior longitudinal fasciculus
fxp	precommissural branch of fornix		
		uf	uncinate fasciculus

(continued)

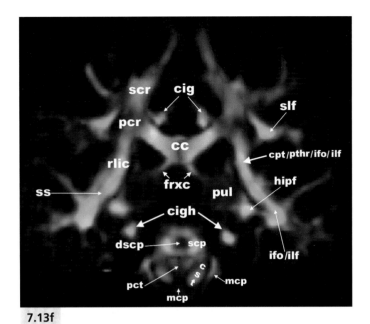

7.13f

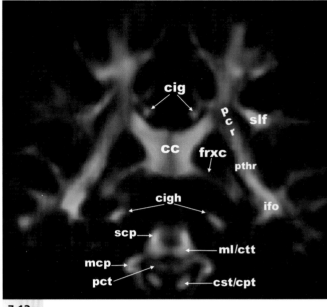

7.13g

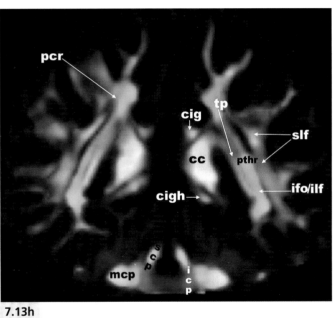

7.13h

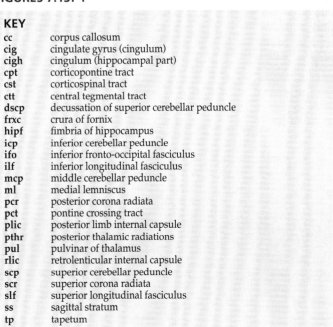

7.13i

FIGURES 7.13f–i

KEY

cc	corpus callosum
cig	cingulate gyrus (cingulum)
cigh	cingulum (hippocampal part)
cpt	corticopontine tract
cst	corticospinal tract
ctt	central tegmental tract
dscp	decussation of superior cerebellar peduncle
frxc	crura of fornix
hipf	fimbria of hippocampus
icp	inferior cerebellar peduncle
ifo	inferior fronto-occipital fasciculus
ilf	inferior longitudinal fasciculus
mcp	middle cerebellar peduncle
ml	medial lemniscus
pcr	posterior corona radiata
pct	pontine crossing tract
plic	posterior limb internal capsule
pthr	posterior thalamic radiations
pul	pulvinar of thalamus
rlic	retrolenticular internal capsule
scp	superior cerebellar peduncle
scr	superior corona radiata
slf	superior longitudinal fasciculus
ss	sagittal stratum
tp	tapetum

(continued)

■ TRACTOGRAPHY IMAGES (FIGURES 7.14a–7.25d)

Parcellation and presentation of some of the white matter tracts is presented in the following images. All images are normal in appearance:

Cingulum

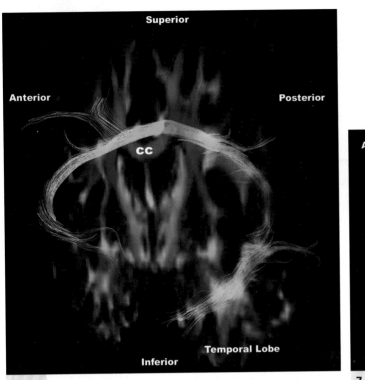
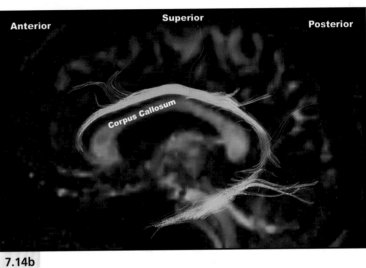

FIGURES 7.14a–b   Coronal oblique (7.14a) and sagittal (7.14b) images of the Cingulum (association tract).

Superior Longitudinal Fasciculus/Arcuate Fasciculus

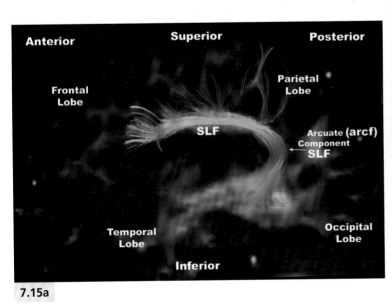
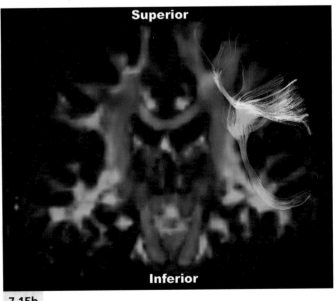

FIGURES 7.15a–b   Sagittal (7.15a) and coronal (7.15b) images of the Superior Longitudinal Fasciculus (association tract).

KEY	
arcf	arcuate fasciculus
cc	corpus callosum
SLF	superior longitudinal fasciculus

Uncinate Fasciculus

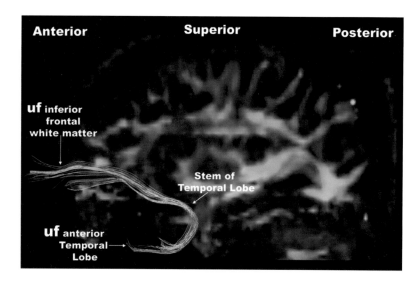

FIGURES 7.16a–c Sagittal (7.16a), coronal oblique (7.16b) and axial (7.16c) images of the Uncinate Fasciculus (association tract). Tracts are displayed as lines in a and b and as tubes in c.

KEY

cc	corpus callosum
uf	uncinate fasciculus

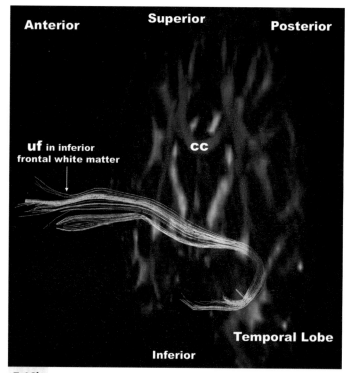

7.16b

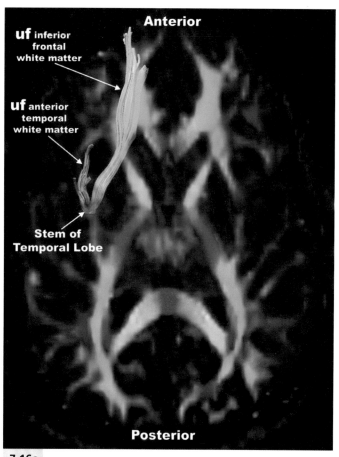

7.16c

Superior Fronto-Occipital Fasciculus

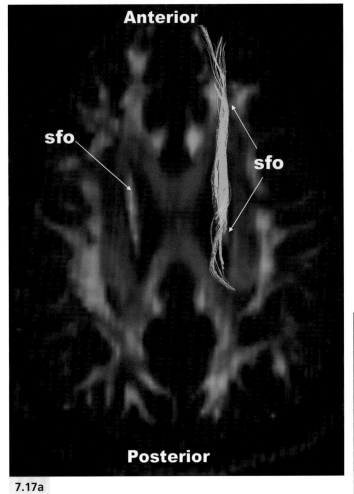

7.17a

FIGURES 7.17a–c   Axial ((7.17a), coronal (7.17b) and sagittal (7.17c) images of the Superior Fronto-Occipital Fasciculus (association tract).

KEY
sfo   superior fronto-occipital fasciculus

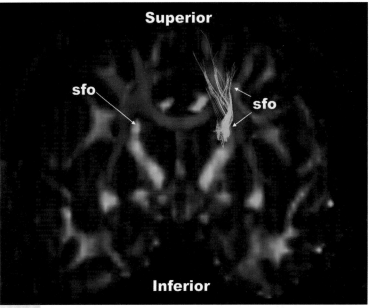

7.17b

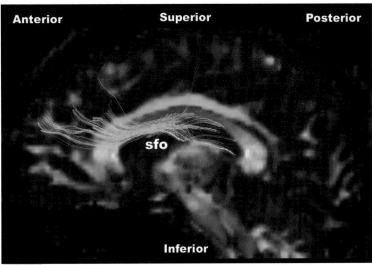

7.17c

Inferior Fronto-Occipital Fasciculus/Inferior Longitudinal Fasciculus/Superior Longitudinal Fasciculus

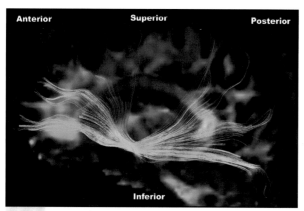

7.18a

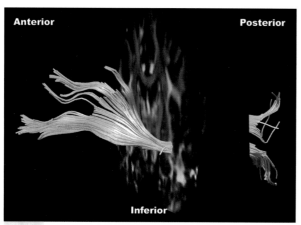

7.18c

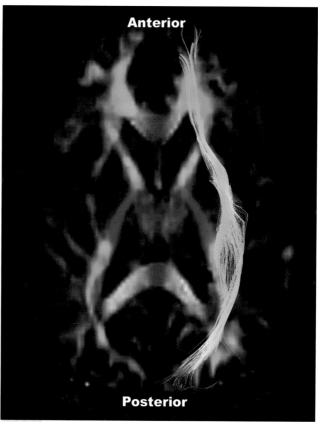

7.18b

FIGURES 7.18a–c Sagittal (7.18a), axial (7.18b) and coronal oblique (7.18c) images of the Inferior Fronto-Occipital Fasciculus (association tract). The tracts are displayed as lines in a and b and as tubes in c.

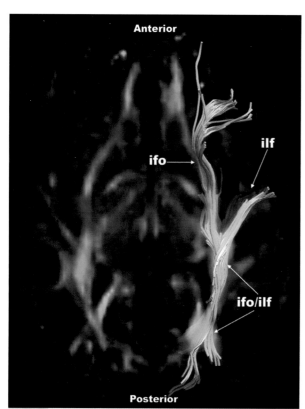

7.19

FIGURE 7.19 Axial image of the Inferior Fronto-Occipital Fasciculus/Inferior Longitudinal Fasciculus (association tracts) displayed as tubes.

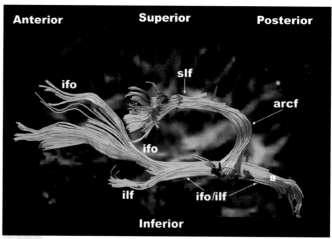

7.20

FIGURE 7.20 Sagittal image of the Inferior Fronto-Occipital Fasciculus/Inferior Longitudinal Fasciculus/Superior Longitudinal Fasciculus (association tracts) displayed as tubes.

KEY

arcf	arcuate fasciculus
ifo	inferior fronto-occipital fasciculus
ilf	inferior longitudinal fasciculus
slf	superior longitudinal fasciculus

Fornix/Fimbria of Hippocampus

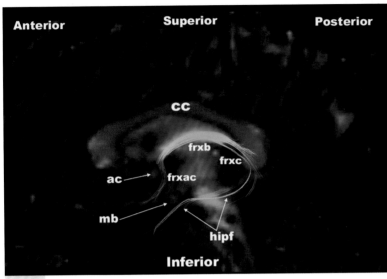

7.21a

FIGURES 7.21a–c Sagittal with slight obliquity (7.21a), coronal oblique (7.21b) and axial (7.21c) images of the Fornix/Hippocampus (contains both projection and commissural fibers).

KEY

ac	anterior commissure
cc	corpus callosum
frxac	ascending columns of fornix
frxb	body of fornix
frxc	crura of fornix
fxp	precommissural branch of fornix
hipf	fimbria of hippocampus
mb	mammillary body

7.21b

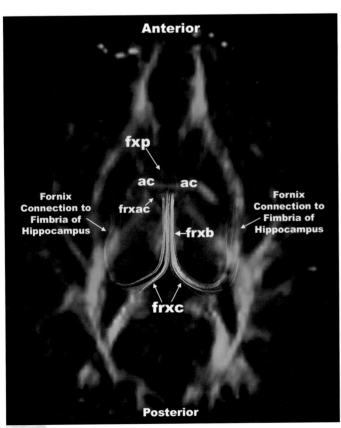

7.21c

Corona Radiata

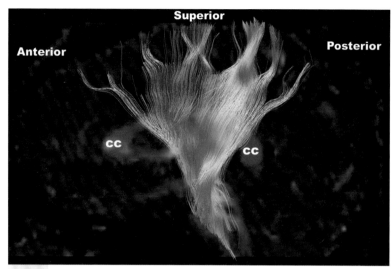

7.22a

FIGURES 7.22a–c Sagittal (7.22a), axial (7.22b) and axial oblique (7.22c) images of the Corona Radiata (composed of multiple different fiber tracts). The tracts are displayed as lines in a and b and as tubes in c.

KEY

cc	corpus callosum
cped	cerebral peduncle
cst	corticospinal tract
fp	frontopontine fibers in cerebral peduncle
tpo	temporoparieto-occipital fibers in cerebral peduncle

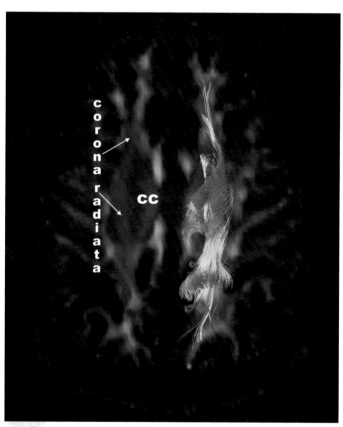

7.22b

7.22c

Corticospinal Tracts

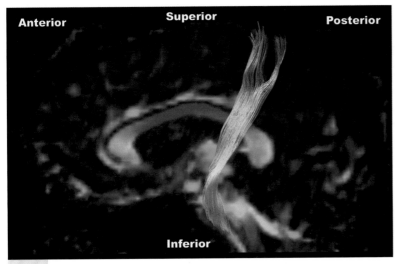

7.23a

FIGURES 7.23a–c   Sagittal (7.23a), coronal (7.23b) and axial (7.23c) images of the Corticospinal Tract (projection tract).

KEY	
cc	corpus callosum
cped	cerebral peduncle
cr	corona radiata
cst	corticospinal tract
plic	posterior limb internal capsule

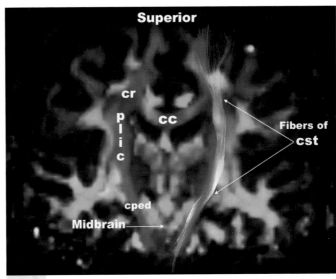

7.23b

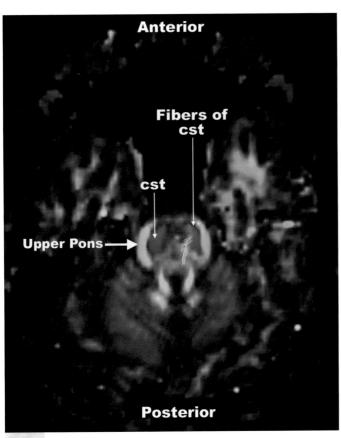

7.23c

Corpus Callosum

7.24a

FIGURES 7.24a–d Sagittal image with fiber tracts displayed as lines (7.24a) and displayed as tubes (7.24b), coronal oblique (7.24c) image with tracts displayed as tubes, and axial (viewing from top down-7.24d) images of the Corpus Callosum (commissural tract).

7.24b

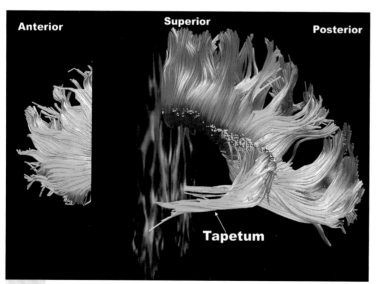

7.24c

7.24d

Forceps Major

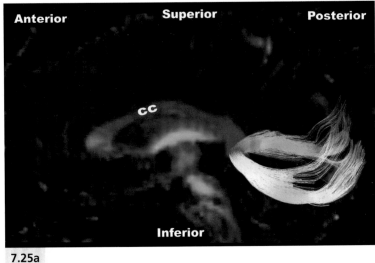

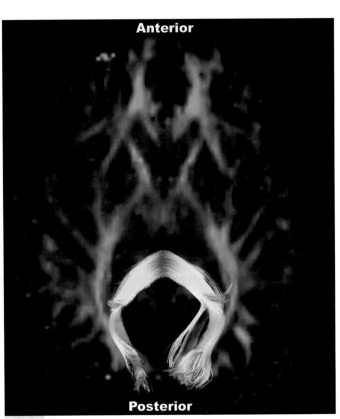

FIGURES 7.25a–b Sagittal (7.25a) and axial (7.25b) images of the Forceps Major.

KEY
cc corpus callosum

Forceps Minor

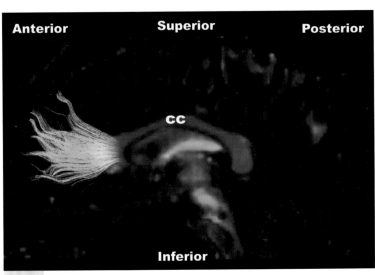

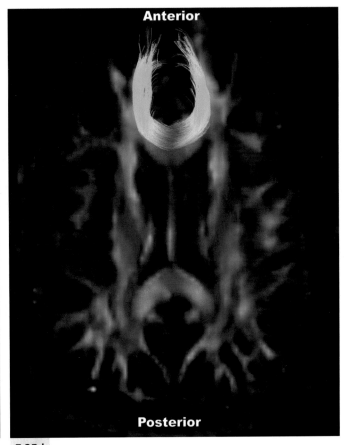

FIGURES 7.25c–d Sagittal (7.25c) and axial (7.25d) images of Forceps Minor.

MR SPECTROSCOPY: INTRODUCTION

MR spectroscopy is an advanced MR technique, which provides information regarding tissue chemistry/metabolites and their concentrations. You might wonder how this can enhance the information we obtain from an MRI scan. It is not uncommon that visual abnormalities identified on routine MR scans are non-specific, meaning the appearance is not limited to a single diagnosis. Quite often we can only describe the signal characteristics on MR and anatomic location of an abnormality and from that generate a list of differential diagnoses. Sometimes a stroke or demyelinating lesion (as in multiple sclerosis) can look like a tumor. In addition we are often unable to differentiate a low-grade (benign behaving) from a high-grade (malignant behaving) tumor using routine MR imaging. MR spectroscopy has also been used to investigate metabolic diseases of the brain. When we are faced with such situations we can perform MR spectroscopy to help determine the precise nature of the abnormality. We should state, however, that sometimes despite obtaining a high quality MR spectroscopy exam we still cannot determine the precise diagnosis.

MR spectroscopy can characterize relative abundances of molecules containing hydrogen (^{1}H), sodium (^{23}Na) or phosphorus (^{31}P) nuclei, but because of its abundance, hydrogen spectroscopy is most often used. Depending on the technical details and the volume of tissue being interrogated, this technique may take between 2 and 15 minutes. Various techniques are used with different MR pulse sequences, using either short or long echo delay times (TE) and acquiring spectra with a single or multi-voxel technique. Advantages of single voxel technique with a short TE time are the higher signal to noise and the potential for viewing peaks corresponding to rarer metabolites. However, as the name states, this technique provides metabolic information in a single relatively small region of the brain. The multi-voxel technique yields a grid of multiple spectra within the applied volume of interest, which can be one two-dimensional slice of voxels or a three-dimensional *box* of voxels. Multi-voxel spectroscopy is also known as *chemical shift imaging* (CSI). Multi-voxel techniques are often helpful in the assessment of tumors since one can identify variations in the metabolites in different portions of the mass. This information can often provide the neurosurgeon with precise regions to target for biopsy and provide a more accurate assessment of the grade (biologic behavior) of the mass.

The data obtained from an MR spectroscopy exam consists of a graphical representation of the relative concentration of metabolites given by the peak heights. Each metabolite in the spectral peaks can be identified according to the position of each peak along the *X*-axis, quantified by the frequency difference in units of hertz (Hz) or parts per million (ppm).

The various brain metabolites seen on spectra reflect specific cellular and biochemical processes. NAA (N-acetylaspartate) reflects the presence of normal neuronal tissue health. This decreases with any disease that affects neuronal integrity. Choline (Cho) is a metabolite reflecting cellular membranes and is increased in diseases that result in cellular breakdown/destruction or with rapid formation of cellular membranes such as with tumors. Creatine (Cr) is a measure of energy metabolism. Certain metabolites such as Lactate or Lipid are only seen in pathologic processes. Lactate (Lac) is the end product of anaerobic metabolism and is seen in hypoxia/stroke and in necrotic tumors. Lipid (Lip) is seen with destructive processes and is often elevated in high grade/malignant tumors and in cases of traumatic brain injury. Myo-inositol (ml) is an osmolyte and is a glial cell marker. This metabolite can be significantly elevated with low-grade gliomas (World Health Organization [WHO] grade 2 astrocytoma). Glutamate (Glu) is the dominant amino acid and cerebral neurotransmitter. Glutamate (Glu) is converted to glutamine (Gln), which is then converted back to glutamate (Glu). This process requires significant energy and has been estimated to require up to 80% to 90% of glucose utilization.

Creatine (Cr) is normally higher in gray matter while choline (Cho) is normally higher in white matter. If one draws a line connecting the peaks of the major metabolites in a normal brain it slopes upward from left to right. This angle has been termed Hunter's angle. Pathologic processes will often disturb this normal appearance.

The MR spectrum in infants differs significantly from that of children (older than the age of about 2 years) and adults because of the immature pattern of myelination in newborns and infants. The immature myelin pattern results in relative increased choline and decrease in NAA. This pattern gradually changes as the pattern of myelination matures. The immature myelin pattern in newborns and infants results in a reversal of the normal Hunter's angle seen in adults.

There are regional differences in the concentrations of the various metabolites such as higher levels of Choline and Creatine in the cerebellum (see Figures 7.26e and f) compared with the supratentorial brain. Higher choline is found in the frontal regions of the brain, the thalamus, hypothalamus, and insular cortex. The pons normally demonstrates high levels of NAA and Choline and low levels of Creatine. The glutamate and glutamine peak overlap at 1.5 Tesla MRI units and this composite peak is referred to as Glx. At higher field strengths these metabolites can be better resolved as individual peaks.

Although we are focusing our discussion on imaging of the brain, other organs such as the breast, liver, and prostate can benefit from MR spectroscopic techniques to delineate metabolic or lipid content.

Spectroscopy provides a wealth of biological information not available from structural images. However, it should be noted that there are several technical details associated with acquiring MR spectra that must be considered to perform the technique properly (it is not a *plug-and-play* imaging sequence). For the reader who is interested in the implementation of MR spectroscopy or in the technical details, please refer to the overview of technical guidelines within Oz et al. or the detailed discussion of Drost et al. as listed in suggested readings.

Metabolite Peaks:

- lactate peak (Lac): resonates at 1.33 ppm
- lipid peak (Lip): resonates between .9 and 1.3 ppm
- NAA peak (N-acetylaspartate): resonates at 2.0
- glutamine/glutamate peak (Glx): resonate sat 2.2 to 2.4 ppm
- gamma-aminobutyric acid (GABA) peak: resonates at 2.2 to 2.4 ppm
- creatine peak (Cr): resonates at 3.0 ppm
- choline peak (Cho): resonates at 3.2 ppm
- myo-inositol (ml) Peak: peak (ml): resonates at 3.56 ppm

■ MR SPECTROSCOPY IMAGES (FIGURES 7.26a–7.30)

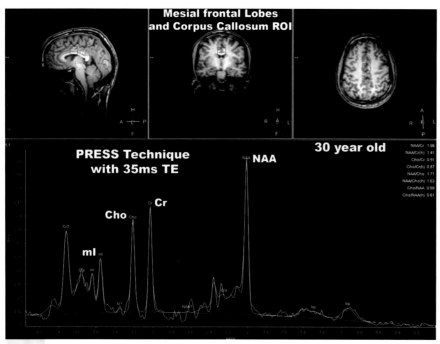

7.26a

FIGURES 7.26a–g   Figures 7.26a-g. Normal single voxel MR spectroscopy using PRESS (point resolved spectroscopy) technique with a short TE (35ms) in a healthy 30-year-old subject using various regions of interest (ROI). Note the differences in the spectra at different ROI. The locations of the ROI are annotated on each of the various spectra and indicated by the location of the voxel (red box) presented.

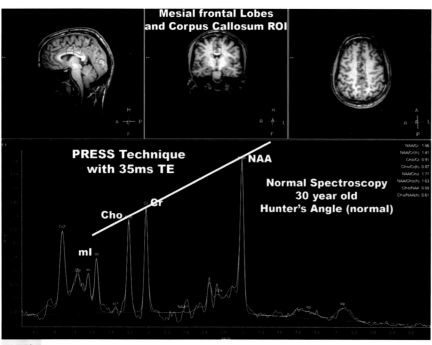

7.26b

FIGURE 7.26b   A white line is drawn along the peaks of the spectra. Note that this line extends from left inferior to right superior and is generally a good indicator of a normal adult spectrum. This line is referred to a Hunter's angle, which is roughly at 45 degrees. If there is deviation from this general pattern consider an abnormal spectrum but remember that there are regional variations in the spectrum based upon where the ROI is placed.

KEY

Cho	Choline
Cr	Creatine
ml	myo-inositol
NAA	N-acetylaspartate

(continued)

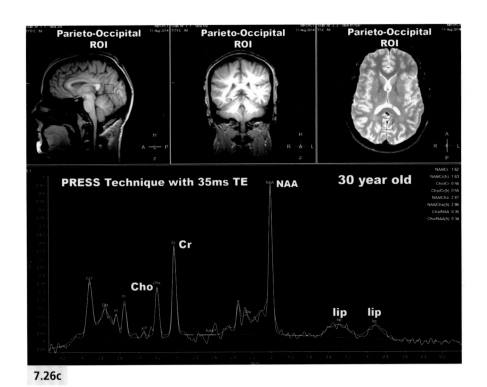

7.26c

7.26d

FIGURES 7.26c,d

KEY
Cho	Choline
Cr	Creatine
Lip	Lipid
NAA	N-acetylaspartate

(continued)

FIGURE 7.26e

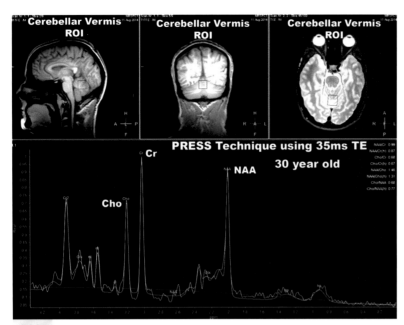

7.26e

FIGURE 7.26f

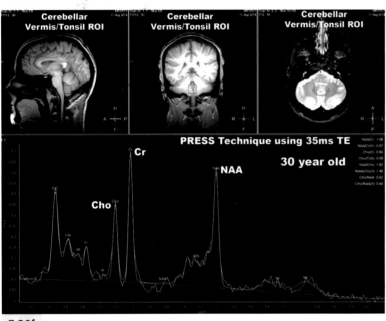

7.26f

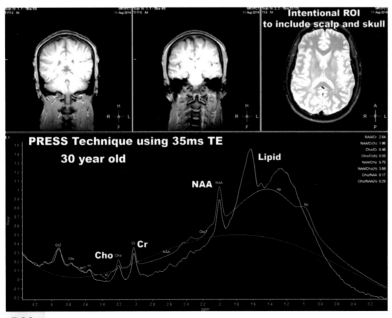

7.26g

FIGURE 7.26g The ROI/voxel was placed intentionally to include the skull and scalp adjacent to the left frontal lobe. This was done to demonstrate the spectrum obtained with the lipid signal (from fatty marrow and scalp) which has the highest peak. Normally there is no lipid peak present in a healthy brain spectrum. Lipid may also be present if the ROI includes the midline where small amounts of fat may normally be present (in ossified falx cerebri with fatty marrow or congenital fat inclusions in the region of the falx). The presence of lipid can also be seen in necrotic regions of brain.

KEY

Cho	Choline
Cr	Creatine
NAA	N-acetylaspartate

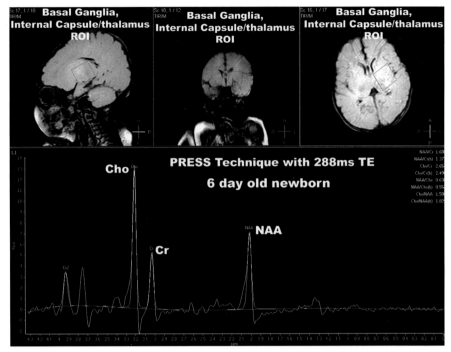

FIGURE 7.27 This is a normal single voxel MR spectroscopy exam performed on a 6-day-old infant. Note the significant differences between this normal study and the normal study from the adult in the previous figures. The immature brain normally demonstrates increased choline and myo-inositol with decrease in NAA as in this case (looks like a reverse Hunter's angle), although the myo-inositol peak at 3.5ppm is not readily identified here. As the brain matures NAA increases and the choline and myo-inositol decrease. The major metabolic changes occur in the first year of life with more gradual changes thereafter until the full adult pattern/values are reached at about the age of 20.

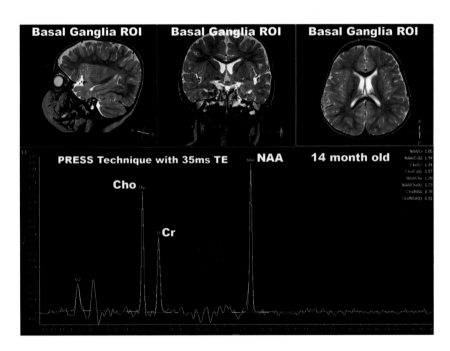

FIGURE 7.28 Normal single voxel spectroscopic exam on a 14-month-old infant. Note the decreasing choline and the increase of NAA in this older infant compared with the MR spectrum of the 6-day-old infant in Figure 7.27.

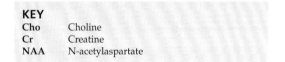

KEY

Cho	Choline
Cr	Creatine
NAA	N-acetylaspartate

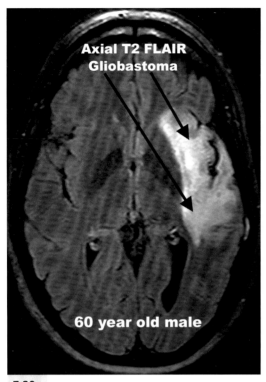

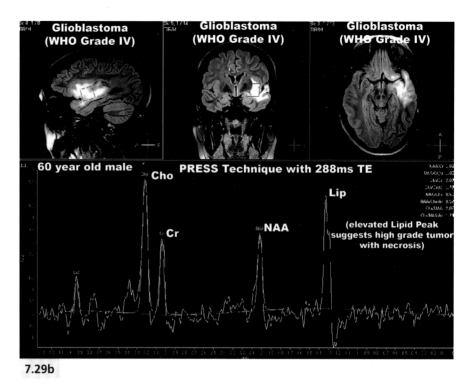

7.29a

7.29b

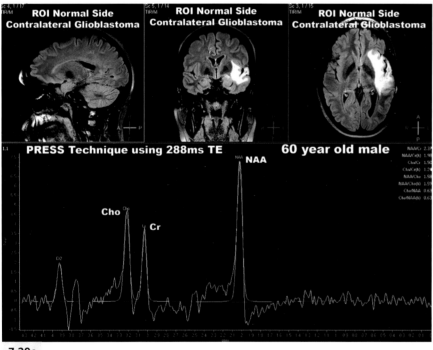

7.29c

FIGURES 7.29a–c 60 year old with newly diagnosed brain tumor.

FIGURE 7.29a This axial T2 FLAIR (fluid-attenuated inversion recovery) image shows extensive increased signal intensity in the left temporal lobe, which extended through the stem of the temporal lobe into the insular/subinsular region. Subsequent biopsy indicated that this was a glioblastoma (WHO Grade IV) tumor.

FIGURES 7.29b,c Single voxel spectroscopy using PRESS technique with a long TE of 288ms. In 7.29b the ROI over the T2 FLAIR signal abnormality shows significant elevation of the choline peak and decrease in NAA. There is also a prominent lipid peak. This pattern is consistent with a high grade, necrotic mass. 7.29c is also a single voxel PRESS technique but placed over the normal appearing right cerebral hemisphere (within the basal ganglia region). This comparison spectrum is normal.

KEY

Cho	Choline
Cr	Creatine
Lip	Lipid
NAA	N-acetylaspartate

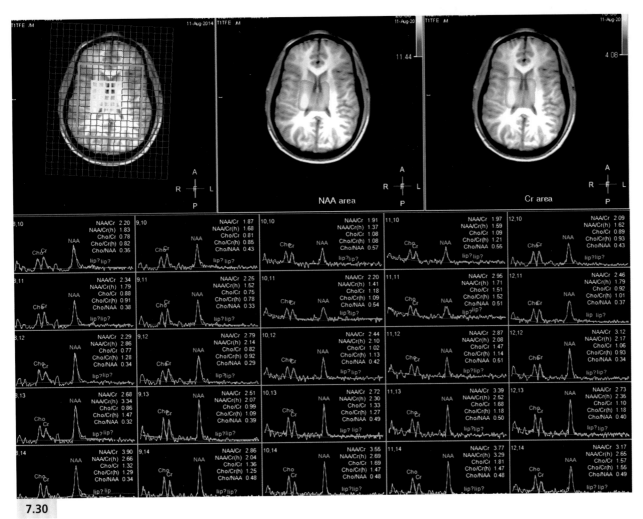

7.30

FIGURE 7.30   This is an example of what a normal multi-voxel MR spectroscopy would look like. The sampling region is indicated by the yellow boxes (left upper corner of image) in the midline, straddling the lateral ventricles and mesial portions of both cerebral hemispheres. Spectra are obtained from each box within the overall sampling region and displayed as a spectrum unique to the box chosen, as seen in the multiple spectra shown in the lower portion of the image. The grid of the various spectra has a 1 to 1 correlation with the grid used for the multi-voxel regions of interest (yellow grid in left upper corner). The color enhanced boxes in the middle and upper right hand side of the image depicts regional variations in the levels of NAA (in the middle image) and Creatine (Cr) on the right, over the entire multi-voxel ROI chosen.

CT Imaging

8

INTRODUCTION TO PRINCIPLES OF CT IMAGING

Since its introduction in the 1970s, computed tomography (CT) has become an invaluable tool in diagnostic imaging. Unlike traditional X-rays that create an image from a single plain projection, CT acquires images from projections of X-rays through the patient at multiple angles to reconstruct anatomical images or "slices" showing a cross section of anatomy. The X-ray source emits a specific number of photons per unit of time (controlled by the tube current) with a specific energy level between 20 and 150 kiloelectron volts (KeV), as it rotates around the patient. The detector, which is placed on the side of the patient opposite from the X-ray source, receives the fan of transmitted X-rays after penetrating that specific body section. The X-ray tube and the detector array rotate 360° about the patient to obtain a number of projections (e.g., 720 projections at 0.5° intervals).

Depending on the type of CT, the table with the patient either moves incrementally and stops for each "slice" (scan), or moves continuously during the scanning process, such that the detectors move in a "spiral" trajectory from the patient's perspective (Helical CT). Newer multi-slice helical scanners have been developed that collect data for reconstruction of several slices in each rotation, allowing for faster scanning time.

The image of the section irradiated by the X-ray beam is reconstructed from a series of measurements of "attenuation coefficients." Each tissue has a different relative attenuation characteristic, expressed in Hounsfield units (HU). By convention, the HU value for water is zero, for air is −1000, for compact bone is +1000 or higher, for fat is −60 to −120, for soft tissue 40 and for acute hemorrhage 50 to 90, meaning that an equal thickness of water attenuates X-rays more weakly than dense bone. Attenuation depends on a few different factors, such as material density as well as the atomic mass and atomic number of the constituent atoms in a given molecule being scanned. Density generally drives the CT image contrast for conventional CT. Because the attenuation coefficients depend on photon energy (KeV), the HU values are approximate and related to the tube voltage used to generate the image.

Advantages of CT are that it is widely available, can be used more safely in some patients with hardware incompatible with magnetic resonance imaging (although image quality may be poor in some circumstances), and allow a quick assessment of intracranial contents. CT imaging also has several limitations that should be kept in mind. Most importantly is the exposure to ionizing radiation and the risk of cancer, especially in young patients. As a comparison, a plain X-ray film involves a radiation dose of 0.01 to 0.15 milligray (mGy), while a CT scan entails doses in the range of 10 to 20 mGy. The use of iodine-based contrast agents may be risky in patients with an unknown contrast allergy when there is a need to further evaluate a specific lesion in the brain or for evaluation of the arterial and venous system, as in the case of CT angiography. Another limitation is that of image artifacts that can interfere with accurate interpretation, such as those occuring in the region of the brainstem and posterior fossa that are generally degraded by the close proximity of bone. It is beyond the scope of this book to review all the artifacts in details, but some of the most common include:

> *Streak Artifact*: seen around materials that block X-rays (bone, metal implants).
> *Motion Artifact*: blurring and/or streaking caused by movement.
> *Ring Artifact*: seen with miscalibration or detector array malfunction.
> *Partial Volume Effect*: blurring at the edges of structures within the image when the scanner is unable to differentiate between two tissues of similar density.
> *Noise*: grainy image caused by a low signal to noise ratio, most commonly present when a thin slice thickness is used or the current supplied by the X-ray tube provides a limited number of X-rays that penetrate the body for some number of views.

HEAD CT

Images from a head CT can emphasize soft-tissue detail as well as emphasizing the bony structures. It can provide considerable detail of the bones in the skull and the skull base, and be very sensitive to detect an acute hemorrhage or calcifications. The CT image will depend on the attenuation of the X-ray beam as it passes through various tissues. Cortical bone has high attenuation (high HU value) and will therefore appear white, while those structures with low attenuation will appear black (air in the sinuses). In the brain, white matter has a lower HU value than gray matter such that it appears slightly darker on a head CT. Pathological conditions of the central nervous system can have either high or low attenuation, producing a bright or dark image, respectively.

CT head exams are performed without and with the intravenous administration of a contrast agent depending upon the clinical question to be answered. All water soluble contrast agents are iodinated and can be classified as high or low osmolarity and ionic or non-ionic. The iodine atoms in the contrast medium absorb X-rays in proportion to its concentration in the area being imaged. Low osmolar contrast agents have a lower overall incidence of adverse reactions than high osmolar agents, including nephrotoxicity; however, they are also more expensive.

CT has become an important diagnostic imaging modality to evaluate certain patients with a variety of suspected abnormalities including stroke, suspected traumatic brain injury, acute intracerebral hemorrhage and in the initial investigation for dementia, hydrocephalus, or intracranial tumors.

■ NORMAL YOUNG ADULT CT HEAD WITHOUT CONTRAST (FIGURES 8.1a–m)

Axial Plane

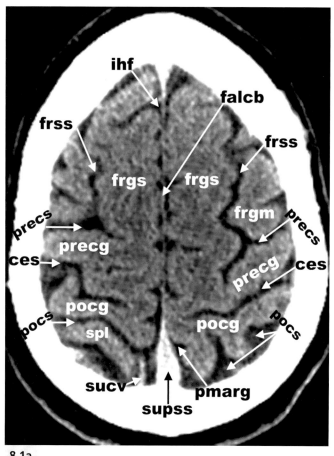

8.1a

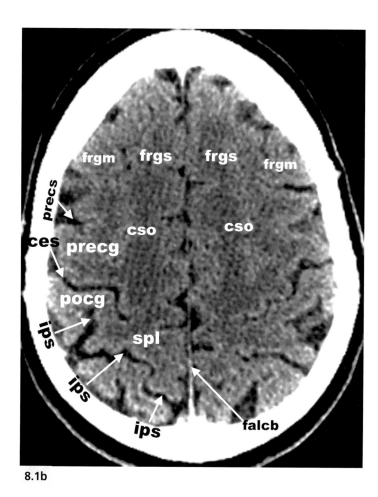

8.1b

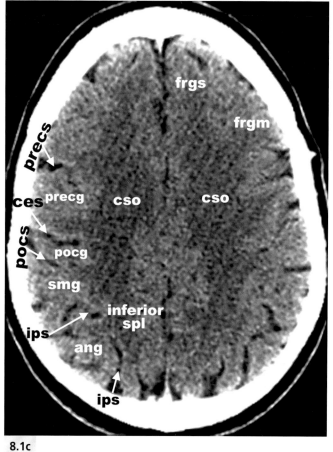

8.1c

FIGURES 8.1a–m Normal axial non-contrast CT of the head with images presented from superior/cranial (Figure 8.1a) to inferior/caudal (Figure 8.1m).

KEY	
ang	angular gyrus
ces	central sulcus
cso	centrum semiovale
falcb	falx cerebri
frgm	middle frontal gyrus
frgs	superior frontal gyrus
frss	superior frontal sulcus
ihf	interhemispheric fissure
ips	intraparietal sulcus
pmarg	pars marginalis (ascending ramus of cingulate sulcus)
pocg	post-central gyrus
pocs	post-central sulcus
precg	pre-central gyrus
precs	pre-central sulcus
smg	supramarginal gyrus
spl	superior parietal lobule
sucv	superficial cortical vein(s)
supss	superior sagittal sinus

(continued)

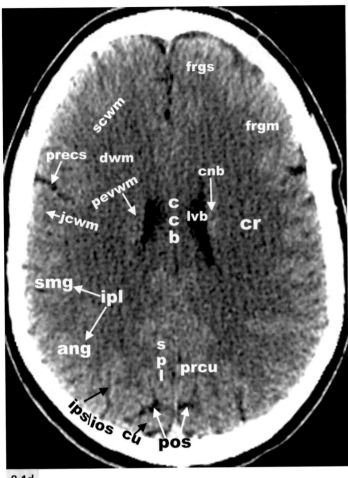

8.1d

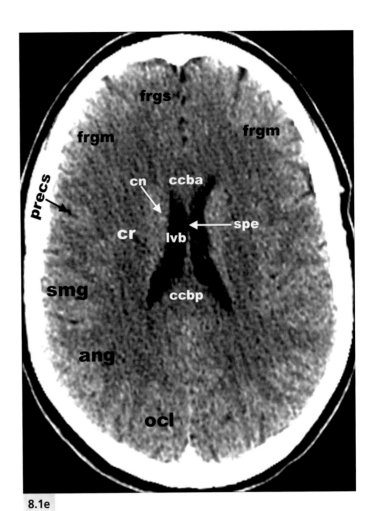

8.1e

FIGURES 8.1d–f

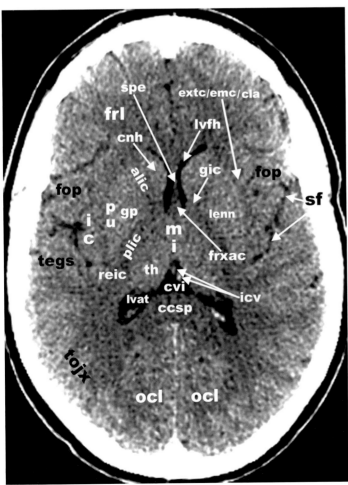

8.1f

KEY

alic	anterior limb of internal capsule	ios	intra-occipital sulcus
ang	angular gyrus	ipl	inferior parietal lobule
ccb	body of corpus callosum	ips	intraparietal sulcus
ccba	anterior body corpus callosum	jcwm	juxtacortical white matter
		lenn	lenticular nucleus
ccbp	posterior body corpus callosum	lvat	atrium (trigone) of lateral ventricle
ccsp	splenium of corpus callosum	lvb	body of lateral ventricle
		lvfh	frontal horn of lateral ventricle
cla	claustrum	mi	massa intermedia
cn	caudate nucleus	ocl	occipital lobe
cnb	caudate nucleus body	pevwm	periventricular white matter
cnh	caudate nucleus head		
cr	corona radiata	plic	posterior limb of internal capsule
cu	cuneus	pos	parieto-occipital sulcus
cvi	cistern of velum interpositum	prcu	precuneus
		precs	pre-central sulcus
dwm	deep white matter	pu	putamen
emc	extreme capsule	reic	retrolenticular internal capsule
extc	external capsule		
fop	frontal operculum	scwm	subcortical white matter
frgm	middle frontal gyrus	sf	Sylvian fissure (lateral sulcus)
frgs	superior frontal gyrus		
frl	frontal lobe	smg	supramarginal gyrus
frxac	ascending columns of fornix	spe	septum pellucidum
		spl	superior parietal lobule
gic	genu of internal capsule	tegs	superior temporal gyrus
		th	thalamus
gp	glopus pallidus	tojx	temporal occipital junction
ic	insular cortex		
icv	internal cerebral vein		

(continued)

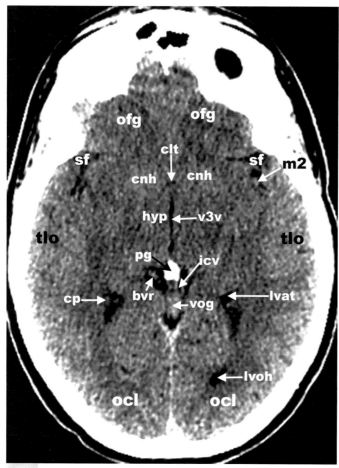

8.1g

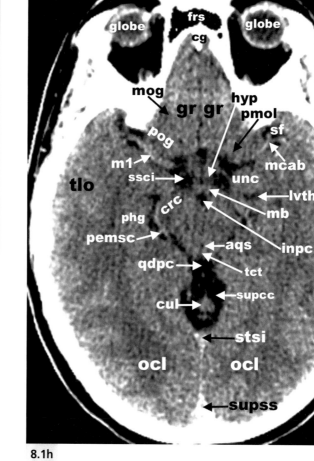

8.1h

FIGURES 8.1g–i

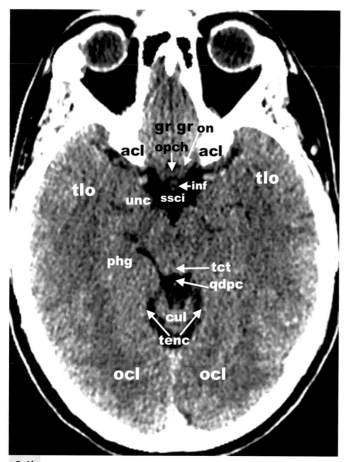

8.1i

KEY

acl	anterior clinoid process	mcab	mca bifurcation/trifurcation
aqs	aqueduct of Sylvius	mog	medial orbital gyrus
bvr	basal vein of Rosenthal	ocl	occipital lobe
cg	crista galli	ofg	orbital-frontal gyri
clt	cistern of lamina terminalis	on	optic nerve
cnh	caudate nucleus head	opch	optic chiasm
cp	choroid plexus	pemsc	perimesencephalic (ambient) cistern
crc	crus cerebri		
cul	culmen (lobules IV and V)	pg	pineal gland
frs	frontal sinus	phg	parahippocampal gyrus
gr	gyrus rectus	pmol	posteromedial orbital lobule
hyp	hypothalamus		
icv	internal cerebral vein	pog	posterior orbital gyrus
inf	infundibulum	qdpc	quadrigeminal plate cistern
inpc	interpeduncular cistern	sf	Sylvian fissure (lateral sulcus)
lvat	atrium (trigone) of lateral ventricle		
		ssci	suprasellar cistern
lvoh	occipital horn of lateral ventricle	stsi	straight sinus
		supcc	supracerebellar cistern
lvth	temporal horn of lateral ventricle	supss	superior sagittal sinus
		tct	tectum
m1	m1 (horizontal segment mca)	tenc	tentorial incisura
m2	m2 (Sylvian/insular branches mca)	tlo	temporal lobe
		unc	uncus
		v3v	third ventricle
mb	mammillary body	vog	vein of Galen
mca	middle cerebral artery		

(continued)

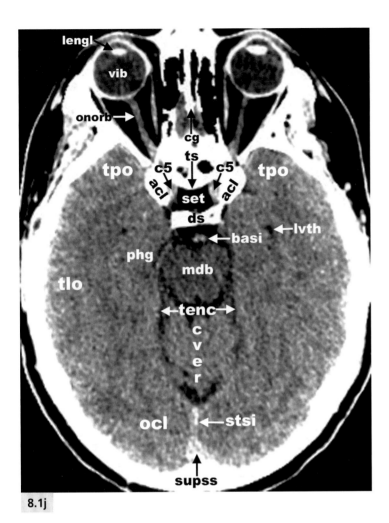

8.1j

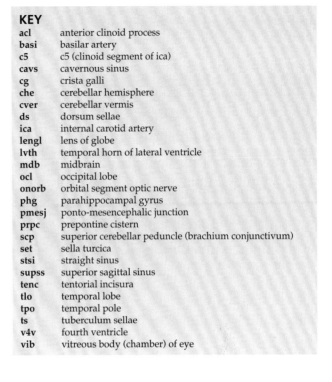

KEY

acl	anterior clinoid process
basi	basilar artery
c5	c5 (clinoid segment of ica)
cavs	cavernous sinus
cg	crista galli
che	cerebellar hemisphere
cver	cerebellar vermis
ds	dorsum sellae
ica	internal carotid artery
lengl	lens of globe
lvth	temporal horn of lateral ventricle
mdb	midbrain
ocl	occipital lobe
onorb	orbital segment optic nerve
phg	parahippocampal gyrus
pmesj	ponto-mesencephalic junction
prpc	prepontine cistern
scp	superior cerebellar peduncle (brachium conjunctivum)
set	sella turcica
stsi	straight sinus
supss	superior sagittal sinus
tenc	tentorial incisura
tlo	temporal lobe
tpo	temporal pole
ts	tuberculum sellae
v4v	fourth ventricle
vib	vitreous body (chamber) of eye

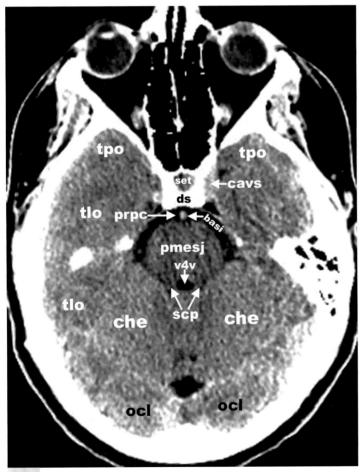

8.1k

(*continued*)

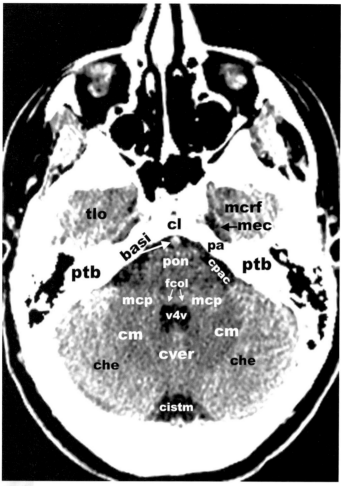

8.1l

FIGURES 8.1l,m

KEY

basi	basilar artery
che	cerebellar hemisphere
cistm	cisterna magna
cl	clivus
cm	corpus medullare
cpac	cerebellopontine angle cistern
cto	cerebellar tonsil
cver	cerebellar vermis
fcol	facial colliculus
icp	inferior cerebellar peduncle (restiform body)
infoc	inferior olivary complex
mcp	middle cerebellar peduncle (brachium pontis)
mcrf	middle cranial fossa
mec	Meckel's cave
med	medulla
ms	maxillary sinus
pa	petrous apex
polis	post-olivary sulcus
pon	pons
prols	pre-olivary sulcus
ptb	petrous temporal bone
pyem	pyramidal eminence
tlo	temporal lobe
v4v	fourth ventricle

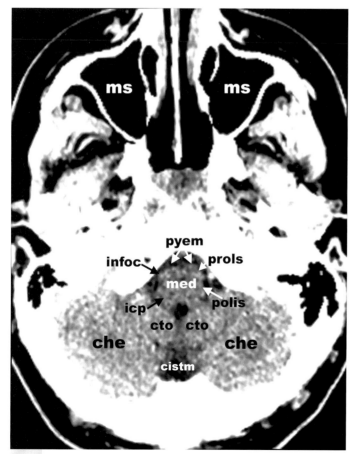

8.1m

■ **ELDERLY SUBJECT CT HEAD WITHOUT CONTRAST (FIGURES 8.2a–8.4e)**

Axial Plane

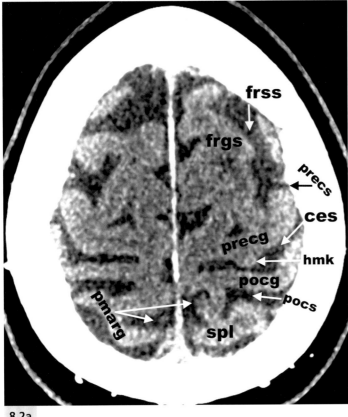

8.2a

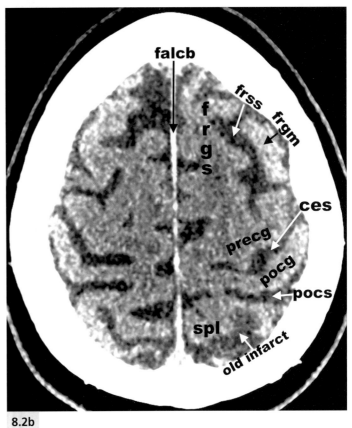

8.2b

FIGURES 8.2a–8.4e   Figures 8.2a–h Axial plane from superior/cranial to inferior/caudal, Figures 8.3a–h Coronal plane from anterior to posterior and Figures 8.4a–e Sagittal plane from medial to lateral.

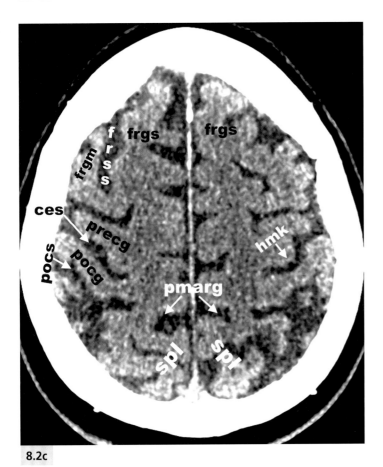

8.2c

KEY	
ces	central sulcus
falcb	falx cerebri
frgm	middle frontal gyrus
frgs	superior frontal gyrus
frss	superior frontal sulcus
hmk	hand motor knob
pmarg	pars marginalis (ascending ramus of cingulate sulcus)
pocg	post-central gyrus
pocs	post-central sulcus
precg	pre-central gyrus
precs	pre-central sulcus
spl	superior parietal lobule

(continued)

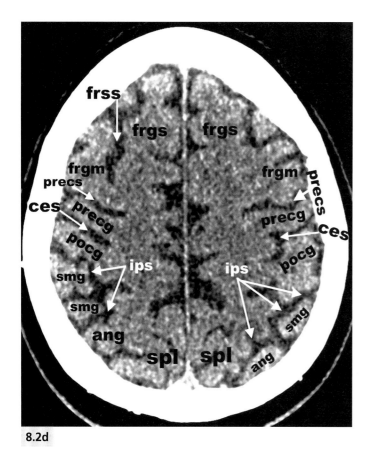

8.2d

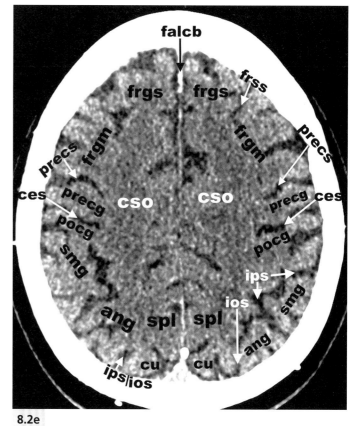

8.2e

FIGURES 8.2d–f

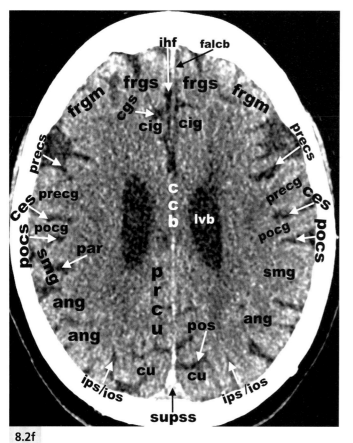

8.2f

KEY

ang	angular gyrus
ccb	body of corpus callosum
ces	central sulcus
cgs	cingulate sulcus
cig	cingulate gyrus
cso	centrum semiovale
cu	cuneus
falcb	falx cerebri
frgm	middle frontal gyrus
frgs	superior frontal gyrus
frss	superior frontal sulcus
ihf	interhemispheric fissure
ios	intra-occipital sulcus
ips	intraparietal sulcus
lvb	body of lateral ventricle
par	posterior ascending ramus of Sylvian fissure
pocg	post-central gyrus
pocs	post-central sulcus
pos	parieto-occipital sulcus
prcu	precuneus
precg	pre-central gyrus
precs	pre-central sulcus
smg	supramarginal gyrus
spl	superior parietal lobule
supss	superior sagittal sinus

(continued)

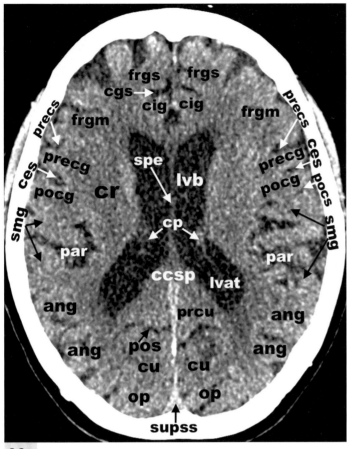

8.2g

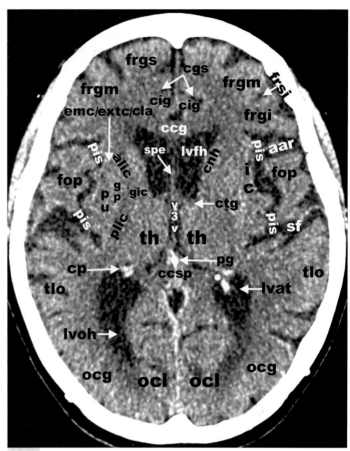

8.2h

FIGURES 8.2g–i

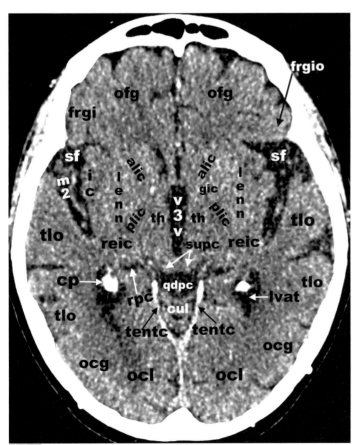

8.2i

KEY

aar	anterior ascending ramus of Sylvian fissure	**mca**	middle cerebral artery
alic	anterior limb of internal capsule	**m2**	m2 (Sylvian/insular branches mca)
ang	angular gyrus	**ocg**	occipital gyri
ccsp	splenium of corpus callosum	**ocl**	occipital lobe
		ofg	orbital-frontal gyri
ccg	genu of corpus callosum	**op**	occipital pole
ces	central sulcus	**par**	posterior ascending ramus of Sylvian fissure
cgs	cingulate sulcus		
cig	cingulate gyrus	**pg**	pineal gland
cla	claustrum	**pis**	peri-insular (circular) sulcus
cnh	caudate nucleus head		
ctg	caudo-thalamic groove (notch)	**plic**	posterior limb of internal capsule
cp	choroid plexus	**pocg**	post-central gyrus
cr	corona radiata	**pocs**	post-central sulcus
cu	cuneus	**pos**	parieto-occipital sulcus
cul	culmen	**prcu**	precuneus
emc	extreme capsule	**precg**	pre-central gyrus
extc	external capsule	**precs**	pre-central sulcus
fop	frontal operculum	**pu**	putamen
frgi	inferior frontal gyrus	**qdpc**	quadrigeminal plate cistern
frgio	pars orbitalis of inferior frontal gyrus	**reic**	retrolenticular internal capsule
frgm	middle frontal gyrus		
frgs	superior frontal gyrus	**rpc**	retro-pulvinar (thalamic) cistern (wings of ambient cistern)
frsi	inferior frontal sulcus		
gic	genu of internal capsule		
gp	glopus pallidus	**sf**	Sylvian fissure (lateral sulcus)
ic	insular cortex		
lenn	lenticular nucleus	**smg**	supramarginal gyrus
lvat	atrium (trigone) of lateral ventricle	**spe**	septum pellucidum
		supc	superior colliculus
lvb	body of lateral ventricle	**supss**	superior sagittal sinus
lvfh	frontal horn of lateral ventricle	**tentc**	tentorium cerebelli
		th	thalamus
lvoh	occipital horn of lateral ventricle	**tlo**	temporal lobe
		v3v	third ventricle

(continued)

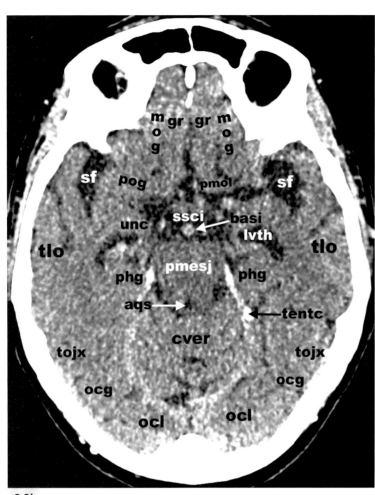

8.2j

FIGURES 8.2j,k

KEY

aqs	aqueduct of Sylvius
basi	basilar artery
che	cerebellar hemisphere
cver	cerebellar vermis
gr	gyrus rectus
hsc	horizontal Sylvian cistern (Sylvian fissure)
lvth	temporal horn of lateral ventricle
m1	m1 (horizontal segment mca)
mca	middle cerebral artery
mog	medial orbital gyrus
ocg	occipital gyri
ocl	occipital lobe
opch	optic chiasm
phg	parahippocampal gyrus
pmesj	ponto-mesencephalic junction
pmol	posteromedial orbital lobule
pog	posterior orbital gyrus
scp	superior cerebellar peduncle (brachium conjunctivum)
sf	Sylvian fissure (lateral sulcus)
ssci	suprasellar cistern
tentc	tentorium cerebelli
tlo	temporal lobe
tojx	temporal occipital junction
tpo	temporal pole
trs	transverse sinus
unc	uncus

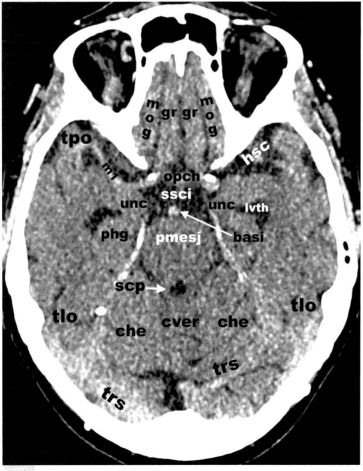

8.2k

(continued)

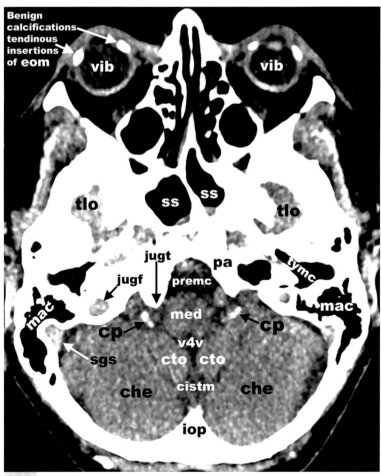

8.2l

FIGURES 8.2l,m

KEY

cavs	cavernous sinus
che	cerebellar hemisphere
cistm	cisterna magna
cp	choroid plexus
cto	cerebellar tonsil
cver	cerebellar vermis
dent	dentate nucleus
eom	extra-ocular muscles
falci	falx cerebelli
iop	internal occipital protuberance
jugf	jugular foramen
jugt	jugular tubercle of occipital bone
mac	mastoid air cells
mcp	middle cerebellar peduncle (brachium pontis)
med	medulla
nodu	nodulus of vermis (lobule X)
pa	petrous apex
ponbp	basis pontis of pons
pont	tegmentum of pons
premc	premedullary cistern
set	sella turcica
sgs	sigmoid sinus
ss	sphenoid sinus
tlo	temporal lobe
tpo	temporal pole
tymc	tympanic cavity
v4v	fourth ventricle
vib	vitreous body (chamber) of eye

8.2m

Coronal Plane

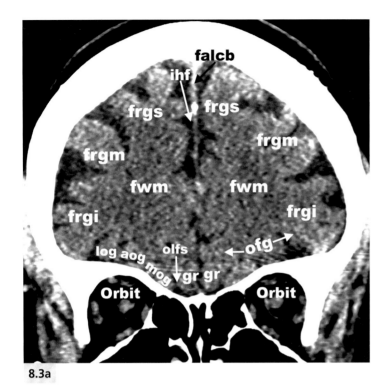

8.3a

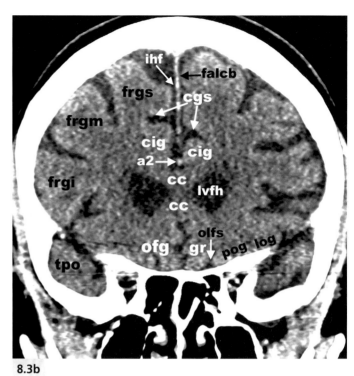

8.3b

FIGURES 8.3a–c

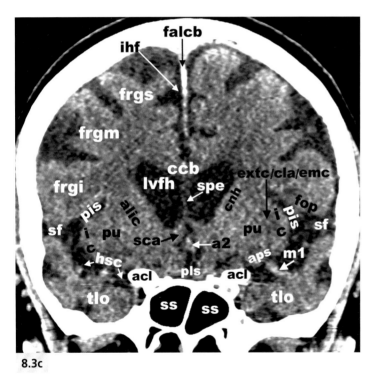

8.3c

KEY

a2	a2 (postcommunicating segment aca)	hsc	horizontal Sylvian cistern (Sylvian fissure)
aca	anterior cerebral artery	ic	insular cortex
acl	anterior clinoid process	ihf	interhemispheric fissure
alic	anterior limb of internal capsule	log	lateral orbital gyrus
		lvfh	frontal horn of lateral ventricle
aog	anterior orbital gyrus		
aps	anterior perforated substance	m1	m1 (horizontal segment mca)
cc	corpus callosum	mca	middle cerebral artery
ccb	body of corpus callosum	mog	medial orbital gyrus
cgs	cingulate sulcus	ofg	orbital-frontal gyri
cig	cingulate gyrus	olfs	olfactory sulcus
cla	claustrum	pis	peri-insular (circular) sulcus
cnh	caudate nucleus head		
emc	extreme capsule	pls	planum sphenoidale
extc	external capsule	pog	posterior orbital gyrus
falcb	falx cerebri	pu	putamen
fop	frontal operculum	sca	subcallosal area
frgi	inferior frontal gyrus	sf	Sylvian fissure (lateral sulcus)
frgm	middle frontal gyrus		
frgs	superior frontal gyrus	spe	septum pellucidum
fwm	frontal white matter	ss	sphenoid sinus
gr	gyrus rectus	tlo	temporal lobe
		tpo	temporal pole

(continued)

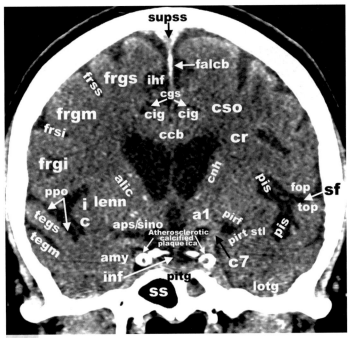

8.3d

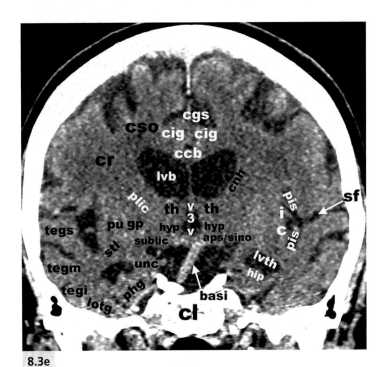

8.3e

FIGURES 8.3d–f

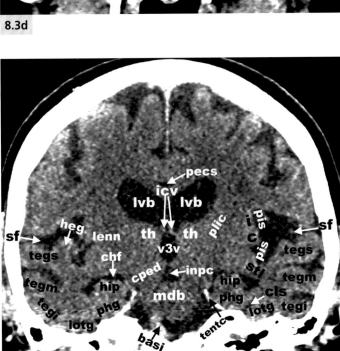

8.3f

KEY

a1	a1 (precommunicating segment aca)	inpc	interpeduncular cistern
aca	anterior cerebral artery	lenn	lenticular nucleus
alic	anterior limb of internal capsule	lotg	lateral occipital temporal gyrus (lotg)/fusiform gyrus
amy	amygdala	lvb	body of lateral ventricle
aps	anterior perforated substance	lvth	temporal horn of lateral ventricle
basi	basilar artery	mdb	midbrain
c7	c7 (communicating segment of ica)	pecs	pericallosal cistern (sulcus)
ccb	body of corpus callosum	phg	parahippocampal gyrus
cgs	cingulate sulcus	pirf	piriform cortex, frontal part
chf	choroidal fissure	pirt	piriform cortex, temporal part
cig	cingulate gyrus	pis	peri-insular (circular) sulcus
cl	clivus		
cls	collateral sulcus	pitg	pituitary gland
cnh	caudate nucleus head	plic	posterior limb of internal capsule
cped	cerebral peduncle		
cr	corona radiata	ppo	planum polare
cso	centrum semiovale	pu	putamen
falcb	falx cerebri	sf	Sylvian fissure (lateral sulcus)
fop	frontal operculum		
frgi	inferior frontal gyrus	sino	substantia innominata
frgm	middle frontal gyrus	ss	sphenoid sinus
frgs	superior frontal gyrus	stl	stem of temporal lobe
frsi	inferior frontal sulcus	sublic	sublenticular internal capsule
frss	superior frontal sulcus		
gp	glopus pallidus	supss	superior sagittal sinus
heg	Heschl's gyrus (transverse temporal gyrus)	tegi	inferior temporal gyrus
		tegm	middle temporal gyrus
hip	hippocampus	tegs	superior temporal gyrus
hyp	hypothalamus	tentc	tentorium cerebelli
ic	insular cortex	th	thalamus
ica	internal carotid artery	top	temporal operculum
icv	internal cerebral vein	unc	uncus
ihf	interhemispheric fissure	v3v	third ventricle
inf	infundibulum		

(continued)

FIGURES 8.3g,h

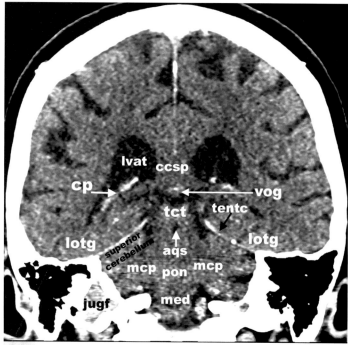

8.3g

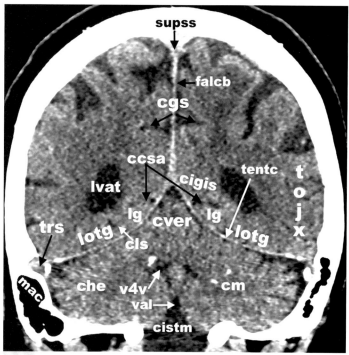

8.3h

KEY

aqs	aqueduct of Sylvius
ccsa	anterior calcarine sulcus
ccsp	splenium of corpus callosum
cgs	cingulate sulcus
che	cerebellar hemisphere
cigis	isthmus of cingulate gyrus
cistm	cisterna magna
cls	collateral sulcus
cm	corpus medullare
cp	choroid plexus
cver	cerebellar vermis
falcb	falx cerebri
jugf	jugular foramen
lg	lingual gyrus (motg)
lotg	lateral occipital temporal gyrus (lotg)/fusiform gyrus
lvat	atrium (trigone) of lateral ventricle
mac	mastoid air cells
mcp	middle cerebellar peduncle (brachium pontis)
med	medulla
pon	pons
supss	superior sagittal sinus
tct	tectum
tentc	tentorium cerebelli
tojx	temporal occipital junction
trs	transverse sinus
v4v	fourth ventricle
val	vallecula space
vog	vein of Galen

Sagittal Plane

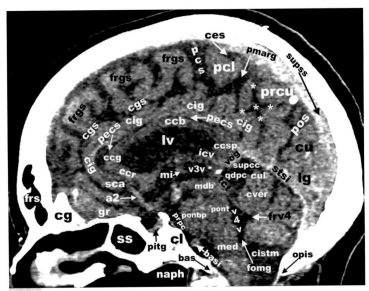

8.4a

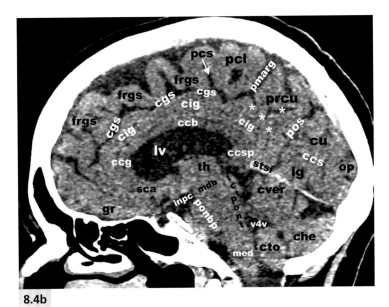

8.4b

FIGURES 8.4a,b   White asterisks outline the subparietal sulcus.

KEY

a2	a2 (postcommunicating segment aca)
aca	anterior cerebral artery
bas	basion
basi	basilar artery
ccb	body of corpus callosum
ccg	genu of corpus callosum
ccr	rostrum of corpus callosum
ccs	calcarine sulcus
ccsp	splenium of corpus callosum
ces	central sulcus
cg	crista galli
cgs	cingulate sulcus
che	cerebellar hemisphere
cig	cingulate gyrus
cistm	cisterna magna
cl	clivus
cto	cerebellar tonsil
cu	cuneus
cul	culmen (lobules IV and V)
cver	cerebellar vermis
fomg	foramen of Magendie
frgs	superior frontal gyrus
frs	frontal sinus
frv4	fastigial recess of fourth ventricle
gr	gyrus rectus
icv	internal cerebral vein
inpc	interpeduncular cistern
lg	lingual gyrus (motg)
lv	lateral ventricle
mdb	midbrain
med	medulla
mi	massa intermedia
naph	nasopharynx
op	occipital pole
opis	opisthion
pcl	paracentral lobule
pcs	paracentral sulcus
pecs	pericallosal cistern (sulcus)
pitg	pituitary gland
pmarg	pars marginalis (ascending ramus of cingulate sulcus)
ponbp	basis pontis of pons
pont	tegmentum of pons
pos	parieto-occipital sulcus
prcu	precuneus
prpc	prepontine cistern
qdpc	quadrigeminal plate cistern
sca	subcallosal area
ss	sphenoid sinus
stsi	straight sinus
supcc	supracerebellar cistern
supss	superior sagittal sinus
tct	tectum
th	thalamus
v3v	third ventricle
v4v	fourth ventricle
vog	vein of Galen

(continued)

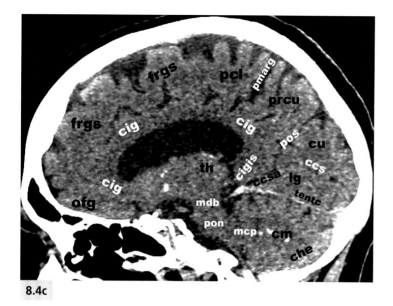

8.4c

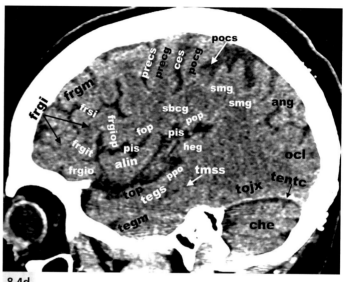

8.4d

FIGURES 8.4c–e

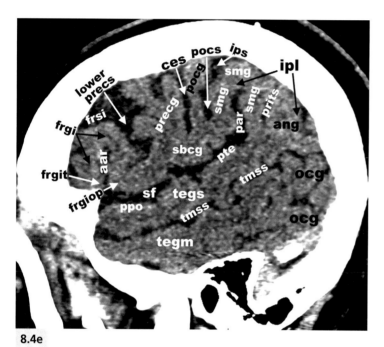

8.4e

KEY

aar	anterior ascending ramus of Sylvian fissure
alin	anterior lobule of insula
ang	angular gyrus
ccs	calcarine sulcus
ccsa	anterior calcarine sulcus
ces	central sulcus
che	cerebellar hemisphere
cig	cingulate gyrus
cigis	isthmus of cingulate gyrus
cm	corpus medullare
cu	cuneus
fop	frontal operculum
frgi	inferior frontal gyrus
frgio	pars orbitalis of inferior frontal gyrus
frgiop	pars opercularis of inferior frontal gyrus
frgit	pars triangularis of inferior frontal gyrus
frgm	middle frontal gyrus
frgs	superior frontal gyrus
frsi	inferior frontal sulcus
heg	Heschl's gyrus (transverse temporal gyrus)
ipl	inferior parietal lobule
ips	intraparietal sulcus
lg	lingual gyrus (motg)
mcp	middle cerebellar peduncle (brachium pontis)
mdb	midbrain
ocg	occipital gyri
ocl	occipital lobe
ofg	orbital-frontal gyri
par	posterior ascending ramus of Sylvian fissure
pcl	paracentral lobule
pis	peri-insular (circular) sulcus
pmarg	pars marginalis (ascending ramus of cingulate sulcus)
pocg	post-central gyrus
pocs	post-central sulcus
pon	pons
pop	parietal operculum
pos	parieto-occipital sulcus
ppo	planum polare
prcu	precuneus
precg	pre-central gyrus
precs	pre-central sulcus
prits	primary intermediate sulcus
pte	planum temporale
sbcg	subcentral gyrus
sf	Sylvian fissure (lateral sulcus)
smg	supramarginal gyrus
tegm	middle temporal gyrus
tegs	superior temporal gyrus
tentc	tentorium cerebelli
th	thalamus
tmss	superior temporal sulcus
tojx	temporal occipital junction
top	temporal operculum

■ SELECT CT HEAD IMAGES WITHOUT CONTRAST (FIGURES 8.5a–d)

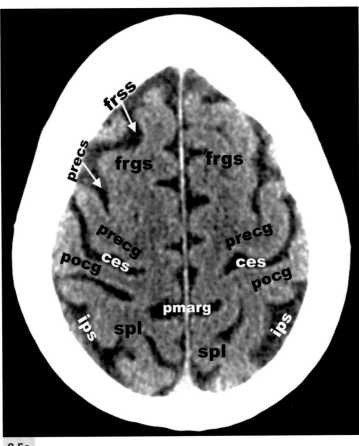

8.5a

FIGURES 8.5a–d Normal typical, textbook appearance of the gyri and sulci in the superior cerebral hemispheres in 8.5a–c and at the level of the basal ganglia/thalamus/internal capsule (Figure 8.5d).

KEY

ang	angular gyrus
ces	central sulcus
frgs	superior frontal gyrus
frss	superior frontal sulcus
frgm	middle frontal gyrus
hmk	hand motor knob
ips	intraparietal sulcus
ipl	inferior parietal lobule
pmarg	pars marginalis (ascending ramus of cingulate sulcus)
pocg	post-central gyrus
precg	pre-central gyrus
precs	pre-central sulcus
spl	superior parietal lobule
smg	supramarginal gyrus

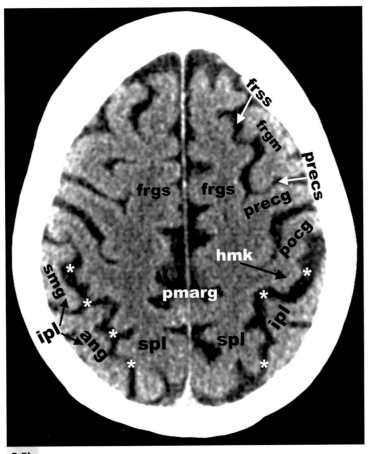

8.5b

FIGURE 8.5b White asterisks in this image outline the intraparietal sulci separating the superior parietal lobule from the inferior parietal lobule (supramarginal and angular gyri).

(continued)

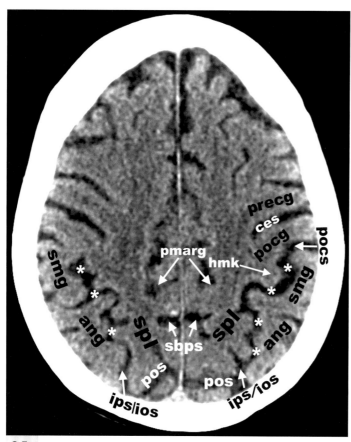

8.5c

FIGURE 8.5c White asterisks in this image outline the intraparietal sulci separating the superior parietal lobule from the inferior parietal lobule (supramarginal and angular gyri).

KEY

alic	anterior limb of internal capsule
ang	angular gyrus
ccg	genu of corpus callosum
ccsp	splenium of corpus callosum
ces	central sulcus
cla	claustrum
cnh	caudate nucleus head
cp	choroid plexus
cvi	cistern of velum interpositum
emc	extreme capsule
extc	external capsule
frxac	ascending columns of fornix
fwm	frontal white matter
gic	genu of internal capsule
gp	glopus pallidus
hmk	hand motor knob
ios	intra-occipital sulcus
ips	intraparietal sulcus
jx	junction
lenn	lenticular nucleus
lvat	atrium (trigone) of lateral ventricle
owm	occipital white matter
plic	posterior limb of internal capsule
pmarg	pars marginalis (ascending ramus of cingulate sulcus)
pocg	post-central gyrus
pocs	post-central sulcus
pos	parieto-occipital sulcus
precg	pre-central gyrus
pu	putamen
reic	retrolenticular internal capsule
sbps	subparietal sulcus
smg	supramarginal gyrus
spl	superior parietal lobule
stsi	straight sinus
th	thalamus
vog	vein of Galen

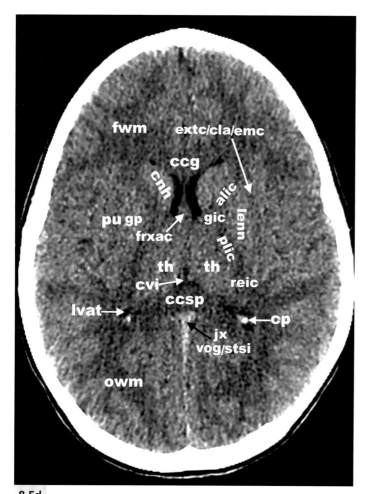

8.5d

FIGURE 8.5d

■ **ARACHNOID GRANULATIONS CT (FIGURES 8.6a–f)**

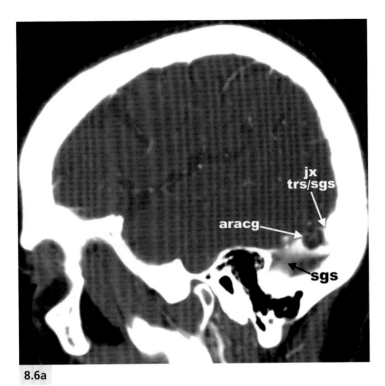

8.6a

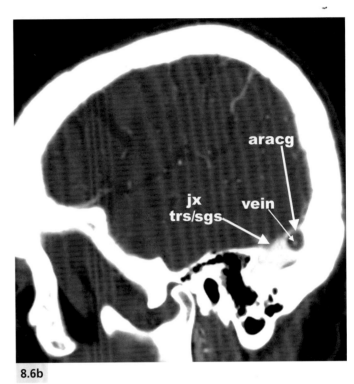

8.6b

FIGURES 8.6a,b   Post-contrast sagittal reformatted images showing a round filling defect in the distal right transverse sinus near its junction with the sigmoid sinus which contains a small central vein. Findings are typical for an arachnoid granulation.

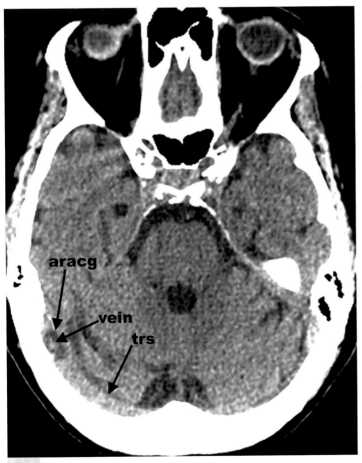

8.6c

KEY	
aracg	arachnoid granulations
jx	junction
sgs	sigmoid sinus
trs	transverse sinus

FIGURE 8.6c   Non-contrast axial CT image in same patient shows a defect in the distal right transverse sinus.

(*continued*)

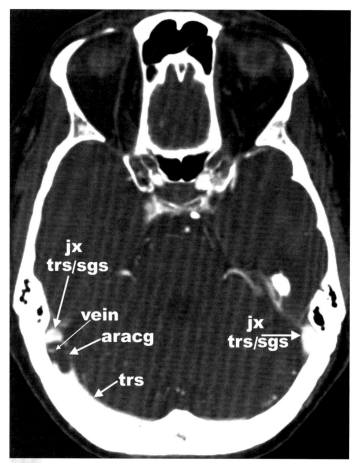

8.6d

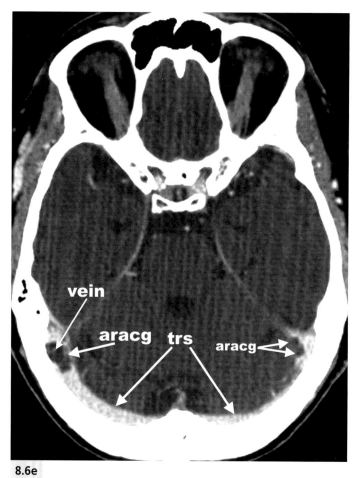

8.6e

FIGURES 8.6d–f Post-contrast axial images demonstrate similar findings as previous images compatible with an arachnoid granulation. Smaller filling defect at junction of left transverse and sigmoid sinuses also represents an arachnoid granulation.

KEY

aracg	arachnoid granulations
jx	junction
sgs	sigmoid sinus
trs	transverse sinus

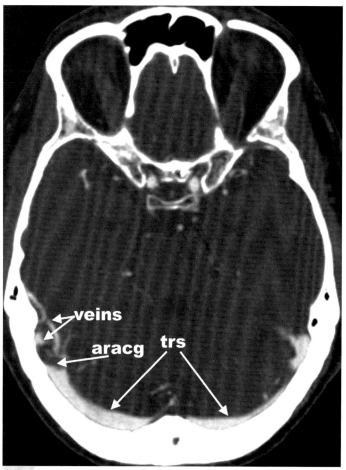

8.6f

3D SKULL AND FACIAL BONES—CT RECONSTRUCTIONS (FIGURES 8.7a–8.8i)

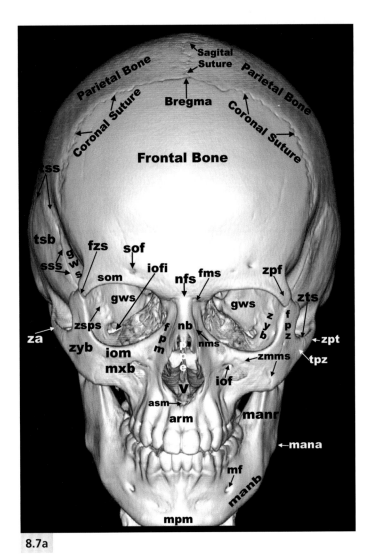

8.7a

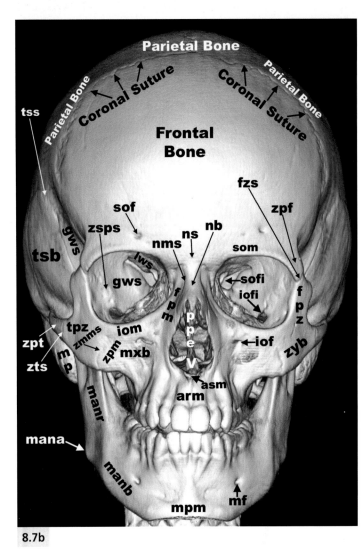

8.7b

FIGURES 8.7a–8.8i   These 3D CT reconstructions demonstrate normal bony anatomy. These detailed images can be reconstructed and rotated in any plane if the appropriate thin section helical CT exam is obtained.

KEY

arm	alveolar ridge of maxilla
asm	anterior spine of maxilla
fms	frontomaxillary suture
fpm	frontal process of maxilla
fpz	frontal process of zygomatic bone
fzs	frontozygomatic suture
gws	greater wing of the sphenoid bone
iof	infraorbital foramen
iofi	inferior orbital fissure
iom	infraorbital margin
lws	lesser wing of the sphenoid bone
mana	angle of mandible
manb	mandible body
manr	ramus of mandible
mf	mental foramen
mp	mastoid process
mpm	mental protuberance of mandible
mxb	maxillary bone
nb	nasal bone
nfs	nasofrontal suture

nms	nasomaxillary suture
ns	nasion
ppe	perpendicular plate of ethmoid
sof	supra-orbital foramen
sofi	superior orbital fissure
som	supraorbital margin
sss	sphenosquamosal suture
tpz	temporal process of zygomatic bone
tsb	temporal squamosal bone
tss	temporal squamosal suture
v	vomer
za	zygomatic arch
zmms	zygomaticomaxillary suture
zpf	zygomatic process of frontal bone
zpm	zygomatic process of maxilla
zpt	zygomatic process of temporal bone
zsps	zygomaticosphenoid suture
zts	zygomaticotemporal suture
zyb	zygomatic bone

(continued)

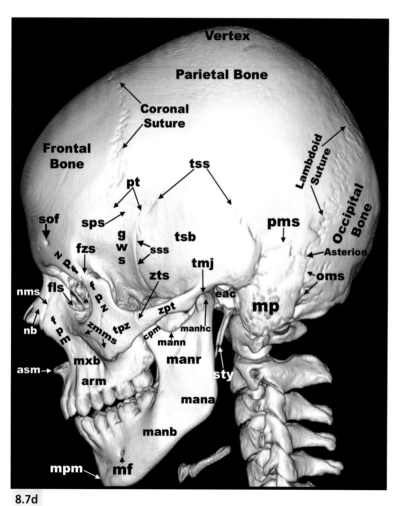

8.7c

8.7d

FIGURES 8.7c,d

KEY

arm	alveolar ridge of maxilla
asm	anterior spine of maxilla
cpm	coronoid process of mandible
eac	external auditory canal
fls	fossa for lacrimal sac
fpm	frontal process of maxilla
fpz	frontal process of zygomatic bone
fzs	frontozygomatic suture
gws	greater wing of the sphenoid bone
iof	infraorbital foramen
iom	infraorbital margin
lws	lesser wing of the sphenoid bone
mana	angle of mandible
manb	mandible body
mancn	neck of mandibular condyle
manhc	head of mandibular condyle
mann	mandibular notch
manr	ramus of mandible
mf	mental foramen
mp	mastoid process
mpm	mental protuberance of mandible
mxb	maxillary bone
nb	nasal bone
nms	nasomaxillary suture
ns	nasion
oms	occipitomastoid suture
opf	orbital plate of frontal bone
pms	parietomastoid suture
ppe	perpendicular plate of ethmoid
pt	pterion
sfs	sphenofrontal suture
sof	supra-orbital foramen
sofi	superior orbital fissure
som	supraorbital margin
sps	sphenoparietal suture
sss	sphenosquamosal suture
sty	styloid process
tmj	temporal mandibular joint
tpz	temporal process of zygomatic bone
tsb	temporal squamosal bone
tss	temporal squamosal suture
v	vomer
zmms	zygomaticomaxillary suture
zpf	zygomatic process of frontal bone
zpm	zygomatic process of maxilla
zpt	zygomatic process of temporal bone
zsps	zygomaticosphenoid suture
zts	zygomaticotemporal suture
zyb	zygomatic bone

(continued)

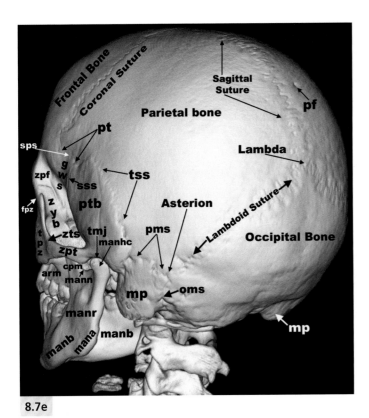

8.7e

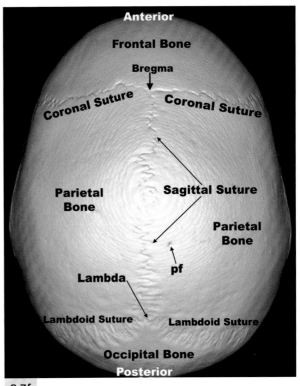

8.7f

FIGURES 8.7e–g

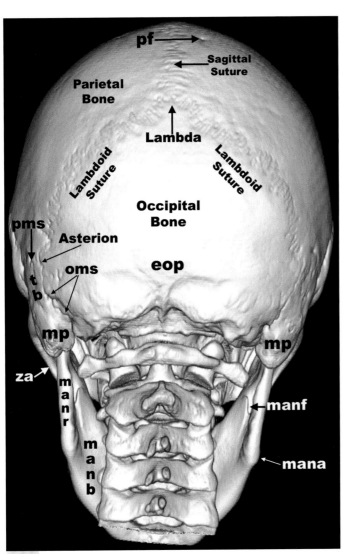

8.7g

KEY	
arm	alveolar ridge of maxilla
cpm	coronoid process of mandible
eop	external occipital protuberance (inion)
fpz	frontal process of zygomatic bone
gws	greater wing of the sphenoid bone
mana	angle of mandible
manb	mandible body
manf	mandibular foramen
manhc	head of mandibular condyle
mann	mandibular notch
manr	ramus of mandible
mp	mastoid process
oms	occipitomastoid suture
pf	parietal foramina
pms	parietomastoid suture
pt	pterion
ptb	petrous temporal bone
sps	sphenoparietal suture
sss	sphenosquamosal suture
tb	temporal bone
tmj	temporal mandibular joint
tpz	temporal process of zygomatic bone
tss	temporal squamosal suture
za	zygomatic arch
zpf	zygomatic process of frontal bone
zpt	zygomatic process of temporal bone
zts	zygomaticotemporal suture
zyb	zygomatic bone

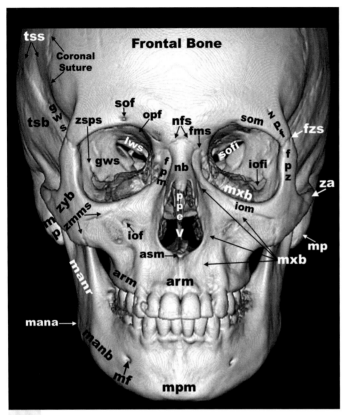

8.8a

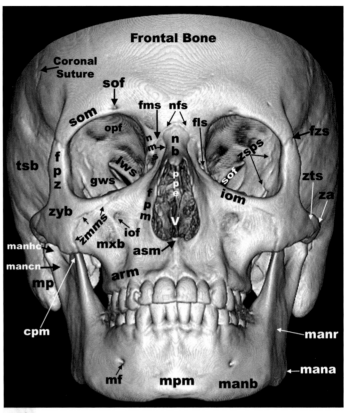

8.8b

FIGURES 8.8a–c

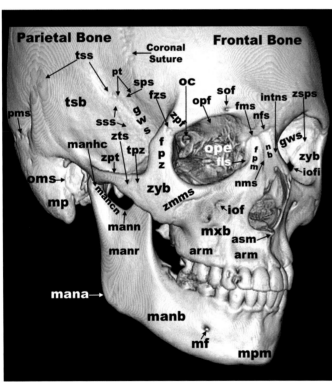

8.8c

KEY

arm	alveolar ridge of maxilla	**oc**	optic canal
asm	anterior spine of maxilla	**oms**	occipitomastoid suture
cpm	coronoid process of mandible	**ope**	orbital plate of ethmoid bone
fls	fossa for lacrimal sac	**opf**	orbital plate of frontal bone
fms	frontomaxillary suture		
fpm	frontal process of maxilla	**pms**	parietomastoid suture
fpz	frontal process of zygomatic bone	**ppe**	perpendicular plate of ethmoid
fzs	frontozygomatic suture	**pt**	pterion
gws	greater wing of the sphenoid bone	**sof**	supra-orbital foramen
		sofi	superior orbital fissure
intns	internasal bone suture	**som**	supraorbital margin
iof	infraorbital foramen	**sps**	sphenoparietal suture
iofi	inferior orbital fissure	**sss**	sphenosquamosal suture
iom	infraorbital margin	**tpz**	temporal process of zygomatic bone
lws	lesser wing of the sphenoid bone	**tsb**	temporal squamosal bone
mana	angle of mandible	**tss**	temporal squamosal suture
manb	mandible body		
mancn	neck of mandibular condyle	**v**	vomer
		za	zygomatic arch
mann	mandibular notch	**zmms**	zygomaticomaxillary suture
manhc	head of mandibular condyle		
		zpf	zygomatic process of frontal bone
manr	ramus of mandible		
mf	mental foramen	**zpt**	zygomatic process of temporal bone
mp	mastoid process		
mpm	mental protuberance of mandible	**zsps**	zygomaticosphenoid suture
mxb	maxillary bone	**zts**	zygomaticotemporal suture
nb	nasal bone		
nfs	nasofrontal suture	**zyb**	zygomatic bone
nms	nasomaxillary suture		

(continued)

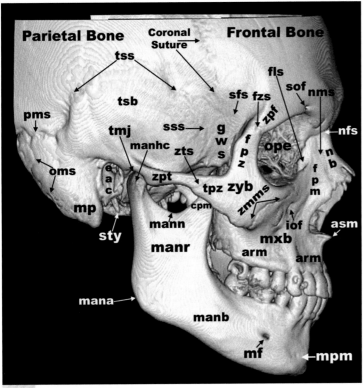

8.8d

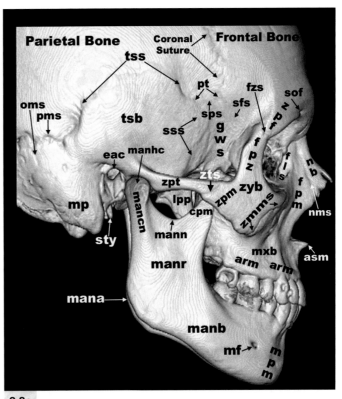

8.8e

FIGURES 8.8d–f

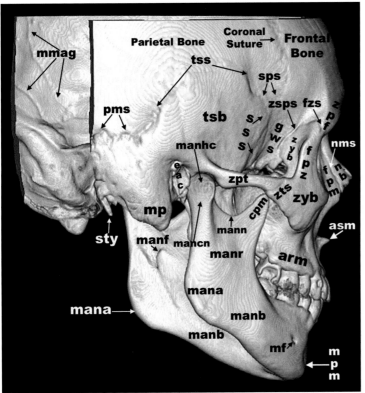

8.8f

KEY

arm	alveolar ridge of maxilla
asm	anterior spine of maxilla
cpm	coronoid process of mandible
eac	external auditory canal
fls	fossa for lacrimal sac
fpm	frontal process of maxilla
fpz	frontal process of zygomatic bone
fzs	frontozygomatic suture
gws	greater wing of the sphenoid bone
iof	infraorbital foramen
lpp	lateral pterygoid plate
mana	angle of mandible
manb	mandible body
mancn	neck of mandibular condyle
manf	mandibular foramen
manhc	head of mandibular condyle
mann	mandibular notch
manr	ramus of mandible
mf	mental foramen
mmag	middle meningeal artery grooves
mp	mastoid process
mpm	mental protuberance of mandible
mxb	maxillary bone
nb	nasal bone
nfs	nasofrontal suture
nms	nasomaxillary suture
oms	occipitomastoid suture
ope	orbital plate of ethmoid bone
pms	parietomastoid suture
pt	pterion
sfs	sphenofrontal suture
sof	supra-orbital foramen
sps	sphenoparietal suture
sss	sphenosquamosal suture
sty	styloid process
tmj	temporal mandibular joint
tpz	temporal process of zygomatic bone
tsb	temporal squamosal bone
tss	temporal squamosal suture
zmms	zygomaticomaxillary suture
zpf	zygomatic process of frontal bone
zpm	zygomatic process of maxilla
zpt	zygomatic process of temporal bone
zsps	zygomaticosphenoid suture
zts	zygomaticotemporal suture
zyb	zygomatic bone

(*continued*)

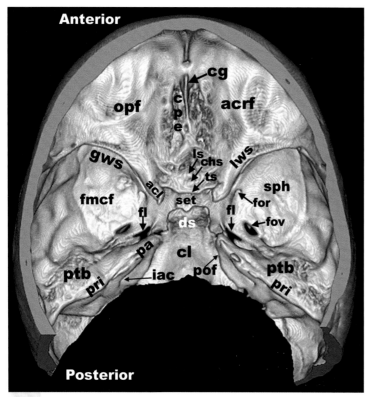

8.8g

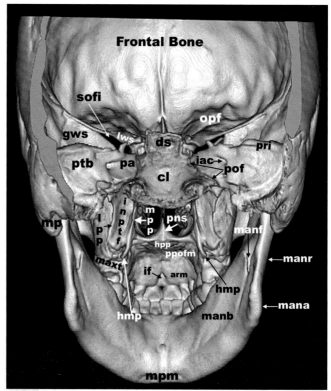

8.8h

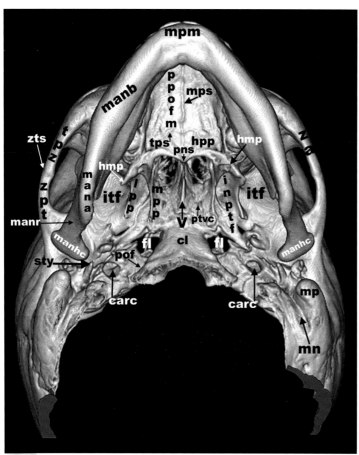

8.8i

FIGURES 8.8g–i Figure 8.8g is a top (superior) down (inferior) view, Figure 8.8h is a posterior (from the back of the head) view and Figure 8.8i is a bottom (inferior) up (superior) view. The uppermost aspect of the skull and the occipital bone was intentionally removed at time of reconstruction.

KEY

acl	anterior clinoid process	manr	ramus of mandible
acrf	anterior cranial fossa	maxt	maxillary tuberosity
arm	alveolar ridge of maxilla	mn	mastoid notch
		mp	mastoid process
carc	carotid canal	mpm	mental protuberance of mandible
cg	crista galli		
chs	chiasmatic sulcus	mpp	medial pterygoid plate
cl	clivus	mps	median palatine suture
cpe	cribriform plate of ethmoid bone	opf	orbital plate of frontal bone
ds	dorsum sellae	pa	petrous apex
fl	foramen lacerum	pns	posterior nasal spine
fmcf	floor of middle cranial fossa	pof	petro-occipital fissure
		ppofm	palatine process of maxilla
for	foramen rotundem		
fov	foramen ovale	pri	petrous ridge
gws	greater wing of the sphenoid bone	ptb	petrous temporal bone
		ptvc	pterygovaginal (palatovaginal or pharyngeal canal)
hmp	hamulus of medial pterygoid plate		
hpp	horizontal plate of palatine bone	set	sella turcica
		sofi	superior orbital fissure
iac	internal auditory canal	sph	sphenoid bone
if	incisive fossa	sty	styloid process
inptf	interpterygoid fossa	tps	transverse palatine suture
itf	infratemporal fossa		
lpp	lateral pterygoid plate	tpz	temporal process of zygomatic bone
ls	limbus sphenoidale		
lws	lesser wing of the sphenoid bone	ts	tuberculum sellae
		v	vomer
mana	angle of mandible	za	zygomatic arch
manb	mandible body	zpt	zygomatic process of temporal bone
manf	mandibular foramen		
manhc	head of mandibular condyle	zts	zygomaticotemporal suture

SKULL BASE CT (FIGURES 8.9a–8.11g)

Axial Plane

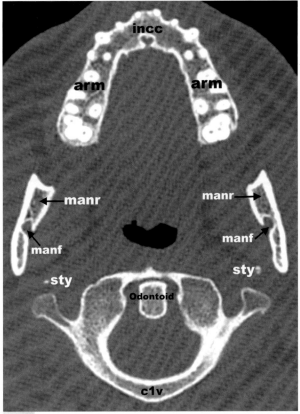

8.9a

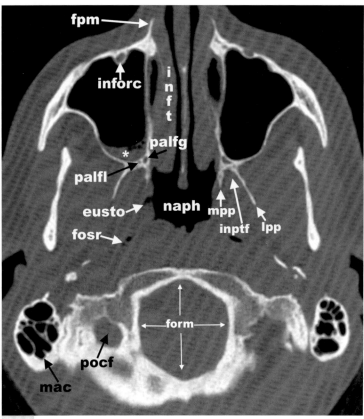

8.9b

FIGURES 8.9a–k   Axial images from inferior (caudal) to superior (cranial) demonstrate normal bony anatomy.

FIGURES 8.9b–g   Demonstrates a small amount of fluid/mucus in the posterior, dependent portion of the right maxillary sinus indicated by the single white asterisk.

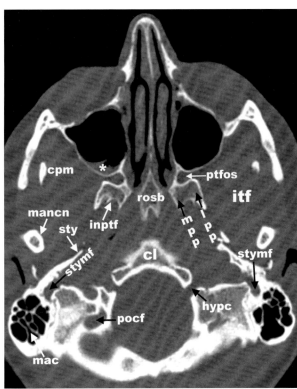

8.9c

KEY

arm	alveolar ridge of maxilla	**lpp**	lateral pterygoid plate
c1v	first vertebral segment	**mac**	mastoid air cells
cl	clivus	**mancn**	neck of mandibular condyle
cpm	coronoid process of mandible	**manf**	mandibular foramen
		manr	ramus of mandible
eusto	eustachian tube orifice	**mpp**	medial pterygoid plate
form	foramen magnum	**naph**	nasopharynx
fosr	fossa of Rosenmüller	**palfg**	greater palatine foramina
fpm	frontal process of maxilla	**palfl**	lesser palatine foramina
hypc	hypoglossal canal	**pocf**	posterior condylar foramen
incc	incisive/nasopalatine canal	**ptfos**	pterygopalatine fossa
inforc	infra-orbital canal	**rosb**	rostrum of sphenoid bone
inft	inferior nasal turbinate	**sty**	styloid process
inptf	interpterygoid fossa	**stymf**	stylomastoid foramen
itf	infratemporal fossa		

(*continued*)

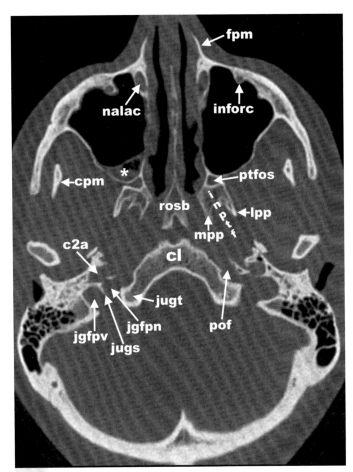

8.9d

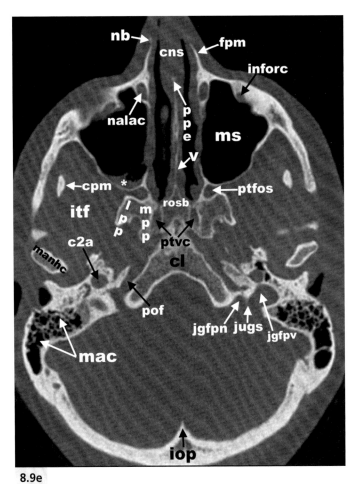

8.9e

FIGURES 8.9d–f

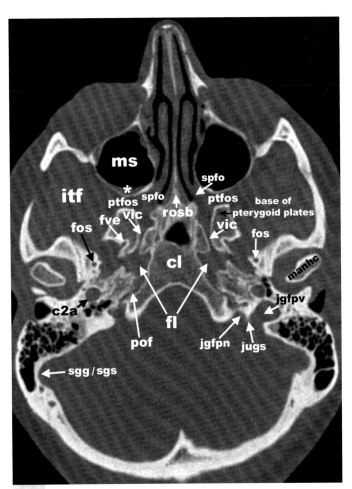

8.9f

KEY

c2a	c2a (vertical petrous segment ica)	lpp	lateral pterygoid plate
		mac	mastoid air cells
cl	clivus	manhc	head of mandibular condyle
cns	cartilaginous nasal septum		
cpm	coronoid process of mandible	mpp	medial pterygoid plate
		ms	maxillary sinus
fl	foramen lacerum	nalac	nasolacrimal duct
fos	foramen spinosum	nb	nasal bone
fpm	frontal process of maxilla	pof	petro-occipital fissure
fve	foramen of Vesalius	ppe	perpendicular plate of ethmoid
ica	internal carotid artery		
inforc	infra-orbital canal	ptfos	pterygopalatine fossa
inptf	interpterygoid fossa	ptvc	pterygovaginal (palatovaginal or pharyngeal canal)
iop	internal occipital protuberance		
		rosb	rostrum of sphenoid bone
itf	infratemporal fossa		
jgfpn	pars nervosa-jugular foramen	sgg	sigmoid groove
		sgs	sigmoid sinus
jgfpv	pars vascularis-jugular foramen	spfo	sphenopalatine foramen
		v	vomer
jugs	jugular spine	vic	vidian canal
jugt	jugular tubercle of occipital bone		

(continued)

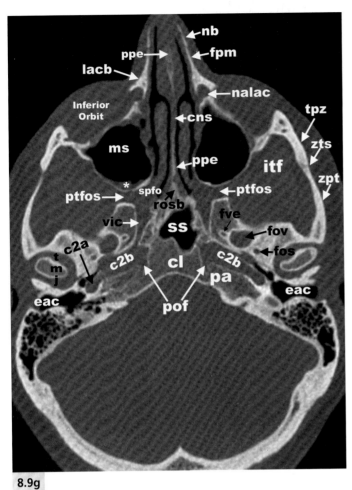

8.9g

FIGURE 8.9g

8.9h

FIGURES 8.9h,i   shows mucosal thickening (multiple white asterisks) in right ethmoid air cells.

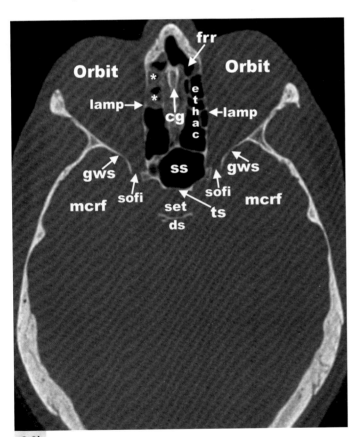

8.9i

KEY

c2a	c2a (vertical petrous segment ica)	nms	nasomaxillary suture
c2b	c2b (horizontal petrous segment of ica)	olfr	olfactory recess of nasal cavity
cg	crista galli	pa	petrous apex
cl	clivus	pcrf	posterior cranial fossa
cns	cartilaginous nasal septum	pof	petro-occipital fissure
ds	dorsum sellae	ppe	perpendicular plate of ethmoid
eac	external auditory canal	ptfos	pterygopalatine fossa
ethac	ethmoid air cells	rosb	rostrum of sphenoid bone
for	foramen rotundem	set	sella turcica
fos	foramen spinosum	sgg	sigmoid groove
fov	foramen ovale	sgs	sigmoid sinus
fpm	frontal process of maxilla	sofi	superior orbital fissure
frr	frontal recess	spfo	sphenopalatine foramen
fve	foramen of Vesalius	sphs	sphenoid sinus septum
gws	greater wing of the sphenoid bone	ss	sphenoid sinus
		tmj	temporal mandibular joint
ica	internal carotid artery	tpz	temporal process of zygomatic bone
iofi	inferior orbital fissure	ts	tuberculum sellae
itf	infratemporal fossa	tymc	tympanic cavity
lacb	lacrimal bone	vesa	vestibular aqueduct
lamp	lamina papyracea	vic	vidian canal
mac	mastoid air cells	zpt	zygomatic process of temporal bone
mcrf	middle cranial fossa	zts	zygomaticotemporal suture
ms	maxillary sinus		
nalac	nasolacrimal duct		
nb	nasal bone		

(continued)

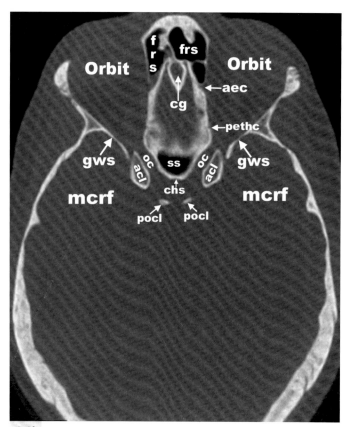

8.9j

FIGURES 8.9j,k

KEY

acl	anterior clinoid process
aec	anterior ethmoidal canal
cg	crista galli
chs	chiasmatic sulcus
frs	frontal sinus
gws	greater wing of the sphenoid bone
ls	limbus sphenoidale
mcrf	middle cranial fossa
oc	optic canal
pethc	posterior ethmoidal canal
pocl	posterior clinoid process
ss	sphenoid sinus

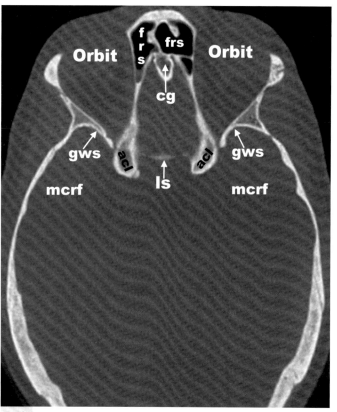

8.9k

Coronal Plane

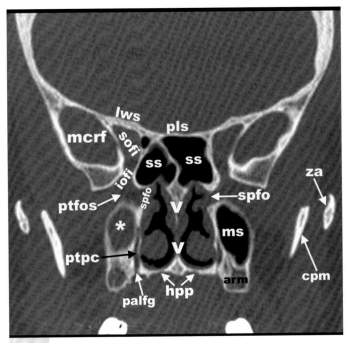

8.10a

FIGURE 8.10a   shows a small amount of fluid/mucus (white asterisk) in the posterior right maxillary sinus.

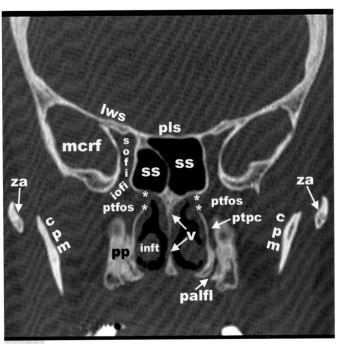

8.10b

FIGURE 8.10b   White asterisks indicate the sphenopalatine foramen.

FIGURES 8.10a–m   Coronal images from anterior to posterior demonstrate normal bony anatomy.

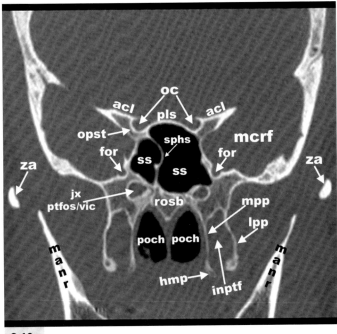

8.10c

FIGURE 8.10c

KEY	
acl	anterior clinoid process
arm	alveolar ridge of maxilla
cpm	coronoid process of mandible
for	foramen rotundem
hmp	hamulus of medial pterygoid plate
hpp	horizontal plate of palatine bone
inft	inferior nasal turbinate
inptf	interpterygoid fossa
iofi	inferior orbital fissure
jx	junction
lpp	lateral pterygoid plate
lws	lesser wing of the sphenoid bone
manr	ramus of mandible
mcrf	middle cranial fossa
mpp	medial pterygoid plate
ms	maxillary sinus
oc	optic canal
opst	optic strut
palfg	greater palatine foramina
palfl	lesser palatine foramina
pls	planum sphenoidale
poch	posterior choana
pp	pterygoid plates
ptfos	pterygopalatine fossa
ptpc	pterygopalatine canal
rosb	rostrum of sphenoid bone
sofi	superior orbital fissure
spfo	sphenopalatine foramen
sphs	sphenoid sinus septum
ss	sphenoid sinus
v	vomer
vic	vidian canal
za	zygomatic arch

(continued)

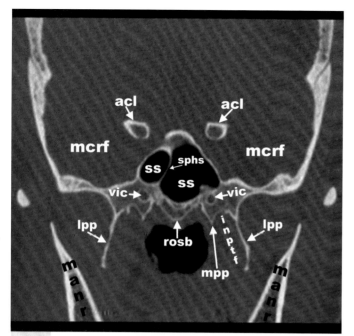

8.10d

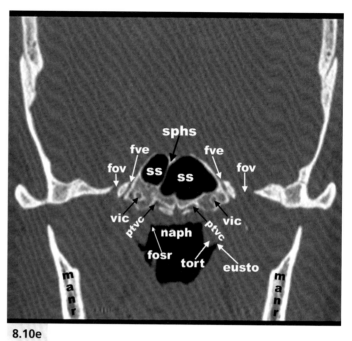

8.10e

FIGURES 8.10d–f

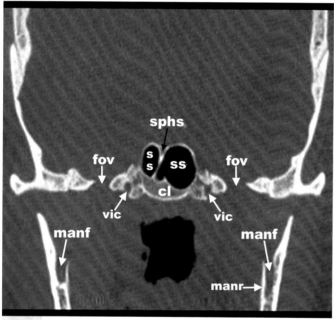

8.10f

KEY

acl	anterior clinoid process
cl	clivus
eusto	eustachian tube orifice
fosr	fossa of Rosenmüller
fov	foramen ovale
fve	foramen of Vesalius
inptf	interpterygoid fossa
lpp	lateral pterygoid plate
manf	mandibular foramen
manr	ramus of mandible
mcrf	middle cranial fossa
mpp	medial pterygoid plate
naph	nasopharynx
ptvc	pterygovaginal (palatovaginal or pharyngeal canal)
rosb	rostrum of sphenoid bone
sphs	sphenoid sinus septum
ss	sphenoid sinus
tort	torus tubarius
vic	vidian canal

(continued)

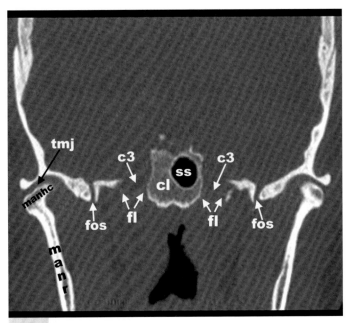

8.10g

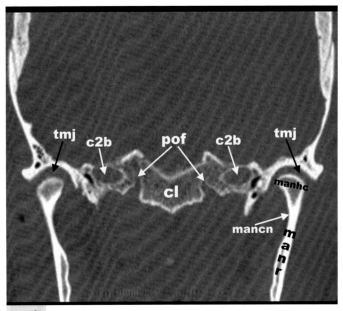

8.10h

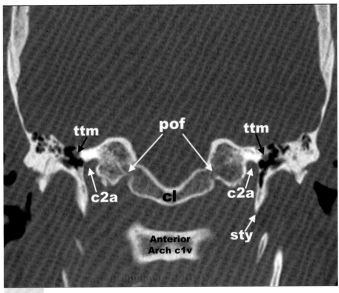

8.10i

FIGURES 8.10g–i

KEY

c1v	first vertebral segment
c2a	c2a (vertical petrous segment ica)
c2b	c2b (horizontal petrous segment of ica)
c3	c3 (lacerum segment of ica)
cl	clivus
fl	foramen lacerum
fos	foramen spinosum
ica	internal carotid artery
mancn	neck of mandibular condyle
manhc	head of mandibular condyle
manr	ramus of mandible
pof	petro-occipital fissure
ss	sphenoid sinus
sty	styloid process
tmj	temporal mandibular joint
ttm	tensor tympani muscle

(*continued*)

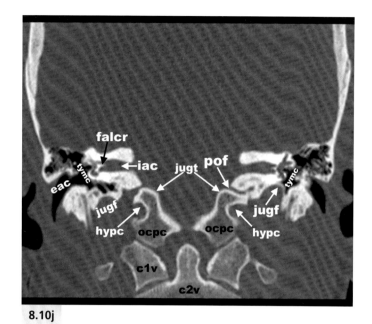

8.10j

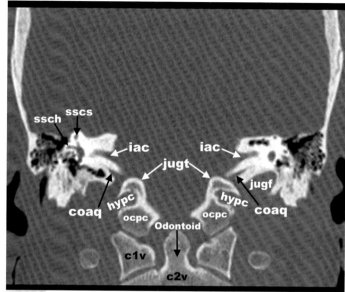

8.10k

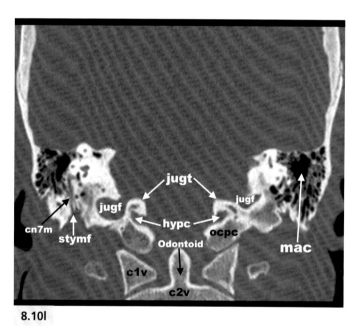

8.10l

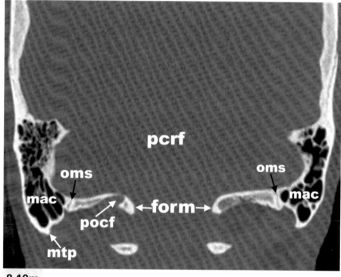

8.10m

FIGURES 8.10j–m

KEY

c1v	first vertebral segment		mac	mastoid air cells
c2v	second vertebral segment		mtp	mastoid tip
cn7m	mastoid segment facial nerve		ocpc	occipital condyle
coaq	cochlear aqueduct		oms	occipitomastoid suture
eac	external auditory canal		pcrf	posterior cranial fossa
falcr	falciform crest		pocf	posterior condylar foramen
form	foramen magnum		pof	petro-occipital fissure
hypc	hypoglossal canal		ssch	horizontal semicircular canal
iac	internal auditory canal		sscs	superior semicircular canal
jugf	jugular foramen		stymf	stylomastoid foramen
jugt	jugular tubercle of occipital bone		tymc	tympanic cavity

Sagittal Plane

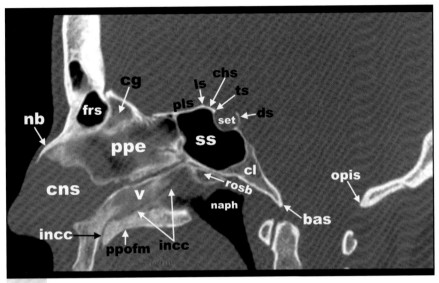

8.11a

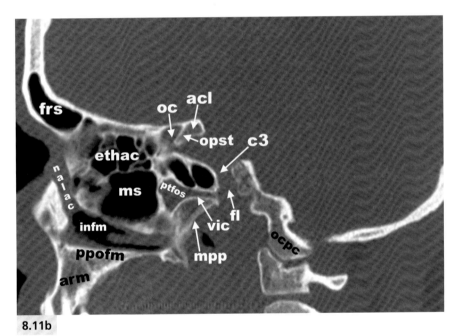

8.11b

FIGURES 8.11a–g   Sagittal images from medial to lateral demonstrate normal bony anatomy.

KEY

acl	anterior clinoid process
arm	alveolar ridge of maxilla
bas	basion
c3	c3 (lacerum segment of ica)
cg	crista galli
chs	chiasmatic sulcus
cl	clivus
cns	cartilaginous nasal septum
ds	dorsum sellae
ethac	ethmoid air cells
fl	foramen lacerum
frs	frontal sinus
ica	internal carotid artery
incc	incisive/nasopalatine canal
infm	inferior meatus
ls	limbus sphenoidale
mpp	medial pterygoid plate
ms	maxillary sinus

nalac	nasolacrimal duct
naph	nasopharynx
nb	nasal bone
oc	optic canal
ocpc	occipital condyle
opis	opisthion
opst	optic strut
pls	planum sphenoidale
ppe	perpendicular plate of ethmoid
ppofm	palatine process of maxilla
ptfos	pterygopalatine fossa
rosb	rostrum of sphenoid bone
set	sella turcica
ss	sphenoid sinus
ts	tuberculum sellae
v	vomer
vic	vidian canal

(continued)

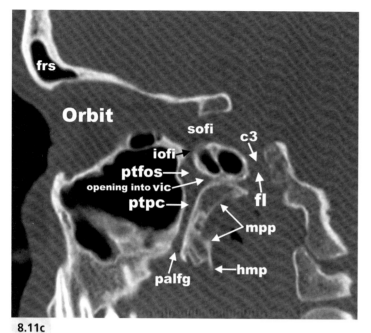

8.11c

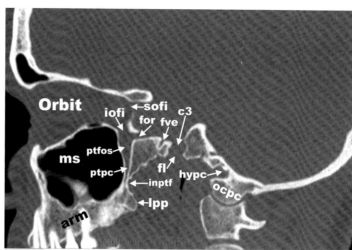

8.11d

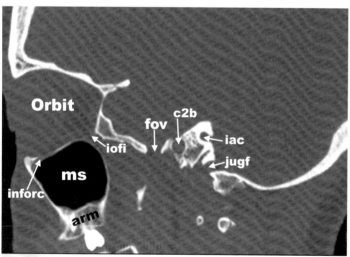

8.11e

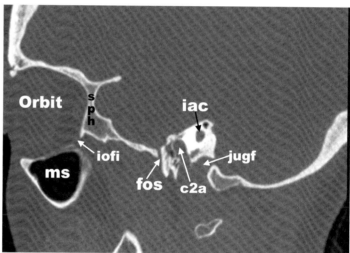

8.11f

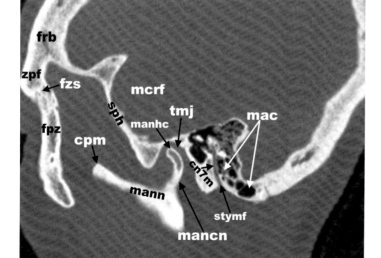

8.11g

FIGURES 8.11c–g

KEY

arm	alveolar ridge of maxilla	**inforc**	infra-orbital canal
c2a	c2a (vertical petrous segment ica)	**inptf**	interpterygoid fossa
		iofi	inferior orbital fissure
c2b	c2b (horizontal petrous segment of ica)	**jugf**	jugular foramen
		lpp	lateral pterygoid plate
c3	c3 (lacerum segment of ica)	**mac**	mastoid air cells
cn7m	mastoid segment facial nerve	**mancn**	neck of mandibular condyle
cpm	coronoid process of mandible	**manhc**	head of mandibular condyle
fl	foramen lacerum	**mann**	mandibular notch
for	foramen rotundem	**mcrf**	middle cranial fossa
fos	foramen spinosum	**mpp**	medial pterygoid plate
fov	foramen ovale	**ms**	maxillary sinus
fpz	frontal process of zygomatic bone	**ocpc**	occipital condyle
		palfg	greater palatine foramina
frb	frontal bone	**ptfos**	pterygopalatine fossa
frs	frontal sinus	**ptpc**	pterygopalatine canal
fve	foramen of Vesalius	**sofi**	superior orbital fissure
fzs	frontozygomatic suture	**sph**	sphenoid bone
hmp	hamulus of medial pterygoid plate	**stymf**	stylomastoid foramen
		tmj	temporal mandibular joint
hypc	hypoglossal canal	**vic**	vidian canal
iac	internal auditory canal	**zpf**	zygomatic process of frontal bone
ica	internal carotid artery		

PARANASAL SINUSES CT (FIGURES 8.12a–8.14g)

Axial Plane

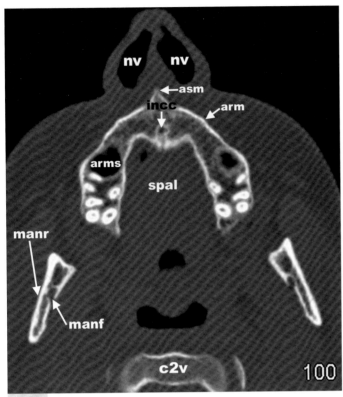

8.12a

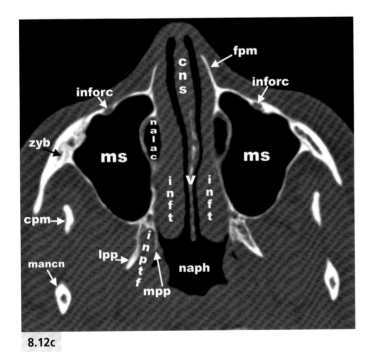

8.12c

8.12b

FIGURE 8.12b   A bony spur projecting from the nasal septum to the left of midline is noted by the white asterisk.

FIGURES 8.12a–j (Axial), 8.13a–i (Coronal) and 8.14a–g (Sagittal)   Images through the paranasal sinuses demonstrating normal anatomy.

KEY			
arm	alveolar ridge of maxilla	lpp	lateral pterygoid plate
arms	alveolar recess of maxillary sinus	mancn	neck of mandibular condyle
asm	anterior spine of maxilla	manf	mandibular foramen
c2v	second vertebral segment	mann	mandibular notch
cns	cartilaginous nasal septum	manr	ramus of mandible
cpm	coronoid process of mandible	mpp	medial pterygoid plate
		ms	maxillary sinus
eusto	eustachian tube orifice	nalac	nasolacrimal duct
fosr	fossa of Rosenmüller	naph	nasopharynx
fpm	frontal process of maxilla	nv	nasal vestibule
incc	incisive/nasopalatine canal	palfg	greater palatine foramina
infm	inferior meatus	palfl	lesser palatine foramina
inforc	infra-orbital canal	spal	soft palate
inft	inferior nasal turbinate	tort	torus tubarius
inptf	interpterygoid fossa	v	vomer
		zyb	zygomatic bone

(continued)

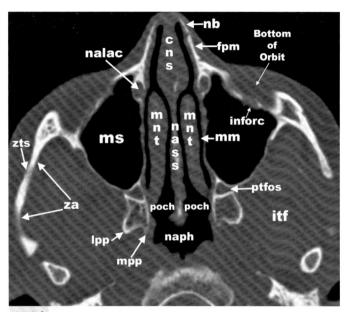

8.12d

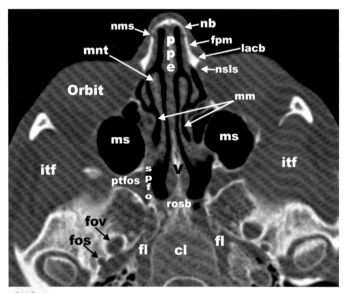

8.12e

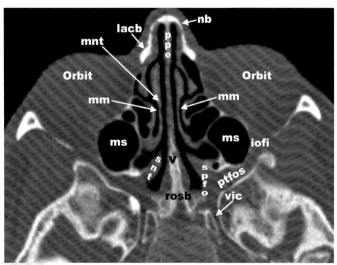

8.12f

FIGURES 8.12d–f

KEY

cl	clivus
cns	cartilaginous nasal septum
fl	foramen lacerum
fos	foramen spinosum
fov	foramen ovale
fpm	frontal process of maxilla
inforc	infra-orbital canal
iofi	inferior orbital fissure
itf	infratemporal fossa
lacb	lacrimal bone
lpp	lateral pterygoid plate
mm	middle meatus
mnt	middle nasal turbinate
mpp	medial pterygoid plate
ms	maxillary sinus
nalac	nasolacrimal duct
naph	nasopharynx
nass	nasal septum
nb	nasal bone
nms	nasomaxillary suture
nsls	nasolacrimal saccule
poch	posterior choana
ppe	perpendicular plate of ethmoid
ptfos	pterygopalatine fossa
rosb	rostrum of sphenoid bone
snt	superior nasal turbinate
spfo	sphenopalatine foramen
v	vomer
vic	vidian canal
za	zygomatic arch
zts	zygomaticotemporal suture

(continued)

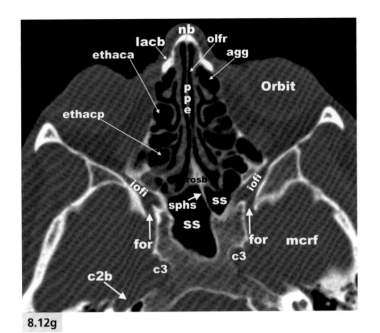

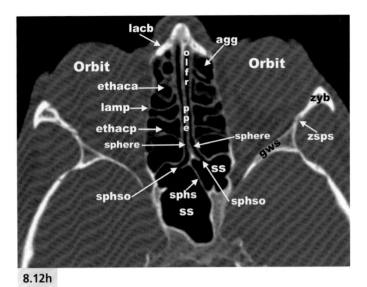

8.12g

8.12h

8.12i

8.12j

FIGURES 8.12g–j

KEY

acl	anterior clinoid process
acrf	anterior cranial fossa
aec	anterior ethmoidal canal
agg	agger nasi cell
c2b	c2b (horizontal petrous segment of ica)
c3	c3 (lacerum segment of ica)
cg	crista galli
ds	dorsum sellae
ethaca	anterior ethmoid air cells
ethacp	posterior ethmoid air cells
for	foramen rotundem
frs	frontal sinus
gr	gyrus rectus
gws	greater wing of the sphenoid bone
ica	internal carotid artery
intfs	intersinus septum (frontal)
iofi	inferior orbital fissure
lacb	lacrimal bone
lamp	lamina papyracea
ls	limbus sphenoidale
mcrf	middle cranial fossa
nb	nasal bone
oc	optic canal
olfr	olfactory recess of nasal cavity
pethc	posterior ethmoidal canal
ppe	perpendicular plate of ethmoid
rosb	rostrum of sphenoid bone
set	sella turcica
sofi	superior orbital fissure
sphere	sphenoethmoidal recess
sphso	sphenoid sinus ostia
sphs	sphenoid sinus septum
ss	sphenoid sinus
zsps	zygomaticosphenoid suture
zyb	zygomatic bone

Coronal Plane

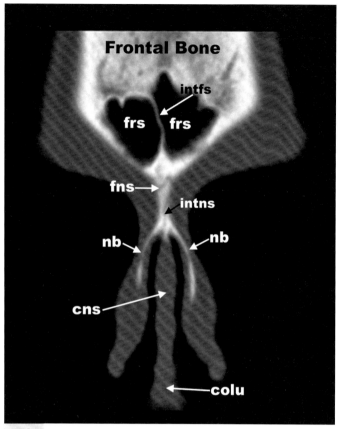

8.13a

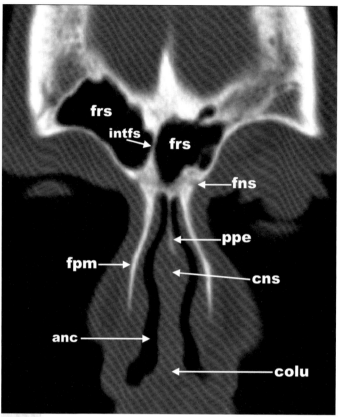

8.13b

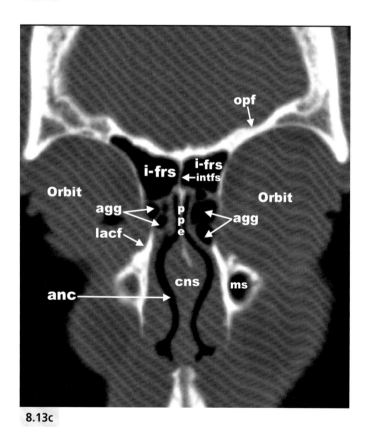

8.13c

FIGURES 8.13a–c

KEY

agg	agger nasi cell
anc	anterior nasal cavity
cns	cartilaginous nasal septum
colu	columella
fns	frontonasal suture
fpm	frontal process of maxilla
frs	frontal sinus
i-frs	inferior frontal sinus
intfs	intersinus septum (frontal)
intns	internasal bone suture
lacf	lacrimal sac fossa
ms	maxillary sinus
nb	nasal bone
opf	orbital plate of frontal bone
ppe	perpendicular plate of ethmoid

(continued)

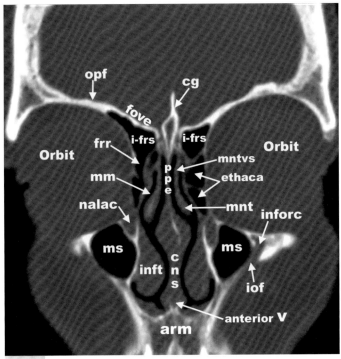

8.13d

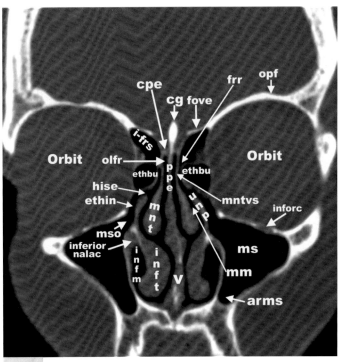

8.13e

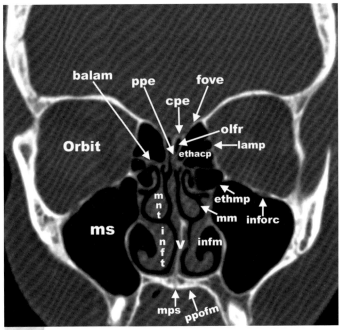

8.13f

FIGURES 8.13d–f

KEY	
arm	alveolar ridge of maxilla
arms	alveolar recess of maxillary sinus
balam	basal lamella
cg	crista galli
cns	cartilaginous nasal septum
cpe	cribriform plate of ethmoid bone
ethbu	ethmoidal bulla
ethacp	posterior ethmoid air cells
ethaca	anterior ethmoid air cells
ethin	ethmoid infundibulum
ethmp	ethmomaxillary plate
fove	fovea ethmoidales
frr	frontal recess
hise	hiatus semilunaris
i-frs	inferior frontal sinus
infm	inferior meatus
inforc	infra-orbital canal
inft	inferior nasal turbinate
iof	infraorbital foramen
lamp	lamina papyracea
mm	middle meatus
mnt	middle nasal turbinate
mntvs	vertical strut/insertion middle nasal turbinate
mps	median palatine suture
ms	maxillary sinus
mso	maxillary sinus ostium
nalac	nasolacrimal duct
olfr	olfactory recess of nasal cavity
opf	orbital plate of frontal bone
ppe	perpendicular plate of ethmoid
ppofm	palatine process of maxilla
unp	uncinate process
v	vomer

(continued)

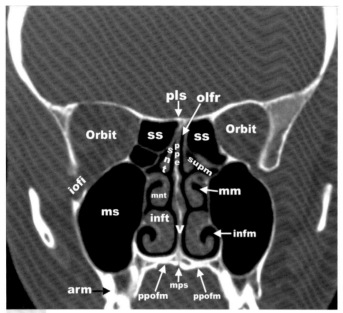

8.13g

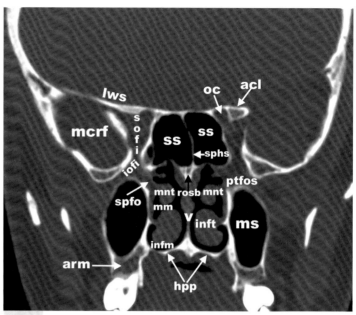

8.13h

FIGURES 8.13g–i

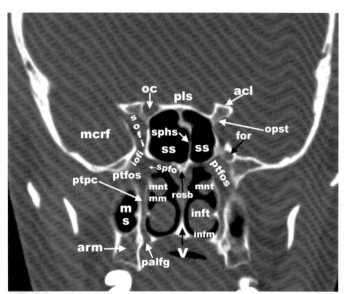

8.13i

KEY

acl	anterior clinoid process
arm	alveolar ridge of maxilla
for	foramen rotundem
hpp	horizontal plate of palatine bone
infm	inferior meatus
inft	inferior nasal turbinate
iofi	inferior orbital fissure
lws	lesser wing of the sphenoid bone
mcrf	middle cranial fossa
mm	middle meatus
mnt	middle nasal turbinate
mps	median palatine suture
ms	maxillary sinus
oc	optic canal
olfr	olfactory recess of nasal cavity
opst	optic strut
palfg	greater palatine foramina
pls	planum sphenoidale
ppe	perpendicular plate of ethmoid
ppofm	palatine process of maxilla
ptfos	pterygopalatine fossa
ptpc	pterygopalatine canal
rosb	rostrum of sphenoid bone
snt	superior nasal turbinate
sofi	superior orbital fissure
spfo	sphenopalatine foramen
sphs	sphenoid sinus septum
ss	sphenoid sinus
supm	superior meatus
v	vomer

Sagittal Plane

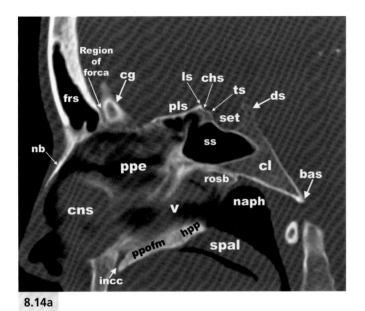

8.14a

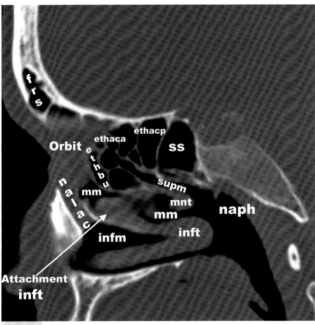

8.14c

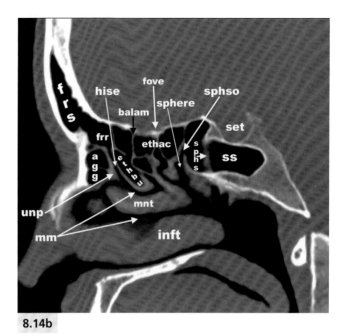

8.14b

FIGURES 8.14a–c

KEY

agg	agger nasi cell
balam	basal lamella
bas	basion
cg	crista galli
chs	chiasmatic sulcus
cl	clivus
cns	cartilaginous nasal septum
ds	dorsum sellae
ethac	ethmoid air cells
ethaca	anterior ethmoid air cells
ethacp	posterior ethmoid air cells
ethbu	ethmoidal bulla
fove	fovea ethmoidales
forca	foramen caecum
frr	frontal recess
frs	frontal sinus
hise	hiatus semilunaris
hpp	horizontal plate of palatine bone
incc	incisive/nasopalatine canal
infm	inferior meatus
inft	inferior nasal turbinate
ls	limbus sphenoidale
mm	middle meatus
mnt	middle nasal turbinate
nalac	nasolacrimal duct
naph	nasopharynx
nb	nasal bone
pls	planum sphenoidale
ppe	perpendicular plate of ethmoid
ppofm	palatine process of maxilla
rosb	rostrum of sphenoid bone
set	sella turcica
spal	soft palate
sphere	sphenoethmoidal recess
sphs	sphenoid sinus septum
sphso	sphenoid sinus ostia
ss	sphenoid sinus
supm	superior meatus
ts	tuberculum sellae
unp	uncinate process
v	vomer

(continued)

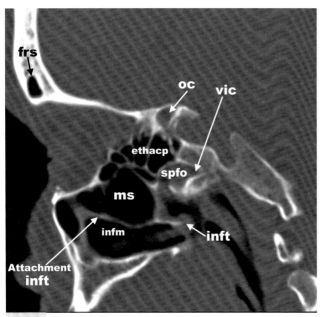

8.14d

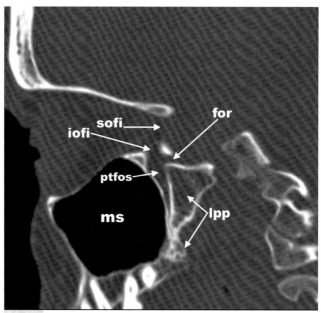

8.14e

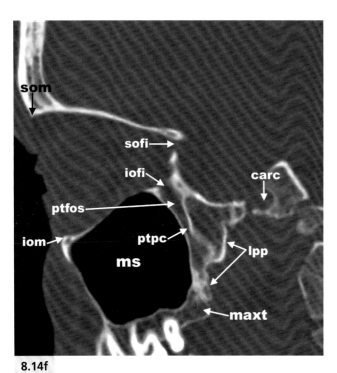

8.14f

FIGURES 8.14d–f

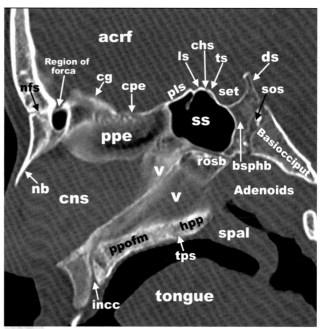

8.14g

FIGURE 8.14g Midsagittal image in another subject who is 16 years old demonstrates normal anatomy with an open sphenooccipital synchondrosis. This normally closes between the ages of 15 and 18.

KEY

acrf	anterior cranial fossa	**infm**	inferior meatus	**ptfos**	pterygopalatine fossa
bsphb	basisphenoid bone	**inft**	inferior nasal turbinate	**ptpc**	pterygopalatine canal
carc	carotid canal	**iofi**	inferior orbital fissure	**rosb**	rostrum of sphenoid bone
cg	crista galli	**iom**	infraorbital margin	**set**	sella turcica
chs	chiasmatic sulcus	**lpp**	lateral pterygoid plate	**sofi**	superior orbital fissure
cns	cartilaginous nasal septum	**ls**	limbus sphenoidale	**som**	supraorbital margin
cpe	cribriform plate of ethmoid bone	**maxt**	maxillary tuberosity	**sos**	spheno-occipital synchondrosis
ds	dorsum sellae	**ms**	maxillary sinus	**spal**	soft palate
ethacp	posterior ethmoid air cells	**nb**	nasal bone	**spfo**	sphenopalatine foramen
forca	foramen caecum	**nfs**	nasofrontal suture	**ss**	sphenoid sinus
for	foramen rotundem	**oc**	optic canal	**tps**	transverse palatine suture
frs	frontal sinus	**pls**	planum sphenoidale	**ts**	tuberculum sellae
hpp	horizontal plate of palatine bone	**ppe**	perpendicular plate of ethmoid	**vic**	vidian canal
incc	incisive/nasopalatine canal	**ppofm**	palatine process of maxilla	**v**	vomer

TEMPORAL BONE CT (FIGURES 8.15a–8.20b)

Imaging Planes for Orientation

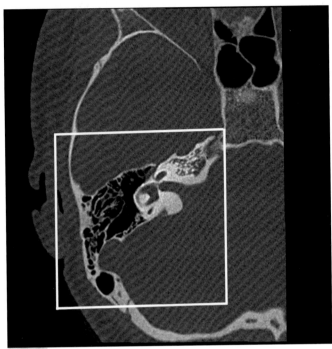

8.15a

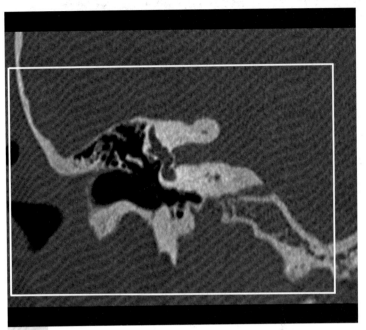

8.15b

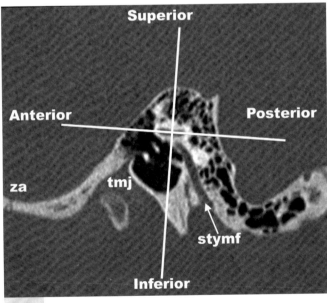

8.15c

FIGURES 8.15a–c   Orientation and planes of imaging.

8.15a. Large field of view axial CT image with bone detail showing the field of view used (box outlined with white lines) for targeted axial images (Figures 8.16a–m).

8.15b. Coronal CT image with bone detail showing the field of view used (box outlined with white lines) for targeted coronal images (Figures 8.17a–n).

8.15c. Sagittal CT image with bone detail shows the planes of imaging used for axial and coronal reconstructions. The plane of the horizontal semicircular canal is used to prescribe the axial slices and a line perpendicular to this for the coronal reconstructions.

KEY
stymf	stylomastoid foramen
tmj	temporal mandibular joint
za	zygomatic arch

Axial Plane

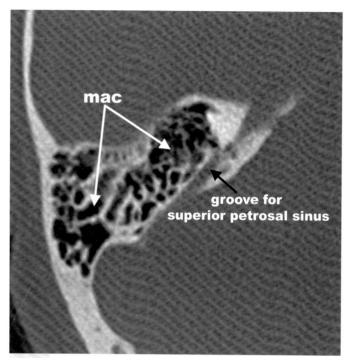

8.16a

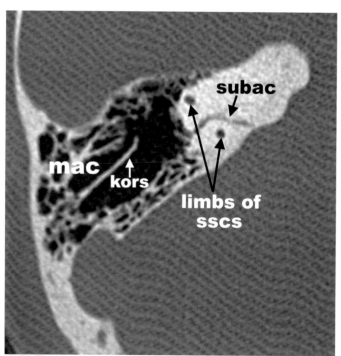

8.16c

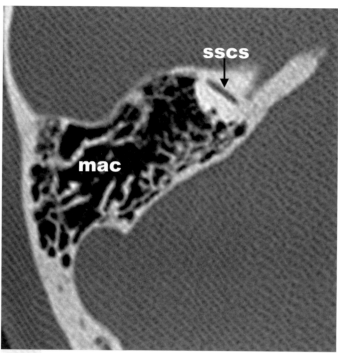

8.16b

FIGURES 8.16a–m Images in the axial plane demonstrate normal anatomy. Black asterisk in Figure 8.16d indicates Bill's bar.

KEY

kors	Korner's septum
mac	mastoid air cells
sscs	superior semicircular canal
subac	subarcuate canal

(*continued*)

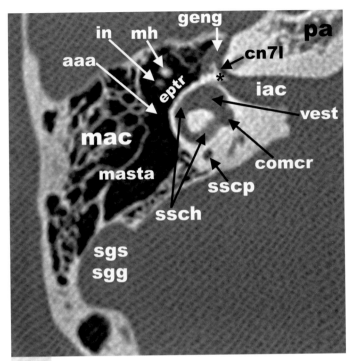

8.16d

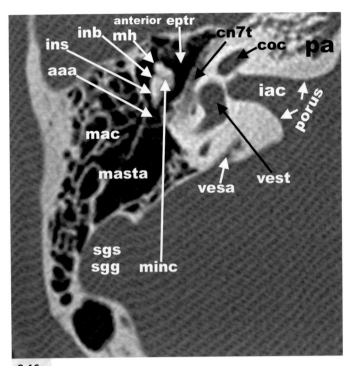

8.16e

FIGURES 8.16d–f

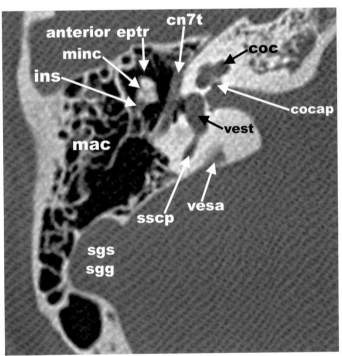

8.16f

KEY

aaa	aditus ad antrum
cn7l	labyrinthine segment facial nerve
cn7t	tympanic segment of facial nerve
coc	cochlea
cocap	cochlear aperture
comcr	common crus
eptr	epitympanic recess (attic)
geng	geniculate ganglion
iac	internal auditory canal
in	incus
inb	body of incus
ins	short process of incus
mac	mastoid air cells
masta	mastoid antrum
mh	head of malleus
minc	malleo-incudal articulation
pa	petrous apex
porus	porus acousticus
sgg	sigmoid groove
sgs	sigmoid sinus
ssch	horizontal semicircular canal
sscp	posterior semicircular canal
vesa	vestibular aqueduct
vest	vestibule

(continued)

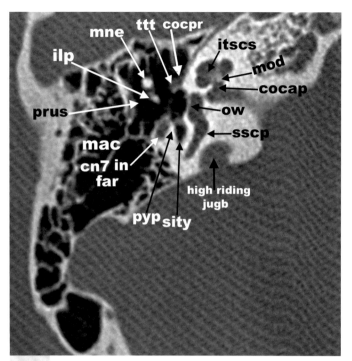

8.16g

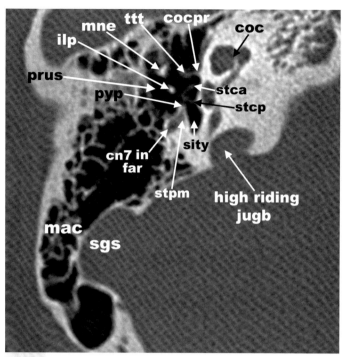

8.16h

FIGURES 8.16g–i

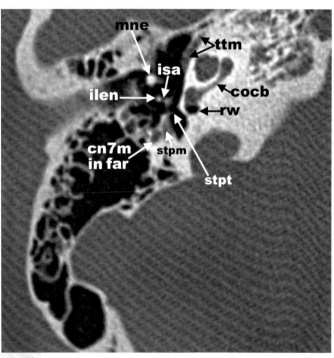

8.16i

KEY

cn7	facial nerve
cn7m	mastoid segment facial nerve
coc	cochlea
cocap	cochlear aperture
cocb	basal turn of cochlea
cocpr	cochleariform process
far	facial recess
ilen	lenticular process of incus
ilp	long process of incus
isa	incudo-stapedial articulation
itscs	interscalar septum
jugb	jugular bulb
mac	mastoid air cells
mne	neck of malleus
mod	modiolus
ow	oval window
prus	Prussak's space
pyp	pyramidal process
rw	round window
sgs	sigmoid sinus
sity	sinus tympani
sscp	posterior semicircular canal
stca	anterior crus of stapes
stcp	posterior crus of stapes
stpm	stapedius muscle
stpt	tendon of stapedius muscle
ttm	tensor tympani muscle
ttt	tensor tympani tendon

(continued)

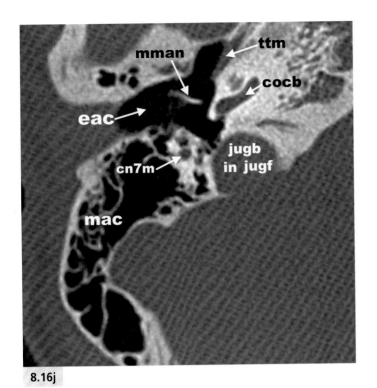

8.16j

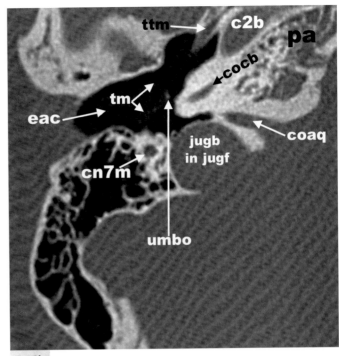

8.16k

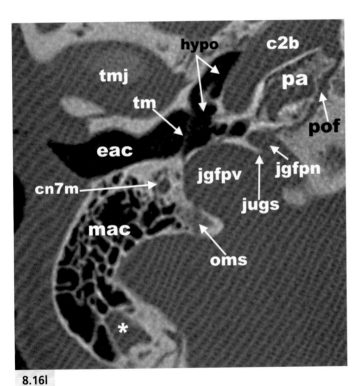

8.16l

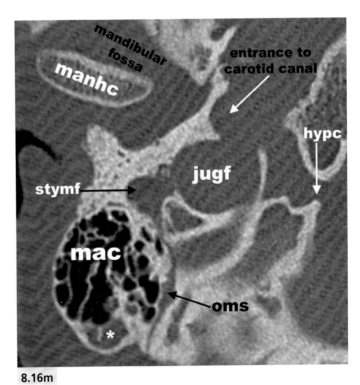

8.16m

FIGURES 8.16l,m White asterisks indicate opacification of a few mastoid air cells.

FIGURES 8.16j,k,m

KEY

c2b	c2b (horizontal petrous segment of ica)
cn7m	mastoid segment facial nerve
coaq	cochlear aqueduct
cocb	basal turn of cochlea
eac	external auditory canal
hypc	hypoglossal canal
hypo	hypotympanum
ica	internal carotid artery
jgfpn	pars nervosa-jugular foramen
jgfpv	pars vascularis-jugular foramen
jugb	jugular bulb
jugf	jugular foramen

jugs	jugular spine
mac	mastoid air cells
manhc	head of mandibular condyle
mman	manubrium of malleus
oms	occipitomastoid suture
pa	petrous apex
pof	petro-occipital fissure
stymf	stylomastoid foramen
tmj	temporal mandibular joint
tm	tympanic membrane
ttm	tensor tympani muscle
umbo	umbo of malleus

Coronal Plane

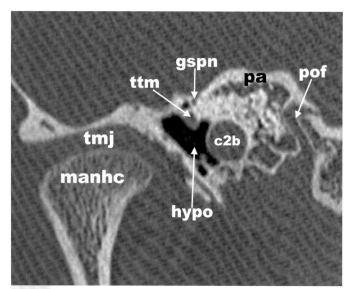

8.17a

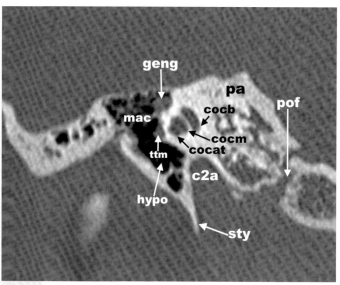

8.17b

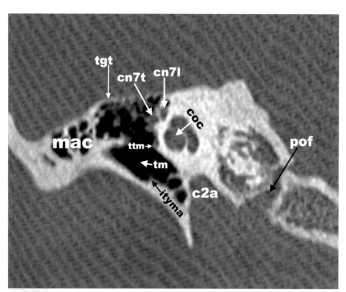

8.17c

FIGURES 8.17a–n   Images in the coronal plane demonstrate normal anatomy.

KEY

c2a	c2a (vertical petrous segment ica)
c2b	c2b (horizontal petrous segment of ica)
cn7l	labyrinthine segment facial nerve
cn7t	tympanic segment of facial nerve
coc	cochlea
cocat	apical turn of cochlea
cocb	basal turn of cochlea
cocm	middle turn of cochlea
geng	geniculate ganglion
gspn	greater superficial petrosal nerve
hypo	hypotympanum
ica	internal carotid artery
ityma	inferior tympanic annulus
mac	mastoid air cells
manhc	head of mandibular condyle
pa	petrous apex
pof	petro-occipital fissure
sty	styloid process
tgt	tegmen tympani
tm	tympanic membrane
tmj	temporal mandibular joint
ttm	tensor tympani muscle

(*continued*)

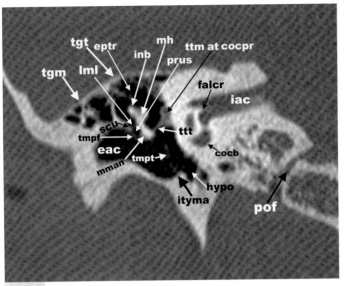

8.17d

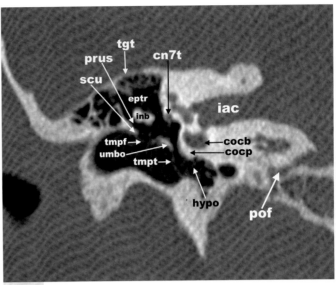

8.17e

FIGURES 8.17d–f

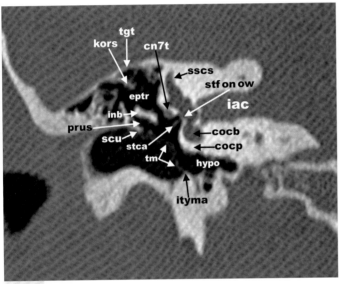

8.17f

KEY

cn7t	tympanic segment of facial nerve
cocb	basal turn of cochlea
cocpr	cochleariform process
cocp	cochlear promontory
eac	external auditory canal
eptr	epitympanic recess (attic)
falcr	falciform crest
hypo	hypotympanum
iac	internal auditory canal
inb	body of incus
ityma	inferior tympanic annulus
kors	Korner's septum
lml	lateral malleolar ligament (in tympanic cavity)
mh	head of malleus
mman	manubrium of malleus
ow	oval window
pof	petro-occipital fissure
prus	Prussak's space
scu	scutum
sscs	superior semicircular canal
stca	anterior crus of stapes
stf	stapes footplate
tgm	tegmen mastoideum
tgt	tegmen tympani
tm	tympanic membrane
tmpf	tympanic membrane pars flaccida
tmpt	tympanic membrane pars tensa
ttm	tensor tympani muscle
ttt	tensor tympani tendon
umbo	umbo of malleus

(continued)

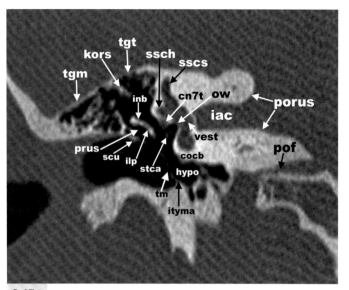

8.17g

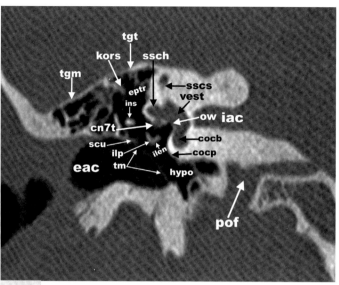

8.17h

FIGURES 8.17g–i

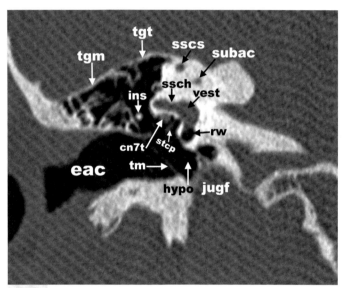

8.17i

KEY

cn7t	tympanic segment of facial nerve
cocb	basal turn of cochlea
cocp	cochlear promontory
eac	external auditory canal
eptr	epitympanic recess (attic)
hypo	hypotympanum
iac	internal auditory canal
ilen	lenticular process of incus
ilp	long process of incus
inb	body of incus
ins	short process of incus
ityma	inferior tympanic annulus
jugf	jugular foramen
kors	Korner's septum
ow	oval window
pof	petro-occipital fissure
porus	porus acousticus
prus	Prussak's space
rw	round window
scu	scutum
ssch	horizontal semicircular canal
sscs	superior semicircular canal
stca	anterior crus of stapes
stcp	posterior crus of stapes
subac	subarcuate canal
tgm	tegmen mastoideum
tgt	tegmen tympani
tm	tympanic membrane
vest	vestibule

(continued)

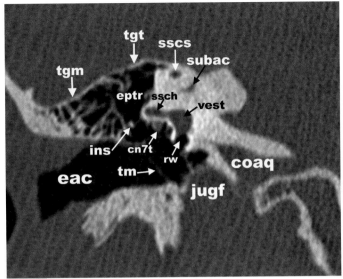

8.17j

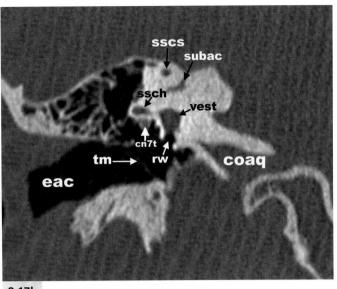

8.17k

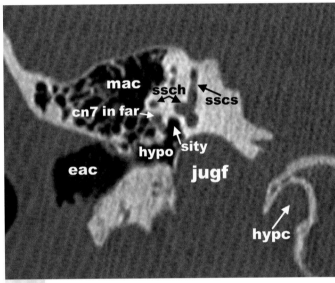

8.17l

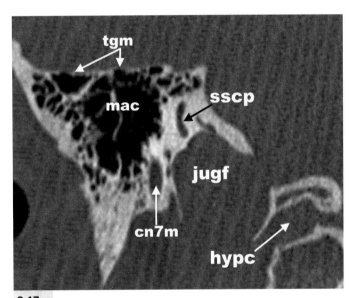

8.17m

FIGURES 8.17j–n

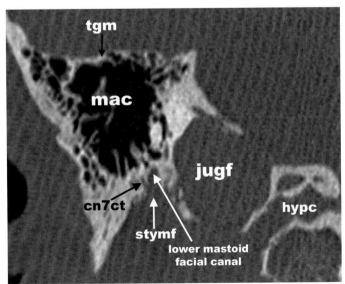

8.17n

KEY

cn7	facial nerve
cn7ct	chorda tympani branch facial nerve
cn7m	mastoid segment facial nerve
cn7t	tympanic segment of facial nerve
coaq	cochlear aqueduct
eac	external auditory canal
eptr	epitympanic recess (attic)
far	facial recess
hypc	hypoglossal canal
hypo	hypotympanum
ins	short process of incus
jugf	jugular foramen
mac	mastoid air cells
rw	round window
sity	sinus tympani
ssch	horizontal semicircular canal
sscp	posterior semicircular canal
sscs	superior semicircular canal
stymf	stylomastoid foramen
subac	subarcuate canal
tgm	tegmen mastoideum
tgt	tegmen tympani
tm	tympanic membrane
vest	vestibule

Axial Plane - Off Axis

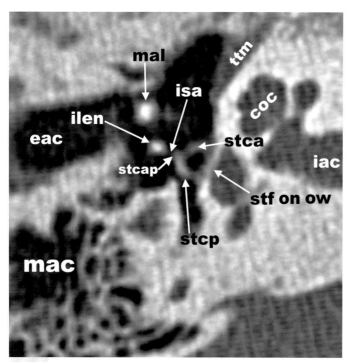

8.18a

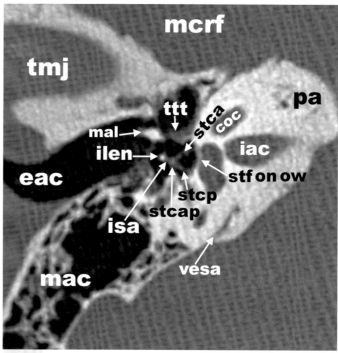

8.18b

FIGURES 8.18a–20b Off axis (not routine) imaging planes with thick slice slabs are used to better demonstrate anatomic structures.

FIGURES 8.18a–c Off axis axial images. 8.18a,b beautifully demonstrate the region of the incudostapedial joint and the anatomy of the stapes. 8.18c shows the chorda tympani branch of CN VII just beyond its takeoff from the main mastoid segment of CN VII.

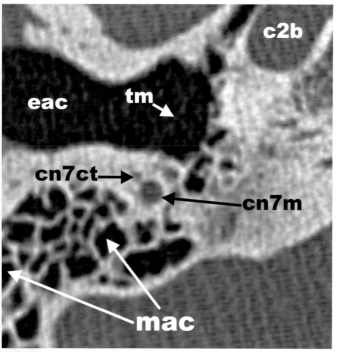

8.18c

KEY

c2b	c2b (horizontal petrous segment of ica)
cn7ct	chorda tympani branch facial nerve
cn7m	mastoid segment facial nerve
coc	cochlea
eac	external auditory canal
iac	internal auditory canal
ica	internal carotid artery
ilen	lenticular process of incus
isa	incudo-stapedial articulation
mac	mastoid air cells
mal	malleus
mcrf	middle cranial fossa
ow	oval window
pa	petrous apex
stca	anterior crus of stapes
stcap	capitellum (head) of stapes
stcp	posterior crus of stapes
stf	stapes footplate
tm	tympanic membrane
tmj	temporal mandibular joint
ttm	tensor tympani muscle
ttt	tensor tympani tendon
vesa	vestibular aqueduct

Coronal Plane - Off Axis

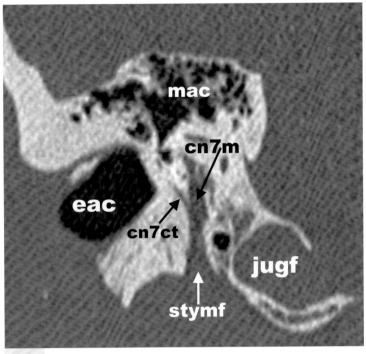

8.19a

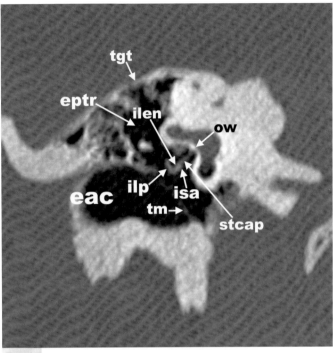

8.19b

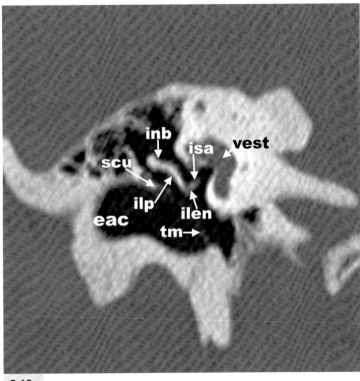

8.19c

FIGURE 8.19a   An oblique coronal view demonstrating the takeoff of the chorda tympani branch from the mastoid segment of CN VII.

FIGURES 8.19b–e   Thick slab and oblique coronal views improve the conspicuity of middle ear anatomy.

KEY

cn7ct	chorda tympani branch facial nerve
cn7m	mastoid segment facial nerve
eac	external auditory canal
eptr	epitympanic recess (attic)
ilen	lenticular process of incus
ilp	long process of incus
inb	body of incus
isa	incudo-stapedial articulation
jugf	jugular foramen
mac	mastoid air cells
ow	oval window
scu	scutum
stcap	capitellum (head) of stapes
stymf	stylomastoid foramen
tgt	tegmen tympani
tm	tympanic membrane
vest	vestibule

(continued)

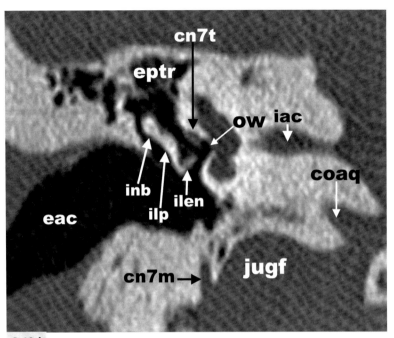

8.19d

FIGURES 8.19d,e

KEY

cn7m	mastoid segment facial nerve
cn7t	tympanic segment of facial nerve
coaq	cochlear aqueduct
cocpr	cochleariform process
eac	external auditory canal
eptr	epitympanic recess (attic)
hypo	hypotympanum
iac	internal auditory canal
ilen	lenticular process of incus
ilp	long process of incus
inb	body of incus
jugf	jugular foramen
lml	lateral malleolar ligament (in tympanic cavity)
mh	head of malleus
mman	manubrium of malleus
mne	neck of malleus
ow	oval window
scu	scutum
tmpt	tympanic membrane pars tensa
tmpf	tympanic membrane pars flaccida
ttt	tensor tympani tendon
umbo	umbo of malleus

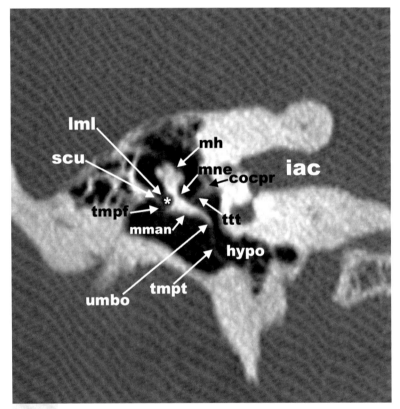

8.19e

FIGURE 8.19e White asterisk indicates Prussak's space.

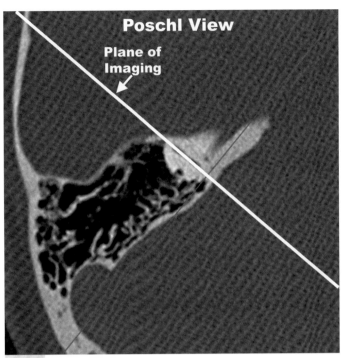

8.20a

FIGURE 8.20a   This image indicates the plane of imaging through the axis of the superior semicircular canal, prescribed off an axial image. This plane is roughly at 45° to the sagittal plane and will yield a Poschl view.

FIGURE 8.20b   Poschl view demonstrating the complete ring of the superior semicircular canal with intact bony margins. The black asterisk indicates the subarcuate canal. This is a good view to assess for dehiscence of the superior semicircular canal.

KEY

cn7t	tympanic segment of facial nerve
jugf	jugular foramen
mal	malleus
sscs	superior semicircular canal
tm	tympanic membrane
tmj	temporal mandibular joint

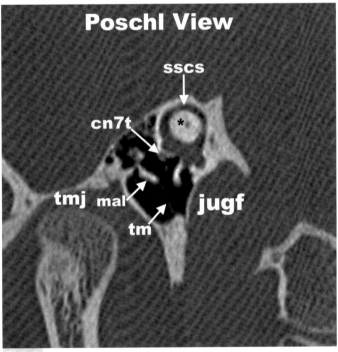

8.20b

ORBITAL CT (FIGURES 8.21a–8.23e)

Axial Plane

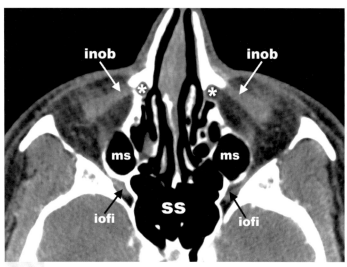

8.21a

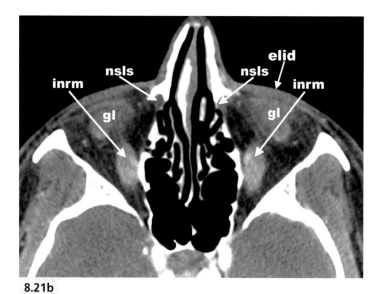

8.21b

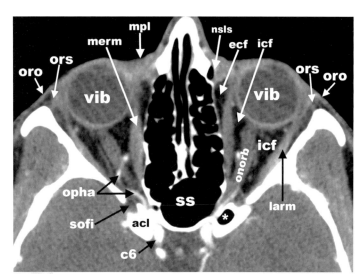

8.21c

FIGURES 8.21a–h   Normal contrast enhanced axial images through the orbits from inferior (caudal) to superior (cranial).

FIGURE 8.21a   White asterisks indicate the proximal nasolacrimal ducts in the inferomedial orbits. Note deviation of the nasal septum.

FIGURE 8.21c   White asterisk indicates a pneumatized (air filled) anterior clinoid process.

KEY

acl	anterior clinoid process
c6	c6 (ophthalmic segment of ica)
ecf	extraconal orbital fat
elid	orbicularis oculi/eyelid
gl	globe
ica	internal carotid artery
icf	intraconal orbital fat
inob	inferior oblique muscle
inrm	inferior rectus muscle
iofi	inferior orbital fissure
larm	lateral rectus muscle
merm	medial rectus muscle
mpl	medial palpebral ligament
ms	maxillary sinus
nsls	nasolacrimal saccule
onorb	orbital segment optic nerve
opha	ophthalmic artery
oro	orbicularis oculi muscle
ors	orbital septum
sofi	superior orbital fissure
ss	sphenoid sinus
vib	vitreous body (chamber) of eye

(continued)

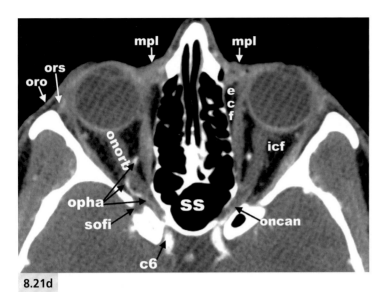

8.21d

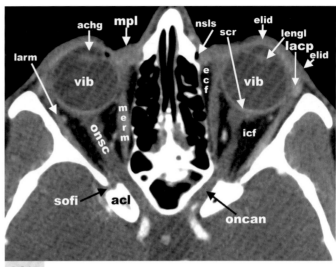

8.21e

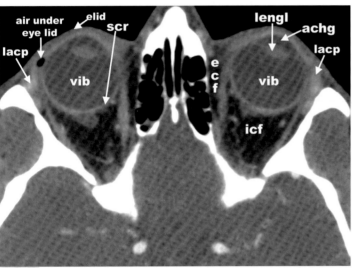

8.21f

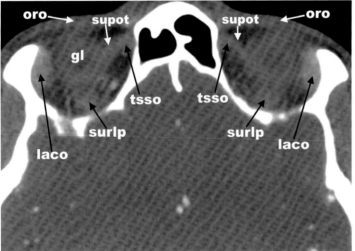

8.21g

FIGURES 8.21d–h

8.21h

KEY

achg	anterior chamber of eye	onorb	orbital segment optic nerve
acl	anterior clinoid process		
c6	c6 (ophthalmic segment of ica)	onsc	optic nerve/sheath complex
ecf	extraconal orbital fat	opha	ophthalmic artery
elid	orbicularis oculi/eyelid	oro	orbicularis oculi muscle
gl	globe	ors	orbital septum
ica	internal carotid artery	scr	3 ocular coats of eye (sclera, choroid, retina)
icf	intraconal orbital fat		
laco	orbital portion of lacrimal gland	sofi	superior orbital fissure
		sov	superior ophthalmic vein
lacp	palpebral portion of lacrimal gland	ss	sphenoid sinus
		supob	superior oblique muscle
larm	lateral rectus muscle	supot	tendon of superior oblique muscle
lengl	lens of globe		
merm	medial rectus muscle	surlp	superior rectus/levator palpebrae muscle
mpl	medial palpebral ligament		
		surm	superior rectus muscle
nsls	nasolacrimal saccule	tsso	trochlear sling of superior oblique muscle
oncan	canalicular segment of optic nerve		
		vib	vitreous body (chamber) of eye

Coronal Plane

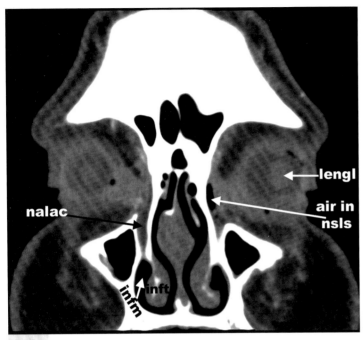

8.22a

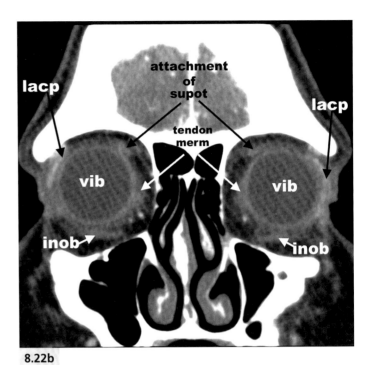

8.22b

FIGURES 8.22a–j   Normal contrast enhanced coronal images through the orbits from anterior to posterior.

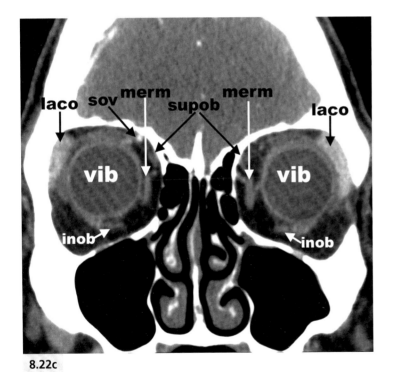

8.22c

KEY

inob	inferior oblique muscle
inft	inferior nasal turbinate
infm	inferior meatus
laco	orbital portion of lacrimal gland
lacp	palpebral portion of lacrimal gland
lengl	lens of globe
merm	medial rectus muscle
nalac	nasolacrimal duct
nsls	nasolacrimal saccule
sov	superior ophthalmic vein
supob	superior oblique muscle
supot	tendon of superior oblique muscle
vib	vitreous body (chamber) of eye

(continued)

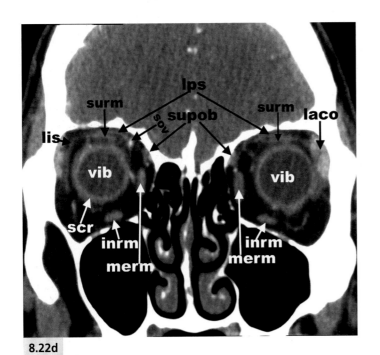

8.22d

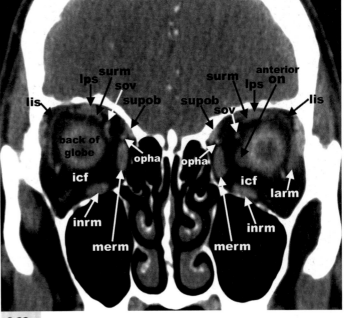

8.22e

FIGURES 8.22d–f

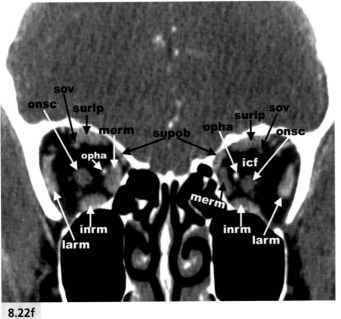

8.22f

KEY

icf	intraconal orbital fat
inrm	inferior rectus muscle
laco	orbital portion of lacrimal gland
larm	lateral rectus muscle
lis	lateral intermuscular septum
lps	levator palpebrae superioris
merm	medial rectus muscle
on	optic nerve
onsc	optic nerve/sheath complex
opha	ophthalmic artery
scr	3 ocular coats of eye (sclera, choroid, retina)
sov	superior ophthalmic vein
supob	superior oblique muscle
surlp	superior rectus/levator palpebrae muscle
surm	superior rectus muscle
vib	vitreous body (chamber) of eye

(continued)

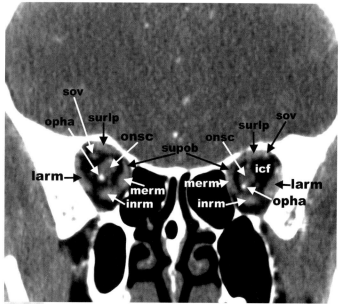

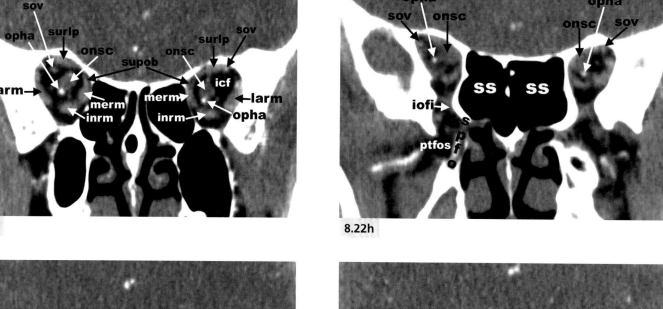

8.22g

8.22h

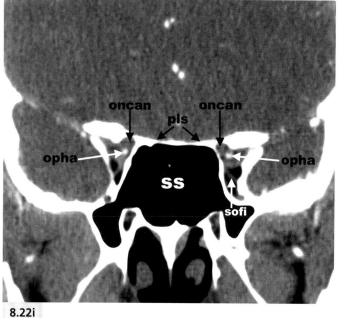

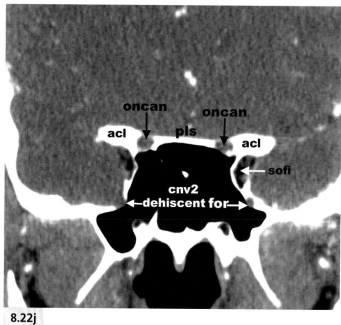

8.22i

8.22j

FIGURES 8.22g–i

FIGURE 8.22j Incidental note is made of dehiscence of the inferomedial bony margin of foramen rotundem bilaterally with the maxillary (V2) division of CN V projecting minimally into the adjacent sphenoid sinus.

KEY

acl	anterior clinoid process
cnv2	maxillary branch (v2) of trigeminal nerve
for	foramen rotundem
icf	intraconal orbital fat
inrm	inferior rectus muscle
iofi	inferior orbital fissure
larm	lateral rectus muscle
merm	medial rectus muscle
oncan	canalicular segment of optic nerve
onsc	optic nerve/sheath complex

opha	ophthalmic artery
pls	planum sphenoidale
ptfos	pterygopalatine fossa
sofi	superior orbital fissure
sov	superior ophthalmic vein
spfo	sphenopalatine foramen
ss	sphenoid sinus
supob	superior oblique muscle
surlp	superior rectus/levator palpebrae muscle

Sagittal Oblique Plane

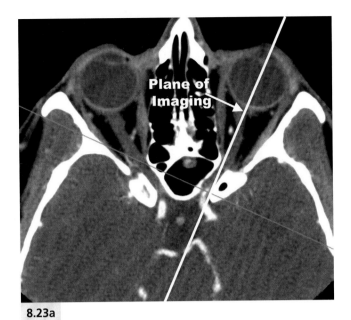

8.23a

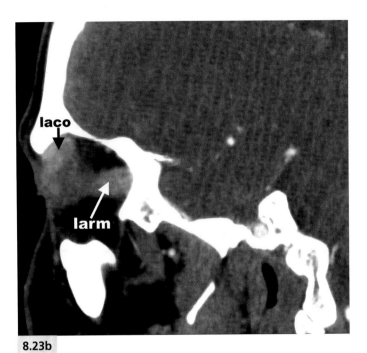

8.23b

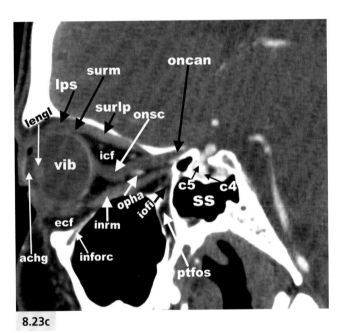

8.23c

FIGURES 8.23a–e   8.23a is the plane of imaging prescribed off the axial slice. 8.23b–e are normal sagittal oblique images through the left orbit along the axis of the optic nerve from lateral to medial.

KEY

achg	anterior chamber of eye
c4	c4 (cavernous segment of ica)
c5	c5 (clinoid segment of ica)
ecf	extraconal orbital fat
ica	internal carotid artery
icf	intraconal orbital fat
inforc	infra-orbital canal
inrm	inferior rectus muscle
iofi	inferior orbital fissure
laco	orbital portion of lacrimal gland
larm	lateral rectus muscle
lengl	lens of globe
lps	levator palpebrae superioris
onsc	optic nerve/sheath complex
oncan	canalicular segment of optic nerve
opha	ophthalmic artery
ptfos	pterygopalatine fossa
ss	sphenoid sinus
surlp	superior rectus/levator palpebrae muscle
surm	superior rectus muscle
vib	vitreous body (chamber) of eye

(continued)

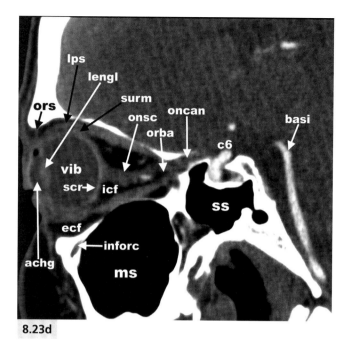

8.23d

FIGURES 8.23d,e

KEY

achg	anterior chamber of eye
basi	basilar artery
c6	c6 (ophthalmic segment of ica)
ecf	extraconal orbital fat
ica	internal carotid artery
icf	intraconal orbital fat
inf	infundibulum
inforc	infra-orbital canal
inob	inferior oblique muscle
lengl	lens of globe
lps	levator palpebrae superioris
merm	medial rectus muscle
ms	maxillary sinus
oncan	canalicular segment of optic nerve
onsc	optic nerve/sheath complex
orba	orbital apex
ors	orbital septum
pitg	pituitary gland
scr	3 ocular coats of eye (sclera, choroid, retina)
set	sella turcica
ss	sphenoid sinus
supob	superior oblique muscle
surm	superior rectus muscle
vib	vitreous body (chamber) of eye

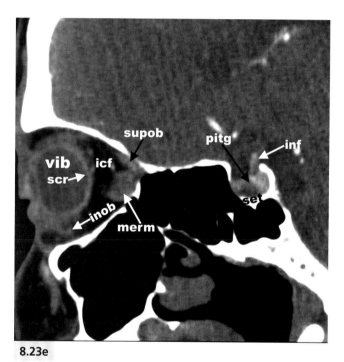

8.23e

Vascular Imaging

9

INTRODUCTION TO VASCULAR IMAGING

In my lifetime, neurovascular imaging has evolved from an invasive procedure where risk of stroke and rarely death was a reality to a non-invasive procedure requiring no more than an injection of an intravenous contrast agent and a few minutes of being scanned, either by computed tomography (CT) for CT angiography (CTA)/CT venography (CTV) or by magnetic resonance imaging (MRI) for MR angiography (MRA)/MR venography (MRV). MRA/MRV can also be done without any contrast injection. The resolution of CTA/CTV exceeds that of MRA/MRV, however, both can provide significant information regarding the state of the subject's vasculature. 3D images can be generated from these exams allowing real-time manipulation into innumerable different views, which may provide information not achievable through what was once felt to be the gold standard, conventional catheter angiography.

INTRODUCTION TO MRA/MRV

Techniques available to image the vascular system with MR technology include 2D or 3D time-of-flight (TOF), contrast enhanced MRA (CE-MRA), and 2D or 3D phase contrast.

The basis of the TOF technique for vascular imaging utilizing MR technology is the exploitation of flow-related enhancement of blood on T1W gradient echo images secondary to the entry of fully magnetized (unsaturated) blood into the imaging slice. This results in the white (or bright) appearance of flowing blood. On the other hand, static tissues within the imaging slice on a T1W gradient echo sequence are exposed to many radiofrequency (RF) pulses at the time of imaging resulting in saturated, poorly magnetized protons incapable of generating much signal. These physical properties lead to high contrast between flowing blood and static background tissue.

Another widely used MR angiographic technique is CE-MRA. This is based upon the first pass of contrast (gadolinium) through the arterial system resulting in shortening of the T1 relaxation time of flowing blood yielding an image with high contrast of enhancing vasculature relative to background tissues.

An entirely different technique for vascular MR imaging is phase contrast. This technique is based upon the velocity-induced phase shifts that occur with flowing blood not present in static background tissue.

The technique of TOF MRA and MRV is essentially the same. Both sequences use gradient echo T1W images. What determines whether you create arterial or venous images is the placement of a saturation band/pulse, which is positioned parallel to the acquired slice to eliminate signal from blood flowing in the opposite direction. In the case of MRA, the saturation band is placed above the acquired slice to eliminate venous flow, and for MRV, the band is placed inferior to the slice to eliminate inflow of arterial blood.

Detailed discussion of these techniques is beyond the scope of this atlas.

The MRA images of the brain in this atlas utilize 3D TOF technique without contrast enhancement while the MRA neck images utilize CE-MRA.

INTRODUCTION TO CTA

CTA combines high-resolution helical CT acquisitions with intravenous administration of iodinated contrast material. CTA has become an invaluable adjunct for imaging of the vascular structures in the head and neck. It is useful for the detection and evaluation of cerebral aneurysms, estimate vessel stenosis due to atherosclerotic disease, or to assess for post traumatic vascular injury (for example, arterial dissections).

The time between the start of contrast injection and scanning can be tailored to a particular clinical question. The intravenous administration of a contrast bolus can thus be timed to maximize vascular opacification of the arterial or venous circulation, depending upon the clinical question one is presented with. Common indications for evaluation of the arterial system include, atherosclerotic vascular disease, embolic phenomenon, vascular malformations, such as arterial venous malformations (AVM), traumatic injury and to evaluate abnormal vasculature in and around tumors and to assess for vascular tumor invasion. CTV is very useful in the detection and evaluation of dural venous sinus thrombosis or stenosis.

CTA can accurately identify and characterize a variety of suspected vascular abnormalities whether they are arterial or venous in nature. CT perfusion (CTP) can be combined with a

CTA examination and is discussed seperately in this chapter. CTP can provide qualitative and quantitative assessment of cerebral blood volume (CBV), cerebral blood flow (CBF), mean transit time (MTT), and time to peak (TTP), which can be useful in the setting of acute stroke, and in evaluating brain tumors.

INTRODUCTION TO 2D DSA AND 3D ROTATIONAL ANGIOGRAPHY

Conventional catheter angiography is an X-ray technique that involves the injection of a positive contrast agent directly into the blood vessels through an indwelling vascular catheter (long thin hollow tube) with acquisition of X-rays over the desired area of interest. These catheters are generally inserted percutaneously (via needles inserted through the skin).

The original technique of angiography generated X-ray images of the desired region of interest in addition to the other types of tissues present in the field of view, such as bone and soft tissue. The simultaneous X-ray appearance of these additional structures (bone and soft tissue) often partially obscured visualization of the desired vasculature.

Digital subtraction angiography (DSA) provides an improvement over conventional angiography by increasing the conspicuity of vessels. One of the images acquired before contrast administration is considered to be a "mask." In real time, this image is subtracted from all subsequent images, revealing changes between the mask and all subsequent images. The net effect is that tissues other than the vasculature are greatly de-emphasized. DSA has replaced the original, conventional technique of angiography without subtraction.

Cerebral angiography using catheter technology involves accessing the arterial tree most often from the femoral artery in the groin. Occasionally, the brachial, axillary, or rarely the carotid arteries may be used as the access point.

An angiographic catheter is passed into the vasculature through the point of access and positioned in the artery of interest. The head or neck is positioned in the desired image projection and will remain so for the entire acquisition of X-rays. At this point, a bolus injection of a positive contrast agent through the catheter is performed followed by acquisition of X-rays for varying periods of time. This allows one to obtain images of the contrast agent as it progresses through the vascular tree from artery to capillary and then into the venous phase of circulation. Different views of the blood vessels of interest can be obtained either by moving the patient relative to the X-ray tube or changing the position of the X-ray tube relative to a stationary subject. This is the basis for 2D angiographic imaging.

The technique of 3D rotational angiography (3DRA) is that during the bolus injection of the positive contrast into the vascular tree a movable X-ray tube rotates in an arc around the patient during acquisition of the X-rays. The X-ray data obtained from this series of exposures undergo computer processing, which then creates a 3D model of the vessels studied. This 3D model can then be manipulated in real time to provide an infinite number of projections (views) of the vessels imaged with only a single injection of contrast. This is in contrast to 2D DSA where every change in the desired projection (view) requires repeated injections of the contrast agent. This can result in the injection of large volumes of contrast, which can have deleterious effects on the patient's kidneys (contrast-induced nephropathy).

The goal of imaging with 3DRA is to obtain all of the X-ray images in the same phase of circulation, as opposed to standard 2D DSA where the contrast bolus is visualized as it progresses through the vascular tree. Most often the arterial phase is desired although imaging parameters can be altered so that the venous phase can be the predominant portion of the vascular bed imaged.

There are certain limitations inherent in the technique of 3DRA which include poor visualization of small/distal vessels, the lack of bony landmarks on the final 3D image, and the lack of sequential visualization of angiographic images showing the progression of contrast through the various phases of circulation. For this reason, 3DRA should complement but not replace traditional high-resolution 2D DSA.

INTRODUCTION TO CTP

CTP is a valuable technique to assess tissue vascularity. The wide availability of CT, the speed of data acquisition, and rapid post-processing time make this technique an important tool. It can be used for a variety of indications, yet in neuroradiology it is most often used in the setting of stroke.

This technique requires the rapid injection of a bolus of iodinated contrast agent with acquisition of serial images over a certain period of time. It not only provides a qualitative assessment through evaluation of color maps, but it can also provide quantitative information. CTP is commonly performed in conjunction with CTA for evaluation of vascular anatomy and pathology.

The underlying principle of CTP is the serial changes in tissue density over time, which is directly correlated with the temporal variation of iodine concentration. These changes reflect tissue vascularity, probed by the bolus of the contrast agent passing through capillary beds in the tissue.

Typical parameters to perform CTP include a bolus of iodinated contrast of approximately 40–50 milliliters (mL) injected at a rate of 4–7 mL/s with imaging over a period of 40–60 s.

Either the technologist or radiologist easily performs post processing of the perfusion data. Certain computer workstations can perform the post-processing automatically.

The post-processed images consist of parametric maps of CBF, CBV, MTT, and TTP. Typically, these maps are color-coded to show small variations more readily. Each one of these imaging metrics quantifies a particular physiological tissue characteristic. Quantitative measurement of CBF indicates the flow rate through the tissue vasculature and is expressed in mL of blood passing through 100 g of tissue per minute (or mL/100 g/min). Quantitative measurement of CBV indicates the volume of blood within the tissue vasculature and is expressed in mL of blood per 100 g of tissue (mL/100 g). Quantitative measurement of MTT indicates the average time for a particular volume of blood to circulate through the capillary bed, and it is expressed in seconds. MTT is given as the ratio of CBV to CBF (MTT = CBV/CBF). Quantitative measurement of TTP indicates the time from arrival of contrast in the major arteries to the peak image enhancement and is also expressed in seconds.

Utilization of CTP in acute stroke helps to identify areas of irreversible damage (infarction) and the presence or absence of tissue at risk (ischemic penumbra). A typical infarction without an ischemic penumbra will have matching reductions in CBV and CBF and prolongation of MTT and TTP. Infarction with ischemic penumbra will demonstrate a matching reduction in CBF and CBV but will also have a surrounding region of decreased CBF and prolongation of MTT without corresponding reduction in CBV. Prolongation of MTT and TTP are very sensitive to steno-occlusive vascular changes but are not the best indicator of final infarct volume. CBV can be thought of as a correlate to diffusion weighted MRI (DWI) in that it is the best CTP parameter to predict final infarct volume. In MRI, the most sensitive and specific indicator of final infarct volume is the DWI (b1000) and its apparent diffusion coefficient (ADC) map. However, it is important to note that CBV measured using MR-based perfusion techniques, such as dynamic susceptibility contrast MR (DSC-MR) or arterial spin labeling (ASL) may show a volumetric mismatch for the infarct in comparison to the ADC map/DWI-b1000 images. Very low CBV (as measured by MR-based perfusion techniques) is the single best indicator of irreversible infarction.

LEGEND FOR BRANCHES OF THE EXTERNAL CAROTID AND MAXILLARY ARTERIES

BRANCHES OF THE EXTERNAL CAROTID ARTERY

ascpha	= ascending pharyngeal artery
facial	= facial artery
linga	= lingual artery
maxa	= maxillary artery
occa	= occipital artery
paur	= posterior auricular artery
sta	= superficial temporal artery
supthy	= superior thyroid artery
trvfa	= transverse facial artery

BRANCHES OF THE MAXILLARY ARTERY

masma	= masseteric muscular artery
bucma	= buccinator muscular branches
grpa	= greater palatine artery
iaa	= inferior alveolar artery
infoa	= infraorbital artery
ln	= lateral nasal branch of sphenopalatine artery
mma(a)	= accessory meningeal artery
mma	= middle meningeal artery
psaa	= posterior superior alveolar artery
sb	= septal branch of sphenopalatine artery
sphpa	= sphenopalatine artery
afr	= artery of the foramen rotundem

ARTERIAL NECK

■ MR ANGIOGRAPHY (MRA) (FIGURES 9.1a,b)

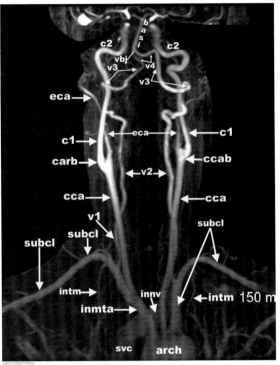

9.1a

FIGURES 9.1a,b   Contrast enhanced **magnetic resonance angiography (MRA)** with frontal (9.1a) and left anterior oblique (LAO) (9.1b), maximum intensity projection (MIP) images from the aortic arch to the skull base demonstrating normal arterial vascular anatomy.

KEY

arch	aortic arch
basi	basilar artery
c1	c1 (cervical segment ica)
c2	c2 (petrous segment of ica)
c3	c3 (lacaum segment of ica)
carb	carotid bulb
cca	common carotid artery
ccab	common carotid artery bifurcation
eca	external carotid artery
ica	internal carotid artery
inmta	innominate artery
innv	innominate vein
intm	internal mammary artery
subcl	subclavian artery
svc	superior vena cava
v1	V1 segment of vertebral artery (pre-foraminal)
v2	V2 segment of vertebral artery (foraminal)
v3	V3 segment of vertebral artery (from C1 to dura)
v4	v4 intracranial/intradural segment vertebral artery
vbj	vertebral basilar junction

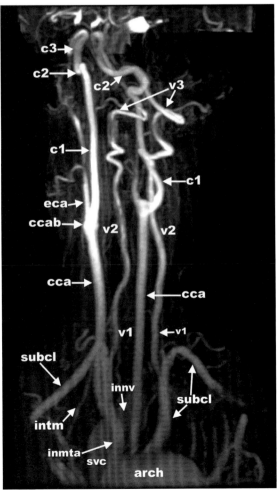

9.1b

■ CT ANGIOGRAPHY (CTA) (FIGURES 9.2a–9.6g)

Axial Plane

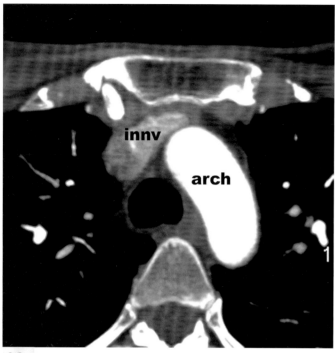

9.2a

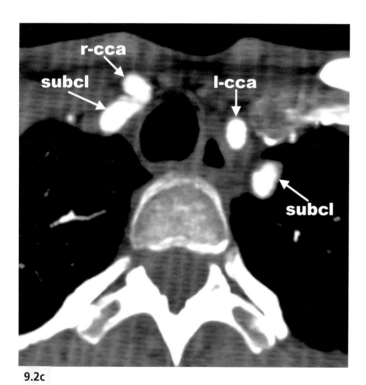

9.2c

9.2b

FIGURES 9.2a–j   Axial CTA source images (from inferior/caudal to superior/cranial) demonstrate normal arterial vascular anatomy.

KEY

arch	aortic arch
inmta	innominate artery
innv	innominate vein
l-cca	left common carotid artery
r-cca	right common carotid artery
subcl	subclavian artery

(*continued*)

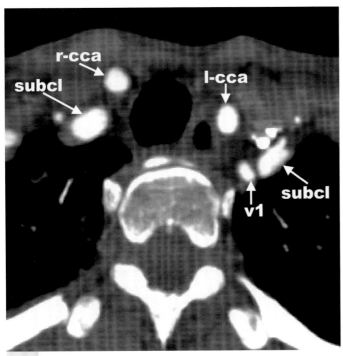

9.2d

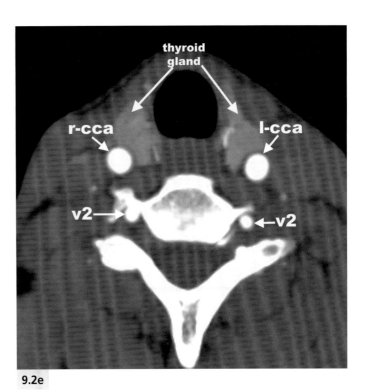

9.2e

FIGURES 9.2d–f

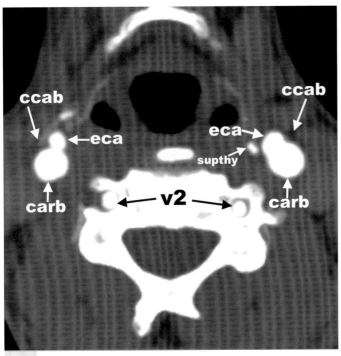

9.2f

KEY

carb	carotid bulb
ccab	common carotid artery bifurcation
eca	external carotid artery
l-cca	left common carotid artery
r-cca	right common carotid artery
subcl	subclavian artery
supthy	superior thyroid artery branch of eca
v1	V1 segment of vertebral artery (pre-foraminal)
v2	V2 segment of vertebral artery (foraminal)

(continued)

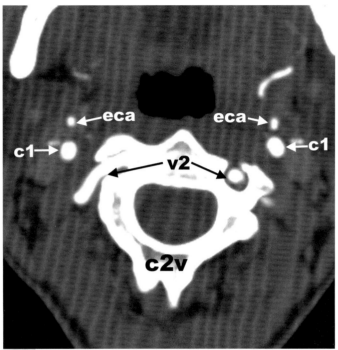

9.2g

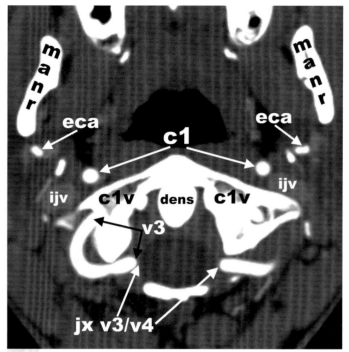

9.2h

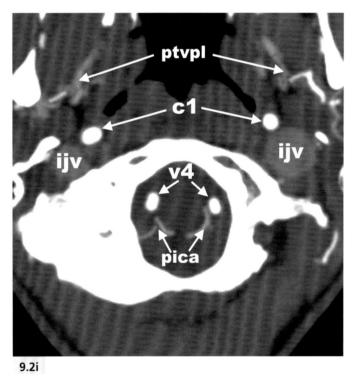

9.2i

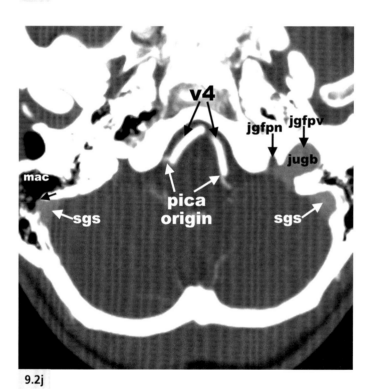

9.2j

FIGURES 9.2g–j

FIGURE 9.2j Incidental note is made of dehiscence of the bony plate separating the right sigmoid sinus from the adjacent right mastoid air cells (dehiscent sigmoid plate), indicated by the black arrow. The sigmoid sinus minimally protrudes into the mastoid air cells.

KEY

c1	c1 (cervical segment ica)	**mac**	mastoid air cells
c1v	first vertebral segment	**manr**	ramus of mandible
c2v	second vertebral segment	**pica**	posterior inferior cerebellar artery
dens	odontoid process of c2V	**ptvpl**	pterygoid venous plexus
eca	external carotid artery		
ica	internal carotid artery	**sgs**	sigmoid sinus
ijv	internal jugular vein	**v2**	V2 segment of vertebral artery (foraminal)
jgfpn	pars nervosa-jugular foramen	**v3**	V3 segment of vertebral artery (from C1 to dura)
jgfpv	pars vascularis-jugular foramen	**v4**	v4 intracranial/ intradural segment vertebral artery
jugb	jugular bulb		
jx	junction		

Coronal Plane

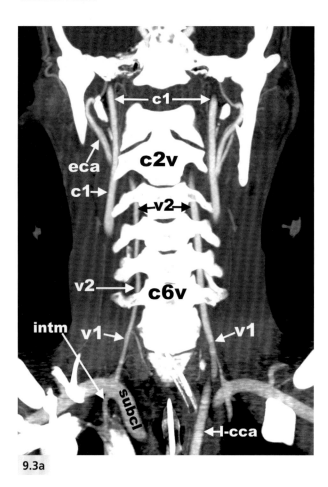

9.3a

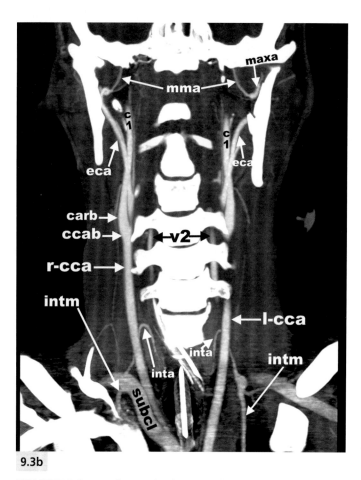

9.3b

FIGURES 9.3a–c   Coronal reformatted images from posterior to anterior demonstrate normal vascular anatomy.

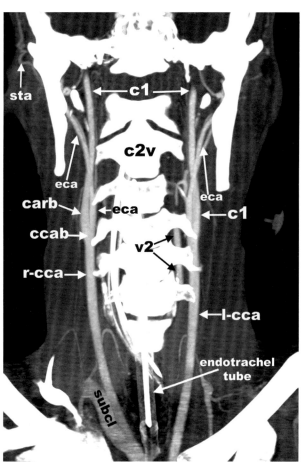

9.3c

KEY

c1	c1 (cervical segment ica)
c2v	second vertebral segment
c6v	sixth vertebral segment
carb	carotid bulb
ccab	common carotid artery bifurcation
eca	external carotid artery
ica	internal carotid artery
inta	inferior thyroid artery
intm	internal mammary artery
l-cca	left common carotid artery
maxa	maxillary artery
mma	middle meningeal artery
r-cca	right common carotid artery
sta	superficial temporal artery
subcl	subclavian artery
v1	V1 segment of vertebral artery (pre-foraminal)
v2	V2 segment of vertebral artery (foraminal)

Sagittal Plane

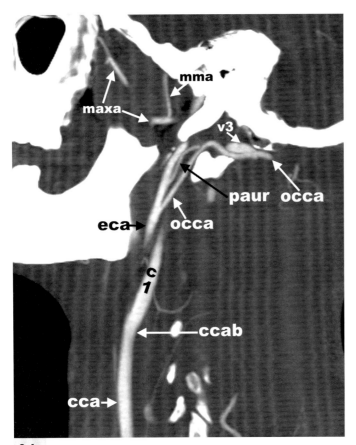

9.4a

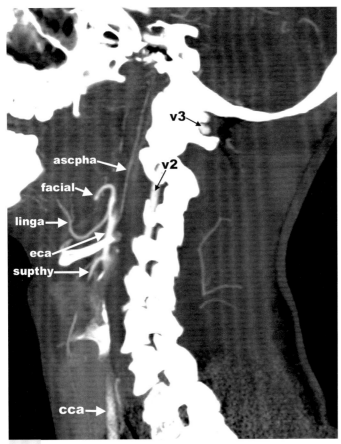

9.4c

9.4b

FIGURES 9.4a–c Sagittal reformatted images of the cervical carotid artery and its branches and the cervical vertebral artery from lateral to medial demonstrate normal vascular anatomy.

KEY

ascpha	ascending pharyngeal artery of eca
c1	c1 (cervical segment ica)
carb	carotid bulb
cca	common carotid artery
ccab	common carotid artery bifurcation
eca	external carotid artery
facial	facial artery
ica	internal carotid artery
linga	lingual artery - branch of eca
maxa	maxillary artery
mma	middle meningeal artery
occa	occipital artery
paur	posterior auricular artery
supthy	superior thyroid artery branch of eca
v2	V2 segment of vertebral artery (foraminal)
v3	V3 segment of vertebral artery (from C1 to dura)

(continued)

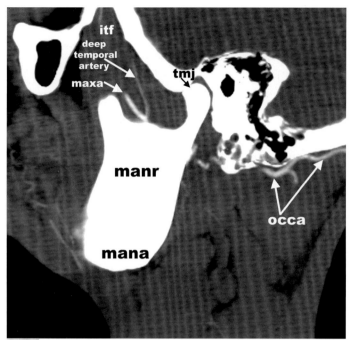

9.4d

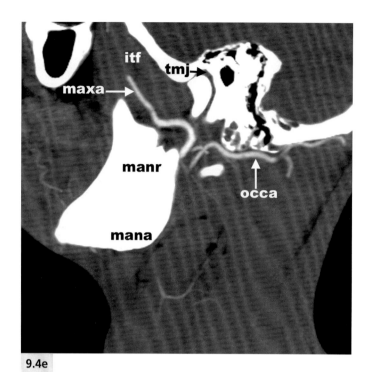

9.4e

FIGURES 9.4d–f   Sagittal images of external carotid and maxillary artery branches from lateral to medial.

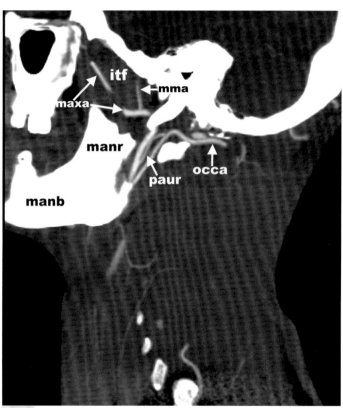

9.4f

KEY

itf	infratemporal fossa
mana	angle of mandible
manb	mandible body
manr	ramus of mandible
maxa	maxillary artery
mma	middle meningeal artery
occa	occipital artery
paur	posterior auricular artery
tmj	temporal mandibular joint

Curved Reformatted Images

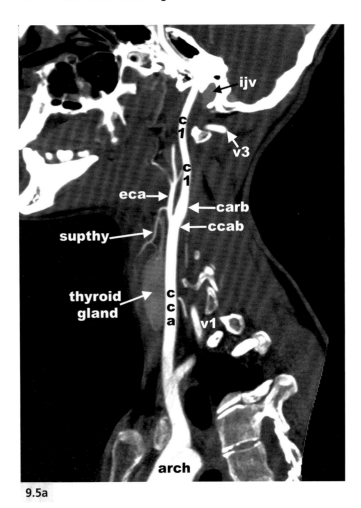

9.5a

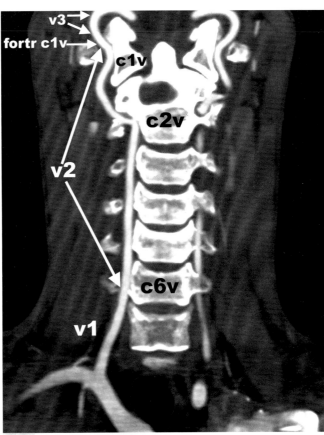

9.5c

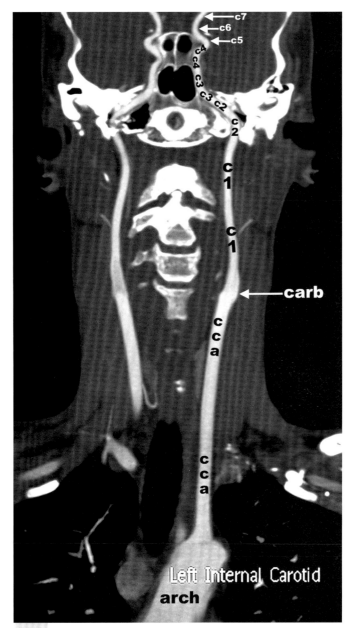

9.5b

FIGURES 9.5a–c   Radial curved reformatted images highlights the normal anatomy of the right carotid artery (9.5a), the left carotid artery (9.5b), and the right vertebral artery (9.5c).

KEY

arch	aortic arch	**carb**	carotid bulb
c1	c1 (cervical segment ica)	**cca**	common carotid artery
c1v	first vertebral segment	**ccab**	common carotid artery bifurcation
c2	c2 (petrous segment of ica)	**eca**	external carotid artery
c2v	second vertebral segment	**fortr**	foramen transversarium
c3	c3 (lacaum segment of ica)	**ica**	internal carotid artery
c4	c4 (cavernous segment of ica)	**ijv**	internal jugular vein
		supthy	superior thyroid artery branch of eca
c5	c5 (clinoid segment of ica)	**v1**	V1 segment of vertebral artery (pre-foraminal)
c6	c6 (ophthalmic segment of ica)	**v2**	V2 segment of vertebral artery (foraminal)
c6v	sixth vertebral segment	**v3**	V3 segment of vertebral artery (from C1 to dura)
c7	c7 (communicating segment of ica)		

3D CT Reconstructions

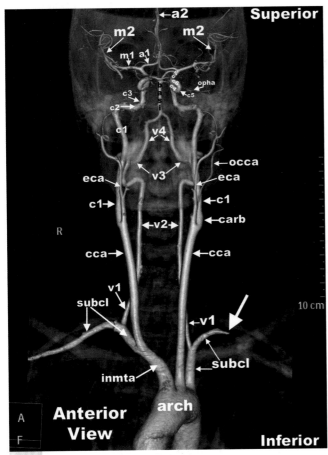

9.6a

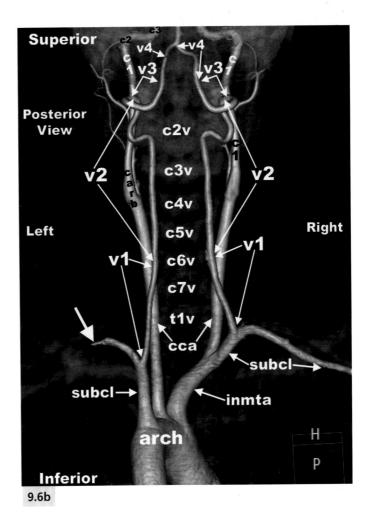

9.6b

FIGURES 9.6a–g 3D CTA reconstructions demonstrate normal vasculature.

FIGURES 9.6a–e Anterior (9.6a), posterior (9.6b), lateral (9.6c), and smaller field of view oblique views (9.6d,e) 3D reconstructions demonstrate only faint visualization of the background skeletal structures.

FIGURES 9.6a,b Cutoff of the left subclavian artery (large white arrows) distal to the takeoff of the left vertebral artery is artifactual related to inadvertent removal at the time of image reconstruction.

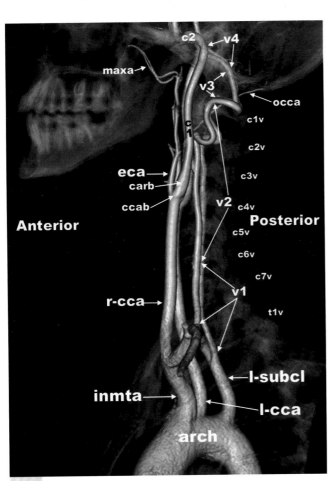

9.6c

KEY			
a1	a1 (precommunicating segment aca)	**ccab**	common carotid artery bifurcation
a2	a2 (postcommunicating segment aca)	**eca**	external carotid artery
aca	anterior cerebral artery	**ica**	internal carotid artery
arch	aortic arch	**inmta**	innominate artery
basi	basilar artery	**l-cca**	left common carotid artery
c1	c1 (cervical segment ica)	**m1**	m1 (horizontal segment mca)
c1v	first vertebral segment	**m2**	m2 (Sylvian/insular branches mca)
c2	c2 (petrous segment of ica)		
c2v	second vertebral segment	**maxa**	maxillary artery
c3	c3 (lacaum segment of ica)	**mca**	middle cerebral artery
c3v	third vertebral segment	**occa**	occipital artery
c4	c4 (cavernous segment of ica)	**opha**	ophthalmic artery
c4v	fourth vertebral segment	**r-cca**	right common carotid artery
c5	c5 (clinoid segment of ica)	**l-subcl**	left subclavian artery
c5v	fifth vertebral segment	**t1v**	t1 vertebral segment
c6	c6 (ophthalmic segment of ica)	**v1**	V1 segment of vertebral artery (pre-foraminal)
c6v	sixth vertebral segment	**v2**	V2 segment of vertebral artery (foraminal)
c7	c7 (communicating segment of ica)		
c7v	seventh vertebral segment	**v3**	V3 segment of vertebral artery (from C1 to dura)
carb	carotid bulb	**v4**	v4 intracranial/intradural segment vertebral artery
cca	common carotid artery		

(continued)

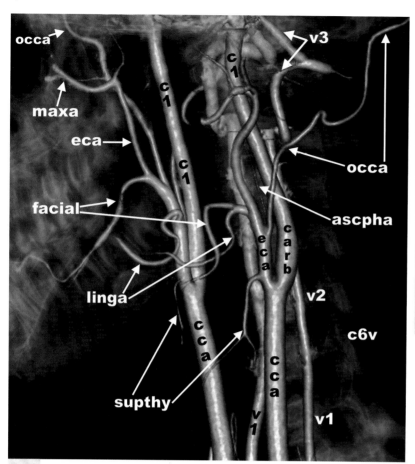

9.6d

FIGURES 9.6c,d Oblique magnified, smaller field of view 3D CTA reconstructions demonstrate the smaller vessels to better advantage.

KEY

ascpha	ascending pharyngeal artery of eca
c1	c1 (cervical segment ica)
c2v	second vertebral segment
c6v	sixth vertebral segment
carb	carotid bulb
cca	common carotid artery
ccab	common carotid artery bifurcation
eca	external carotid artery
facial	facial artery
ica	internal carotid artery
linga	lingual artery - branch of eca
maxa	maxillary artery
occa	occipital artery
supthy	superior thyroid artery branch of eca
v1	V1 segment of vertebral artery (pre-foraminal)
v2	V2 segment of vertebral artery (foraminal)
v3	V3 segment of vertebral artery (from C1 to dura)

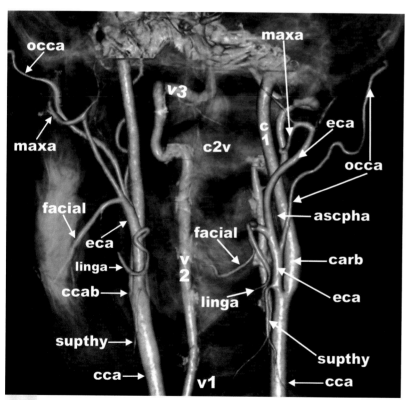

9.6e

(continued)

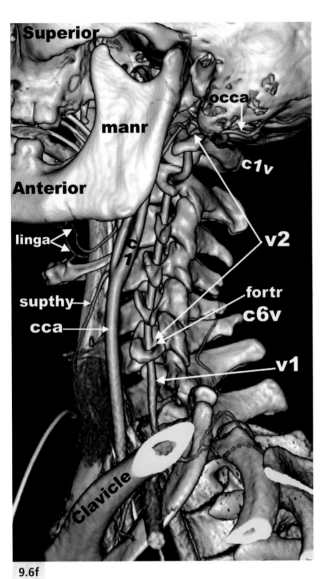

9.6f

FIGURES 9.6f,g   Lateral oblique (9.6f) and posterior (9.6g) 3D CTA reconstructions using different software demonstrate that the skeletal structures are well visualized which results in decreased ability to visualize the vascular structures.

KEY

c1	c1 (cervical segment ica)
c1v	first vertebral segment
c2v	second vertebral segment
c3v	third vertebral segment
c6v	sixth vertebral segment
carb	carotid bulb
cca	common carotid artery
eca	external carotid artery
fortr	foramen transversarium
ica	internal carotid artery
linga	lingual artery - branch of eca
manr	ramus of mandible
occa	occipital artery
r-cca	right common carotid artery
supthy	superior thyroid artery branch of eca
v1	V1 segment of vertebral artery (pre-foraminal)
v2	V2 segment of vertebral artery (foraminal)
v3	V3 segment of vertebral artery (from C1 to dura)

9.6g

■ CATHETER ANGIOGRAPHY (FIGURES 9.7a–9.8n)

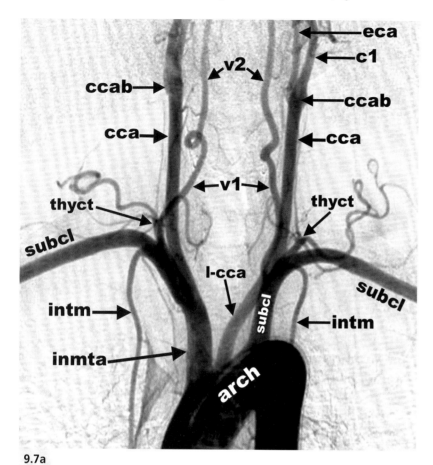

9.7a

FIGURES 9.7a,b Left anterior oblique (LAO) projections from aortic arch catheter angiograms demonstrating normal vascular anatomy.

KEY	
arch	aortic arch
c1	c1 (cervical segment ica)
cca	common carotid artery
ccab	common carotid artery bifurcation
eca	external carotid artery
ica	internal carotid artery
inmta	innominate artery
intm	internal mammary artery
l-cca	left common carotid artery
subcl	subclavian artery
thyct	thyrocervical trunk
v1	V1 segment of vertebral artery (pre-foraminal)
v2	V2 segment of vertebral artery (foraminal)

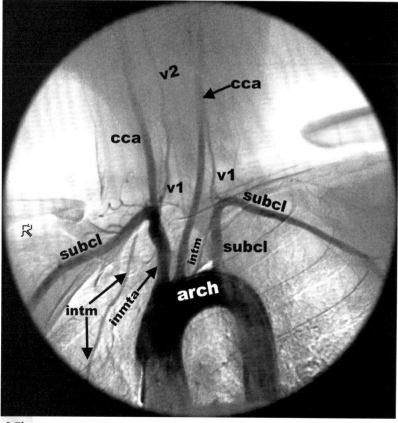

9.7b

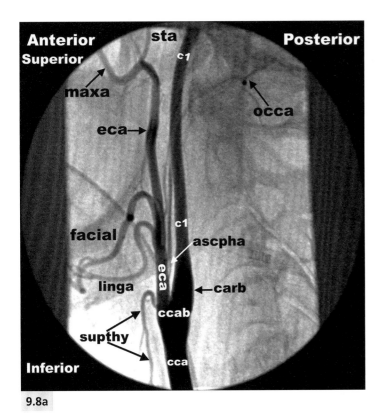

9.8a

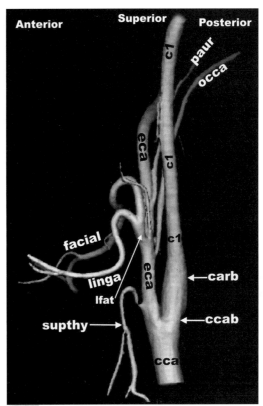

9.8b

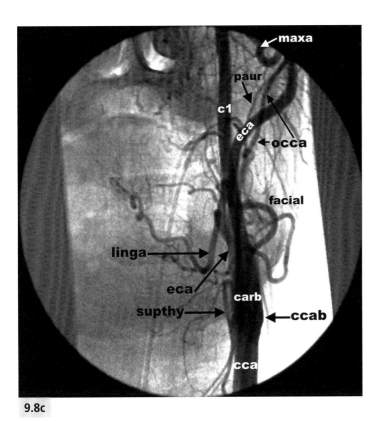

9.8c

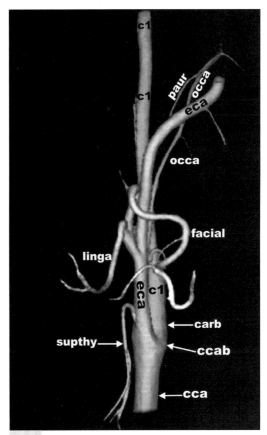

9.8d

KEY

ascpha	ascending pharyngeal artery of eca	linga	lingual artery - branch of eca
c1	c1 (cervical segment ica)	maxa	maxillary artery
carb	carotid bulb	occa	occipital artery
cca	common carotid artery	paur	posterior auricular artery
ccab	common carotid artery bifurcation		
		sta	superficial temporal artery
eca	external carotid artery		
facial	facial artery	supthy	superior thyroid artery branch of eca
ica	internal carotid artery		
lfat	lingual-facial artery trunk		

FIGURES 9.8a–d Lateral (9.8a,b) and frontal (9.8c,d) projections from a 2D, DSA (9.8a,c) and 3D rotational angiogram (9.8b,d) via injection of the common carotid artery shows normal vascular anatomy.

(*continued*)

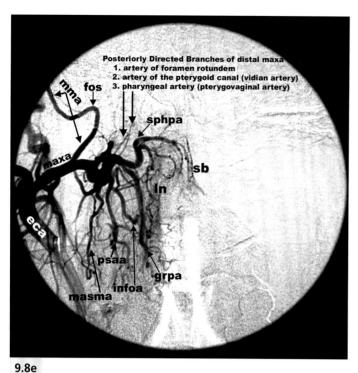

9.8e

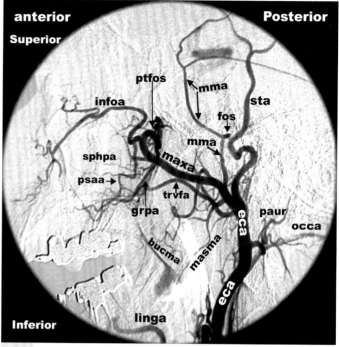

9.8f

FIGURES 9.8e–g   Frontal Towne's (9.8e), lateral (9.8f) and frontal Caldwell (9.8g) projections from a 2D DSA via selective external carotid artery injection shows normal vascular anatomy.

KEY

bucma	buccinator muscular branches of eca
eca	external carotid artery
facial	facial artery
fos	foramen spinosum
grpa	greater palatine artery
infoa	infraorbital artery
linga	lingual artery - branch of eca
ln	lateral nasal branch of sphenopalatine artery
masma	masseteric muscular artery branches of eca
maxa	maxillary artery
mma	middle meningeal artery
occa	occipital artery
paur	posterior auricular artery
psaa	posterior superior alveolar artery
ptfos	pterygopalatine fossa
sb	septal branch of sphenopalatine artery
sphpa	sphenopalatine artery
sta	superficial temporal artery
trvfa	transverse facial artery

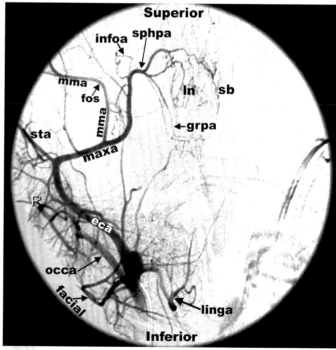

9.8g

(continued)

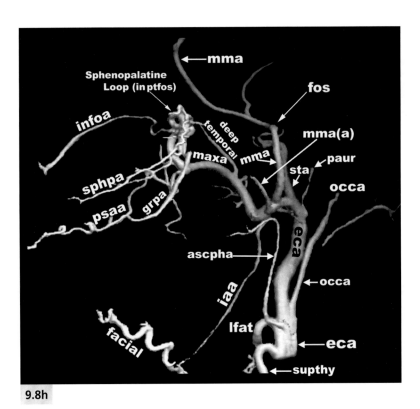

9.8h

FIGURES 9.8h,i   3D rotational catheter external carotid artery angiogram in the lateral (9.8h) and frontal (9.8i) projections demonstrates normal vascular anatomy.

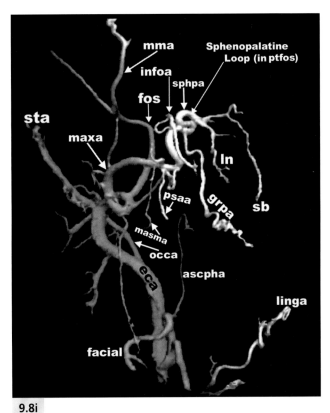

9.8i

KEY

ascpha	ascending pharyngeal artery of eca
eca	external carotid artery
facial	facial artery
fos	foramen spinosum
grpa	greater palatine artery
iaa	inferior alveolar artery
infoa	infraorbital artery
lfat	lingual-facial artery trunk
linga	lingual artery - branch of eca
ln	lateral nasal branch of sphenopalatine artery
masma	masseteric muscular artery branches of eca
maxa	maxillary artery
mma(a)	accessory meningeal artery
mma	middle meningeal artery
occa	occipital artery
paur	posterior auricular artery
psaa	posterior superior alveolar artery
ptfos	pterygopalatine fossa
sb	septal branch of sphenopalatine artery
sphpa	sphenopalatine artery
sta	superficial temporal artery
supthy	superior thyroid artery branch of eca

(continued)

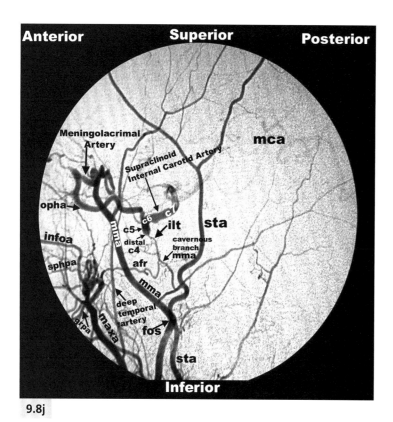

9.8j

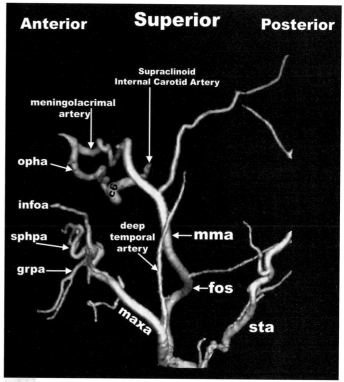

9.8k

FIGURES 9.8j,k Lateral 2D digital subtraction common carotid artery catheter angiogram (9.8j) and corresponding lateral projection from a 3D rotational catheter angiogram (9.8k) in same patient shows occlusion of the cervical internal carotid artery extending intracranially to the c4/5 junction where there is retrograde filling of the ophthalmic artery via a meningolacrimal branch of the middle meningeal artery. There is also collateral flow into the distal cavernous (c4) segment of the internal carotid artery via external carotid artery collaterals which opacify the inferolateral trunk (ilt) and then the internal carotid artery. Note the lack of visualization of the smaller branches on the 3D angiogram, which is one of its drawbacks.

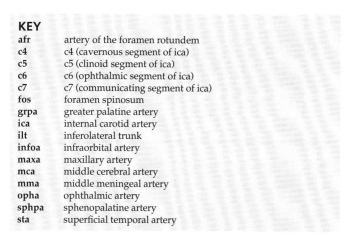

KEY

afr	artery of the foramen rotundem
c4	c4 (cavernous segment of ica)
c5	c5 (clinoid segment of ica)
c6	c6 (ophthalmic segment of ica)
c7	c7 (communicating segment of ica)
fos	foramen spinosum
grpa	greater palatine artery
ica	internal carotid artery
ilt	inferolateral trunk
infoa	infraorbital artery
maxa	maxillary artery
mca	middle cerebral artery
mma	middle meningeal artery
opha	ophthalmic artery
sphpa	sphenopalatine artery
sta	superficial temporal artery

(continued)

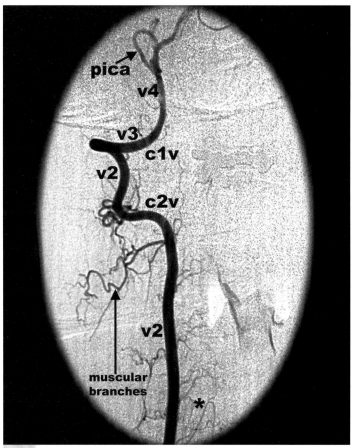

9.8l

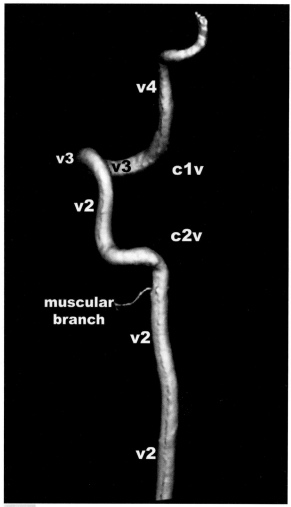

9.8m

FIGURES 9.8l,m Frontal projection, selective right vertebral artery 2D catheter DSA image (9.8l), and corresponding frontal projection 3D catheter angiographic image (9.8m) demonstrate normal vascular anatomy. Again note the relative lack of visualization of smaller branches on the 3D image compared with the 2D DSA image. The black asterisk in Figure 9.8l indicates a radiculomedullary arterial feeder to the anterior spinal artery arising from the lower cervical right vertebral artery.

KEY

asa	anterior spinal artery
c1v	first vertebral segment
c2v	second vertebral segment
intm	internal mammary artery
pica	posterior inferior cerebellar artery
subcl	subclavian artery
thyct	thyrocervical trunk
thyctac	ascending cervical branch of thyrocervical trunk
v1	V1 segment of vertebral artery (pre-foraminal)
v2	V2 segment of vertebral artery (foraminal)
v3	V3 segment of vertebral artery (from C1 to dura)
v4	v4 intracranial/intradural segment vertebral artery

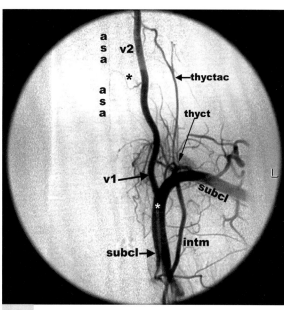

9.8n

FIGURE 9.8n Frontal projection from a selective left subclavian artery 2D DSA angiogram demonstrating normal vascular anatomy. The white asterisk indicates the tip of the vascular catheter in the subclavian artery just proximal to the origin of the left vertebral artery. The black asterisk indicates a radiculomedullary arterial feeder to the anterior spinal artery, which arises from the lower cervical vertebral artery.

ARTERIAL BRAIN

■ MRA (FIGURES 9.9a–9.14b)

Axial Plane

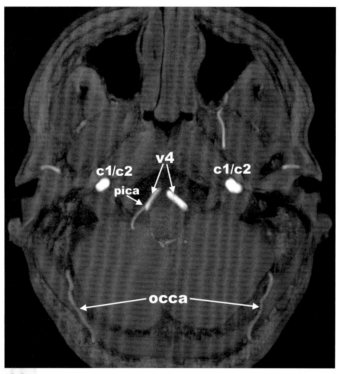

9.9a

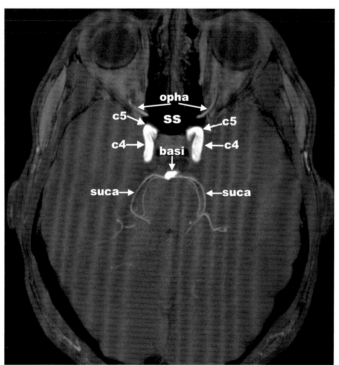

9.9c

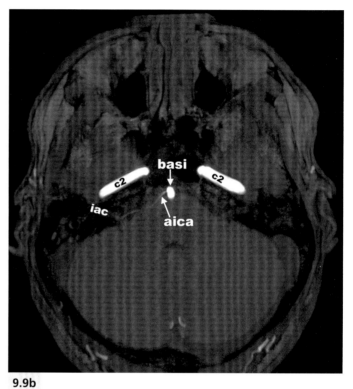

9.9b

FIGURES 9.9a–9.11b   Source 3D time-of-flight (TOF) non-contrast axial (9.9a–j) magnetic resonance angiographic images presented with thicker slice slabs than typically generated for routine clinical use with reformation into coronal (9.10a–d) and sagittal (9.11a,b) planes demonstrates normal vascular anatomy.

KEY

aica	anterior inferior cerebellar artery
basi	basilar artery
c1	c1 (cervical segment ica)
c2	c2 (petrous segment of ica)
c4	c4 (cavernous segment of ica)
c5	c5 (clinoid segment of ica)
iac	internal auditory canal
ica	internal carotid artery
occa	occipital artery
opha	ophthalmic artery
pica	posterior inferior cerebellar artery
ss	sphenoid sinus
suca	superior cerebellar artery
v4	v4 intracranial/intradural segment vertebral artery

(continued)

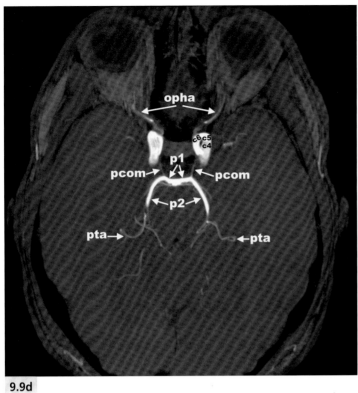

9.9d

9.9e

FIGURES 9.9d–f

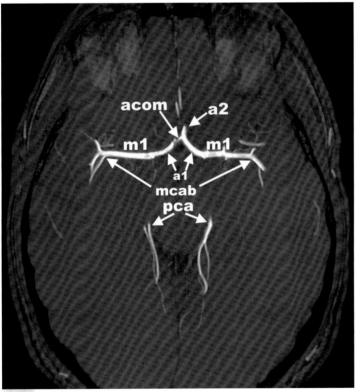

9.9f

KEY	
a1	a1 (precommunicating segment aca)
a2	a2 (postcommunicating segment aca)
aca	anterior cerebral artery
acha	anterior choroidal artery
acom	anterior communicating artery
c4	c4 (cavernous segment of ica)
c5	c5 (clinoid segment of ica)
c6	c6 (ophthalmic segment of ica)
c7	c7 (communicating segment of ica)
ica	internal carotid artery
m1	m1 (horizontal segment mca)
mca	middle cerebral artery
mcab	mca bifurcation/trifurcation
opha	ophthalmic artery
p1	p1 (precommunicating/mesencephalic segment pca)
p2	p2 (ambient segment of pca)
pca	posterior cerebral artery
pcom	posterior communicating artery
pta	posterior temporal branch of pca

(continued)

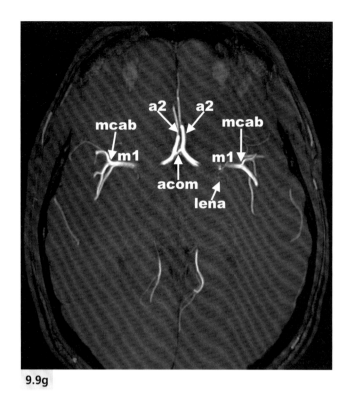

9.9g

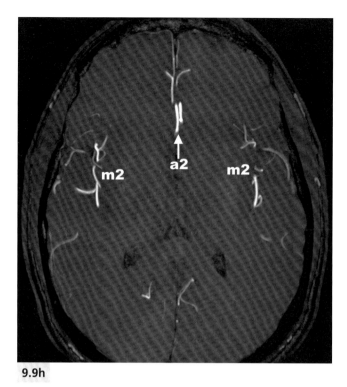

9.9h

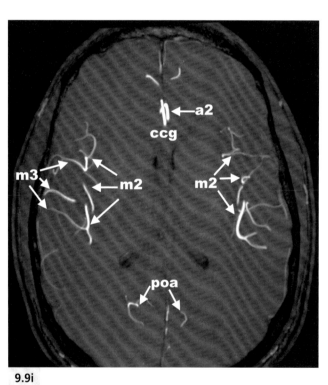

9.9i

9.9j

FIGURES 9.9g–j

KEY

a2	a2 (postcommunicating segment aca)
aca	anterior cerebral artery
acom	anterior communicating artery
ccg	genu of corpus callosum
lena	lenticulostriate arteries
m1	m1 (horizontal segment mca)
m2	m2 (Sylvian/insular branches mca)
m3	m3 (opercular branches mca)
m4	m4 (cortical branches mca)
mca	middle cerebral artery
mcab	mca bifurcation/trifurcation
pca	posterior cerebral artery
peric	pericallosal branch of aca
poa	parieto-occipital branch of pca

Frontal Views

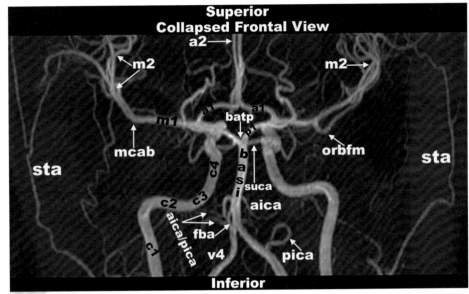

9.10a

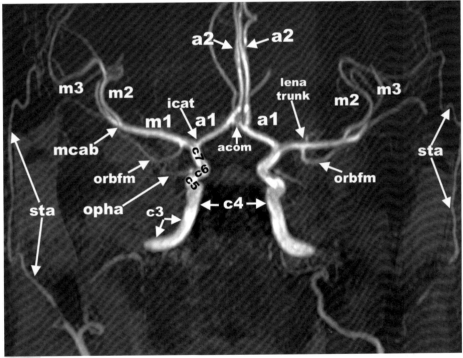

9.10b

FIGURES 9.10a,b

KEY

a1	a1 (precommunicating segment aca)
a2	a2 (postcommunicating segment aca)
aca	anterior cerebral artery
acom	anterior communicating artery
aica	anterior inferior cerebellar artery
aica/pica	medial branch of aica supplying pica
basi	basilar artery
batp	basilar artery tip
c1	c1 (cervical segment ica)
c2	c2 (petrous segment of ica)
c3	c3 (lacerum segment of ica)
c4	c4 (cavernous segment of ica)
c5	c5 (clinoid segment of ica)
c6	c6 (ophthalmic segment of ica)
c7	c7 (communicating segment of ica)
fba	fenestration of basilar artery
ica	internal carotid artery
icat	ica terminus/bifurcation
lena	lenticulostriate arteries
m1	m1 (horizontal segment mca)
m2	m2 (Sylvian/insular branches mca)
m3	m3 (opercular branches mca)
mca	middle cerebral artery
mcab	mca bifurcation/trifurcation
opha	ophthalmic artery
orbfm	orbitofrontal branch of mca
p1	p1 (precommunicating/mesencephalic segment pca)
pca	posterior cerebral artery
pica	posterior inferior cerebellar artery
sta	superficial temporal artery
suca	superior cerebellar artery
v4	v4 intracranial/intradural segment vertebral artery

(continued)

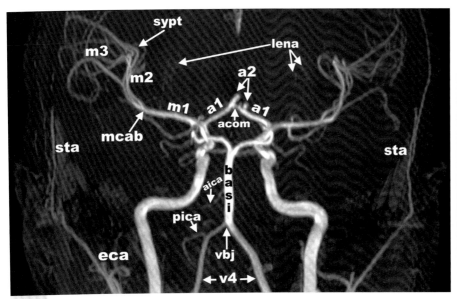

9.10c

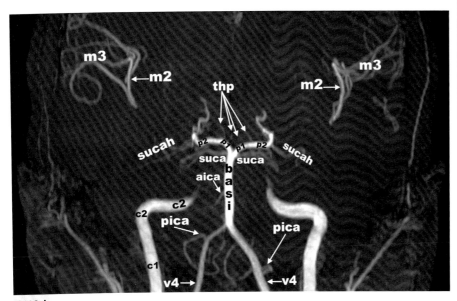

9.10d

FIGURES 9.10c,d

KEY

a1	a1 (precommunicating segment aca)
a2	a2 (postcommunicating segment aca)
aca	anterior cerebral artery
acom	anterior communicating artery
aica	anterior inferior cerebellar artery
basi	basilar artery
c1	c1 (cervical segment ica)
c2	c2 (petrous segment of ica)
eca	external carotid artery
ica	internal carotid artery
lena	lenticulostriate arteries
m1	m1 (horizontal segment mca)
m2	m2 (Sylvian/insular branches mca)
m3	m3 (opercular branches mca)
mca	middle cerebral artery
mcab	mca bifurcation/trifurcation
p1	p1 (precommunicating/mesencephalic segment pca)
p2	p2 (ambient segment of pca)
pca	posterior cerebral artery
pica	posterior inferior cerebellar artery
sta	superficial temporal artery
suca	superior cerebellar artery
sucah	hemispheric branch of suca
sypt	Sylvian point
thp	thalamoperforators
v4	v4 intracranial/intradural segment vertebral artery
vbj	vertebral basilar junction

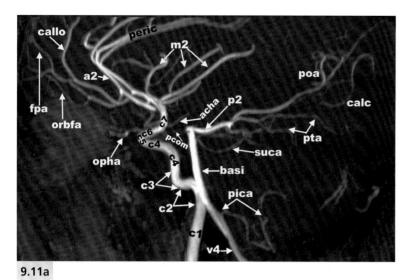

9.11a

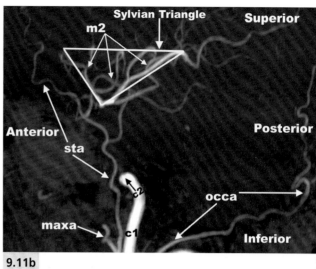

9.11b

FIGURES 9.11a,b Maximum intensity projection (MIP) sagittal (lateral) views illustrate the "angiographic Sylvian triangle" which is the geometric representation of the insular middle cerebral artery branches (m2) overlying the insular cortex.

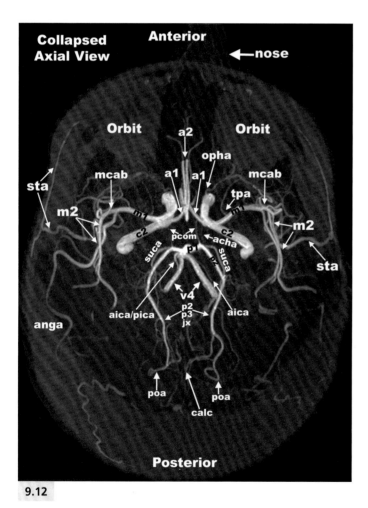

9.12

FIGURE 9.12 This collapsed axial MIP demonstrates normal intracranial vascular anatomy.

FIGURES 9.12–9.14b Maximum intensity projection (MIP) MRA images.

KEY

a1	a1 (precommunicating segment aca)
a2	a2 (postcommunicating segment aca)
aca	anterior cerebral artery
acha	anterior choroidal artery
aica	anterior inferior cerebellar artery
aica/pica	medial branch of aica supplying pica
anga	angular artery
basi	basilar artery
c1	c1 (cervical segment ica)
c2	c2 (petrous segment of ica)
c3	c3 (lacaum segment of ica)
c4	c4 (cavernous segment of ica)
c5	c5 (clinoid segment of ica)
c6	c6 (ophthalmic segment of ica)
c7	c7 (communicating segment of ica)
calc	calcarine branch of pca
callo	callosomarginal branch of aca
fpa	frontopolar branch of aca
ica	internal carotid artery
jx	junction
m1	m1 (horizontal segment mca)
m2	m2 (Sylvian/insular branches mca)
maxa	maxillary artery
mca	middle cerebral artery
mcab	mca bifurcation/trifurcation
occa	occipital artery
opha	ophthalmic artery
orbfa	orbitofrontal branch of aca
p1	p1 (precommunicating/mesencephalic segment pca)
p2	p2 (ambient segment of pca)
p3	p3 (quadrigeminal segment of pca)
pca	posterior cerebral artery
pcom	posterior communicating artery
peric	pericallosal branch of aca
pica	posterior inferior cerebellar artery
poa	parieto-occipital branch of pca
pta	posterior temporal branch of pca
sta	superficial temporal artery
suca	superior cerebellar artery
tpa	temporal polar branch of mca
v4	v4 intracranial/intradural segment vertebral artery

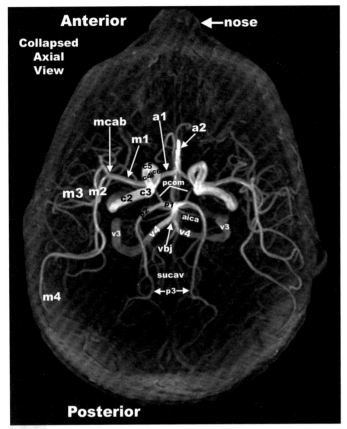

9.13a

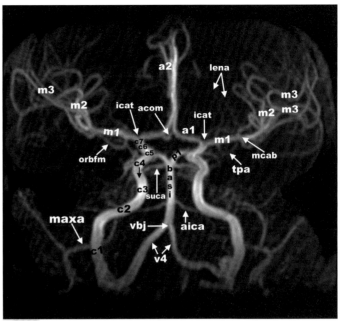

9.13b

FIGURES 9.13a–e Axial collapsed MIP image of another subject (9.13a) and static rotated MIP images from the frontal to the lateral projection (9.13b–e) demonstrate normal intracranial vascular anatomy.

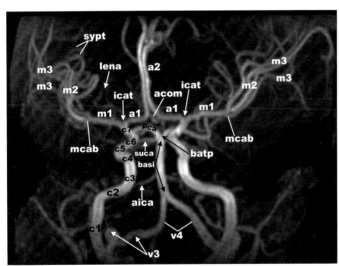

9.13c

KEY

a1	a1 (precommunicating segment aca)
a2	a2 (postcommunicating segment aca)
aca	anterior cerebral artery
acom	anterior communicating artery
aica	anterior inferior cerebellar artery
basi	basilar artery
batp	basilar artery tip
c1	c1 (cervical segment ica)
c2	c2 (petrous segment of ica)
c3	c3 (lacaum segment of ica)
c4	c4 (cavernous segment of ica)
c5	c5 (clinoid segment of ica)
c6	c6 (ophthalmic segment of ica)
c7	c7 (communicating segment of ica)
ica	internal carotid artery
icat	ica terminus/bifurcation
lena	lenticulostriate arteries
m1	m1 (horizontal segment mca)
m2	m2 (Sylvian/insular branches mca)
m3	m3 (opercular branches mca)
m4	m4 (cortical branches mca)
maxa	maxillary artery
mca	middle cerebral artery
mcab	mca bifurcation/trifurcation
orbfm	orbitofrontal branch of mca
p1	p1 (precommunicating/mesencephalic segment pca)
p2	p2 (ambient segment of pca)
p3	p3 (quadrigeminal segment of pca)
pca	posterior cerebral artery
pcom	posterior communicating artery
suca	superior cerebellar artery
sucav	vermin branch of suca
sypt	Sylvian point
tpa	temporal polar branch of mca
v3	V3 segment of vertebral artery (from C1 to dura)
v4	v4 intracranial/intradural segment vertebral artery
vbj	vertebral basilar junction

(continued)

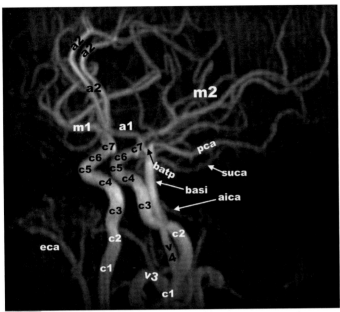

9.13d

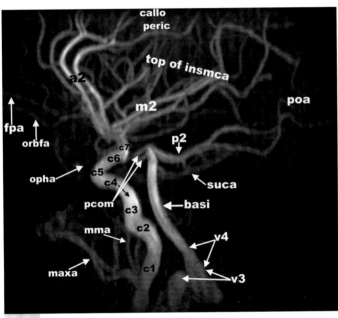

9.13e

FIGURES 9.13d,e

KEY

a1	a1 (precommunicating segment aca)
a2	a2 (postcommunicating segment aca)
aca	anterior cerebral artery
aica	anterior inferior cerebellar artery
basi	basilar artery
batp	basilar artery tip
c1	c1 (cervical segment ica)
c2	c2 (petrous segment of ica)
c3	c3 (lacaum segment of ica)
c4	c4 (cavernous segment of ica)
c5	c5 (clinoid segment of ica)
c6	c6 (ophthalmic segment of ica)
c7	c7 (communicating segment of ica)
callo	callosomarginal branch of aca
eca	external carotid artery
fpa	frontopolar branch of aca
ica	internal carotid artery
insmca	insular branches of mca
m1	m1 (horizontal segment mca)
m2	m2 (Sylvian/insular branches mca)
maxa	maxillary artery
mca	middle cerebral artery
mma	middle meningeal artery
opha	ophthalmic artery
orbfa	orbitofrontal branch of aca
p2	p2 (ambient segment of pca)
pca	posterior cerebral artery
pcom	posterior communicating artery
peric	pericallosal branch of aca
poa	parieto-occipital branch of pca
suca	superior cerebellar artery
v3	V3 segment of vertebral artery (from C1 to dura)
v4	v4 intracranial/intradural segment vertebral artery

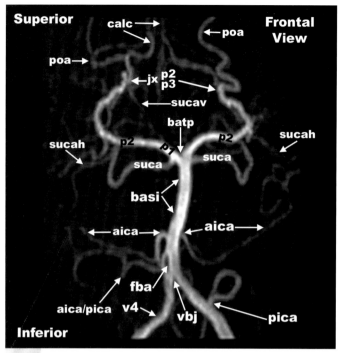

9.14a

FIGURES 9.14a,b Frontal and lateral MIP images with the carotid/anterior circulation removed show normal anatomy in the vertebral-basilar circulation (posterior circulation).

KEY

a-thp	anterior thalamoperforators
aica	anterior inferior cerebellar artery
aica/pica	medial branch of aica supplying pica
basi	basilar artery
batp	basilar artery tip
calc	calcarine branch of pca
fba	fenestration of basilar artery
jx	junction
p1	p1 (precommunicating/mesencephalic segment pca)
p2	p2 (ambient segment of pca)
p3	p3 (quadrigeminal segment of pca)
pca	posterior cerebral artery
pcom	posterior communicating artery
pica	posterior inferior cerebellar artery
poa	parieto-occipital branch of pca
pta	posterior temporal branch of pca
suca	superior cerebellar artery
sucah	hemispheric branch of suca
sucav	vermin branch of suca
v4	v4 intracranial/intradural segment vertebral artery
vbj	vertebral basilar junction

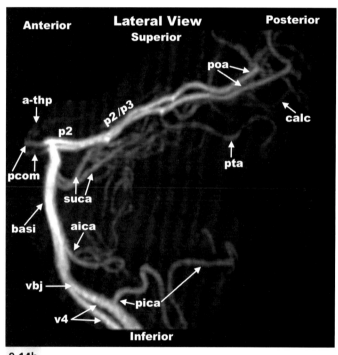

9.14b

■ CTA (FIGURES 9.15a–9.19c)

Axial Plane

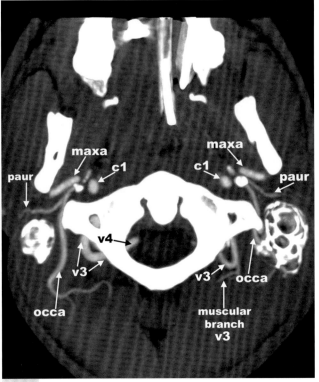

9.15a

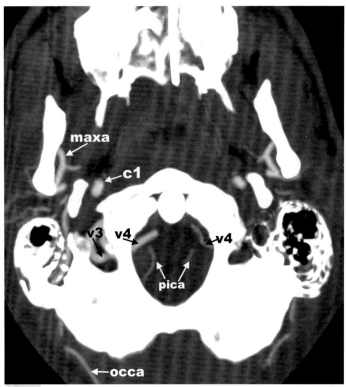

9.15b

FIGURES 9.15a–k   CTA Subject 1. Thick slab reformatted axial images from a CTA demonstrates normal intracranial vascular anatomy.

KEY	
c1	c1 (cervical segment ica)
ica	internal carotid artery
maxa	maxillary artery
occa	occipital artery
paur	posterior auricular artery
pica	posterior inferior cerebellar artery
v3	V3 segment of vertebral artery (from C1 to dura)
v4	v4 intracranial/intradural segment vertebral artery

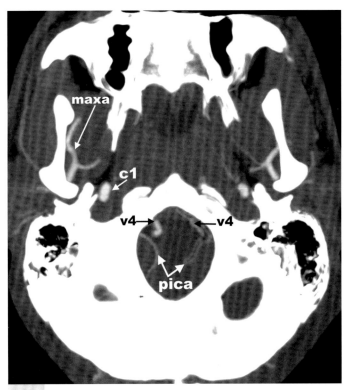

9.15c

(continued)

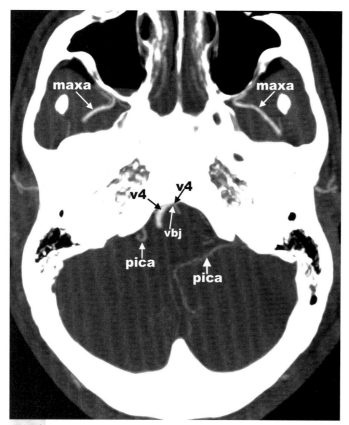

9.15d

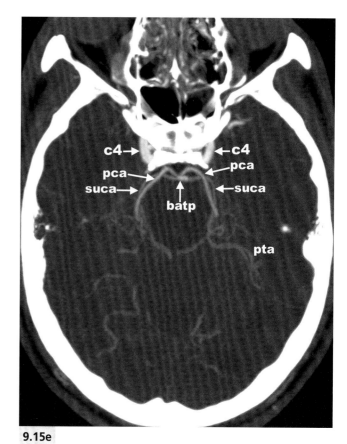

9.15e

FIGURES 9.15d–f

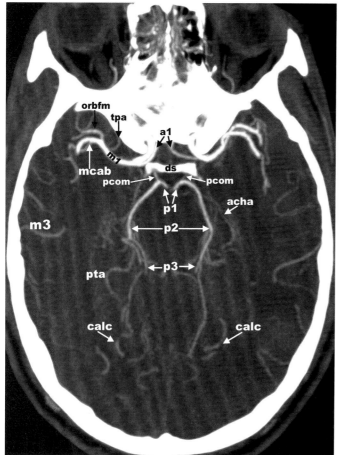

9.15f

KEY

a1	a1 (precommunicating segment aca)
aca	anterior cerebral artery
acha	anterior choroidal artery
batp	basilar artery tip
c4	c4 (cavernous segment of ica)
calc	calcarine branch of pca
ds	dorsum sellae
ica	internal carotid artery
m1	m1 (horizontal segment mca)
m3	m3 (opercular branches mca)
maxa	maxillary artery
mca	middle cerebral artery
mcab	mca bifurcation/trifurcation
orbfm	orbitofrontal branch of mca
p1	p1 (precommunicating/mesencephalic segment pca)
p2	p2 (ambient segment of pca)
p3	p3 (quadrigeminal segment of pca)
pca	posterior cerebral artery
pcom	posterior communicating artery
pica	posterior inferior cerebellar artery
pta	posterior temporal branch of pca
suca	superior cerebellar artery
tpa	temporal polar branch of mca
v4	v4 intracranial/intradural segment vertebral artery
vbj	vertebral basilar junction

(continued)

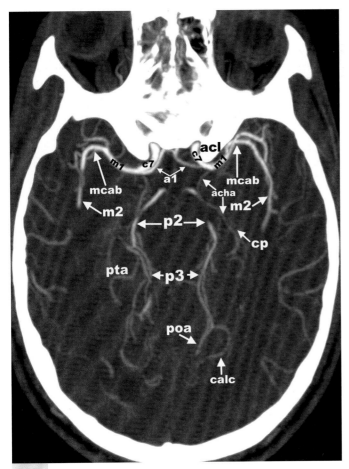

9.15g

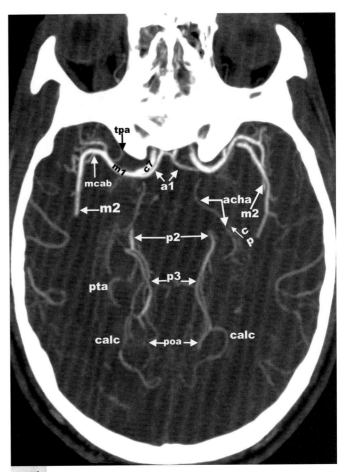

9.15h

FIGURES 9.15g–i

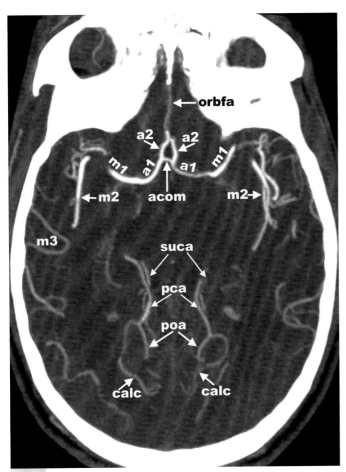

9.15i

KEY

a1	a1 (precommunicating segment aca)
a2	a2 (postcommunicating segment aca)
aca	anterior cerebral artery
acha	anterior choroidal artery
acl	anterior clinoid process
acom	anterior communicating artery
c7	c7 (communicating segment of ica)
calc	calcarine branch of pca
cp	choroid plexus
ica	internal carotid artery
m1	m1 (horizontal segment mca)
m2	m2 (Sylvian/insular branches mca)
m3	m3 (opercular branches mca)
mca	middle cerebral artery
mcab	mca bifurcation/trifurcation
orbfa	orbitofrontal branch of aca
p2	p2 (ambient segment of pca)
p3	p3 (quadrigeminal segment of pca)
pca	posterior cerebral artery
poa	parieto-occipital branch of pca
pta	posterior temporal branch of pca
suca	superior cerebellar artery
tpa	temporal polar branch of mca

(continued)

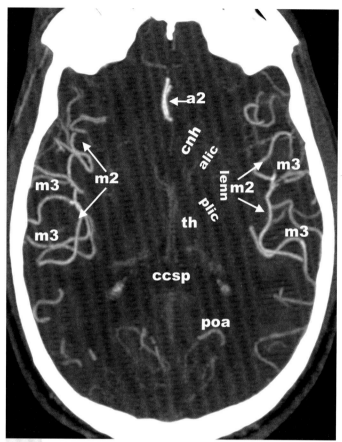

9.15j

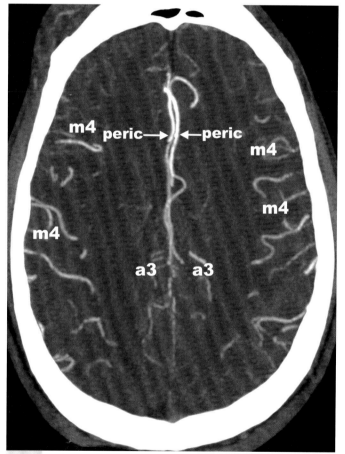

9.15k

FIGURES 9.15j,k

KEY

a2	a2 (postcommunicating segment aca)
a3	a3 (cortical branches of aca)
aca	anterior cerebral artery
alic	anterior limb of internal capsule
ccsp	splenium of corpus callosum
cnh	caudate nucleus head
lenn	lenticular nucleus
m2	m2 (Sylvian/insular branches mca)
m3	m3 (opercular branches mca)
m4	m4 (cortical branches mca)
mca	middle cerebral artery
pca	posterior cerebral artery
peric	pericallosal branch of aca
plic	posterior limb of internal capsule
poa	parieto-occipital branch of pca
th	thalamus

Axial Plane

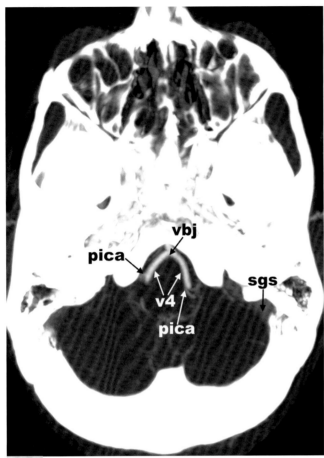

9.16a

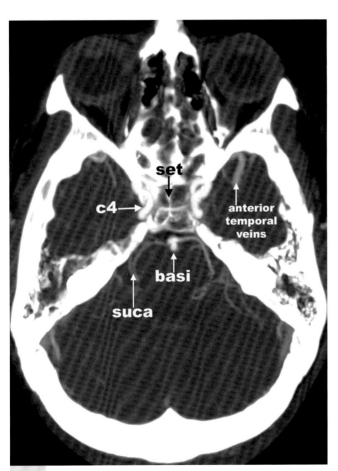

9.16c

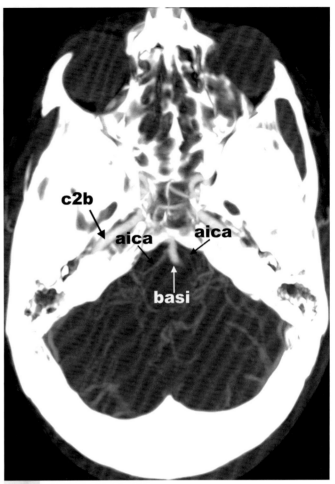

9.16b

FIGURES 9.16a–9.18f   CTA Subject 2. Thick slab reformatted axial (9.16a–j), coronal (9.17a–c), and sagittal (9.18a–f) images demonstrate normal intracranial vascular anatomy. Note the greater degree of visualization of the venous system compared with the previous CTA, which reflects a longer time delay from the point of contrast injection to the start of imaging.

KEY

aica	anterior inferior cerebellar artery
basi	basilar artery
c2b	c2b (horizontal petrous segment of ica)
c4	c4 (cavernous segment of ica)
ica	internal carotid artery
pica	posterior inferior cerebellar artery
set	sella turcica
sgs	sigmoid sinus
suca	superior cerebellar artery
v4	v4 intracranial/intradural segment vertebral artery
vbj	vertebral basilar junction

(continued)

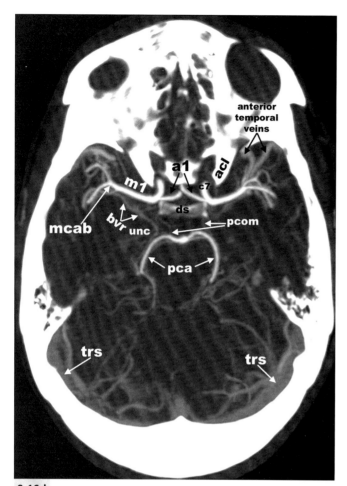

9.16d

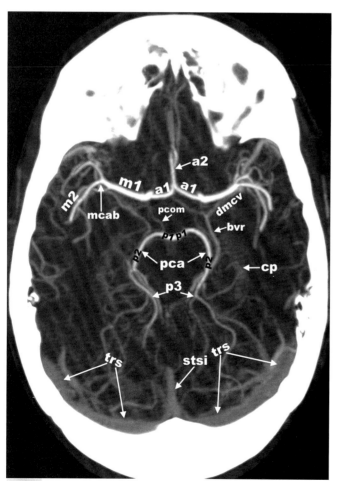

9.16f

9.16e

FIGURES 9.16d–f

KEY

a1	a1 (precommunicating segment aca)
a2	a2 (postcommunicating segment aca)
aca	anterior cerebral artery
acl	anterior clinoid process
antcv	anterior cerebral vein
bvr	basal vein of Rosenthal
c7	c7 (communicating segment of ica)
cp	choroid plexus
dmcv	deep middle cerebral vein
ds	dorsum sellae
ica	internal carotid artery
m1	m1 (horizontal segment mca)
m2	m2 (Sylvian/insular branches mca)
mca	middle cerebral artery
mcab	mca bifurcation/trifurcation
p1	p1 (precommunicating/mesencephalic segment pca)
p2	p2 (ambient segment of pca)
p3	p3 (quadrigeminal segment of pca)
pca	posterior cerebral artery
pcom	posterior communicating artery
spps	sphenoparietal sinus
stsi	straight sinus
trs	transverse sinus
unc	uncus

(continued)

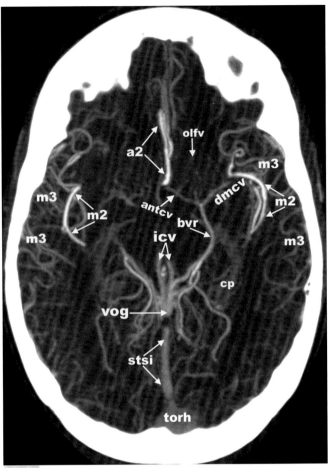

9.16g

FIGURES 9.16g,h

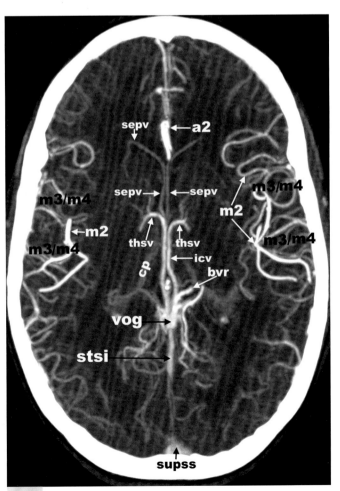

9.16h

(continued)

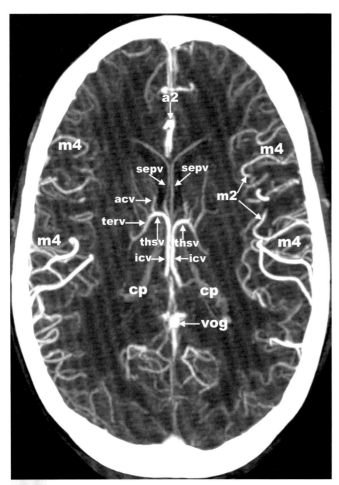

9.16i

FIGURES 9.16i,j

KEY

a2	a2 (postcommunicating segment aca)
a3	a3 (cortical branches of aca)
aca	anterior cerebral artery
acv	anterior caudate vein
cp	choroid plexus
icv	internal cerebral vein
m2	m2 (Sylvian/insular branches mca)
m4	m4 (cortical branches mca)
mca	middle cerebral artery
peric	pericallosal branch of aca
sepv	septal vein
terv	terminal vein
thsv	thalamostriate vein
vog	vein of Galen

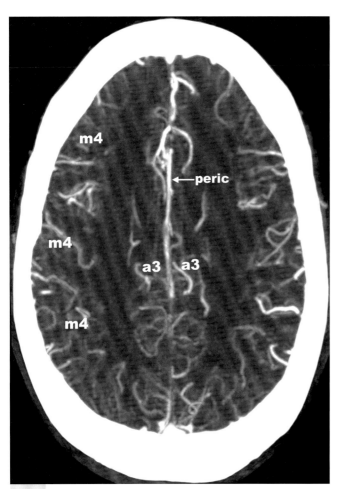

9.16j

Coronal Plane

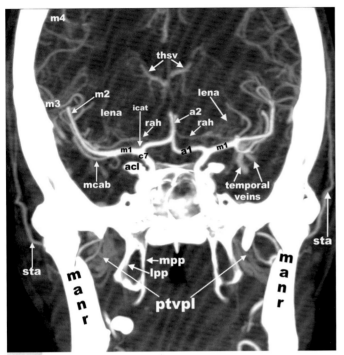

9.17a

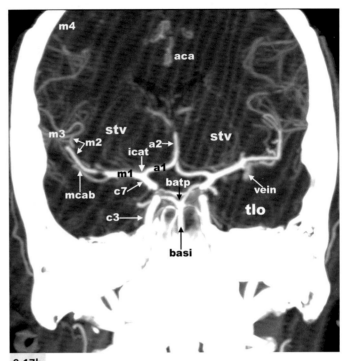

9.17b

FIGURES 9.17a–c

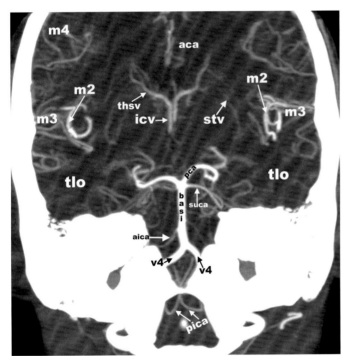

9.17c

KEY

a1	a1 (precommunicating segment aca)
a2	a2 (postcommunicating segment aca)
aca	anterior cerebral artery
acl	anterior clinoid process
aica	anterior inferior cerebellar artery
basi	basilar artery
batp	basilar artery tip
c3	c3 (lacaum segment of ica)
c7	c7 (communicating segment of ica)
ica	internal carotid artery
icat	ica terminus/bifurcation
icv	internal cerebral vein
lena	lenticulostriate arteries
lpp	lateral pterygoid plate
m1	m1 (horizontal segment mca)
m2	m2 (Sylvian/insular branches mca)
m3	m3 (opercular branches mca)
m4	m4 (cortical branches mca)
manr	ramus of mandible
mca	middle cerebral artery
mcab	mca bifurcation/trifurcation
mpp	medial pterygoid plate
pca	posterior cerebral artery
pica	posterior inferior cerebellar artery
ptvpl	pterygoid venous plexus
rah	recurrent artery of Huebner
sta	superficial temporal artery
stv	striate vessels
suca	superior cerebellar artery
thsv	thalamostriate vein
tlo	temporal lobe
v4	v4 intracranial/intradural segment vertebral artery

Sagittal Plane

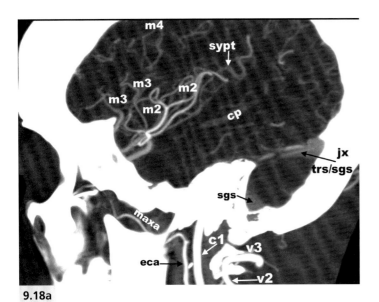

9.18a

FIGURES 9.18a–c

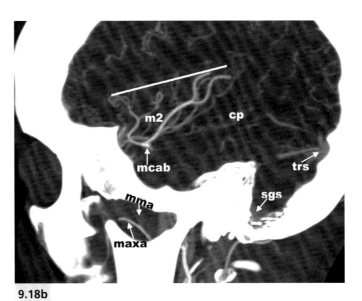

9.18b

FIGURE 9.18b   The solid white line indicates the roof/ superior most aspect of the insular cortex/Sylvian fissure where the insular middle cerebral artery branches (m2) must turn and exit laterally from the Sylvian fissure and become opercular (m3) branches.

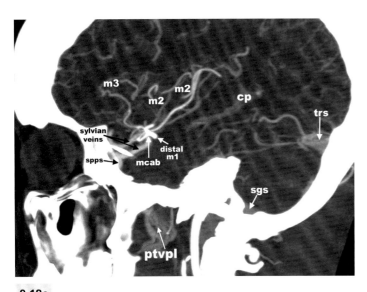

9.18c

KEY

c1	c1 (cervical segment ica)
cp	choroid plexus
eca	external carotid artery
ica	internal carotid artery
jx	junction
m1	m1 (horizontal segment mca)
m2	m2 (Sylvian/insular branches mca)
m3	m3 (opercular branches mca)
m4	m4 (cortical branches mca)
maxa	maxillary artery
mca	middle cerebral artery
mcab	mca bifurcation/trifurcation
mma	middle meningeal artery
ptvpl	pterygoid venous plexus
sgs	sigmoid sinus
spps	sphenoparietal sinus
sypt	Sylvian point
trs	transverse sinus
v2	V2 segment of vertebral artery (foraminal)
v3	V3 segment of vertebral artery (from C1 to dura)

(continued)

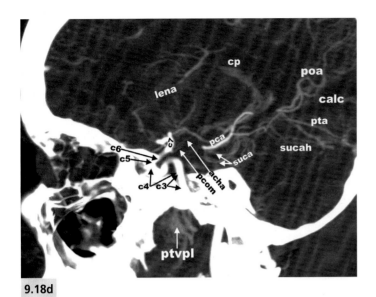

9.18d

FIGURES 9.18d–f

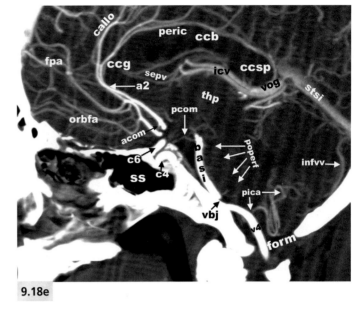

9.18e

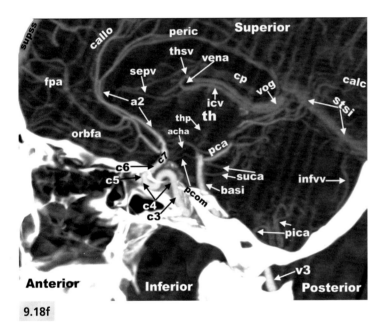

9.18f

KEY

a2	a2 (postcommunicating segment aca)
aca	anterior cerebral artery
acha	anterior choroidal artery
acom	anterior communicating artery
basi	basilar artery
c3	c3 (lacaum segment of ica)
c4	c4 (cavernous segment of ica)
c5	c5 (clinoid segment of ica)
c6	c6 (ophthalmic segment of ica)
c7	c7 (communicating segment of ica)
calc	calcarine branch of pca
callo	callosomarginal branch of aca
ccb	body of corpus callosum
ccg	genu of corpus callosum
ccsp	splenium of corpus callosum
cp	choroid plexus
form	foramen magnum
fpa	frontopolar branch of aca
ica	internal carotid artery
icv	internal cerebral vein
infvv	inferior vermian vein
lena	lenticulostriate arteries
orbfa	orbitofrontal branch of aca
pca	posterior cerebral artery
pcom	posterior communicating artery
peric	pericallosal branch of aca
pica	posterior inferior cerebellar artery
poa	parieto-occipital branch of pca
poperf	pontine perforators
pta	posterior temporal branch of pca
ptvpl	pterygoid venous plexus
sepv	septal vein
ss	sphenoid sinus
stsi	straight sinus
suca	superior cerebellar artery
sucah	hemispheric branch of suca
supss	superior sagittal sinus
th	thalamus
thp	thalamoperforators
thsv	thalamostriate vein
v3	V3 segment of vertebral artery (from C1 to dura)
v4	v4 intracranial/intradural segment vertebral artery
vbj	vertebral basilar junction
vena	venous angle
vog	vein of Galen

3D CTA Reconstructions

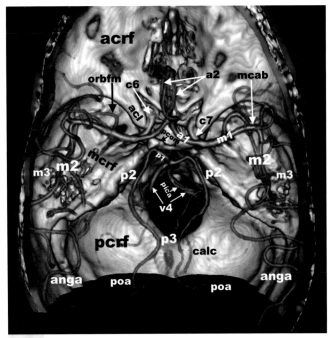

9.19a

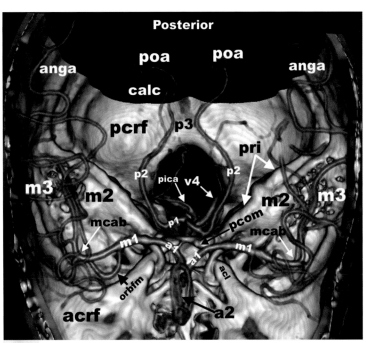

9.19b

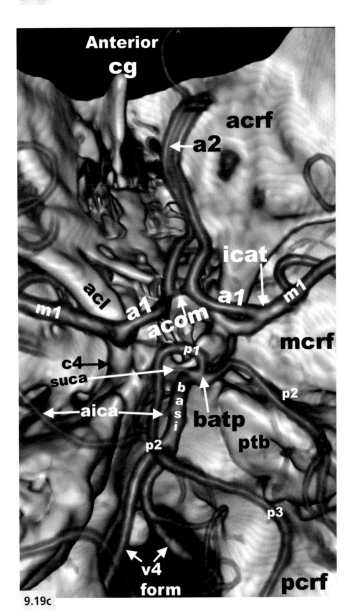

9.19c

FIGURES 9.19a–c 3D CTA reconstructions in the superior/cranial to inferior/caudal (9.19a,b) projections and a complex angle 3D reconstruction (9.19c) targeted to the region of the circle of Willis. These images demonstrate normal vascular anatomy.

KEY

a1	a1 (precommunicating segment aca)
a2	a2 (postcommunicating segment aca)
aca	anterior cerebral artery
acl	anterior clinoid process
acom	anterior communicating artery
acrf	anterior cranial fossa
aica	anterior inferior cerebellar artery
anga	angular artery
basi	basilar artery
batp	basilar artery tip
c4	c4 (cavernous segment of ica)
c6	c6 (ophthalmic segment of ica)
c7	c7 (communicating segment of ica)
calc	calcarine branch of pca
cg	crista galli
form	foramen magnum
ica	internal carotid artery
icat	ica terminus/bifurcation
m1	m1 (horizontal segment mca)
m2	m2 (Sylvian/insular branches mca)
m3	m3 (opercular branches mca)
mca	middle cerebral artery
mcab	mca bifurcation/trifurcation
mcrf	middle cranial fossa
orbfm	orbitofrontal branch of mca
p1	p1 (precommunicating/mesencephalic segment pca)
p2	p2 (ambient segment of pca)
p3	p3 (quadrigeminal segment of pca)
pca	posterior cerebral artery
pcom	posterior communicating artery
pcrf	posterior cranial fossa
pica	posterior inferior cerebellar artery
poa	parieto-occipital branch of pca
pri	petrous ridge
ptb	petrous temporal bone
suca	superior cerebellar artery
v4	v4 intracranial/intradural segment vertebral artery

■ CATHETER ANGIOGRAPHY (FIGURES 9.20a–9.33b)

2D DSA and 3D Rotational Angiography

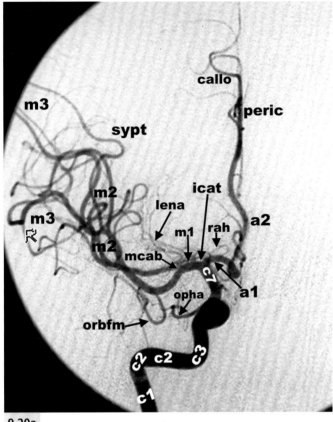

9.20a

FIGURES 9.20a,b Frontal digital subtraction angiographic (DSA) image (9.20a) and a frontal 3D rotational angiographic image (9.20b) following a selective internal carotid artery injection demonstrate normal vascular anatomy. The anterior cerebral artery was intentionally removed on the 3D view. The Sylvian point (sypt) refers to the most superior and medial point where the last Sylvian MCA branch turns inferolateraly to exit the posterior/superior aspect of the Sylvian fissure.

KEY

a1	a1 (precommunicating segment aca)
a2	a2 (postcommunicating segment aca)
aca	anterior cerebral artery
c1	c1 (cervical segment ica)
c2	c2 (petrous segment of ica)
c3	c3 (lacaum segment of ica)
c4	c4 (cavernous segment of ica)
c5	c5 (clinoid segment of ica)
c6	c6 (ophthalmic segment of ica)
c7	c7 (communicating segment of ica)
callo	callosomarginal branch of aca
ica	internal carotid artery
icat	ica terminus/bifurcation
lena	lenticulostriate arteries
m1	m1 (horizontal segment mca)
m2	m2 (Sylvian/insular branches mca)
m3	m3 (opercular branches mca)
mca	middle cerebral artery
mcab	mca bifurcation/trifurcation
opha	ophthalmic artery
orbfm	orbitofrontal branch of mca
pcom	posterior communicating artery
peric	pericallosal branch of aca
rah	recurrent artery of Huebner
sypt	Sylvian point
tpa	temporal polar branch of mca

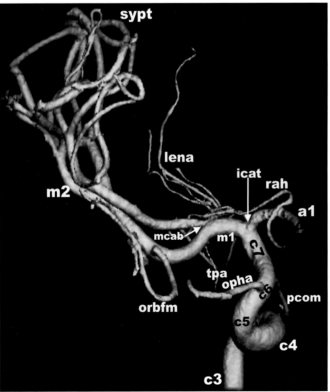

9.20b

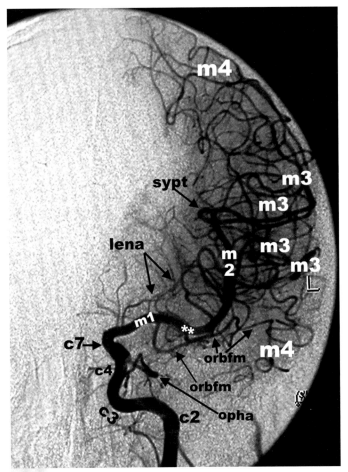

9.21a

9.21b

FIGURES 9.21a–c Frontal DSA image (9.21a) and frontal and lateral 3D rotational angiographic images (9.21b,c) following a selective left internal carotid artery injection demonstrates normal vascular anatomy with a congenitally undeveloped left A1 segment representing a normal variant. The site of the middle cerebral artery bifurcation is more clearly visible on the frontal 3D image (9.21b). This region is marked by white asterisks on the frontal 2D DSA image (9.21a).

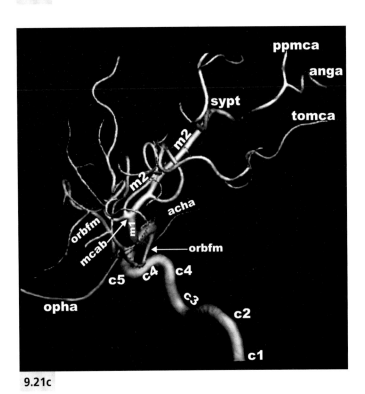

9.21c

KEY

acha	anterior choroidal artery	**m2**	m2 (Sylvian/insular branches mca)
anga	angular artery		
c1	c1 (cervical segment ica)	**m3**	m3 (opercular branches mca)
c2	c2 (petrous segment of ica)		
c3	c3 (lacerum segment of ica)	**m4**	m4 (cortical branches mca)
c4	c4 (cavernous segment of ica)	**mca**	middle cerebral artery
		mcab	mca bifurcation/trifurcation
c5	c5 (clinoid segment of ica)	**opha**	ophthalmic artery
c6	c6 (ophthalmic segment of ica)	**orbfm**	orbitofrontal branch of mca
		ppmca	posterior parietal branch of mca
c7	c7 (communicating segment of ica)	**sypt**	Sylvian point
ica	internal carotid artery	**tomca**	temporal-occipital branch of mca
lena	lenticulostriate arteries		
m1	m1 (horizontal segment mca)		

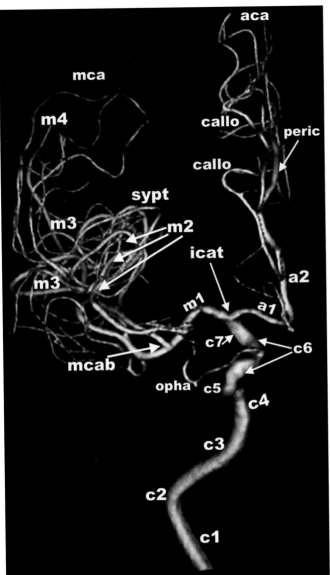

9.22a

FIGURES 9.22a,b Frontal and lateral 3D rotational angiographic images following an internal carotid artery injection demonstrates atherosclerotic irregularity of the intracranial vessels but otherwise demonstrates a normal pattern.

KEY

a1	a1 (precommunicating segment aca)
a2	a2 (postcommunicating segment aca)
aca	anterior cerebral artery
aif	anterior internal frontal branch of aca
anga	angular artery
atmca	anterior temporal mca
c1	c1 (cervical segment ica)
c2	c2 (petrous segment of ica)
c3	c3 (lacaum segment of ica)
c4	c4 (cavernous segment of ica)
c5	c5 (clinoid segment of ica)
c6	c6 (ophthalmic segment of ica)
c7	c7 (communicating segment of ica)
callo	callosomarginal branch of aca
fpa	frontopolar branch of aca
ica	internal carotid artery
icat	ica terminus/bifurcation
m1	m1 (horizontal segment mca)
m2	m2 (Sylvian/insular branches mca)
m3	m3 (opercular branches mca)
m4	m4 (cortical branches mca)
mca	middle cerebral artery
mcab	mca bifurcation/trifurcation
mif	middle internal frontal branch of aca
mtmca	middle temporal branch of mca
opha	ophthalmic artery
orbfa	orbitofrontal branch of aca
pcla	paracentral lobule artery branch of aca
peric	pericallosal branch of aca
pif	posterior internal frontal branch of aca
pmca	parietal branch of mca
ptmca	posterior temporal branch of mca
sipa	superior internal parietal branch of aca
sypt	Sylvian point
tomca	temporal-occipital branch of mca

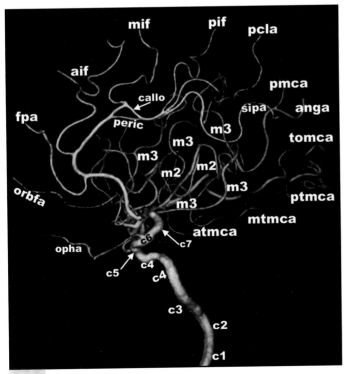

9.22b

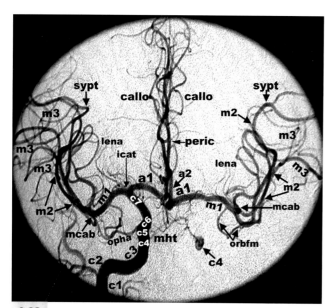

9.23

FIGURE 9.23 2D DSA frontal view following a right common carotid artery injection shows normal vascular anatomy on the patient's right side (viewer's left). A patent anterior communicating artery provides flow into the left anterior circulation and there is a small clival branch of the right meningohypophyseal artery trunk providing flow across the midline into the cavernous segment (c4) of the left internal carotid artery.

FIGURE 9.24 This lateral 2D, DSA image following a common carotid artery injection shows an unobscured view of the anterior cerebral artery and its branches secondary to occlusion of the middle cerebral artery. Atherosclerotic irregularity of the vessels is seen.

FIGURE 9.25 This lateral 2D, DSA image nicely illustrates the middle cerebral artery extending into its distal branches secondary to absent filling of the anterior cerebral artery. The Sylvian triangle is redemonstrated.

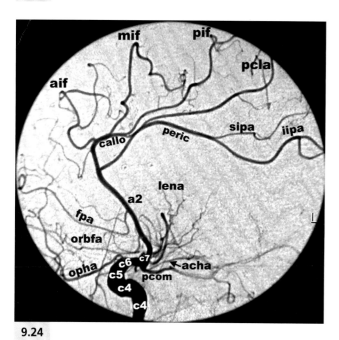

9.24

9.25

KEY

a1	a1 (precommunicating segment aca)	m3	m3 (opercular branches mca)
a2	a2 (postcommunicating segment aca)	m4	m4 (cortical branches mca)
aca	anterior cerebral artery	mca	middle cerebral artery
acha	anterior choroidal artery	mcab	mca bifurcation/trifurcation
aif	anterior internal frontal branch of aca	mht	meningohypophyseal artery trunk
anga	angular artery	mif	middle internal frontal branch of aca
apmca	anterior parietal branch of mca	mtmca	middle temporal branch of mca
atmca	anterior temporal mca		
c1	c1 (cervical segment ica)	opha	ophthalmic artery
c2	c2 (petrous segment of ica)	orbfa	orbitofrontal branch of aca
c3	c3 (lacaum segment of ica)	orbfm	orbitofrontal branch of mca
c4	c4 (cavernous segment of ica)	pcla	paracentral lobule artery branch of aca
c5	c5 (clinoid segment of ica)		
c6	c6 (ophthalmic segment of ica)	pcom	posterior communicating artery
c7	c7 (communicating segment of ica)	peric	pericallosal branch of aca
		pif	posterior internal frontal branch of aca
callo	callosomarginal branch of aca		
crmca	central rolandic branches of mca	ppmca	posterior parietal branch of mca
fpa	frontopolar branch of aca	prcmca	pre-central branch(es) of mca
ica	internal carotid artery	prfmca	prefrontal branch of mca
icat	ica terminus/bifurcation	ptmca	posterior temporal branch of mca
iipa	inferior internal parietal branch of aca	sipa	superior internal parietal branch of aca
lena	lenticulostriate arteries		
m1	m1 (horizontal segment mca)	sypt	Sylvian point
m2	m2 (Sylvian/insular branches mca)	tomca	temporal-occipital branch of mca

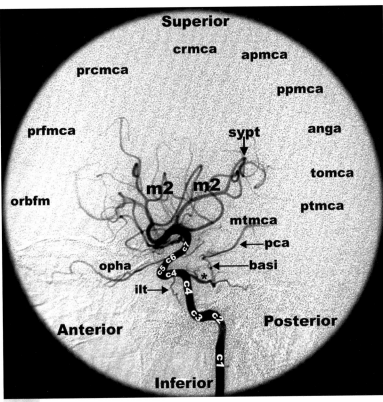

9.26a

FIGURES 9.26a,b Early (9.26a) and late (9.26b) arterial phase, lateral 2D, DSA images following an internal carotid artery injection demonstrate an unobscured view of the middle cerebral artery vascular territory due to a congenitally absent A1 segment of the anterior cerebral artery. The inferolateral trunk (ilt) and a persistent trigeminal artery (black asterisk) are seen in the early arterial phase. Faint opacification of external carotid artery branches in the late arterial phase (9.26b) likely results from filling from the ilt.

KEY

anga	angular artery
apmca	anterior parietal branch of mca
atmca	anterior temporal mca
basi	basilar artery
c1	c1 (cervical segment ica)
c2	c2 (petrous segment of ica)
c3	c3 (lacaum segment of ica)
c4	c4 (cavernous segment of ica)
c5	c5 (clinoid segment of ica)
c6	c6 (ophthalmic segment of ica)
c7	c7 (communicating segment of ica)
crmca	central rolandic branches of mca
eca	external carotid artery
ica	internal carotid artery
ilt	inferolateral trunk
m2	m2 (Sylvian/insular branches mca)
mca	middle cerebral artery
mtmca	middle temporal branch of mca
opha	ophthalmic artery
orbfm	orbitofrontal branch of mca
pca	posterior cerebral artery
ppmca	posterior parietal branch of mca
prcmca	pre-central branch(es) of mca
prfmca	prefrontal branch of mca
ptmca	posterior temporal branch of mca
sypt	Sylvian point
tomca	temporal-occipital branch of mca
tpa	temporal polar branch of mca

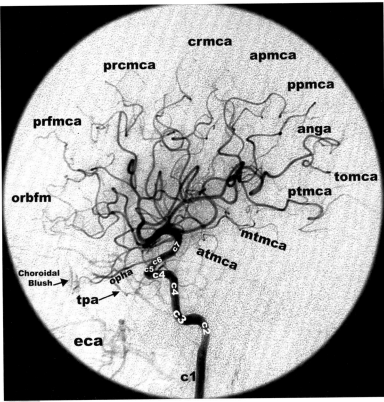

9.26b

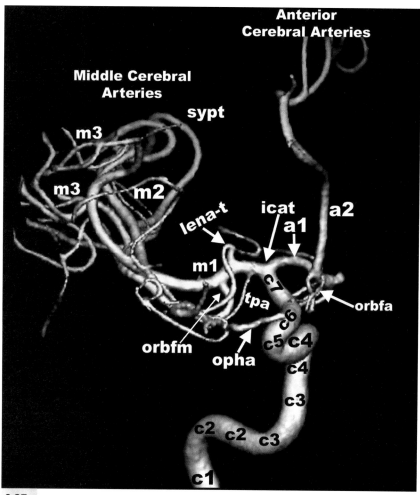

9.27a

FIGURES 9.27a,b Frontal and right posterior oblique (RPO) projections from a 3D rotational catheter angiogram following an internal carotid artery injection demonstrate normal vascular anatomy. Note a large common lateral lenticulostriate trunk which gives rise to numerous smaller branches. This is a common variant. Also note infindibular dilatation at the origins of the posterior communicating and anterior choroidal arteries.

KEY

a1	a1 (precommunicating segment aca)
a2	a2 (postcommunicating segment aca)
aca	anterior cerebral artery
acha	anterior choroidal artery
c1	c1 (cervical segment ica)
c2	c2 (petrous segment of ica)
c3	c3 (lacaum segment of ica)
c4	c4 (cavernous segment of ica)
c5	c5 (clinoid segment of ica)
c6	c6 (ophthalmic segment of ica)
c7	c7 (communicating segment of ica)
icat	ica terminus/bifurcation
ica	internal carotid artery
lena-t	lenticulostriate artery trunk
m1	m1 (horizontal segment mca)
m2	m2 (Sylvian/insular branches mca)
m3	m3 (opercular branches mca)
mca	middle cerebral artery
mht	meningohypophyseal artery trunk
opha	ophthalmic artery
orbfa	orbitofrontal branch of aca
orbfm	orbitofrontal branch of mca
pcom	posterior communicating artery
sypt	Sylvian point
tpa	temporal polar branch of mca

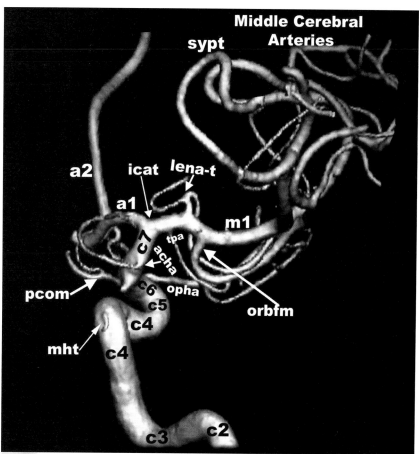

9.27b

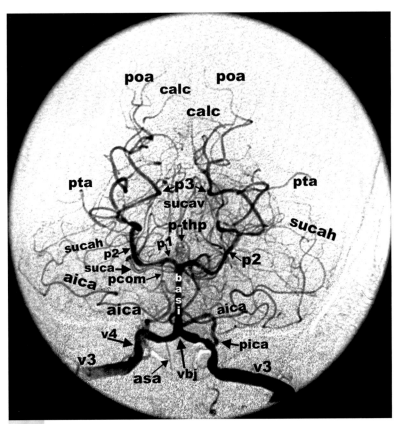

9.28a

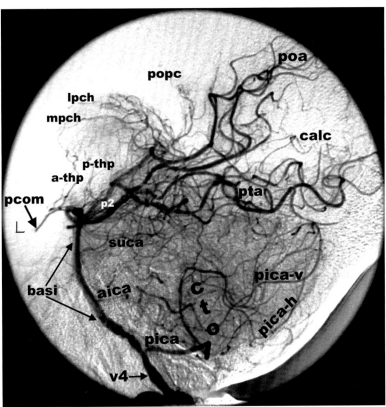

9.28b

FIGURES 9.28a,b   AP Towne's (9.28a) and lateral (9.28b) projections following a selective left vertebral artery injection DSA exam demonstrates diffuse irregularity of the vasculature compatible with a known diagnosis of vasculitis. Otherwise there is a normal pattern and distribution of vascular branches in the posterior/vertebral basilar circulation.

KEY

a-thp	anterior thalamoperforators
aica	anterior inferior cerebellar artery
asa	anterior spinal artery
basi	basilar artery
calc	calcarine branch of pca
cto	cerebellar tonsil
lpch	lateral posterior choroidal artery
mpch	medial posterior choroidal artery
p-thp	posterior thalamoperforators
p1	p1 (precommunicating/mesencephalic segment pca)
p2	p2 (ambient segment of pca)
p3	p3 (quadrigeminal segment of pca)
pca	posterior cerebral artery
pcom	posterior communicating artery
pica	posterior inferior cerebellar artery
pica-h	hemispheric branch of pica
pica-v	vermian branch of pica
poa	parieto-occipital branch of pca
popc	posterior pericallosal/splenial branches pca
pta	posterior temporal branch of pca
suca	superior cerebellar artery
sucah	hemispheric branch of suca
sucav	vermin branch of suca
v3	V3 segment of vertebral artery (from C1 to dura)
v4	v4 intracranial/intradural segment vertebral artery
vbj	vertebral basilar junction

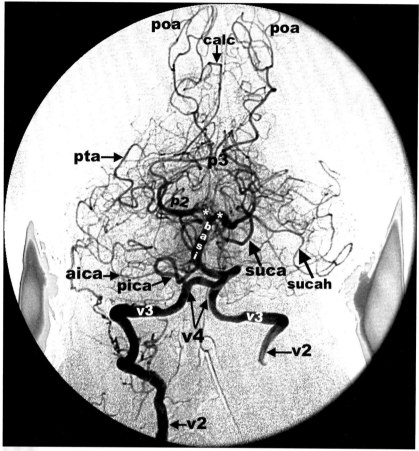

9.29a

FIGURES 9.29a,b AP Towne's (9.29a) and lateral (9.29b) projections following a selective right vertebral artery injection DSA exam demonstrate normal vascular anatomy in the posterior/vertebral-basilar circulation. White asterisks in 9.29a indicate the p1 segments of the posterior cerebral arteries. The white asterisk in 9.29b indicates the vertebral-basilar junction.

KEY

a-thp	anterior thalamoperforators
aica	anterior inferior cerebellar artery
asa	anterior spinal artery
basi	basilar artery
calc	calcarine branch of pca
cto	cerebellar tonsil
lpch	lateral posterior choroidal artery
mpch	medial posterior choroidal artery
p-thp	posterior thalamoperforators
p2	p2 (ambient segment of pca)
p3	p3 (quadrigeminal segment of pca)
pca	posterior cerebral artery
pcom	posterior communicating artery
pica	posterior inferior cerebellar artery
pica-h	hemispheric branch of pica
pica-v	vermian branch of pica
poa	parieto-occipital branch of pca
popc	posterior pericallosal/splenial branches pca
pta	posterior temporal branch of pca
suca	superior cerebellar artery
sucah	hemispheric branch of suca
sucav	vermin branch of suca
v2	V2 segment of vertebral artery (foraminal)
v3	V3 segment of vertebral artery (from C1 to dura)
v4	v4 intracranial/intradural segment vertebral artery

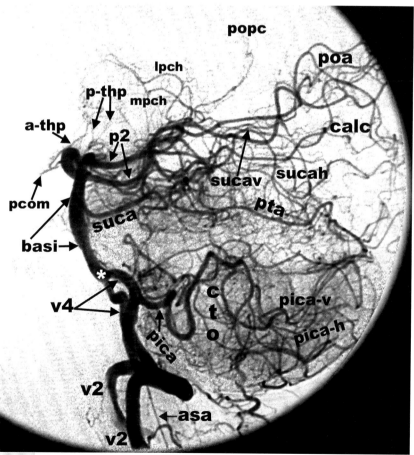

9.29b

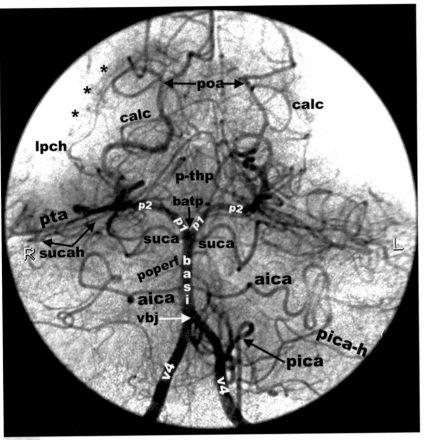

9.30a

FIGURES 9.30a,b   AP Caldwell DSA image (9.30a) and a frontal 3D rotational angiographic image (9.30b) in a similar projection show normal vertebral-basilar vascular anatomy. Black asterisks in 9.30a indicate the blush of the choroid plexus in the atrium of the right lateral ventricle and you can see a prominent but normal lateral posterior choroidal artery branch of the posterior cerebral artery.

KEY

aica	anterior inferior cerebellar artery
basi	basilar artery
batp	basilar artery tip
calc	calcarine branch of pca
lpch	lateral posterior choroidal artery
p-thp	posterior thalamoperforators
p1	p1 (precommunicating/mesencephalic segment pca)
p2	p2 (ambient segment of pca)
pca	posterior cerebral artery
pica	posterior inferior cerebellar artery
pica-h	hemispheric branch of pica
pica-v	vermian branch of pica
poa	parieto-occipital branch of pca
poperf	pontine perforators
pta	posterior temporal branch of pca
suca	superior cerebellar artery
sucah	hemispheric branch of suca
sucav	vermin branch of suca
v4	v4 intracranial/intradural segment vertebral artery
vbj	vertebral basilar junction

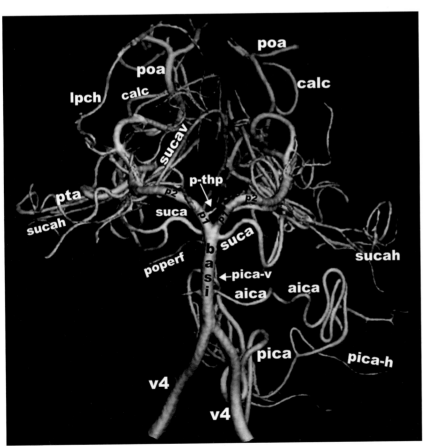

9.30b

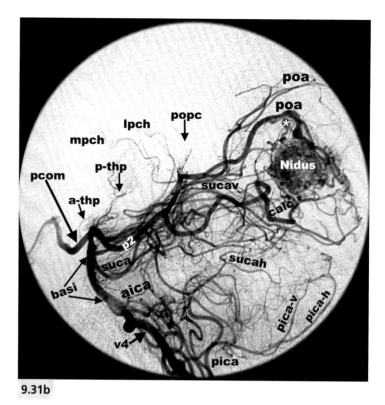

9.31a

9.31b

FIGURES 9.31a,b AP Towne's and lateral projections from a 2D DSA exam following a selective right vertebral artery injection demonstrates an AVM (arterial venous malformation) in the right occipital lobe supplied by enlarged calcarine and parieto-occipital branches of the posterior cerebral artery (pca). There is also enlargement of the entire right pca back to the level of the posterior communicating artery. The AVM nidus is noted on the images and the perinidal aneurysm is noted by the black asterisk in 9.31a and white asterisk in 9.31b.

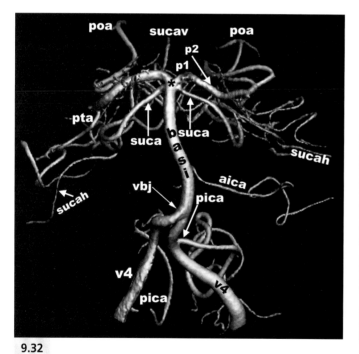

9.32

FIGURE 9.32 AP Caldwell projection from a 3D catheter rotational angiogram demonstrates normal vascular anatomy in the posterior/vertebral-basilar circulation. Black asterisk indicates the tip of the basilar artery.

KEY

a-thp	anterior thalamoperforators	pica-h	hemispheric branch of pica
aica	anterior inferior cerebellar artery	pica-v	vermian branch of pica
basi	basilar artery	poa	parieto-occipital branch of pca
calc	calcarine branch of pca	popc	posterior pericallosal/splenial branches pca
lpch	lateral posterior choroidal artery		
mpch	medial posterior choroidal artery	pta	posterior temporal branch of pca
p-thp	posterior thalamoperforators	suca	superior cerebellar artery
p1	p1 (precommunicating/mesencephalic segment pca)	sucah	hemispheric branch of suca
		sucav	vermin branch of suca
p2	p2 (ambient segment of pca)	v2	V2 segment of vertebral artery (foraminal)
pca	posterior cerebral artery	v3	V3 segment of vertebral artery (from C1 to dura)
pcom	posterior communicating artery		
		v4	v4 intracranial/intradural segment vertebral artery
pica	posterior inferior cerebellar artery	vbj	vertebral basilar junction

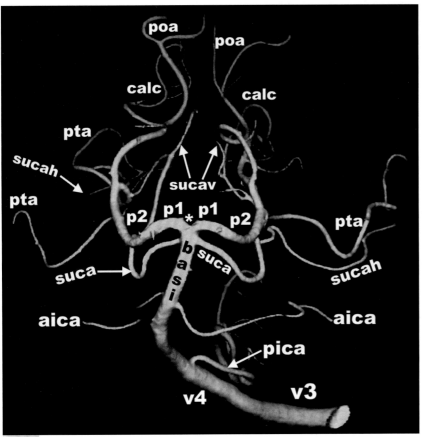

9.33a

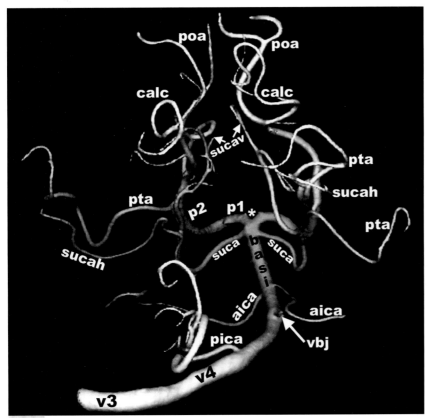

9.33b

FIGURES 9.33a,b Frontal and posterior views from a 3D rotational catheter angiogram demonstrate normal vascular anatomy in the posterior/vertebral-basilar circulation. White asterisk indicates the tip of the basilar artery.

KEY

aica	anterior inferior cerebellar artery
basi	basilar artery
calc	calcarine branch of pca
p1	p1 (precommunicating/mesencephalic segment pca)
p2	p2 (ambient segment of pca)
pca	posterior cerebral artery
pica	posterior inferior cerebellar artery
poa	parieto-occipital branch of pca
pta	posterior temporal branch of pca
suca	superior cerebellar artery
sucah	hemispheric branch of suca
sucav	vermin branch of suca
v3	V3 segment of vertebral artery (from C1 to dura)
v4	v4 intracranial/intradural segment vertebral artery
vbj	vertebral basilar junction

INTRACRANIAL VENOUS SYSTEM

■ MR VENOGRAPHY (MRV) (FIGURES 9.34a–9.35f)

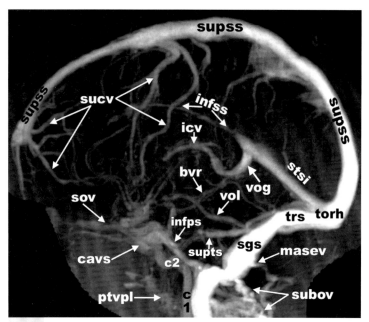

9.34a

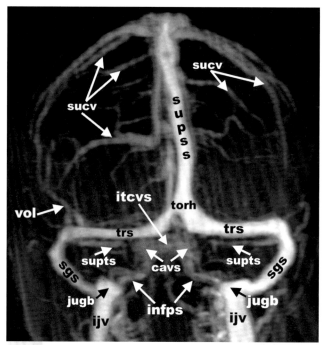

9.34b

FIGURES 9.34a–c Lateral (9.34a), posterior (9.34b), and left posterior oblique (9.34c) projections from an intracranial MRV demonstrate normal intracranial venous anatomy.

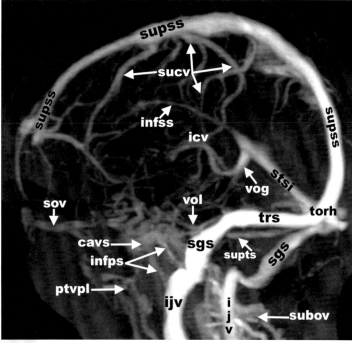

9.34c

KEY

bvr	basal vein of Rosenthal		plexus
		sgs	sigmoid sinus
c1	c1 (cervical segment ica)	sov	superior ophthalmic vein
c2	c2 (petrous segment of ica)	stsi	straight sinus
		subov	suboccipital veins
cavs	cavernous sinus	sucv	superficial cortical vein(s)
ica	internal carotid artery		
icv	internal cerebral vein	supss	superior sagittal sinus
ijv	internal jugular vein	supts	superior petrosal sinus
infps	inferior petrosal sinus		
infss	inferior sagittal sinus	torh	torcular herophili (confluence of sinuses)
itcvs	intercavernous sinus		
jugb	jugular bulb		
masev	mastoid emissary vein	trs	transverse sinus
		vog	vein of Galen
ptvpl	pterygoid venous	vol	vein of Labbe

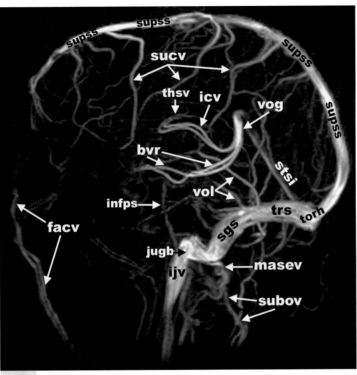

9.35a

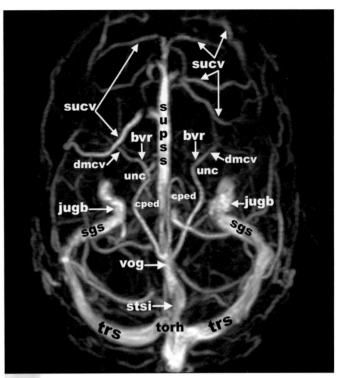

9.35b

FIGURES 9.35a–f Lateral (9.35a,d), superior to inferior (9.35b,e), and posterior (9.35c,f) views from an intracranial MRV performed without contrast in 9.35a–c and with contrast in 9.35d–f. These images demonstrate normal intracranial venous anatomy.

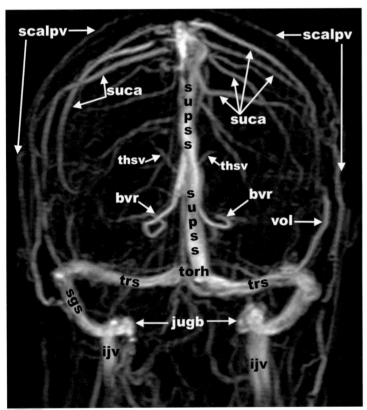

9.35c

KEY

bvr	basal vein of Rosenthal	**subov**	suboccipital veins
cped	cerebral peduncle	**suca**	superior cerebellar artery
dmcv	deep middle cerebral vein	**sucv**	superficial cortical vein(s)
facv	facial vein	**supss**	superior sagittal sinus
icv	internal cerebral vein	**thsv**	thalamostriate vein
ijv	internal jugular vein	**torh**	torcular herophili (confluence of sinuses)
infps	inferior petrosal sinus		
jugb	jugular bulb	**trs**	transverse sinus
masev	mastoid emissary vein	**unc**	uncus
scalpv	scalp vein (s)	**vog**	vein of Galen
sgs	sigmoid sinus	**vol**	vein of Labbe
stsi	straight sinus		

(continued)

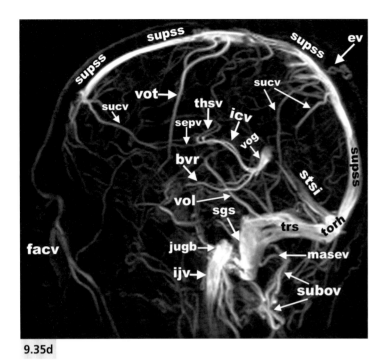

9.35d

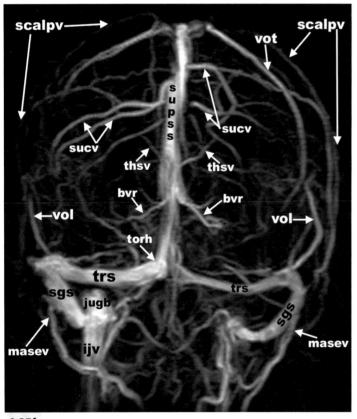

9.35f

9.35e

FIGURES 9.35d–f

KEY

bvr	basal vein of Rosenthal	suca	superior cerebellar artery
ev	emissary vein	sucv	superficial cortical
facv	facial vein		vein(s)
icv	internal cerebral vein	supss	superior sagittal sinus
ijv	internal jugular vein	thsv	thalamostriate vein
jugb	jugular bulb	torh	torcular herophili
masev	mastoid emissary vein		(confluence of sinuses)
scalpv	scalp vein (s)	trs	transverse sinus
sepv	septal vein	vog	vein of Galen
sgs	sigmoid sinus	vol	vein of Labbe
stsi	straight sinus	vot	vein of Trolard
subov	suboccipital veins		

■ CT VENOGRAPHY (FIGURES 9.36a–9.39g)

Axial Plane

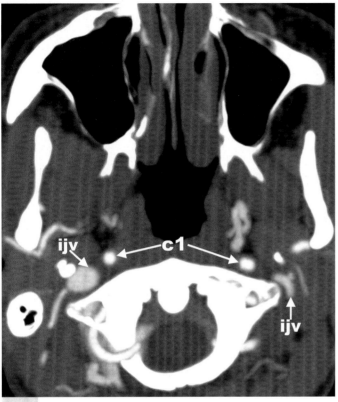

9.36a

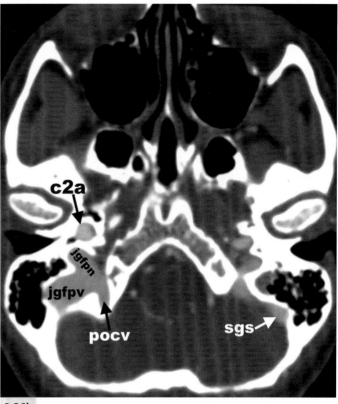

9.36b

FIGURES 9.36a–h, 9.37a–k, and 9.38a–g   CT venogram with reformatted axial (9.36a–h), coronal (9.37a–k), and sagittal (9.38a–g) images from inferior to superior, anterior to posterior and medial to lateral demonstrate normal venous anatomy. Thin subdural hygromas versus chronic subdural hematomas are present. White asterisk in 9.36g indicates the location of the ascending columns of the fornix.

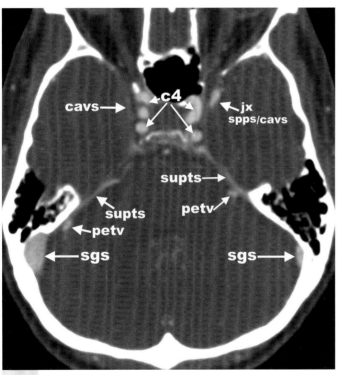

9.36c

KEY

c1	c1 (cervical segment ica)
c2a	c2a (vertical petrous segment ica)
c4	c4 (cavernous segment of ica)
cavs	cavernous sinus
ica	internal carotid artery
ijv	internal jugular vein
jgfpn	pars nervosa-jugular foramen
jgfpv	pars vascularis-jugular foramen
jx	junction
petv	petrosal vein
pocv	posterior condylar vein
sgs	sigmoid sinus
spps	sphenoparietal sinus
supts	superior petrosal sinus

(continued)

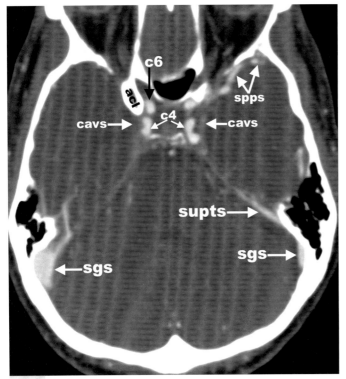

9.36d

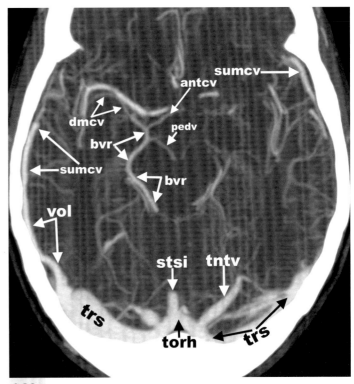

9.36e

FIGURES 9.36d–f

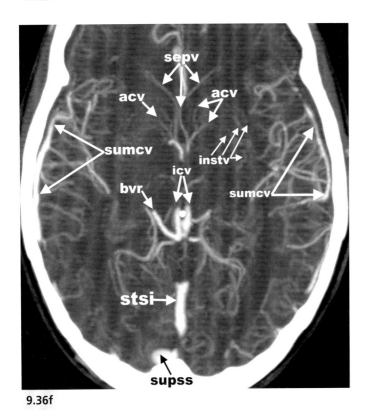

9.36f

KEY

acl	anterior clinoid process
acv	anterior caudate vein
antcv	anterior cerebral vein
bvr	basal vein of Rosenthal
c4	c4 (cavernous segment of ica)
c6	c6 (ophthalmic segment of ica)
cavs	cavernous sinus
dmcv	deep middle cerebral vein
ica	internal carotid artery
icv	internal cerebral vein
instv	inferior striate vein
pedv	peduncular vein
sepv	septal vein
sgs	sigmoid sinus
spps	sphenoparietal sinus
stsi	straight sinus
sumcv	superficial middle cerebral vein
supss	superior sagittal sinus
supts	superior petrosal sinus
tntv	tentorial vein
torh	torcular herophili (confluence of sinuses)
trs	transverse sinus
vol	vein of Labbe

(continued)

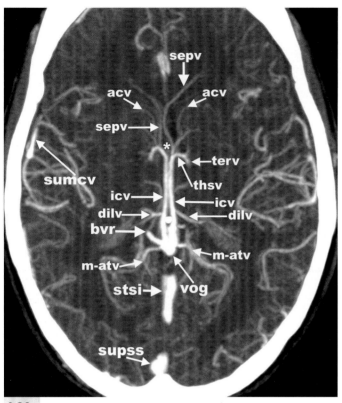

9.36g

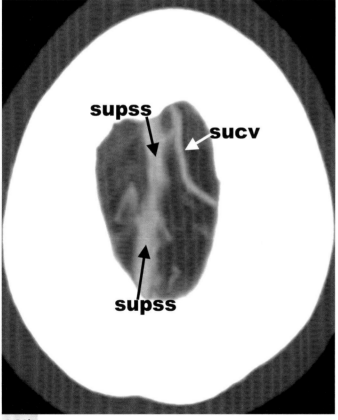

9.36h

FIGURES 9.36g,h

KEY

acv	anterior caudate vein
bvr	basal vein of Rosenthal
dilv	direct lateral vein
icv	internal cerebral vein
m-atv	medial atrial vein
sepv	septal vein
stsi	straight sinus
sucv	superficial cortical vein(s)
sumcv	superficial middle cerebral vein
supss	superior sagittal sinus
terv	terminal vein
thsv	thalamostriate vein
vog	vein of Galen

Coronal Plane

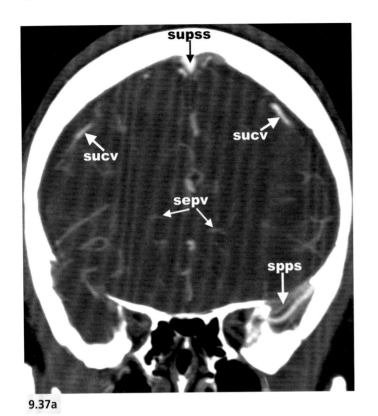

9.37a

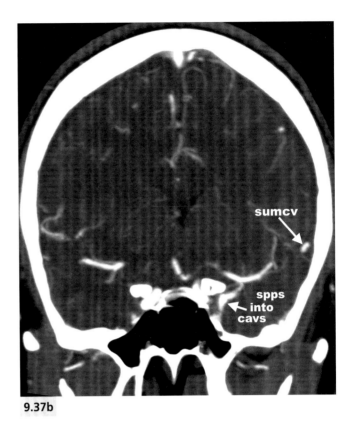

9.37b

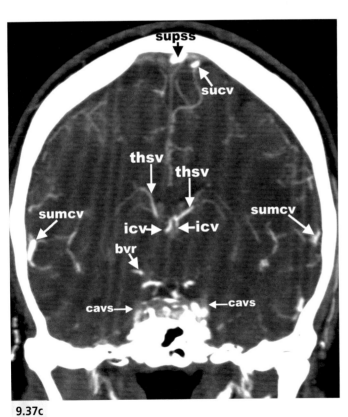

9.37c

9.37d

FIGURES 9.37a–d

KEY

bvr	basal vein of Rosenthal	**sucv**	superficial cortical vein(s)
cavs	cavernous sinus		
icv	internal cerebral vein	**sumcv**	superficial middle cerebral vein
ijv	internal juggular vein		
sepv	septal vein	**supss**	superior sagittal sinus
spps	sphenoparietal sinus	**thsv**	thalamostriate vein
		vol	vein of Labbe

(*continued*)

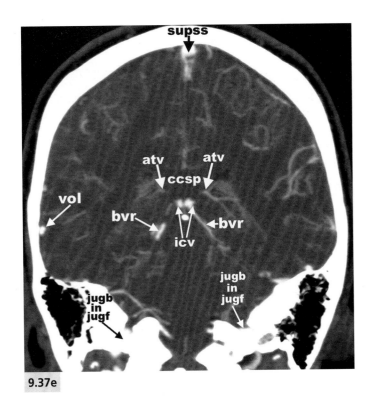

9.37e

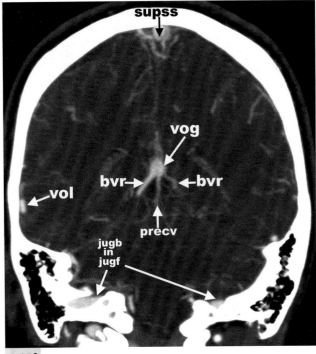

9.37f

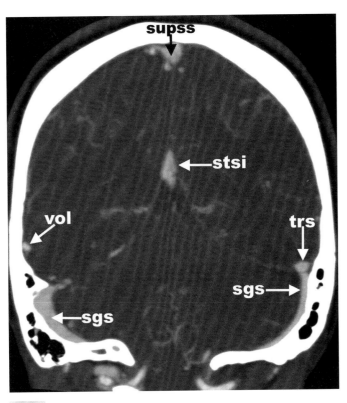

9.37g

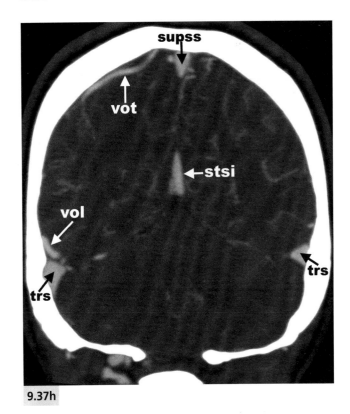

9.37h

FIGURES 9.37e–h

KEY			
atv	atrial vein	**sgs**	sigmoid sinus
bvr	basal vein of Rosenthal	**stsi**	straight sinus
ccsp	splenium of corpus callosum	**supss**	superior sagittal sinus
		trs	transverse sinus
icv	internal cerebral vein	**vog**	vein of Galen
ijv	internal jugular vein	**vol**	vein of Labbe
jugb	jugular bulb	**vot**	vein of Trolard
jugf	jugular foramen		
precv	pre-central cerebellar vein		

(continued)

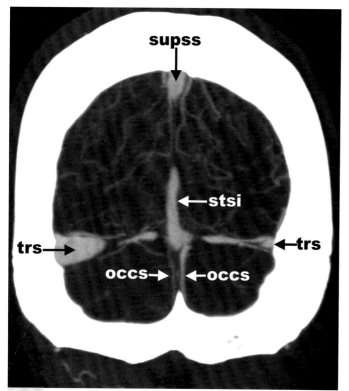

9.37i

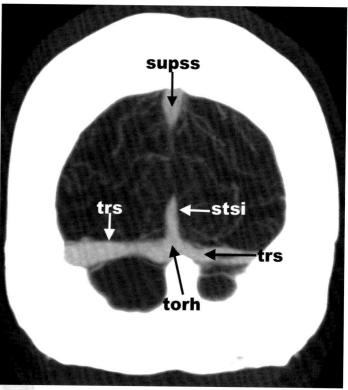

9.37j

FIGURES 9.37i–k

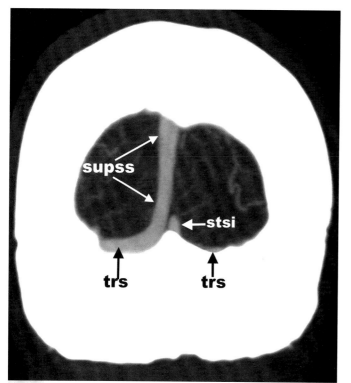

9.37k

Sagittal Plane

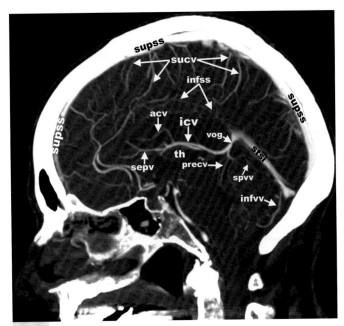

9.38a

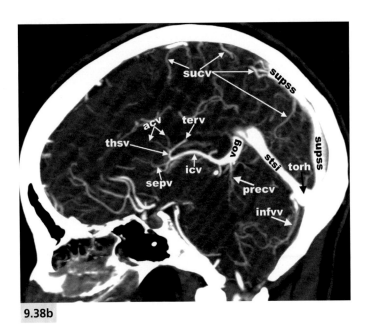

9.38b

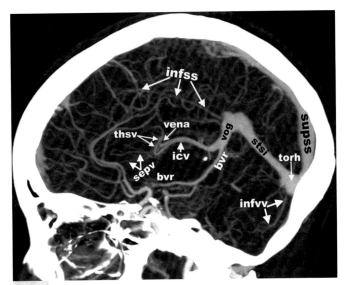

9.38c

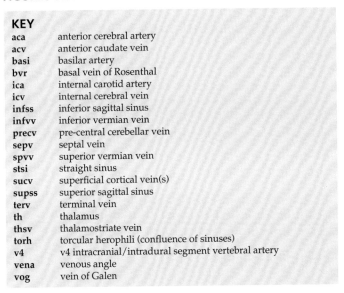

9.38d

FIGURES 9.38a–d

KEY

aca	anterior cerebral artery
acv	anterior caudate vein
basi	basilar artery
bvr	basal vein of Rosenthal
ica	internal carotid artery
icv	internal cerebral vein
infss	inferior sagittal sinus
infvv	inferior vermian vein
precv	pre-central cerebellar vein
sepv	septal vein
spvv	superior vermian vein
stsi	straight sinus
sucv	superficial cortical vein(s)
supss	superior sagittal sinus
terv	terminal vein
th	thalamus
thsv	thalamostriate vein
torh	torcular herophili (confluence of sinuses)
v4	v4 intracranial/intradural segment vertebral artery
vena	venous angle
vog	vein of Galen

(continued)

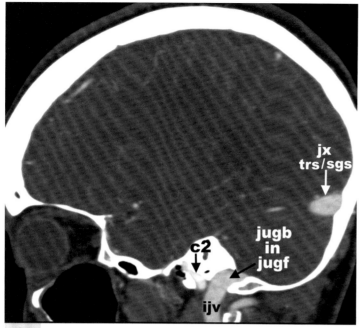

9.38e

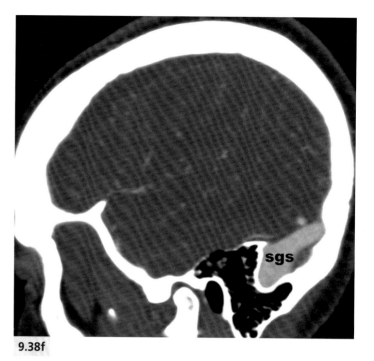

9.38f

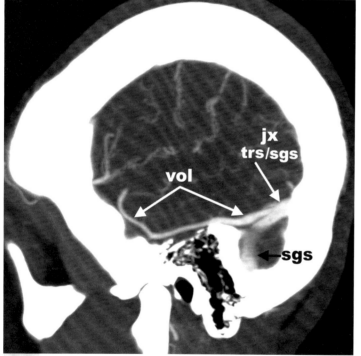

9.38g

FIGURES 9.38e–g

KEY	
c2	c2 (petrous segment of ica)
ica	internal carotid artery
ijv	internal jugular vein
jugb	jugular bulb
jugf	jugular foramen
jx	junction
sgs	sigmoid sinus
trs	transverse sinus
vol	vein of Labbe

3D Reconstructions From CTV
Sagittal (Lateral) Views

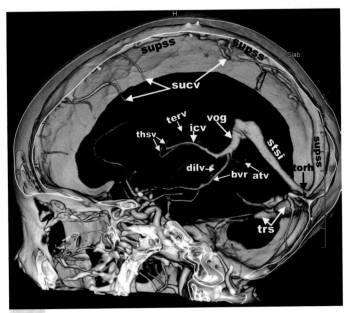

9.39a

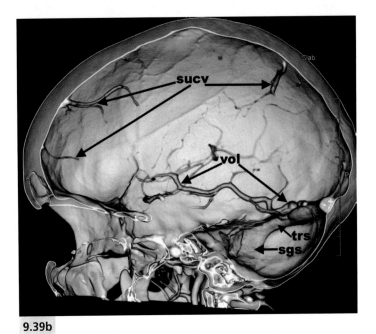

9.39b

FIGURES 9.39a–g   3D reconstructions from a CT venogram with bone visible (9.39a–e) and with bone removed (9.39f,g) demonstrate normal intracranial venous anatomy.

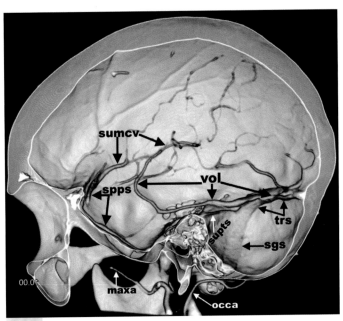

9.39C

KEY

atv	atrial vein
bvr	basal vein of Rosenthal
dilv	direct lateral vein
icv	internal cerebral vein
maxa	maxillary artery
occa	occipital artery
sgs	sigmoid sinus
spps	sphenoparietal sinus
stsi	straight sinus
sucv	superficial cortical vein(s)
sumcv	superficial middle cerebral vein
supss	superior sagittal sinus
supts	superior petrosal sinus
terv	terminal vein
thsv	thalamostriate vein
torh	torcular herophili (confluence of sinuses)
trs	transverse sinus
vog	vein of Galen
vol	vein of Labbe

(continued)

Axial Views

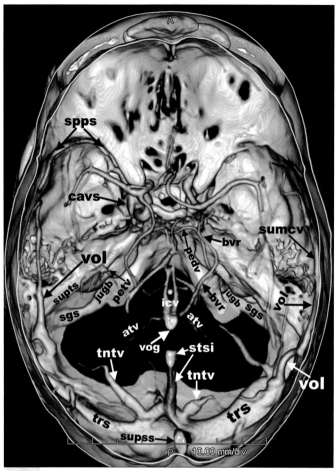

9.39d

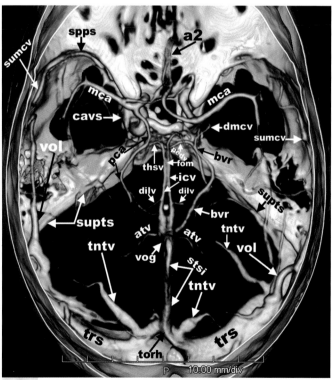

9.39e

FIGURES 9.39d,e

KEY

a2	a2 (postcommunicating segment aca)
aca	anterior cerebral artery
atv	atrial vein
bvr	basal vein of Rosenthal
cavs	cavernous sinus
dilv	direct lateral vein
dmcv	deep middle cerebral vein
fom	foramen of Monro
icv	internal cerebral vein
jugb	jugular bulb
mca	middle cerebral artery
pca	posterior cerebral artery
pedv	peduncular vein
petv	petrosal vein
sgs	sigmoid sinus
spps	sphenoparietal sinus
stsi	straight sinus
sumcv	superficial middle cerebral vein
supss	superior sagittal sinus
supts	superior petrosal sinus
thsv	thalamostriate vein
tntv	tentorial vein
torh	torcular herophili (confluence of sinuses)
trs	transverse sinus
vog	vein of Galen
vol	vein of Labbe

(continued)

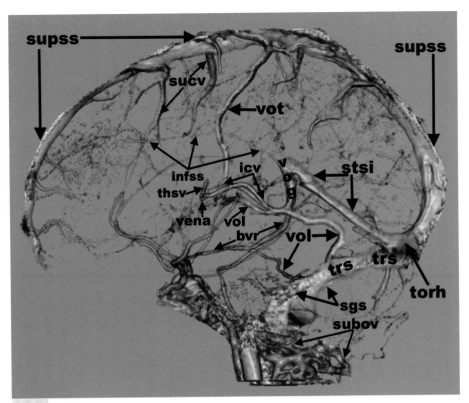

9.39f

FIGURES 9.39f,g

KEY

bvr	basal vein of Rosenthal
icv	internal cerebral vein
infss	inferior sagittal sinus
jugb	jugular bulb
occs	occipital sinus
sgs	sigmoid sinus
stsi	straight sinus
subov	suboccipital veins
sucv	superficial cortical vein(s)
supss	superior sagittal sinus
thsv	thalamostriate vein
torh	torcular herophili (confluence of sinuses)
trs	transverse sinus
vena	venous angle
vog	vein of Galen
vol	vein of Labbe
vot	vein of Trolard

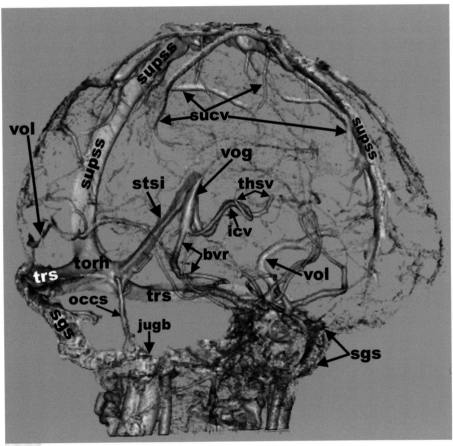

9.39g

■ CATHETER ANGIOGRAPHY (FIGURES 9.40a–9.42d)

2D DSA and 3D Rotational Catheter Angiography

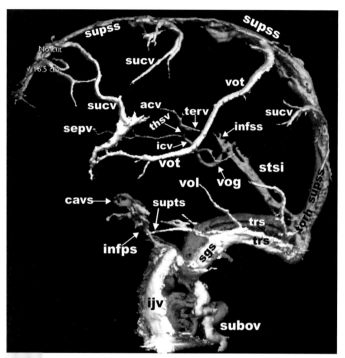

9.40a

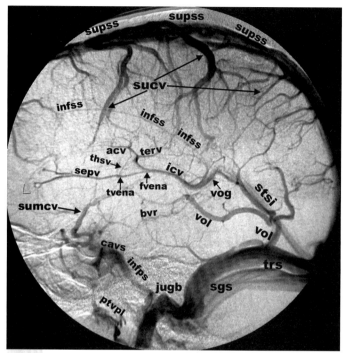

9.40b

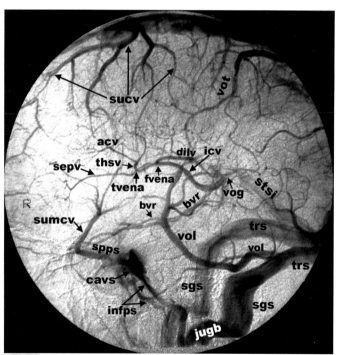

9.40c

FIGURES 9.40a–e Lateral projection venous phase image (9.40a) from a 3D rotational catheter angiogram following injection of contrast into the internal carotid artery, and lateral 2D DSA images in the venous phase following internal carotid artery injections in four different subjects (9.40b–e) demonstrate normal but variable venous drainage patterns.

KEY

acv	anterior caudate vein
bvr	basal vein of Rosenthal
cavs	cavernous sinus
dilv	direct lateral vein
fvena	false venous angle
icv	internal cerebral vein
ijv	internal jugular vein
infps	inferior petrosal sinus
infss	inferior sagittal sinus
jugb	jugular bulb
ptvpl	pterygoid venous plexus
sepv	septal vein
sgs	sigmoid sinus
spps	sphenoparietal sinus
stsi	straight sinus
subov	suboccipital veins
sucv	superficial cortical vein(s)
sumcv	superficial middle cerebral vein
supss	superior sagittal sinus
supts	superior petrosal sinus
terv	terminal vein
thsv	thalamostriate vein
torh	torcular herophili (confluence of sinuses)
trs	transverse sinus
tvena	true venous angle
vog	vein of Galen
vol	vein of Labbe
vot	vein of Trolard

(continued)

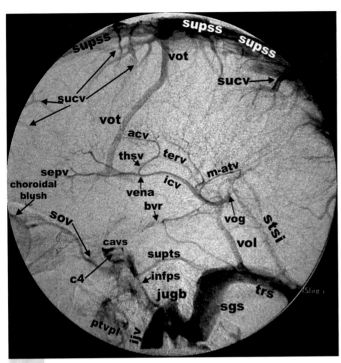

9.40d

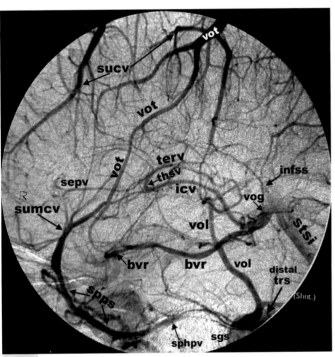

9.40e

FIGURES 9.40d,e

KEY

acv	anterior caudate vein
bvr	basal vein of Rosenthal
c4	c4 (cavernous segment of ica)
cavs	cavernous sinus
ica	internal carotid artery
icv	internal cerebral vein
ijv	internal jugular vein
infps	inferior petrosal sinus
infss	inferior sagittal sinus
jugb	jugular bulb
m-atv	medial atrial vein
ptvpl	pterygoid venous plexus
sepv	septal vein
sgs	sigmoid sinus
sov	superior ophthalmic vein
sphpv	sphenopetrosal vein
spps	sphenoparietal sinus
stsi	straight sinus
sucv	superficial cortical vein(s)
sumcv	superficial middle cerebral vein
supss	superior sagittal sinus
supts	superior petrosal sinus
terv	terminal vein
thsv	thalamostriate vein
trs	transverse sinus
vena	venous angle
vog	vein of Galen
vol	vein of Labbe
vot	vein of Trolard

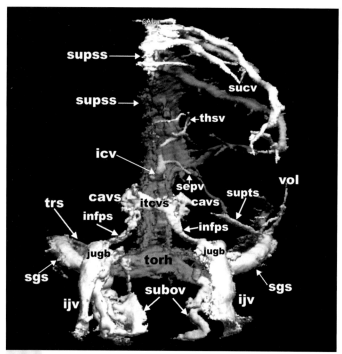

9.41a

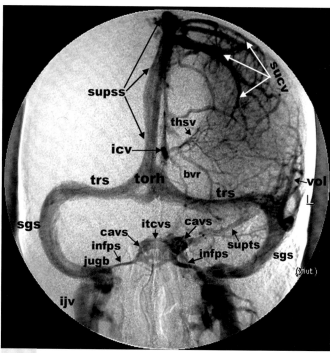

9.41b

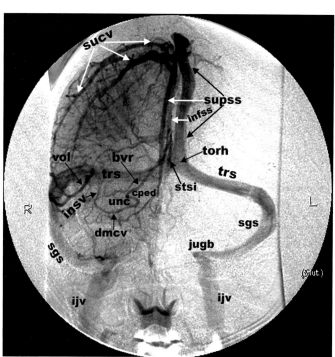

9.41c

FIGURES 9.41a–c Frontal projection venous phase image (9.41a) from a 3D rotational catheter angiogram following an internal carotid artery injection shows normal venous anatomy. AP venous phase images from 2D DSA exams following left (9.41b) and right (9.41c) internal carotid artery injections demonstrate normal venous anatomy.

KEY

bvr	basal vein of Rosenthal
cavs	cavernous sinus
cped	cerebral peduncle
dmcv	deep middle cerebral vein
icv	internal cerebral vein
ijv	internal jugular vein
infps	inferior petrosal sinus
infss	inferior sagittal sinus
insv	insular vein
itcvs	intercavernous sinus
jugb	jugular bulb
sepv	septal vein
sgs	sigmoid sinus
stsi	straight sinus
subov	suboccipital veins
sucv	superficial cortical vein(s)
supss	superior sagittal sinus
supts	superior petrosal sinus
thsv	thalamostriate vein
torh	torcular herophili (confluence of sinuses)
trs	transverse sinus
unc	uncus
vol	vein of Labbe

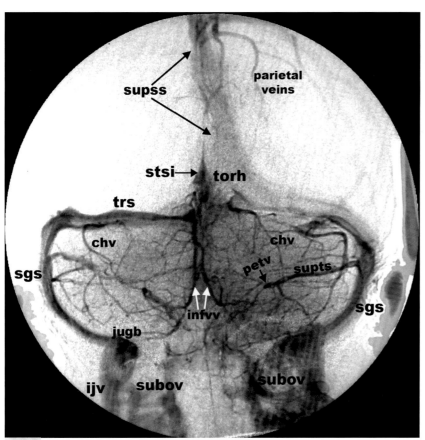

9.42a

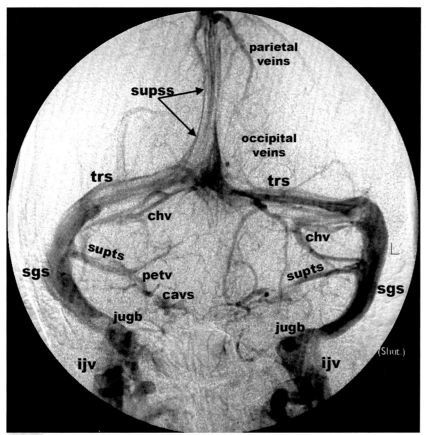

9.42b

FIGURES 9.42a–c   Posterior fossa (vertebral artery injections) AP venous phase DSA images in 9.42a–c show normal but variable patterns of venous drainage.

KEY

cavs	cavernous sinus
chv	cerebellar hemispheric vein
ijv	internal jugular vein
infvv	inferior vermian vein
jugb	jugular bulb
petv	petrosal vein
sgs	sigmoid sinus
stsi	straight sinus
subov	suboccipital veins
supss	superior sagittal sinus
supts	superior petrosal sinus
torh	torcular herophili (confluence of sinuses)
trs	transverse sinus

(*continued*)

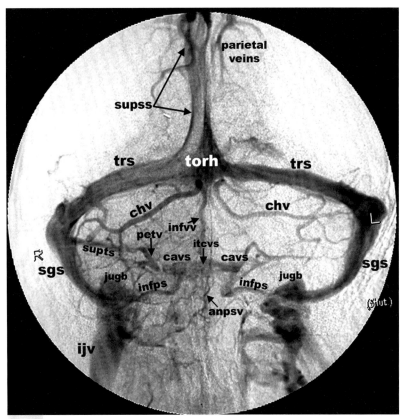

9.42c

FIGURE 9.42c

KEY

a-tve	anterior thalamic vein
anpsv	anterior pontomesencephalic vein
cavs	cavernous sinus
chv	cerebellar hemispheric vein
icv	internal cerebral vein
ijv	internal jugular vein
infps	inferior petrosal sinus
infvv	inferior vermian vein
inpc	interpeduncular cistern
itcvs	intercavernous sinus
jugb	jugular bulb
petv	petrosal vein
pmv	posterior mesencephalic vein
precv	pre-central cerebellar vein
s-tve	superior thalamic vein
schv	superior choroid vein
sgs	sigmoid sinus
spvv	superior vermian vein
stsi	straight sinus
supss	superior sagittal sinus
supts	superior petrosal sinus
torh	torcular herophili (confluence of sinuses)
trs	transverse sinus
vog	vein of Galen

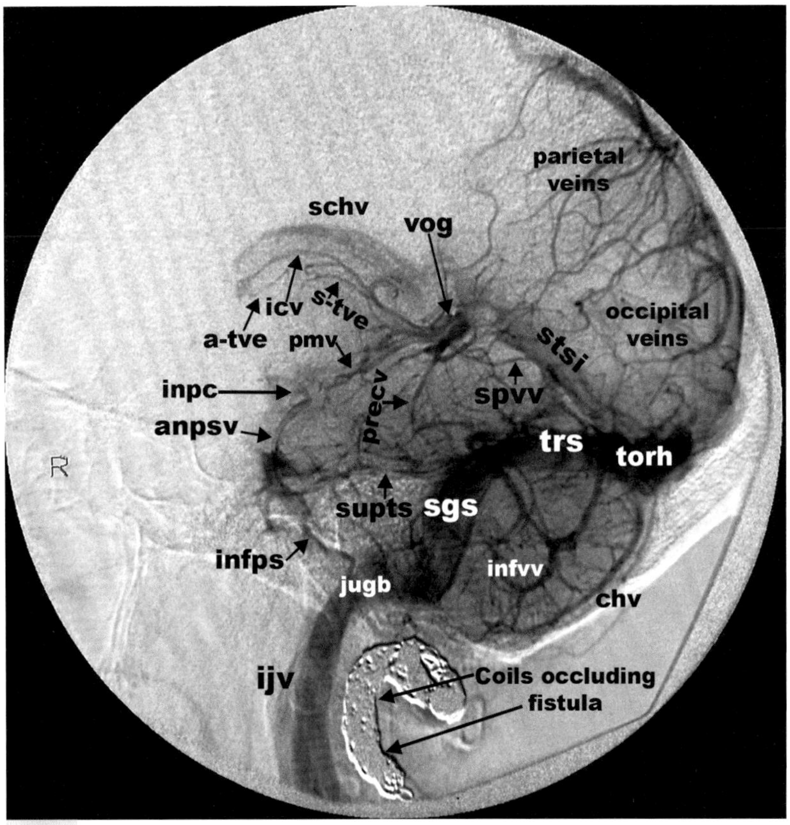

9.42d

FIGURE 9.42d   Posterior fossa (vertebral artery injection) lateral venous phase DSA image shows a normal venous pattern. Note the multiple endovascular coils occluding a suboccipital arterial-venous fistula (AVF).

CT PERFUSION (CTP) (FIGURES 9.43a–9.45e)

Case 1. Normal CTP exam in a patient with possible clinical stroke (Figures 9.43a–e).

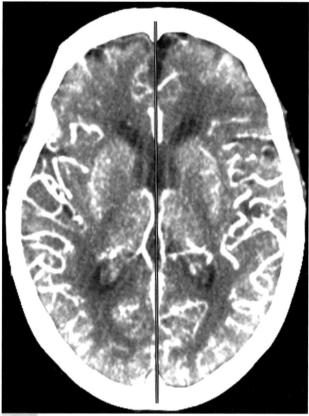

9.43a

FIGURE 9.43a   A contrast enhanced axial CT image through the basal ganglia regions without evidence of ischemic changes.

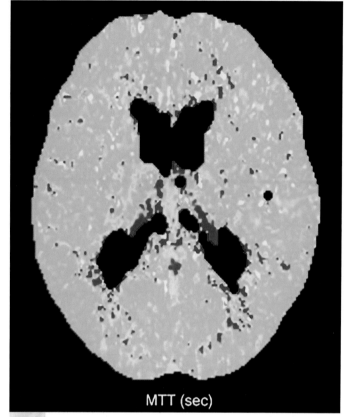

9.43b

FIGURES 9.43b–d   Color maps generated from a CT perfusion study. Normal mean transit time (MTT), cerebral blood flow (CBF), and cerebral blood volume (CBV) are seen without evidence or acute or old infarction.

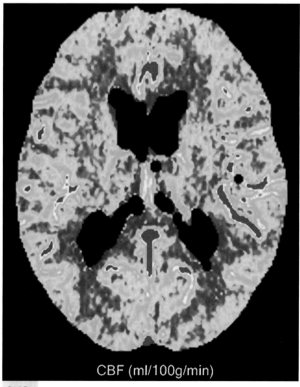

9.43c

(*continued*)

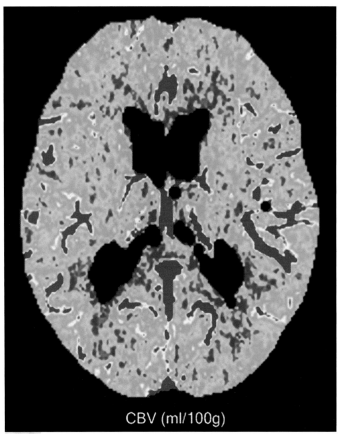

CBV (ml/100g)

9.43d

FIGURE 9.43d

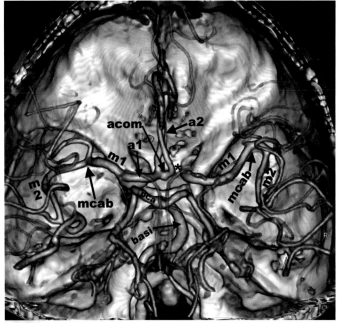

9.43e

FIGURE 9.43e A 3D CTA image that does not show any significant vascular occlusion or stenosis. Developmental hypoplasia versus aplasia of the A1 segment of the right anterior cerebral artery is incidentally noted (indicated by the black asterisk) which is a normal variant of the circle of Willis.

KEY

a1	a1 (precommunicating segment aca)
a2	a2 (postcommunicating segment aca)
aca	anterior cerebral artery
acom	anterior communicating artery
basi	basilar artery
m1	m1 (horizontal segment mca)
m2	m2 (Sylvian/insular branches mca)
mca	middle cerebral artery
mcab	mca bifurcation/trifurcation
pca	posterior cerebral artery

Case 2. CT perfusion data compatible with a region of core infarction with a large region of surrounding ischemic penumbra in the left middle cerebral artery (MCA) vascular territory (Figures 9.44a–k).

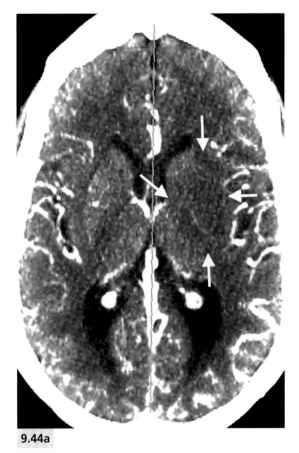

9.44a

FIGURES 9.44a–d   **Level 1. Basal Ganglia/internal capsule region.**

FIGURE 9.44a   A contrast enhanced axial CT image at this level in a patient suspected of having a stroke. This image shows hypodensity with loss of gray white differentiation compatible with cytotoxic (ischemic) edema in the left basal ganglia region, extending laterally to the insular cortex (region surrounded by white arrows).

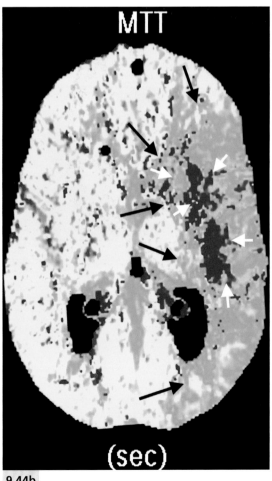

9.44b

FIGURE 9.44b   Color map of MTT demonstrating a large region of delayed transit time (green region surrounded by black arrows) with a smaller region of even greater delayed transit time (blue region surrounded by white arrows) in the left MCA vascular territory.

(continued)

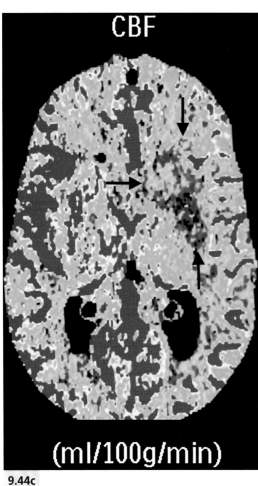

9.44c

FIGURE 9.44c Color map of CBF showing a similar but subtler large region of decreased CBF in the left MCA territory with a smaller region of even lower CBF, which is blue surrounded by black arrows.

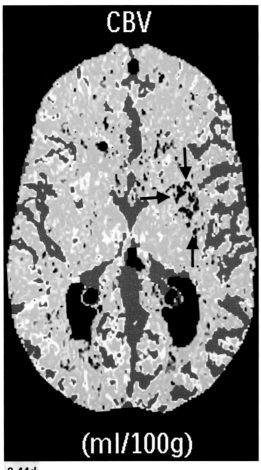

9.44d

FIGURE 9.44d Color map of CBV showing a limited region of decreased CBV (blue region surrounded by black arrows) suggesting that this will be the region of irreversible ischemia/infarction.

(continued)

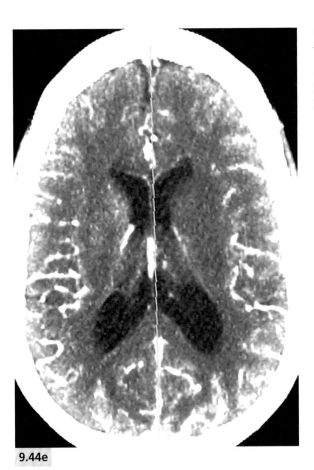

9.44e

FIGURES 9.44e–h   Level 2. Superior to level 1 at bodies of lateral ventricles.

FIGURE 9.44e   A contrast enhanced axial CT at this level. Subtle hypodensity in the left frontal and fronto-parietal white matter and hypodensity in the body of the left caudate nucleus is noted.

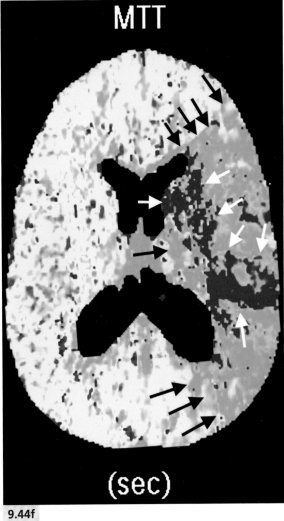

9.44f

FIGURES 9.44f   Color map of MTT showing a large region of delayed transit time (green region surrounded by black arrows) with a smaller region of even greater delayed transit time (blue region surrounded by white arrows).

(continued)

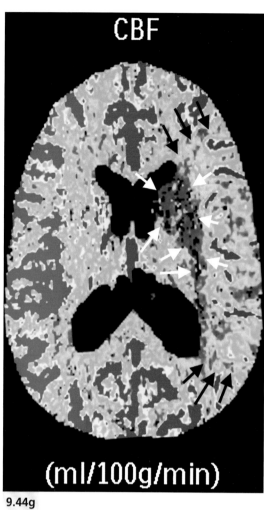

9.44g

FIGURE 9.44g Color map of CBF demonstrating a similar large region of reduced CBF (light blue region surrounded by black arrows) and a more limited region of even greater reduction in CBF centrally (darker blue surrounded by white arrows).

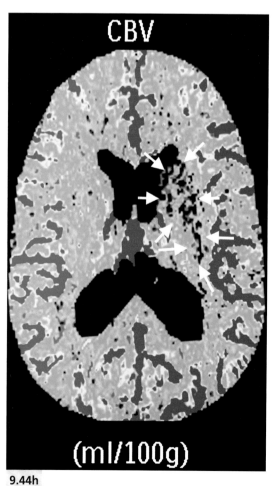

9.44h

FIGURE 9.44h Color map of CBV demonstrating a region of decreased CBV in the central white matter and caudate head outlined by the white arrows.

(continued)

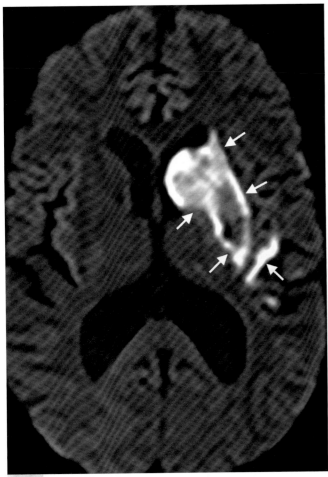

9.44i

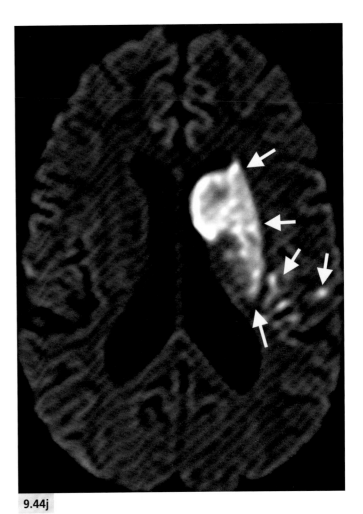
9.44j

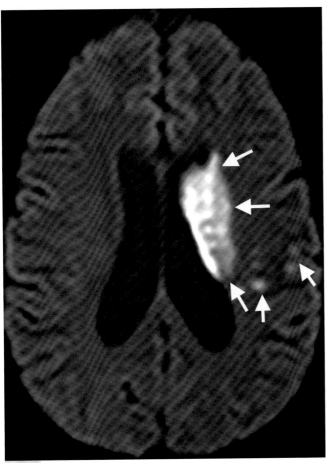
9.44k

FIGURES 9.44i–k   Diffusion weighted images demonstrating a moderately large region of presumed irreversible infarction (white regions surrounded by white arrows) which correlates best with the CBV color maps. The relatively matching abnormalities of delayed transit time and CBF which do not show a reduction in CBV or diffusion restriction (white found on i–k) indicates that this represents a large surrounding region of ischemic penumbra (salvageable brain tissue).

Case 3. CTP data compatible with a small core infarct with surrounding ischemic penumbra (Figures 9.45a–e).

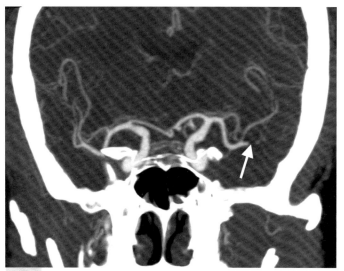

9.45a

FIGURE 9.45a   This coronal CTA image shows abrupt occlusion of the inferior division of the left MCA at the left MCA bifurcation/trifurcation.

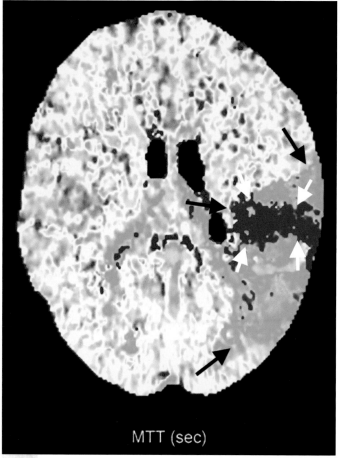

MTT (sec)

9.45b

FIGURE 9.45b   A color MTT map shows an area of delayed mean transit time (green region surrounded by black arrows) in the left temporal/inferior parietal lobe extending posteriorly to the watershed region adjacent to the occipital lobe. A smaller region of even greater delayed transit time is indicated by the blue region surrounded by white arrows.

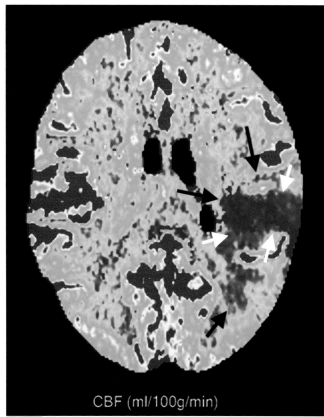

CBF (ml/100g/min)

9.45c

FIGURE 9.45c   A color CBF map shows a matching region of decreased CBF (surrounded by black arrows) in addition to a smaller region of even greater reduction in CBF (surrounded by white arrows).

(*continued*)

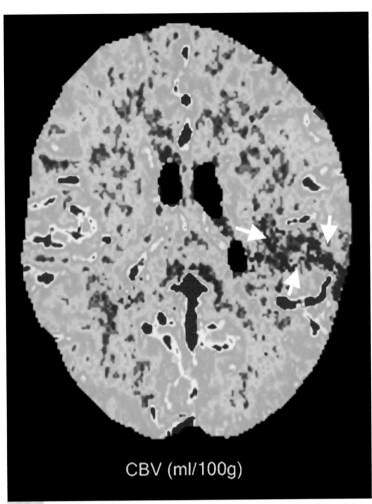

FIGURE 9.45d   A color CBV map shows a small region of diminished CBV in the left temporal/inferior parietal region, which suggests that this represents an area of irreversible ischemia/infarction.

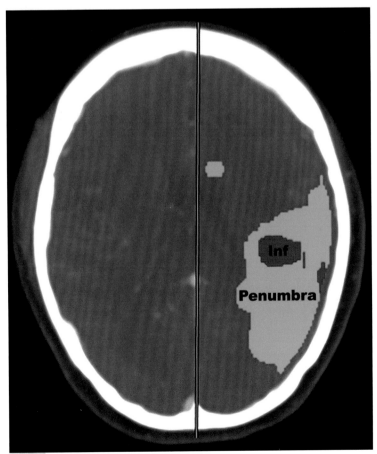

FIGURE 9.45e   This axial color map superimposed upon the CT scan was a computer generated prediction of the core infarction in red and the surrounding ischemic penumbra (tissue at risk) indicated by the green, based upon the CT perfusion data. This underestimated the actual size of the eventual region of infarction (irreversible ischemia).

KEY
Inf   infarction

Neonatal Cranial Ultrasound

10

*U*ltrasonography is the diagnostic application of sound waves beyond the range of human hearing to image the body. The details of ultrasound physics are beyond the scope of this book, but a brief review of some basic concepts is necessary. Using an ultrasound device, a sound wave is generated when a rapidly alternating electric field is applied to individual piezoelectric crystals, or transducers, arranged in an array, causing each crystal to vibrate. The sound wave, which is a wave that compresses and rarifies tissue, penetrates through tissues where it can be reflected, absorbed, or scattered. Differences in the acoustic impedance at tissue interfaces are responsible for the reflection of sound waves back to the probe. The array of transducer crystals acts as the receiver of the reflected waves after the transmitted pulse has terminated, and the resulting image is created from multiple signals. Clinical ultrasound uses frequencies of 2 to 15 MHz, where the velocity of the sound wave depends on the physical characteristics of the tissue that the wave is travelling through. Most tissues exhibit sonic qualities that are similar to liquids, but the denser the tissue, the faster the sound wave. The frequency of the sound waves generated by the ultrasound transducer affects the resolution of the image. Higher frequencies produce greater resolution, but less depth penetration. In a similar fashion, lower frequencies have greater penetration to reach deeper structures, but less resolution of the image. For example, Transcranial Doppler ultrasound uses low-frequency sound waves to produce spectral waveforms of the major intracranial vessels for evaluation of flow velocity, direction, amplitude, and pulsatility.

Cranial ultrasound examination is a safe imaging modality that does not entail the exposure of a patient to ionizing radiation. Additionally, the equipment is portable so that the examination can be performed at the bedside, and the infant does not require sedation. Unfortunately, the quality of the examination and the diagnostic accuracy is operator-dependent. Cranial ultrasonography relies on the presence of an adequate "acoustic window" through which an examination can be performed, so its value diminishes after the fontanels close in infancy.

Modern ultrasound equipment with various transducers capable of scanning at multiple frequencies is necessary to perform an adequate cranial ultrasound examination. The probes must have a footprint that matches the size of the acoustic window and be adequately positioned in the center of the fontanel.

Most commonly, a standard neonatal cranial ultrasound examination begins at the anterior fontanel as the main acoustic window. Scanning is performed with a transducer frequency around 7.5 MHz and it is critical to scan in a systematic manner. Typically, the study begins with static gray-scale anatomical images covering the brain in sagittal and coronal planes through the anterior fontanel. The most frequent use of gray-scale ultrasound imaging in premature neonates is to detect germinal matrix hemorrhage, whose incidence is between 20% and 30% for infants with a birth weight less than 1500 g.

Supplemental cranial acoustic windows allow positioning of the transducer near the area of interest. The mastoid fontanel provides a window to visualize the fourth ventricle, aqueduct of Sylvius, cisterna magna, and cerebellum. The temporal windows can be used to visualize the brainstem, circle of Willis and part of the cerebellum, as well as for Doppler flow measurements. The posterior fontanel allows visualization of the occipital horns of the lateral ventricles, the occipital lobe, and the cerebellum.

In addition to gray-scale anatomical imaging, Transcranial Doppler ultrasound can provide additional information on intracranial abnormalities, vessel anatomy and patency, and the velocity of blood flow to detect, for example, dural sinus venous thrombosis in newborns. The resistive index (RI) of the intracranial vasculature attempts to quantify alterations in blood flow. RI is obtained using Doppler ultrasound along an anterior branch of the circle of Willis, such as the anterior or middle cerebral arteries. The RI value is calculated as the ratio between the maximal end-diastolic and end-systolic flow velocities (Peak Systolic Velocity – End Diastolic Velocity/Peak Systolic Velocity). For full term neonates, the normal RI is 0.65 to 0.75, while preterm infants have a slightly higher RI value (0.77 to 0.90). A large variability of the RI values may indicate impaired intracranial autoregulation. Limitations of cranial ultrasound (US) include operator dependence, variable inter-observer interpretation, and equipment dependence.

Coronal Plane (Figures 10.1a–10.1k)

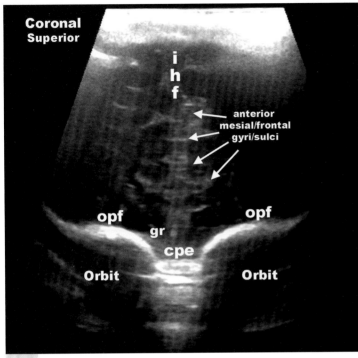

10.1a

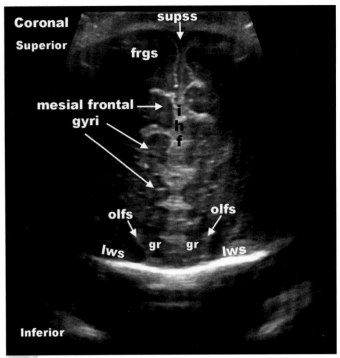

10.1b

FIGURES 10.1a–j   Cranial ultrasound of a full-term infant in the coronal plane from anterior (10.1a) to posterior (10.1j) demonstrating normal anatomy.

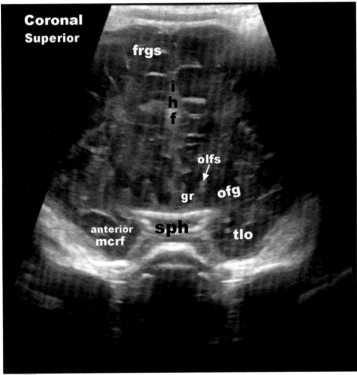

10.1c

KEY	
cpe	cribriform plate of ethmoid bone
frgs	superior frontal gyrus
gr	gyrus rectus
ihf	interhemispheric fissure
lws	lesser wing of the sphenoid bone
mcrf	middle cranial fossa
ofg	orbital-frontal gyri
olfs	olfactory sulcus
opf	orbital plate of frontal bone
sph	sphenoid bone
supss	superior sagittal sinus
tlo	temporal lobe

(continued)

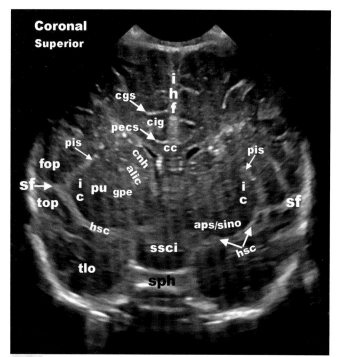

10.1d

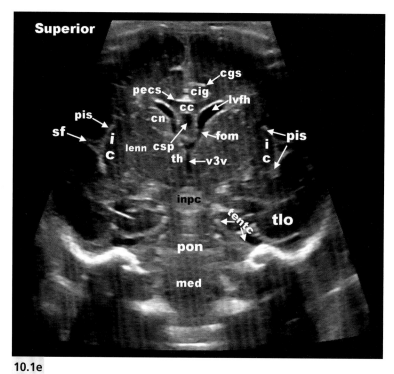

10.1e

FIGURES 10.1d–f

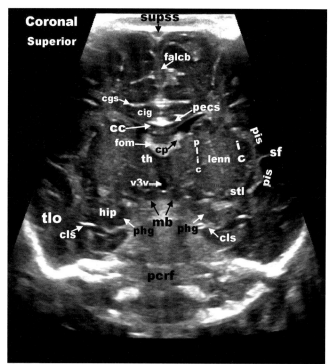

10.1f

KEY

alic	anterior limb of internal capsule	**lvfh**	frontal horn of lateral ventricle
aps	anterior perforated substance	**mb**	mammillary body
cc	corpus callosum	**med**	medulla
cgs	cingulate sulcus	**pcrf**	posterior cranial fossa
cig	cingulate gyrus	**pecs**	pericallosal cistern (sulcus)
cls	collateral sulcus	**phg**	parahippocampal gyrus
cn	caudate nucleus	**pis**	peri-insular (circular) sulcus
cnh	caudate nucleus head	**plic**	posterior limb of internal capsule
cp	choroid plexus	**pon**	pons
csp	cavum septum pellucidum	**pu**	putamen
falcb	falx cerebri	**sf**	Sylvian fissure (lateral sulcus)
fom	foramen of Monro	**sino**	substantia innominata
fop	frontal operculum	**sph**	sphenoid bone
gpe	globus pallidus externa	**ssci**	suprasellar cistern
hip	hippocampus	**stl**	stem of temporal lobe
hsc	horizontal Sylvian cistern (Sylvian fissure)	**supss**	superior sagittal sinus
		tentc	tentorium cerebelli
ic	insular cortex	**th**	thalamus
ihf	interhemispheric fissure	**tlo**	temporal lobe
inpc	interpeduncular cistern	**top**	temporal operculum
lenn	lenticular nucleus	**v3v**	third ventricle

(continued)

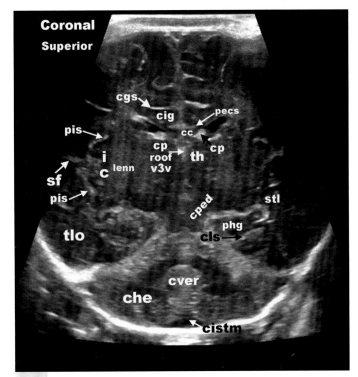

10.1g

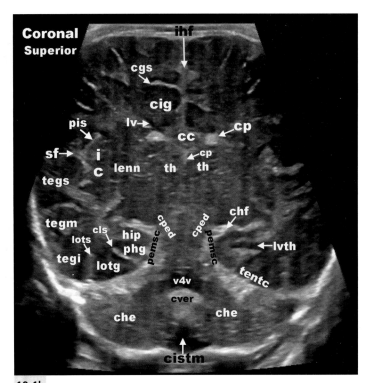

10.1h

FIGURES 10.1g–i

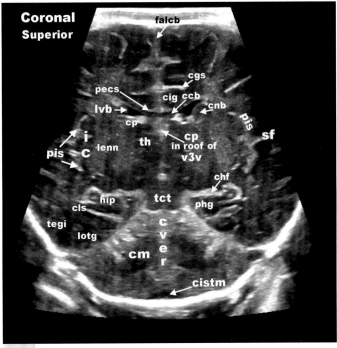

10.1i

KEY

cc	corpus callosum	lv	lateral ventricle
ccb	body of corpus callosum	lvb	body of lateral ventricle
cgs	cingulate sulcus	lvth	temporal horn of lateral ventricle
che	cerebellar hemisphere		
chf	choroidal fissure	pecs	pericallosal cistern (sulcus)
cig	cingulate gyrus	pemsc	perimesencephalic (ambient) cistern
cistm	cisterna magna		
cls	collateral sulcus	phg	parahippocampal gyrus
cm	corpus medullare	pis	peri-insular (circular) sulcus
cnb	caudate nucleus body		
cp	choroid plexus	sf	Sylvian fissure (lateral sulcus)
cped	cerebral peduncle		
cver	cerebellar vermis	stl	stem of temporal lobe
falcb	falx cerebri	tct	tectum
hip	hippocampus	tegi	inferior temporal gyrus
ic	insular cortex	tegm	middle temporal gyrus
ihf	interhemispheric fissure	tegs	superior temporal gyrus
lenn	lenticular nucleus	tentc	tentorium cerebelli
lotg	lateral occipital temporal gyrus (lotg)/fusiform gyrus	th	thalamus
		tlo	temporal lobe
		v3v	third ventricle
lots	lateral occipital temporal sulcus	v4v	fourth ventricle

(continued)

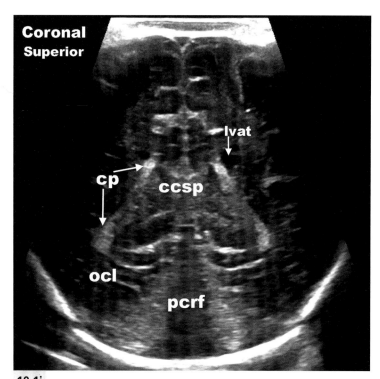

10.1j

FIGURE 10.1j

Sagittal Plane (Figures 10.1l–10.1s)

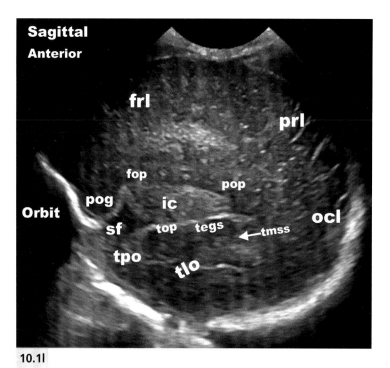

10.1l

FIGURE 10.1l Lateral parasagittal view demonstrates an open Sylvian fissure with visualization of the surface of the insular cortex and the surrounding opercula and diminished sulcation in this pre-term neonate.

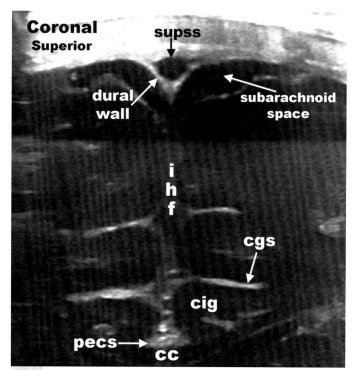

10.1k

FIGURE 10.1k Small field of view coronal image from the level of the body of the corpus callosum to the vertex. Note the superior sagittal sinus and its surrounding dural walls. One can also visualize the subarachnoid space at the vertex, to either side of the midline.

KEY	
cc	corpus callosum
ccsp	splenium of corpus callosum
cgs	cingulate sulcus
cig	cingulate gyrus
cp	choroid plexus
fop	frontal operculum
frl	frontal lobe
ic	insular cortex
ihf	interhemispheric fissure
lvat	atrium (trigone) of lateral ventricle
ocl	occipital lobe
pcrf	posterior cranial fossa
pecs	pericallosal cistern (sulcus)
pog	posterior orbital gyrus
pop	parietal operculum
prl	parietal lobe
sf	Sylvian fissure (lateral sulcus)
supss	superior sagittal sinus
tegs	superior temporal gyrus
tlo	temporal lobe
tmss	superior temporal sulcus
top	temporal operculum
tpo	temporal pole

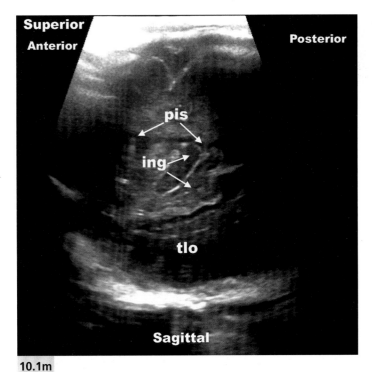

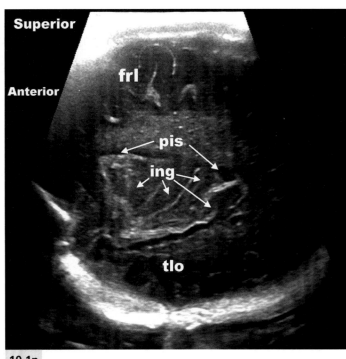

FIGURES 10.1m–n Parasagittal views demonstrate the insular gyri and the peri-insular sulcus (circular sulcus) in a full-term infant.

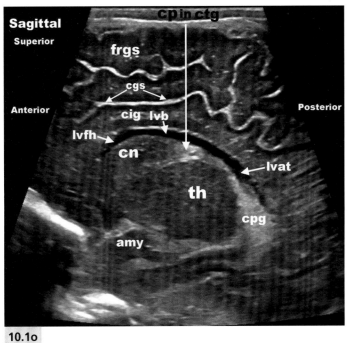

KEY	
amy	amygdala
cgs	cingulate sulcus
cig	cingulate gyrus
cn	caudate nucleus
cp	choroid plexus
cpg	glomus of choroid plexus
ctg	caudo-thalamic groove (notch)
frgs	superior frontal gyrus
frl	frontal lobe
ing	insular gyri
lvat	atrium (trigone) of lateral ventricle
lvb	body of lateral ventricle
lvfh	frontal horn of lateral ventricle
pis	peri-insular (circular) sulcus
th	thalamus
tlo	temporal lobe

FIGURES 10.1o–s Sagittal views from lateral to medial demonstrating normal anatomy in a full-term infant.

(continued)

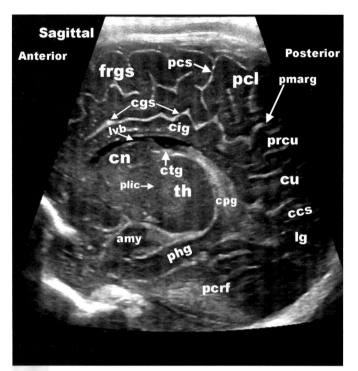

10.1p

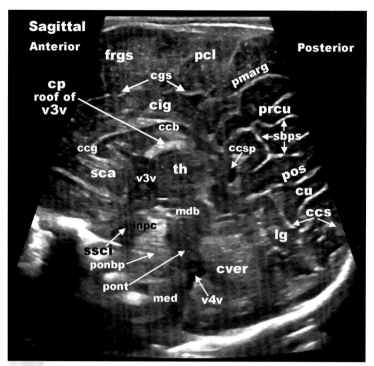

10.1q

FIGURES 10.1p–r

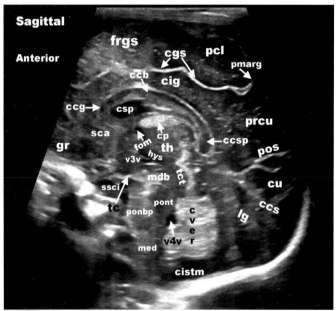

10.1r

KEY

amy	amygdala	**lvb**	body of lateral ventricle
cc	corpus callosum	**mdb**	midbrain
ccb	body of corpus callosum	**med**	medulla
ccg	genu of corpus callosum	**pcl**	paracentral lobule
ccs	calcarine sulcus	**pcrf**	posterior cranial fossa
ccsp	splenium of corpus callosum	**pcs**	paracentral sulcus
cgs	cingulate sulcus	**phg**	parahippocampal gyrus
cig	cingulate gyrus	**plic**	posterior limb of internal
cistm	cisterna magna		capsule
cn	caudate nucleus	**pmarg**	pars marginalis (ascending
cp	choroid plexus		ramus of cingulate sulcus)
cpg	glomus of choroid plexus	**ponbp**	basis pontis of pons
csp	cavum septum pellucidum	**pont**	tegmentum of pons
ctg	caudo-thalamic groove	**pos**	parieto-occipital sulcus
	(notch)	**prcu**	precuneus
cu	cuneus	**sbps**	subparietal sulcus
cver	cerebellar vermis	**sca**	subcallosal area
fom	foramen of Monro	**ssci**	suprasellar cistern
frgs	superior frontal gyrus	**tc**	tuber cinereum
gr	gyrus rectus	**tct**	tectum
hys	hypothalamic sulcus	**th**	thalamus
inpc	interpeduncular cistern	**v3v**	third ventricle
lg	lingual gyrus (motg)	**v4v**	fourth ventricle

(continued)

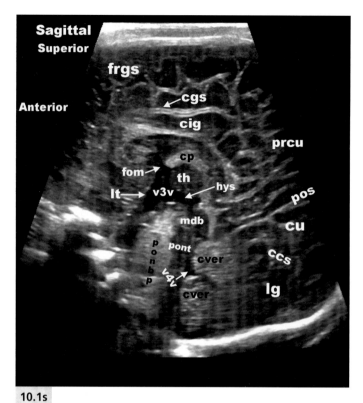

10.1s

FIGURE 10.1s

KEY

a1	a1 (precommunicating segment aca)	m1	m1 (horizontal segment mca)
aca	anterior cerebral artery	mca	middle cerebral artery
acom	anterior communicating artery	mdb	midbrain
		mog	medial orbital gyrus
ccs	calcarine sulcus	olfs	olfactory sulcus
cgs	cingulate sulcus	pca	posterior cerebral artery
cig	cingulate gyrus	pemsc	perimesencephalic (ambient) cistern
cp	choroid plexus		
cped	cerebral peduncle	ponbp	basis pontis of pons
cu	cuneus	pont	tegmentum of pons
cver	cerebellar vermis	pos	parieto-occipital sulcus
fom	foramen of Monro	prcu	precuneus
frgs	superior frontal gyrus	qdpc	quadrigeminal plate cistern
gr	gyrus rectus		
hsc	horizontal Sylvian cistern (Sylvian fissure)	ssci	suprasellar cistern
		supss	superior sagittal sinus
hys	hypothalamic sulcus	th	thalamus
lg	lingual gyrus (motg)	v3v	third ventricle
lt	lamina terminalis	v4v	fourth ventricle

Color Doppler Ultrasound (Figures 10.1t,u)

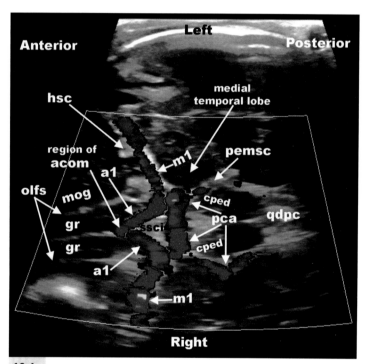

10.1u

FIGURE 10.1u Axial plane through the basal cisterns with Doppler ultrasound shows a patent circle of Willis as labeled.

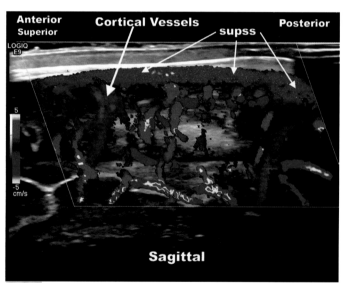

10.1t

FIGURE 10.1t Small field of view mid-sagittal image extending from the vertex to the cingulate sulcus with Doppler ultrasound showing patency of the superior sagittal sinus and patent mesial cortical vessels.

Suggested Readings

Afifi AK, Bergman RA. *Functional Neuroanatomy: Text and Atlas*. 2nd ed. McGraw Hill Professional; 2005:494.

Arslan OE. *Neuroanatomical Basis of Clinical Neurology*. New York: The Parthenon Publishing Group; 2001.

Barker PB, Bizzi A, DeStefano N, et al. *Clinical MR Spectroscopy: Techniques and Applications*. Cambridge University Press; 2009:264.

Benarroch EE, Westmoreland BF, Daube JR, et al. *Medical Neurosciences: An Approach to Anatomy, Pathology, and Physiology by Systems and Levels*. 4th ed. New York: Lippincott, Williams & Wilkins; 1999.

Binder DK, Sonne DC, Fishbein NJ. *Cranial Nerves: Anatomy, Pathology, Imaging*. New York: Thieme Medical Publishers, Inc.; 2010.

Bispro RFM, Ramalho AJC, Gusmao LCB, et al. Cerebellar vermis: topography and variations. *Int J Morphol*. 2010; 28(2): 439–443.

Blumenfeld H. *Neuroanatomy Through Clinical Cases*. 2nd ed. Sinauer Associates; 2011.

Borden NM. *3D Angiographic Atlas of Neurovascular Anatomy and Pathology*. Cambridge University Press; 2007:273.

Borden, NM, Forseen SE. *Pattern Recognition Neuroradiology*. Cambridge University Press; 2011:339.

Brodal P. *The Central Nervous System: Structure and Function*. 4th ed. Oxford University Press; 2010:608.

Campos D, Rieger A, Mohr H, et al. Anatomy and evolution of accessory nerve: cranial or spinal origins? – a review. *J Morphol Sci*. 2011; 28(4): 222–227.

Casselman J, guest ed. Cranial nerves. *Neuroimaging Clin N Am*. 2008; 18(2): 197–444.

Chhabra A, ed. MR neurography. *Neuroimaging Clin N Am*. 2014; 24(1): 1–267.

Chong VFH, ed. Skull base and temporal bone imaging. *Neuroimaging Clin N Am*. 2009; 19(3): 287–516.

Daneman A, Epelman M, Blaser S, et al. Imaging of the brain in full-term neonates: does sonography still play a role? *Pediatr Radiol*. 2006; 36: 636–646.

Dixon RL, Whitlow CT. The physical basis of diagnostic imaging. In: Chen MM, Pope TL, Ott DJ, eds. *Basic Radiology*, 2nd ed. New York, NY: McGraw-Hill; 2011: 15–24.

Drost DJ, Riddle WR, Clarke GD. Proton magnetic resonance spectroscopy in the brain: report of the AAPM MR task group #9. *Med Phys*. 2002; 29(9): 2177–2197.

FitzGerald MJT, Gruener G, Mtui E. *Clinical Neuroanatomy and Neuroscience*, 6th ed. Saunders Elsevier; 2011.

Fushimi Y, Miki Y, Ueba T, et al. Lilliquist membrane: three-dimensional constructive interference in steady state MR imaging. *Radiology*. 2003; 229(2): 360–364.

Ginsberg LE. The posterior condylar canal. *AJNR Am J Neuroradiol*. 1994; 15: 969–972.

Govaert P, deVries LS. *An Atlas of Neonatal Brain Sonography: (CDM 182–183)*. 2nd ed. London: Mac Keith Press; 2010:419.

Haacke EM, Reichenbach JR, eds. *Susceptibility Weighted Imaging in MRI: Basic Concepts and Clinical Applications*. John Wiley & Sons; 2011:743.

Haines DE. *Fundamental Neuroscience for Basic and Clinical Applications*. 4th ed. Philadelphia, PA: Elsevier Saunders; 2012.

Haines DE. *Neuroanatomy: An Atlas of Structures, Sections and Systems*. 8th ed. Wolters Kluver/Lippincott Williams & Wilkins; 2012.

Hendelman WJ. *Atlas of Functional Neuroanatomy*. 2nd ed. Boca Raton, FL: CRC Press; 2006.

Kiernan J, Rajakumar R. *Barr's The Human Nervous System: An Anatomical Viewpoint*. 10th ed. Baltimore: Wolters Kluwer Health/Lippincott, Williams & Wilkins; 2014.

Kingsley RE. *Concise Text of Neuroscience*. 2nd ed. Philadelphia, PA: Lippincott, Williams and Wilkins; 2000.

Hall EJ, Brenner DJ. Cancer risks from diagnostic radiology. *Br J Radiol*. 2008; 81(965): 362–378.

Harnsbergr HR, Osborn AG, Macdonald AJ, Ross JS. *Diagnostic and Surgical Imaging Anatomy: Brain, Head & Neck, Spine.* Lippincott Williams & Wilkins; 2007:225.

Huber P. *Cerebral Angiography.* Georg Thieme Verlag; 1982:585.

Huisman TA, Singhi S, Pinto PS. Non-invasive imaging of intracranial pediatric vascular lesions. *Childs Nerv Syst.* 2010; 26: 1275–1295.

Jellison BJ, Field AS, Medow J, et al. Diffusion tensor imaging of cerebral white matter: a pictorial review of physics, fiber tract anatomy, and tumor imaging patterns. *AJNR Am J Neuroradiol.* 2004; 25: 356–369.

Kapp JP, Schmidek HH, eds. *The Cerebral Venous System and Its Disorders.* Grune & Stratton Inc.; 1984:637.

Kelly WM, guest ed. Cranial neuropathy. *Neuroimaging Clin N Am.* 1993; 3(1): 1–212.

Kretschmann HJ, Weinrich W. *Cranial Neuroimaging and Clinical Neuroanatomy: Magnetic Resonance Imaging and Computed Tomography.* 2nd ed., rev. and expanded. Stuttgart: Georg Thieme Verlag; 1992:375.

Leblanc A. *Anatomy and Imaging of the Cranial Nerves: A Neuroanatomic Method of Investigation Using Magnetic Resonance Imaging (MRI) and Computed Tomography (CT).* Springer-Verlag; 1992:277.

Lowe LH, Bailey Z. State-of-the-art cranial sonography: part I, modern techniques and image interpretation. *AJR Am J Roentgenol.* 2011; 196: 1028–1033.

Mai JK, Paxinos G, Voss T. *Atlas of the Human Brain.* 3rd ed. Elsevier; 2008:271.

Martin J. *Neuroanatomy Text and Atlas.* 4th ed. McGraw-Hill Medical; 2012.

Mason P. *Medical Neurobiology.* Oxford University Press; 2011.

May JK, Paxinos G, Voss T. *Atlas of the Human Brain.* 3rd ed. Academic Press; 2007.

McMinn RMH, Hutchings RT, Logan BM. *Color Atlas of Head and Neck Anatomy.* Chicago: Year Book Medical Publishers; 1981:240.

Nadeau SE, Ferguson TS, Valenstein E, et al. *Medical Neuroscience.* Philadelphia, PA: Saunders/Elsevier; 2004.

Naidich TP, Castillo M, Cha S, Smirniotopoulos JG. *Imaging of the Brain: Expert Radiology Series.* Elsevier-Saunders; 2013:1052.

Naidich TP, Duvernoy HM, Delman BN, et al. *Duvernoy's Atlas of the Human Brain Stem and Cerebellum.* SpringerWienNewYork; 2009:876.

Naidich TP, Yousry TA, Mathews VP, guest eds. Anatomic basis of functional MR imaging. *Neuroimaging Clin N Am.* 2001; 11(2): 151–384.

Nair JR, Van Hecke W, De Belder F, et al. High-resolution susceptibility-weighted imaging at 3 T with a 32-channel head coil: technique and clinical applications. *AJR Am J Roentgenol.* 2010; 195(4): 1007–1014.

Nolte J. *The Human Brain.* 6th ed. Philadelphia PA: Mosby/Elsevier; 2009.

Nolte J. *The Human Brain in Photographs and Diagrams.* 4th ed. Saunders; 2013.

Nolte J. *Elsevier's Integrated Neuroscience.* Philadelphia, PA: Mosby/Elsevier; 2007.

Osborne AG. *Diagnostic Cerebral Angiography.* 2nd ed. Lippincott Williams & Wilkins; 1999:462.

Oz G, Alger JR, Barker PB, et al. Clinical proton MR spectroscopy in central nervous system disorders. *Radiology.* 2014; 270(3): 658–679.

Parent A. *Carpenter's Human Neuroanatomy.* 9th ed. Williams & Wilkins; 1996:2171.

Rumack CM, Wilson SR, Charboneau JW, Levine D. *Diagnostic Ultrasound.* Vol. 2. 4th ed. Elsevier/Mosby; 2011:2031.

Schmahmann JD, Doyon J, McDonald D, et al. Three-dimensional MRI atlas of the human cerebellum in proportional stereotaxic space. *NeuroImage.* 1999; 10: 223–260.

Shankar L, Evans K, Hawke M, Stammberger H. *An Atlas of Imaging of the Paranasal Sinuses.* 1st ed. Lippincott Williams & Wilkins; 1994:208.

Siegel A, Sapru HN. *Essential Neuroscience.* 3rd ed. Lippincott, Williams & Wilkins; 2014:538.

Smith-Bindman R, Lipson J, Marcus R, et al. Radiation dose associated with common computed tomography examinations and the associated lifetime attributable risk of cancer. *Arch Intern Med.* 2009; 169(22): 2078–2086.

Som PM and Curtin HD. *Head and Neck Imaging.* 5th ed., Vol. 2. Elsevier Mosby; 2011:2947.

Steggerda SJ, Leijser LM, Walther FJ, et al. Neonatal cranial ultrasonography: how to optimize its performance. *Early Hum Dev.* 2009; 85: 93–99.

Sundgren PC, guest ed. Advanced imaging techniques in brain tumors. *Neuroimaging Clin N Am.* 2009; 19(4): 517–700.

Swartz JD, Loevner LA. *Imaging of the Temporal Bone.* 4th ed. New York: Thieme; 2008:604.

Tamraz JC, Comair YG. *Atlas of Regional Anatomy of the Brain Using MRI With Functional Correlations.* Springer Verlag; 2000:330.

Tien RD, guest ed. The limbic system normal anatomy and pathology. *Neuroimaging Clin N Am.* 1997; 7(1): 1–170.

Weber AL, guest ed. Imaging of the skull base. *Neuroimaging Clin N Am.* 1994; 4(3): 465–662.

van Wezel-Meijler G, Steggerda SJ, Leijser LM. Cranial ultrasonography in neonates: role and limitations. *Semin Perinatol.* 2010; 34: 28–38.

Wakana S, Jiang H, Nagae-Poetscher LM, et al. Fiber tract-based atlas of human white matter anatomy. *Radiology.* 2004; 230(1): 77–87.

Watson C. *Basic Human Neuroanatomy: A Clinically Oriented Atlas*. 6th ed. Lulu.com (print and electronic versions); 2012.

Waxman SG. *Clinical Neuroanatomy*. 27th ed. Lange McGraw-Hill Medical; 2013: 352.

Weber AL, guest ed. Imaging of the globe, orbit, and visual pathway. *Neuroimaging Clin N Am*. 1996; 6(1): 1–264.

Weissleder R, Wittenberg J, Harisinghani, MG, Chen JW. Chapter 14. Imaging physics. In: Weissleder R, Wittenberg J, Harisinghani, MG, Chen JW, eds. *Primer of Diagnostic Imaging*, 5th ed. St. Louis, MO: Mosby, Inc.; 2011.

Wilson-Pauwels L, Stewart PA, Akesson EG, et al. *Cranial Nerves: Function & Disfunction*. 3rd ed. People's Medical Publishing House – USA; 2010:247.

Woolsey TA, Hanaway J, Gado MH. *The Brain Atlas: A Visual Guide to the Human Central Nervous System*. 3rd ed. Wiley-Liss; 2008:272.

Young PA, Young PH. *Basic Clinical Neuroscience*. 2nd ed. Lippincott, Williams & Wilkins; 2007:384.

Zang-Hee Cho. *7.0 Tesla MRI Brain Atlas: In Vivo Atlas With Cryomacrotome Correlation*. Springer; 2010:560.

Zapadka ME, Bradbury MS, Williams III DW. Brain and its coverings. In: Chen MM, Pope TL, Ott DJ, eds. *Basic Radiology*. 2nd ed. New York, NY: McGraw-Hill; 2011:325–364.

Master Legend Key

A

A = anterior nuclei of thalamus
a-thp = anterior thalamoperforators
a-tve = anterior thalamic vein
a1 = a1 (precommunicating segment anterior cerebral artery)
a2 = a2 (postcommunicating segment anterior cerebral artery)
a3 = a3 (cortical branches of anterior cerebral artery)
aaa = aditus ad antrum
aar = anterior ascending ramus of Sylvian fissure
ac = anterior commissure
aca = anterior cerebral artery
acha = anterior choroidal artery
achg = anterior chamber of eye
acl = anterior clinoid process
acom = anterior communicating artery
acr = anterior corona radiata
acrf = anterior cranial fossa
acv = anterior caudate vein
adh = adenohypophysis
aec = anterior ethmoidal canal
afr = artery of the foramen rotundem
agg = agger nasi cell
ahr = anterior horizontal ramus of Sylvian fissure
aica = anterior inferior cerebellar artery
aica/pica = medial branch of aica supplying pica
aif = anterior internal frontal branch of anterior cerebral artery
alcl = ala of central lobe
alg = anterior long insular gyrus
alic = anterior limb of internal capsule
alin = anterior lobule of insula
amy = amygdala
anc = anterior nasal cavity
ang = angular gyrus
anga = angular artery
anpsv = anterior pontomesencephalic vein
antcv = anterior cerebral vein
aog = anterior orbital gyrus
api = apex of insula
apmca = anterior parietal branch of middle cerebral artery
apofs = anterior parolfactory sulcus
aps = anterior perforated substance
aqs = aqueduct of Sylvius

aracg = arachnoid granulations
arbv = arbor vitae
arcf = arcuate fasciculus
arch = aortic arch
arm = alveolar ridge of maxilla
arms = alveolar recess of maxillary sinus
asa = anterior spinal artery
ascpha = ascending pharyngeal artery of eca
asg = anterior short insular gyrus
asm = anterior spine of maxilla
aspf = anterior superior (primary) fissure
atmca = anterior temporal middle cerebral artery
atr = anterior thalamic radiations
atv = atrial vein
   l-atv = lateral atrial vein
   m-atv = medial atrial vein

B

balam = basal lamella
bas = basion
basi = basilar artery
batp = basilar artery tip
biven = biventral lobule
bsphb = basisphenoid bone
bucm = buccinator muscle
bucma = buccinator muscular branches of eca
bvr = basal vein of Rosenthal

C

c1 = c1 (cervical segment internal carotid artery)
c2 = c2 (petrous segment of internal carotid artery)
c2a = c2a (vertical petrous segment internal carotid artery)
c2b = c2b (horizontal petrous segment of internal carotid artery)
c3 = c3 (lacerum segment of internal carotid artery)
c4 = c4 (cavernous segment of internal carotid artery)
c5 = c5 (clinoid segment of internal carotid artery)
c6 = c6 (ophthalmic segment of internal carotid artery)
c7 = c7 (communicating segment of internal carotid artery)

c1v = first vertebral segment
c2v = second vertebral segment
c3v = third vertebral segment
c4v = fourth vertebral segment
c5v = fifth vertebral segment
c6v = sixth vertebral segment
c7v = seventh vertebral segment
ca = calcar avis
calc = calcarine branch of pca
callo = callosomarginal branch of anterior
    cerebral artery
carb = carotid bulb
carc = carotid canal
cavs = cavernous sinus
cbomc = cerebellomedullary cistern
cc = corpus callosum
cca = common carotid artery
    l-cca = left common carotid artery
    r-cca = right common carotid artery
ccab = common carotid artery bifurcation
ccb = body of corpus callosum
ccba = anterior body corpus callosum
ccbp = posterior body corpus callosum
ccg = genu of corpus callosum
ccr = rostrum of corpus callosum
ccs = calcarine sulcus
ccsa = anterior calcarine sulcus
ccsp = splenium of corpus callosum
ces = central sulcus
cfa = csf flow artifact
cg = crista galli
cgs = cingulate sulcus
che = cerebellar hemisphere
chf = choroidal fissure
chs = chiasmatic sulcus
chv = cerebellar hemispheric vein
cig = cingulate gyrus (cingulum)
cigh = cingulum (hippocampal part)
cigis = isthmus of cingulate gyrus
cistm = cisterna magna
cl = clivus
cla = claustrum
clb = caudato-lenticular bridges
clob = central lobule (lobules II and III)
cls = collateral sulcus
clt = cistern of lamina terminalis
clv = clava
clvp = clival venous plexus
clw = collateral white matter
cm = corpus medullare
cmed = closed medulla
cn = caudate nucleus
cn1 = olfactory nerve
cn2 = optic nerve
cn3 = oculomotor nerve
cn4 = trochlear nerve
cn5 = trigeminal nerve
cn5p = pre-ganglionic segment trigeminal nerve
cn6 = abducens nerve
cn7 = facial nerve
cn7ct = chorda tympani branch facial nerve
cn7l = labyrinthine segment facial nerve
cn7m = mastoid segment facial nerve
cn7t = tympanic segment of facial nerve
cn7/8 = facial and vestibulocochlear nerves
cn8 = vestibulocochlear nerve
cn8c = cochlear branch of vestibulocochlear nerve

cn8iv = inferior division of vestibular nerve
cn8sv = superior division of vestibular nerve
cn9 = glossopharyngeal nerve
cn10 = vagus nerve
cn11 = accessory nerve
cn12 = hypoglossal nerve
cnb = caudate nucleus body
cnh = caudate nucleus head
cns = cartilaginous nasal septum
cnt = caudate nucleus tail
cnv1 = ophthalmic branch (v1) of
    trigeminal nerve
cnv2 = maxillary branch (v2) of trigeminal
    nerve
cnv3 = mandibular division (v3) of trigeminal
    nerve
cnv3lg = lingual nerve (branch of v3)
coam = cornu ammonis
coaq = cochlear aqueduct
coc = cochlea
cocap = cochlear aperture
cocat = apical turn of cochlea
cocb = basal turn of cochlea
cocm = middle turn of cochlea
cocp = cochlear promontory
cocpr = cochleariform process
colu = columella
comcr = common crus
cp = choroid plexus
cpac = cerebellopontine angle cistern
cpe = cribriform plate of ethmoid bone
cped = cerebral peduncle
cpg = glomus of choroid plexus
cpm = coronoid process of mandible
cpt = corticopontine tract
cr = corona radiata
crc = crus cerebri
crmca = central rolandic branches of middle
    cerebral artery
cruci = crural cistern
cs = corticospinal fibers in cerebral peduncle
csf = cerebrospinal fluid
csi = central sulcus of insula
cso = centrum semiovale
csp = cavum septum pellucidum
cst = corticospinal tract
ctg = caudo-thalamic groove (notch)
cto = cerebellar tonsil
ctt = central tegmental tract
cu = cuneus
cul = culmen (lobules IV and V)
cver = cerebellar vermis
cvi = cistern of velum interpositum

D
dec = declive (lobule VI)
dent = dentate nucleus
dg = dentate gyrus
dilv = direct lateral vein
dmcv = deep middle cerebral vein
dorc = Dorello's canal
ds = dorsum sellae
dscp = decussation of superior cerebellar
    peduncles
dur = dura (pachymeninges)
dva = developmental venous anomaly
dwm = deep white matter

E

eac = external auditory canal
eca = external carotid artery
ecf = extraconal orbital fat
elid = orbicularis oculi/eyelid
emc = extreme capsule
enc = entorhinal cortex
eom = extra-ocular muscles
eop = external occipital protuberance (inion)
eptr = epitympanic recess (attic)
ethac = ethmoid air cells
ethaca = anterior ethmoid air cells
ethacp = posterior ethmoid air cells
ethbu = ethmoidal bulla
ethin = ethmoid infundibulum
ethmp = ethmomaxillary plate
eusto = eustachian tube orifice
ev = emissary vein
extc = external capsule

F

facial = facial artery
facv = facial vein
falcb = falx cerebri
falci = falx cerebelli
falcr = falciform crest
far = facial recess
fba = fenestration of basilar artery
fcol = facial colliculus
fl = foramen lacerum
flaq = flow void through aqueduct of Sylvius
floc = flocculus
fls = fossa for lacrimal sac
fmcf = floor of middle cranial fossa
fmi = forceps minor
fmj = forceps major
fms = frontomaxillary suture
fns = frontonasal suture
fof = fields of Forel
fol = folium (lobule VII)
folus = foramen of Luschka
fom = foramen of Monro
fomg = foramen of Magendie
fop = frontal operculum
for = foramen rotundem
forca = foramen caecum
form = foramen magnum
fortr = foramen transversarium
fos = foramen spinosum
fosr = fossa of Rosenmüller
fov = foramen ovale
fove = fovea ethmoidales
fp = frontopontine fibers in cerebral peduncle
fpa = frontopolar branch of anterior cerebral
    artery
fpm = frontal process of maxilla
fpop = fronto-parietal operculum
fpz = frontal process of zygomatic bone
frb = frontal bone
frgi = inferior frontal gyrus
frgio = pars orbitalis of inferior frontal gyrus
frgiop = pars opercularis of inferior frontal gyrus
frgit = pars triangularis of inferior frontal gyrus
frgm = middle frontal gyrus
frgs = superior frontal gyrus
frl = frontal lobe
frms = frontomarginal sulcus

frr = frontal recess
frs = frontal sinus
frsi = inferior frontal sulcus
frsm = middle frontal sulcus
frss = superior frontal sulcus
frv4 = fastigial recess of fourth ventricle
frx = fornix
frxac = ascending columns of fornix
frxb = body of fornix
frxc = crura of fornix
fxp = precommissural branch of fornix
ftj = falco-tentorial junction
fve = foramen of Vesalius
fvena = false venous angle
fwm = frontal white matter
fzs = frontozygomatic suture

G

geng = geniculate ganglion
gic = genu of internal capsule
gl = globe
glm = glossopharyngeal meatus
gp = glopus pallidus
gpe = globus pallidus externa
gpi = globus pallidus interna
gr = gyrus rectus
grac = gracile lobule
grpa = greater palatine artery
gspn = greater superficial petrosal nerve
gws = greater wing of the sphenoid bone
gya = gyrus ambiens

H

h = hypoglossal eminence
hab = habenular trigone
heg = Heschl's gyrus (transverse temporal gyrus)
hif = hippocampal fissure (sulcus)
hip = hippocampus
hipa = alveus of hippocampus
hipb = hippocampal body
hipcom = hippocampal commissure
hipf = fimbria of hippocampus
hiph = hippocampal head
hipt = hippocampal tail
hise = hiatus semilunaris
hmk = hand motor knob
hmp = hamulus of medial pterygoid plate
horzf = great horizontal fissure of cerebellum
hpp = horizontal plate of palatine bone
hsc = horizontal Sylvian cistern (Sylvian fissure)
hsr = hippocampal sulcal remnants
hyp = hypothalamus
hypc = hypoglossal canal
hypo = hypotympanum
hys = hypothalamic sulcus

I

iaa = inferior alveolar artery
iac = internal auditory canal
ian = inferior alveolar nerve (branch of cnv3)
ic = insular cortex
ica = internal carotid artery
icat = internal carotid artery terminus/bifurcation
icf = intraconal orbital fat
icp = inferior cerebellar peduncle (restiform body)

icv = internal cerebral vein
if = incisive fossa
ifo = inferior fronto-occipital fasciculus
i-frs = inferior frontal sinus
ihf = interhemispheric fissure
iipa = inferior internal parietal branch of anterior
    cerebral artery
ijv = internal jugular vein
ilen = lenticular process of incus
ilf = inferior longitudinal fasciculus
ilp = long process of incus
ilt = inferolateral trunk
imlt = internal medullary lamina of
    thalamus
imv = inferior/posterior medullary velum
in = incus
inb = body of incus
incc = incisive/nasopalatine canal
inf = infundibulum
infc = inferior colliculus
infm = inferior meatus
infoa = infraorbital artery
infoc = inferior olivary complex
inforc = infra-orbital canal
infps = inferior petrosal sinus
infslu = inferior semilunar lobule (Crus II)
infss = inferior sagittal sinus
inft = inferior nasal turbinate
infvv = inferior vermian vein
ing = insular gyri
inmta = innominate artery
innv = innominate vein
inob = inferior oblique muscle
inpc = interpeduncular cistern
inptf = interpterygoid fossa
inrm = inferior rectus muscle
ins = short process of incus
insmca = insular branches of middle cerebral
    artery
instv = inferior striate vein
insv = insular vein
inta = inferior thyroid artery
intfs = intersinus septum (frontal)
intm = internal mammary artery
intns = internasal bone suture
intp = inferior temporal polar region
iof = infraorbital foramen
iofi = inferior orbital fissure
iog = inferior occipital gyrus
iom = infraorbital margin
iop = internal occipital protuberance
ios = intra-occipital sulcus
ipl = inferior parietal lobule
ips = intraparietal sulcus
irv3 = infindibular recess of third ventricle
isa = incudo-stapedial articulation
itcvs = intercavernous sinus
itf = infratemporal fossa
itscs = interscalar septum
ityma = inferior tympanic annulus
ivv = inferior ventricular vein

J

jcwm = juxtacortical white matter
jgfpn = pars nervosa-jugular foramen
jgfpv = pars vascularis-jugular foramen
jugb = jugular bulb

jugf = jugular foramen
jugs = jugular spine
jugt = jugular tubercle of occipital bone
jx = junction

K

kors = Korner's septum

L

L = combined ventral and lateral nuclei of
    thalamus
l-cca = left common carotid artery
lac = lacrimal gland
lacb = lacrimal bone
lacf = lacrimal sac fossa
laco = orbital portion of lacrimal gland
lacp = palpebral portion of lacrimal gland
lamp = lamina papyracea
lamss = lateral mesencephalic sulcus
larm = lateral rectus muscle
latl = lateral lenticulostriate arteries
lcv = longitudinal caudate vein
lena = lenticulostriate arteries
lena-t = lenticulostriate artery trunk
lengl = lens of globe
lenn = lenticular nucleus
lfat = lingual-facial artery trunk
lg = lingual gyrus (motg)
lgn = lateral geniculate nucleus
li = limen insulae
lilimd = diencephalic segment of Liliequist's
    membrane
lilimm = mesencephalic segment of Liliequist's
    membrane
lilims = sellar segment of Liliequist's
    membrane
linga = lingual artery – branch of eca
lingula = lingula (lobule I)
lis = lateral intermuscular septum
llln = lateral lamina of lenticular nucleus
lml = lateral malleolar ligament (in
    tympanic cavity)
ln = lateral nasal branch of sphenopalatine
    artery
log = lateral orbital gyrus
los = lateral (inferior) occipital sulcus
lotg = lateral occipital temporal gyrus (lotg)/
    fusiform gyrus
lots = lateral occipital temporal sulcus
lpch = lateral posterior choroidal artery
lpl = lateral palpebral ligament
lpp = lateral pterygoid plate
lps = levator palpebrae superioris
lrv4 = lateral recess of fourth ventricle
ls = limbus sphenoidale
lt = lamina terminalis
lv = lateral ventricle
lvat = atrium (trigone) of lateral
    ventricle
lvb = body of lateral ventricle
lvfh = frontal horn of lateral ventricle
lvoh = occipital horn of lateral
    ventricle
lvth = temporal horn of lateral
    ventricle
lws = lesser wing of the sphenoid bone

M

M = medial nuclei of thalamus
m-atv = medial atrial vein
m1 = m1 (horizontal segment middle cerebral artery)
m2 = m2 (Sylvian/insular branches middle cerebral artery)
m3 = m3 (opercular branches middle cerebral artery)
m4 = m4 (cortical branches middle cerebral artery)
mac = mastoid air cells
mal = malleus
mana = angle of mandible
manb = mandible body
mancn = neck of mandibular condyle
manf = mandibular foramen
manhc = head of mandibular condyle
mann = mandibular notch
manr = ramus of mandible
margs = marginal sinus
masev = mastoid emissary vein
masm = masseter muscle
masma = masseteric muscular artery branches of eca
masta = mastoid antrum
maxa = maxillary artery
maxt = maxillary tuberosity
mb = mammillary body
mca = middle cerebral artery
mcab = middle cerebral artery bifurcation/ trifurcation
mcp = middle cerebellar peduncle (brachium pontis)
mcrf = middle cranial fossa
mdb = midbrain
mdbtg = tegmentum of midbrain
mec = Meckel's cave
med = medulla
medps = median pontine sulcus
medvein = medullary vein(s)
merm = medial rectus muscle
mf = mental foramen
mgn = medial geniculate nucleus
mh = head of malleus
mht = meningohypophyseal artery trunk
mi = massa intermedia
mif = middle internal frontal branch of anterior cerebral artery
minc = malleo-incudal articulation
ml = medial lemniscus
mlln = medial lamina of lenticular nucleus
mm = middle meatus
mma = middle meningeal artery
mma(a) = accessory meningeal artery
mmag = middle meningeal artery grooves
mman = manubrium of malleus
mn = mastoid notch
mne = neck of malleus
mnt = middle nasal turbinate
mntvs = vertical strut/insertion middle nasal turbinate
mocg = middle occipital gyrus
mod = modiolus
mog = medial orbital gyrus
motg = medial occipital temporal gyrus (lingual gyrus)
mp = mastoid process

mpch = medial posterior choroidal artery
mpl = medial palpebral ligament
mpm = mental protuberance of mandible
mpp = medial pterygoid plate
mps = median palatine suture
ms = maxillary sinus
msg = middle short insular gyrus
mso = maxillary sinus ostium
mtmca = middle temporal branch of middle cerebral artery
mtp = mastoid tip
mtt = mammilothalamic tract
mxb = maxillary bone

N

nac = nucleus accumbens
nalac = nasolacrimal duct
naph = nasopharynx
nass = nasal septum
nb = nasal bone
nfs = nasofrontal suture
nh = neurohypophysis
nms = nasomaxillary suture
nodu = nodulus of vermis (lobule X)
ns = nasion
nsls = nasolacrimal saccule
nucc = nucleus cuneatus
nucg = nucleus gracilis
nv = nasal vestibule

O

obx = obex
oc = optic canal
occa = occipital artery
occs = occipital sinus
ocg = occipital gyri
ocl = occipital lobe
ocpc = occipital condyle
ofg = orbital-frontal gyri
olfb = olfactory bulb (cn1)
olfr = olfactory recess of nasal cavity
olfs = olfactory sulcus
olft = olfactory tract (cn1)
olfv = olfactory vein
omed = open medulla
oms = occipitomastoid suture
on = optic nerve (cn2)
oncan = canalicular segment of optic nerve
oncis = cisternal (pre-chiasmatic) segment optic nerve
onorb = orbital segment optic nerve
onsc = optic nerve/sheath complex
op = occipital pole
opch = optic chiasm
ope = orbital plate of ethmoid bone
opf = orbital plate of frontal bone
opha = ophthalmic artery
opis = opisthion
opr = optic radiations
opst = optic strut
opt = optic tract
opts = optic sheath
orba = orbital apex
orbfa = orbitofrontal branch of anterior cerebral artery
orbfm = orbitofrontal branch of middle cerebral artery

oro = orbicularis oculi muscle
ors = orbital septum
ot = outer table of skull
ow = oval window
owm = occipital white matter

P

p1 = p1 (precommunicating/mesencephalic segment posterior cerebral artery)
p2 = p2 (ambient segment of posterior cerebral artery)
p2/3 = p2/3 junction
p3 = p3 (quadrigeminal segment of posterior cerebral artery)
p-thp = posterior thalamoperforators
pa = petrous apex
pag = periaqueductal gray matter
palfg = greater palatine foramina
palfl = lesser palatine foramina
pamp = posterior ampullary nerve
par = posterior ascending ramus of Sylvian fissure
parg = parotid gland
paur = posterior auricular artery
pbr = para-brachial recess
pc = posterior commissure
pca = posterior cerebral artery
pcf = pontocerebellar fibers
pcl = paracentral lobule
pcla = paracentral lobule artery branch of anterior cerebral artery
pcom = posterior communicating artery
pcr = posterior corona radiata
pcrf = posterior cranial fossa
pcs = paracentral sulcus
pct = pontine crossing tract
pecs = pericallosal cistern (sulcus)
pedv = peduncular vein
pemsc = perimesencephalic (ambient) cistern
peric = pericallosal branch of anterior cerebral artery
pethc = posterior ethmoidal canal
petv = petrosal vein
pevwm = periventricular white matter
pf = parietal foramina
pg = pineal gland
phg = parahippocampal gyrus
pica = posterior inferior cerebellar artery
pica-h = hemispheric branch of pica
pica-v = vermian branch of pica
pif = posterior internal frontal branch of anterior cerebral artery
pir = piriform cortex
pirf = piriform cortex, frontal part
pirt = piriform cortex, temporal part
pis = peri-insular (circular) sulcus
pitg = pituitary gland
pits = primary intermediate sulcus
plg = posterior long insular gyrus
pli = posterior lobule of insula
plic = posterior limb of internal capsule
PLN = posterolateral nucleus of thalamus
pls = planum sphenoidale
pmarg = pars marginalis (ascending ramus of cingulate sulcus)
pmca = parietal branch of middle cerebral artery
pmdj = ponto-medullary junction

pmesj = ponto-mesencephalic junction
pmol = posteromedial orbital lobule
pms = parietomastoid suture
pmv = posterior mesencephalic vein
pns = posterior nasal spine
poa = parieto-occipital branch of pca
poc = pre-occipital notch
pocf = posterior condylar foramen
pocg = post-central gyrus
poch = posterior choana
pocl = posterior clinoid process
pocs = post-central sulcus
pocv = posterior condylar vein
pof = petro-occipital fissure
pog = posterior orbital gyrus
polis = post-olivary sulcus
pon = pons
ponbp = basis pontis of pons
pont = tegmentum of pons
pop = parietal operculum
popc = posterior pericallosal/splenial branches pca
poperf = pontine perforators
porus = porus acousticus
pos = parieto-occipital sulcus
pospf = postpyramidal fissure
potms = pontomedullary sulcus
pp = pterygoid plates
ppe = perpendicular plate of ethmoid
ppmca = posterior parietal branch of middle cerebral artery
ppo = planum polare
ppofm = palatine process of maxilla
pps = posterior parolfactory sulcus
prcmca = pre-central branch(es) of middle cerebral artery
prcu = precuneus
precg = pre-central gyrus
precs = pre-central sulcus
preculf = preculminate fissure
precv = pre-central cerebellar vein
premc = premedullary cistern
prepf = prepyramidal fissure of cerebellum
prfmca = prefrontal branch of middle cerebral artery
pri = petrous ridge
prl = parietal lobe
prols = pre-olivary sulcus
prpc = prepontine cistern
prus = Prussak's space
psaa = posterior superior alveolar artery
psf = posterior superior fissure of cerebellum
psg = posterior short insular gyrus
psrv4 = posterior superior recess of fourth ventricle
pt = pterion
pta = posterior temporal branch of pca
ptb = petrous temporal bone
pte = planum temporale
ptfos = pterygopalatine fossa
ptg = paraterminal gyrus
pthr = posterior thalamic radiations
ptmca = posterior temporal branch of middle cerebral artery
ptml = lateral pterygoid muscle
ptmm = medial pterygoid muscle
ptpc = pterygopalatine canal
ptr = porus trigeminus

ptvc = pterygovaginal (palatovaginal or
      pharyngeal canal)
ptvpl = pterygoid venous plexus
pu = putamen
pul = pulvinar of thalamus (part of lateral
      thalamic nuclear group)
pyem = pyramidal eminence
pymd = pyramid of vermis (lobule VIII)
pyp = pyramidal process

Q
qdpc = quadrigeminal plate cistern
quad = quadrangular lobule (anterior
       quadrangular lobule)

R
r-cca = right common carotid artery
rah = recurrent artery of Huebner
reic = retrolenticular internal capsule
rez = root entry zone of trigeminal nerve
rg = rostral gyrus
rgi = inferior rostral gyrus
rgis = inferior rostral sulcus
rgss = superior rostral sulcus
rgsu = superior rostral gyrus
rhs = rhinal sulcus
rlic = retrolenticular internal capsule
rn = red nucleus
rosb = rostrum of sphenoid bone
rpc = retro-pulvinar (thalamic) cistern (wings
      of ambient cistern)
rw = round window

S
s-tve = superior thalamic vein
sb = septal branch of sphenopalatine artery
sbcg = subcentral gyrus
sbepv = subependymal veins
sbps = subparietal sulcus
sca = subcallosal area
scalpv = scalp vein (s)
schv = superior choroid vein
scp = superior cerebellar peduncle (brachium
      conjunctivum)
scr = 3 ocular coats of eye (sclera, choroid, retina)
scu = scutum
scwm = subcortical white matter
sepv = septal vein
set = sella turcica
sf = Sylvian fissure (lateral sulcus)
sfo = superior fronto-occipital fasciculus
sfs = sphenofrontal suture
sgg = sigmoid groove
sgs = sigmoid sinus
simp = simple lobule (posterior quadrangular
       lobule)
sino = substantia innominata
sipa = superior internal parietal branch of
       anterior cerebral artery
sity = sinus tympani
slf = superior longitudinal fasciculus
sli = sulcus limitans
sma = supplementary motor area
smg = supramarginal gyrus
smt = stria medullaris thalami
smv = superior/anterior medullary velum
sn = substantia nigra

snpc = pars compacta of substantia nigra
snpr = pars reticulata of substantia nigra
snt = superior nasal turbinate
sof = supra-orbital foramen
sofi = superior orbital fissure
som = supraorbital margin
sorv3 = supra-optic recess of third ventricle
sos = spheno-occipital synchondrosis
sov = superior ophthalmic vein
spal = soft palate
spe = septum pellucidum
spfo = sphenopalatine foramen
sph = sphenoid bone
sphere = sphenoethmoidal recess
sphpa = sphenopalatine artery
sphpv = sphenopetrosal vein
sphs = sphenoid sinus septum
sphso = sphenoid sinus ostia
spl = superior parietal lobule
spps = sphenoparietal sinus
sps = sphenoparietal suture
spvv = superior vermian vein
ss = sphenoid sinus
ssch = horizontal semicircular canal
ssci = suprasellar cistern
sscp = posterior semicircular canal
sscs = superior semicircular canal
sss = sphenosquamosal suture
st = stria terminalis
sta = superficial temporal artery
stca = anterior crus of stapes
stcap = capitellum (head) of stapes
stcp = posterior crus of stapes
stf = stapes footplate
sth = subthalamic nucleus
stl = stem of temporal lobe
stpm = stapedius muscle
stpt = tendon of stapedius muscle
str = superior thalamic radiations
stsi = straight sinus
stv = striate vessels
sty = styloid process
stymf = stylomastoid foramen
sub = subiculum
subac = subarcuate canal
subcl = subclavian artery
sublic = sublenticular internal capsule
subov = suboccipital veins
suca = superior cerebellar artery
sucah = hemispheric branch of superior
        cerebellar artery
sucav = vermin branch of superior cerebellar
        artery
sucv = superficial cortical vein(s)
sumcv = superficial middle cerebral vein
supc = superior colliculus
supcc = supracerebellar cistern
supm = superior meatus
supob = superior oblique muscle
supot = tendon of superior oblique muscle
supslu = superior semilunar lobule (Crus I)
supss = superior sagittal sinus
supthy = superior thyroid artery branch of eca
supts = superior petrosal sinus
surlp = superior rectus/levator palpebrae muscle
surm = superior rectus muscle
svc = superior vena cava
sypt = Sylvian point

T
t1v = t1 vertebral segment
tb = temporal bone
tc = tuber cinereum
tct = tectum
tegi = inferior temporal gyrus
tegm = middle temporal gyrus
tegs = superior temporal gyrus
tenc = tentorial incisura
tentc = tentorium cerebelli
tentv = tentorial vein
terv = terminal vein
tgm = tegmen mastoideum
tgt = tegmen tympani
th = thalamus
   A = anterior nuclei of thalamus
   M = medial nuclei of thalamus
   L = combined ventral and lateral nuclei of
      thalamus
   pul = pulvinar is part of lateral thalamic
      nuclear group
PLN = posterolateral nucleus of thalamus
thp = thalamoperforators
   a-thp = anterior thalamoperforators
   p-thp = posterior thalamoperforators
thsv = thalamostriate vein
thv = thalamic vein(s)
thyct = thyrocervical trunk
thyctac = ascending cervical branch of
      thyrocervical trunk
tlo = temporal lobe
tm = tympanic membrane
tmj = temporal mandibular joint
tmpf = tympanic membrane pars flaccida
tmpt = tympanic membrane pars tensa
tmsi = inferior temporal sulcus
tmss = superior temporal sulcus
tntv = tentorial vein
tojx = temporal occipital junction
tomca = temporal-occipital branch of middle
      cerebral artery
top = temporal operculum
torh = torcular herophili (confluence of sinuses)
tort = torus tubarius
tos = transverse occipital sulcus
tp = tapetum
tpa = temporal polar branch of middle cerebral
      artery
tpf = transverse pontine fibers
tpj = temporal parietal junction
tpo = temporal pole
tps = transverse palatine suture
tpz = temporal process of zygomatic bone
trs = transverse sinus
trvfa = transverse facial artery
ts = tuberculum sellae
tsb = temporal squamosal bone

tss = temporal squamosal suture
tsso = trochlear sling of superior oblique muscle
ttm = tensor tympani muscle
ttt = tensor tympani tendon
tub = tuber of vermis (lobule VII)
tvena = true venous angle
tymc = tympanic cavity

U
uf = uncinate fasciculus
umbo = umbo of malleus
unc = uncus of temporal lobe
unp = uncinate process
uvu = uvula of the vermis (lobule IX)

V
v = vomer
v1 = V1 segment of vertebral artery (pre-foraminal)
v2 = V2 segment of vertebral artery (foraminal)
v3 = V3 segment of vertebral artery (from
      C1 to dura)
v3sup = supra-pineal recess of third ventricle
v3v = third ventricle
v4 = v4 intracranial/intradural segment
      vertebral artery
v4v = fourth ventricle
val = vallecula space
vbj = vertebral basilar junction
ve = vagal eminence
vena = venous angle
vesa = vestibular aqueduct
vesar = vestibular area
vest = vestibule
vg = vagal meatus
vib = vitreous body (chamber) of eye
vic = vidian canal
vn = vidian nerve
vog = vein of Galen
vol = vein of Labbe
vot = vein of Trolard
vpm/vpl = ventroposterior medialis/
      ventroposterior lateralis thalamus
vrs = Virchow–Robin spaces
vta = ventral tegmental area

Z
za = zygomatic arch
zmms = zygomaticomaxillary suture
zpf = zygomatic process of frontal bone
zpm = zygomatic process of maxilla
zpt = zygomatic process of temporal bone
zsps = zygomaticosphenoid suture
zts = zygomaticotemporal suture
zyb = zygomatic bone

Index